AHA Hospital Statistics™

W9-BKR-317

2018 Edition

2018 Institutional Member $250.00
Nonmember $295.00
AHA Catalog NUMBER 080143
telephone ORDERS: 800-AHA-2626

ISSN 0090-6662
ISBN 978-0-87258-980-3

AHA Institutional Members $230.00
Nonmembers $295.00
AHA Catalog NUMBER 082018
Telephone ORDERS 1-800-AHA-2626

ISSN 0090-6662
ISBN-13: 978-0-87258-980-3

Contents

Acknowledgments
& Advisements

Acknowledgments

The 2018 edition of *AHA Hospital Statistics* is published by Health Forum, an affiliate of the American Hospital Association, Rick Pollack, President and CEO.

Advisements

The data published here should be used with the following advisements: The data are based on replies to an annual survey that seeks a variety of information, not all of which is published in this book. The information gathered by the survey includes specific services, but not all of each hospital's services. Therefore, the data do not reflect an exhaustive list of all services offered by all hospitals. For information on the availability of additional data, please contact Health Forum, (800) 821-2039.

Health Forum does not assume responsibility for the accuracy of information voluntarily reported by the individual institutions surveyed. The purpose of this publication is to provide basic data reflecting the delivery of health care in the United States and associated areas, and is not to serve an official and all-inclusive list of services offered by individual hospitals.

Caring for Communities: How Hospitals are Engaging in New Payment Models and Addressing Community Needs

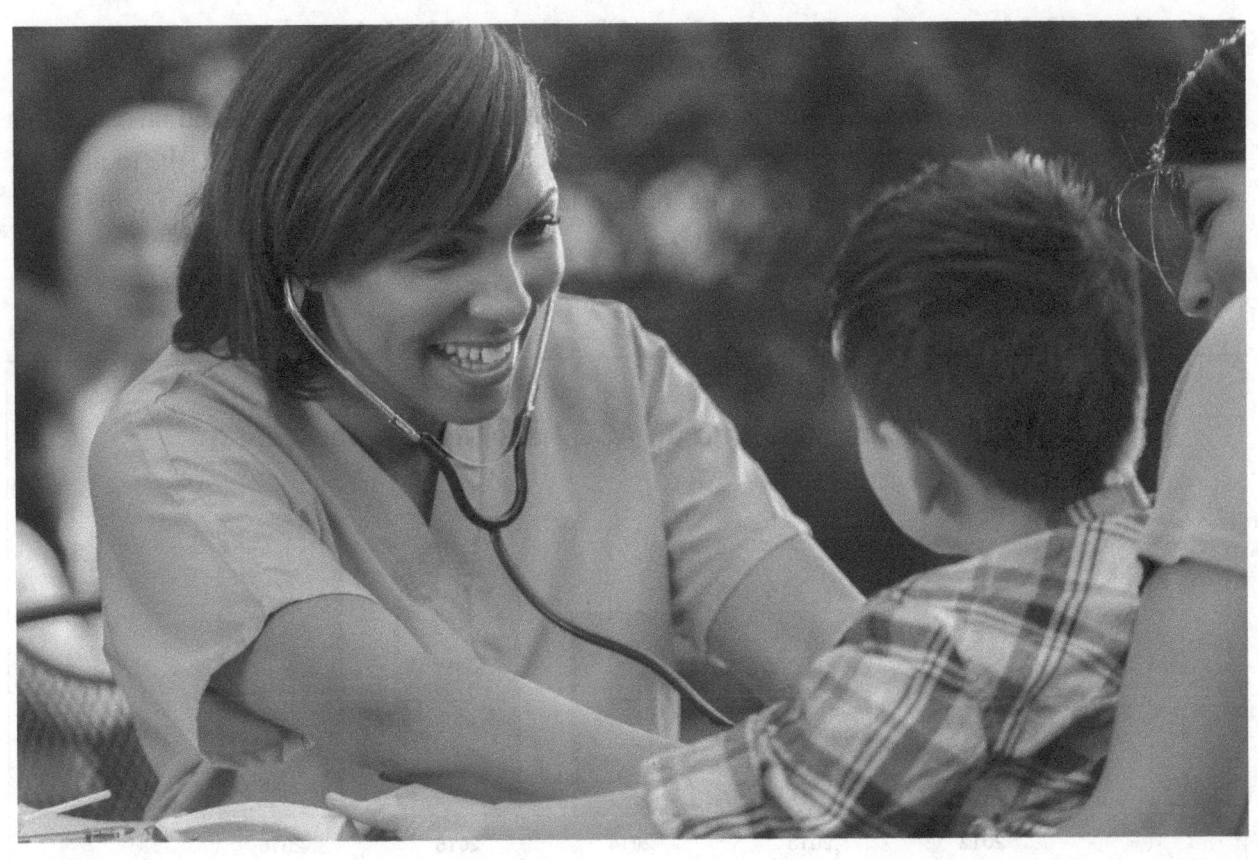

Introduction

Hospitals and health systems continue to test and adopt alternative payment and delivery models, such as accountable care organizations, medical homes, and performance-based payment. Ongoing implementation of the Quality Payment Program (QPP) under the Medicare Access and CHIP Reauthorization Act (MACRA) of 2015, as well as new Medicare and Medicaid demonstration initiatives support these efforts. Hospitals and health systems also increasingly recognize the large impact that social, economic, and environmental factors have on health outcomes and costs. They are engaged in developing approaches to addressing these factors and integrating them into the delivery of health care services.

Adoption of Alternative Payment and Delivery Models
Accountable Care Organizations (ACOs)

Hospitals and health systems continue to establish ACOs, networks of physicians and hospitals that share financial and medical responsibility for providing care to patients. Since 2012, the total percentage of hospitals or health systems that have established an ACO almost tripled from 13 percent to 37 percent (Figure 1).[i]

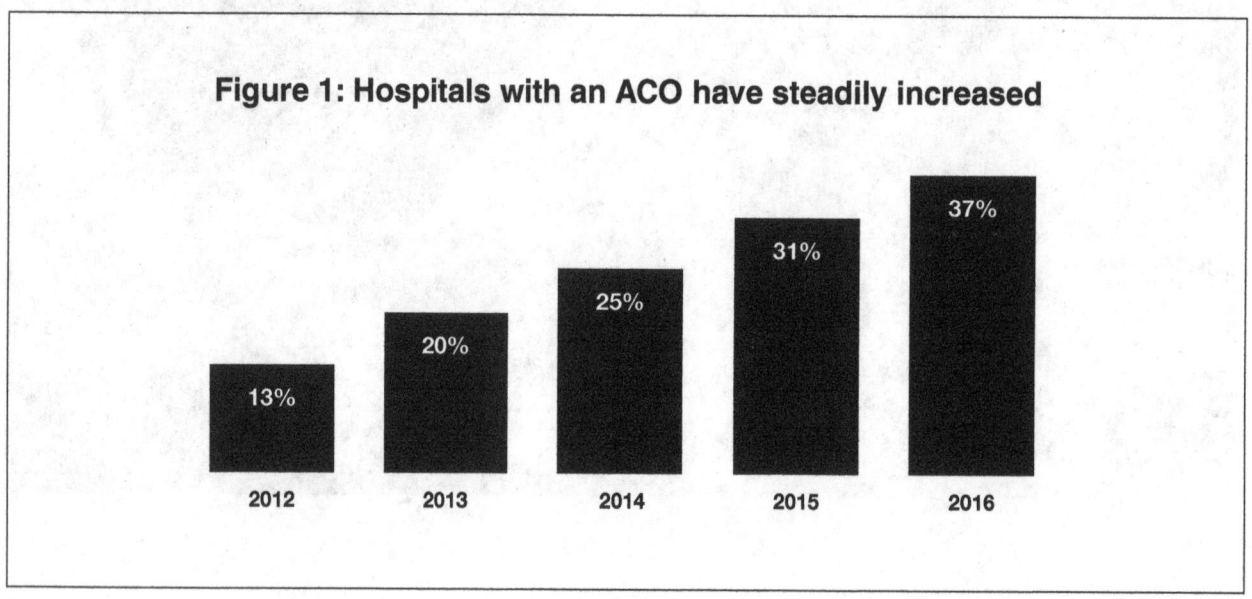

Figure 1: Hospitals with an ACO have steadily increased

Of these hospitals and health systems, ACO participation varies across patient populations. Generally, these ACOs tend to be comprised of Medicare populations. In 2016, 83 percent of respondents to the AHA Hospital Survey participated in a Medicare ACO model, and half participated in an ACO with a private insurer (Figure 2).[ii] These rates varied by region and bed size.

---

[i] Source: American Hospital Association, Annual Survey data 2012-2016
[ii] Source: American Hospital Association, Annual Survey data 2016

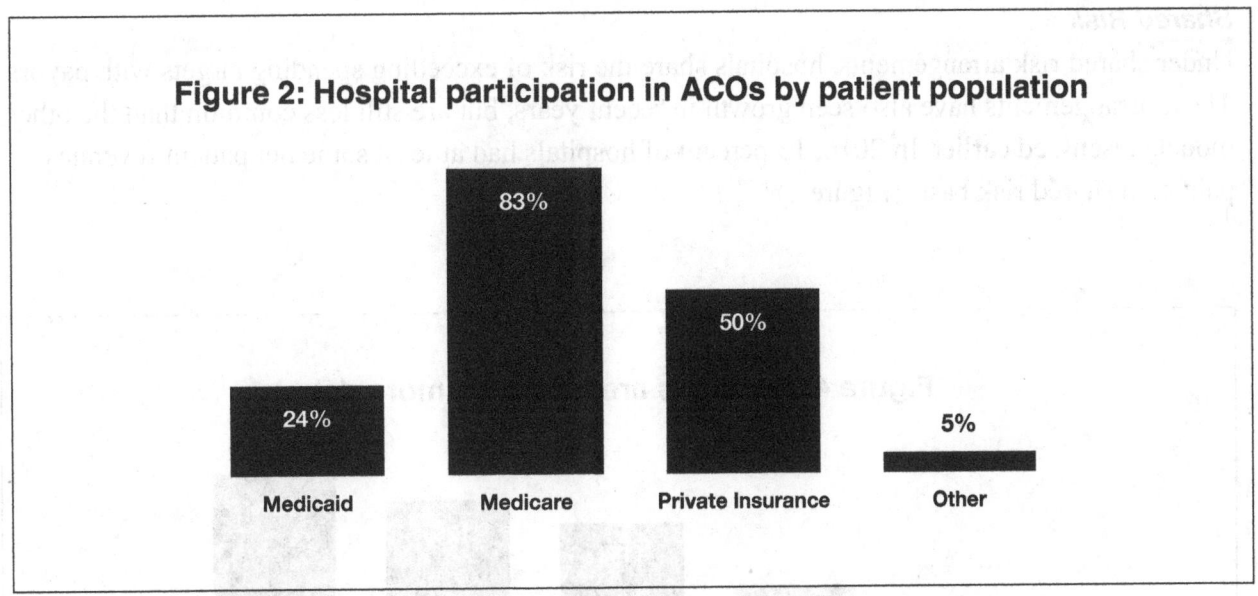

Figure 2: Hospital participation in ACOs by patient population

Medical Homes

The percentage of hospitals that have established a medical home program, where the patient has a direct relationship with a provider responsible for coordinating their care, has also grown in recent years. The rate of growth, however, has not been as steep as with ACOs. Between 2012 and 2016, the percentage of hospitals that had established a medical home grew from 18 percent to 28 percent (Figure 3). Facilities are also increasingly likely to have both an ACO and medical home program, rising from 6 percent in 2012 to 18 percent in 2016.[iii]

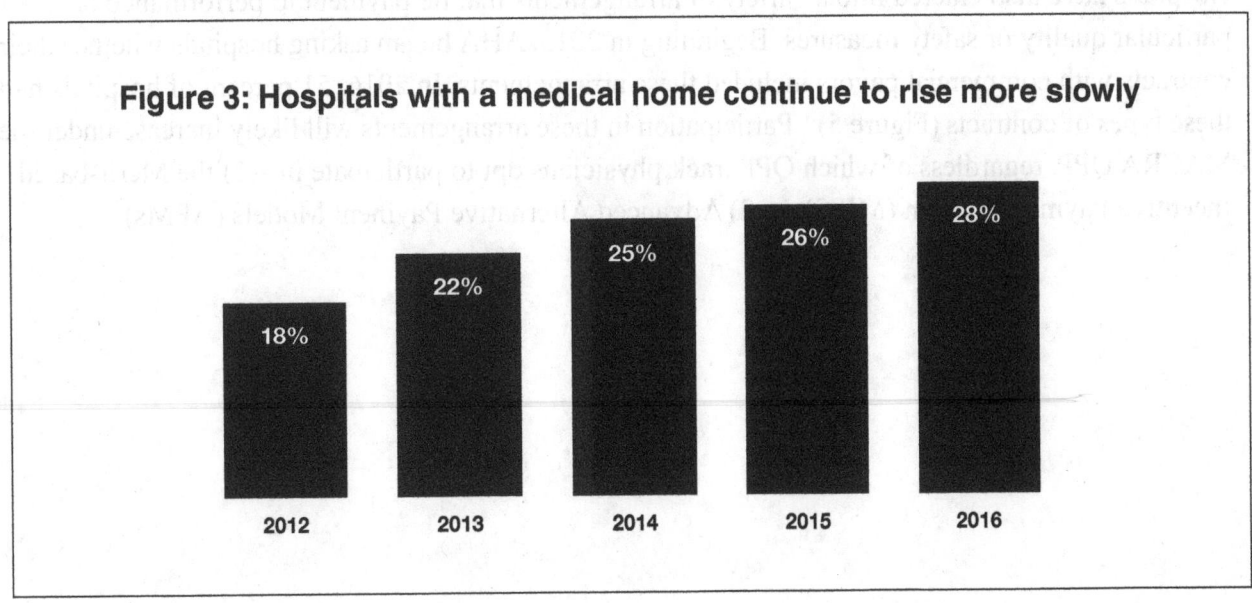

Figure 3: Hospitals with a medical home continue to rise more slowly

---

[iii] Source: American Hospital Association, Annual Survey data 2012-2016

Shared Risk

Under shared risk arrangements, hospitals share the risk of exceeding spending targets with payors. These arrangements have also seen growth in recent years, but are still less common than the other models discussed earlier. In 2016, 13 percent of hospitals had at least some net patient revenues paid on a shared risk basis (Figure 4).[iv]

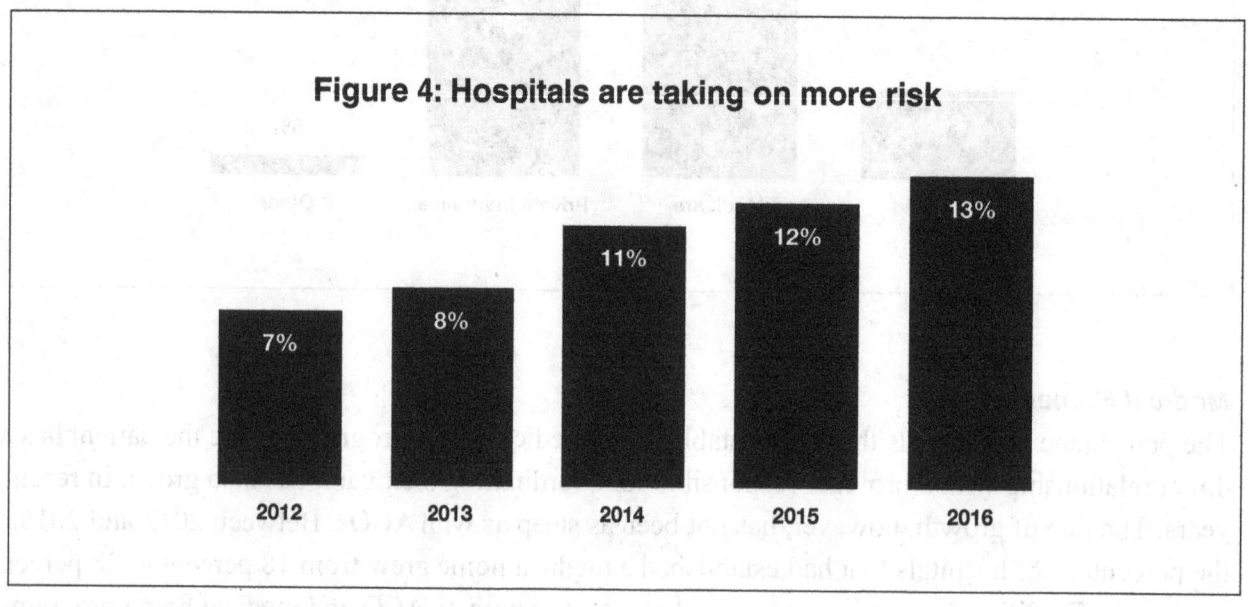

Figure 4: Hospitals are taking on more risk

Payment Tied to Performance

Hospitals have also entered into a variety of arrangements that tie payment to performance on particular quality or safety measures. Beginning in 2013, AHA began asking hospitals whether their contracts with commercial payors included these arrangements. In 2016, 51 percent of hospitals had these types of contracts (Figure 5).[v] Participation in these arrangements will likely increase under the MACRA QPP, regardless of which QPP track physicians opt to participate in – 1) the Merit-based Incentive Payment System (MIPS), or 2) Advanced Alternative Payment Models (APMs).

---

iv Source: American Hospital Association, Annual Survey data 2012-2016
v Source: American Hospital Association, Annual Survey data 2013-2016

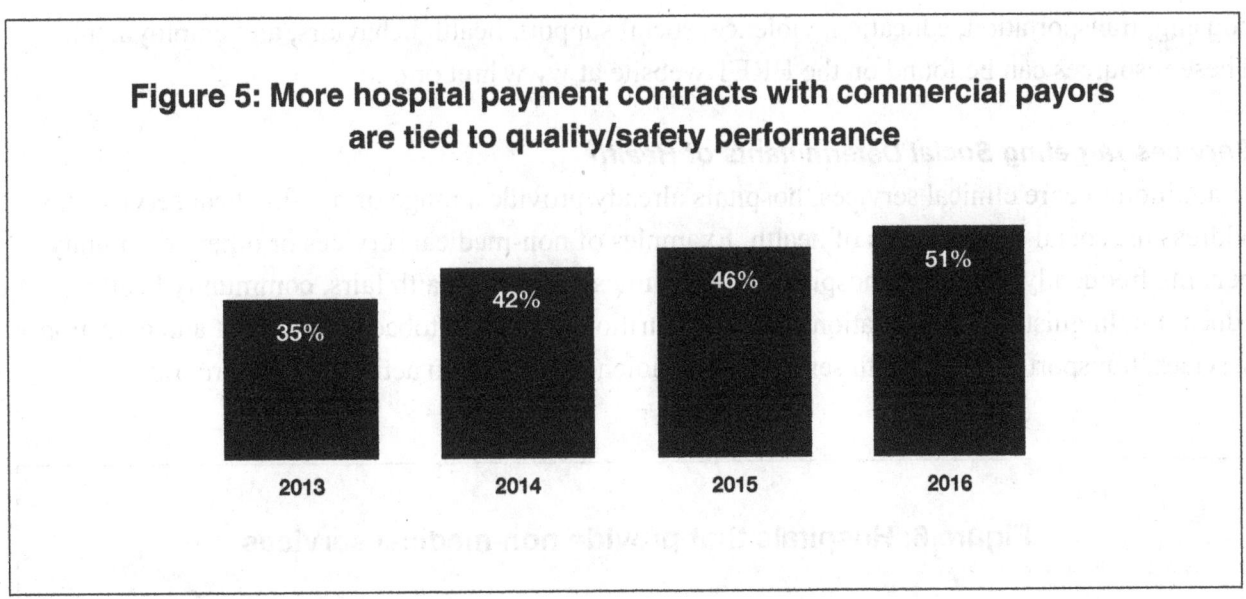

Figure 5: More hospital payment contracts with commercial payors are tied to quality/safety performance

- 2013: 35%
- 2014: 42%
- 2015: 46%
- 2016: 51%

Trends in Hospitals Addressing Social Determinants of Health and Community Partnerships

In April 2017, the Centers for Medicare & Medicaid Services (CMS) announced the selection of participants in the Center for Medicare and Medicaid Innovation's Accountable Health Communities Model. This initiative will provide support to local communities seeking to address the "health-related social needs of Medicare and Medicaid beneficiaries by bridging the gap between clinical and community service providers."

Of the 32 organizations selected, 20 are hospitals, health systems, or organizations affiliated with hospitals, such as foundations or networks. Over a five-year period, the model will provide support to organizations testing approaches aimed at connecting beneficiaries to community services that may address their unmet health-related social needs. Examples of these social needs are housing instability, food insecurity, utility needs, interpersonal violence, and transportation. Organizations participating in the model will seek to bridge clinical and community services through:

- Screening to identify unmet health-related social needs;
- Referral to community services;
- Provision of navigation services to assist with accessing community services; and
- Alignment between clinical and community services to ensure availability and responsiveness of community services.

In 2017, the AHA, through its Health Research & Educational Trust (HRET) and Association for Community Health Improvement (ACHI) began releasing a series of resources to help hospitals address the social determinants of health. These resources include strategies and interventions that hospitals are using to address priority needs in their communities. Topics include food insecurity, housing, transportation, education, violence, social support, health behaviors, and employment. These resources can be found on the HRET website at www.hret.org.

Services Targeting Social Determinants of Health

In addition to core clinical services, hospitals already provide a range of non-medical services that address the social determinants of health. Examples of non-medical services or other community benefits frequently offered by hospitals include fitness centers, health fairs, community health education, linguistic and translation services, nutrition programs, tobacco treatment and cessation services, transportation to health services, and violence prevention activities. (Figure 6).[vi]

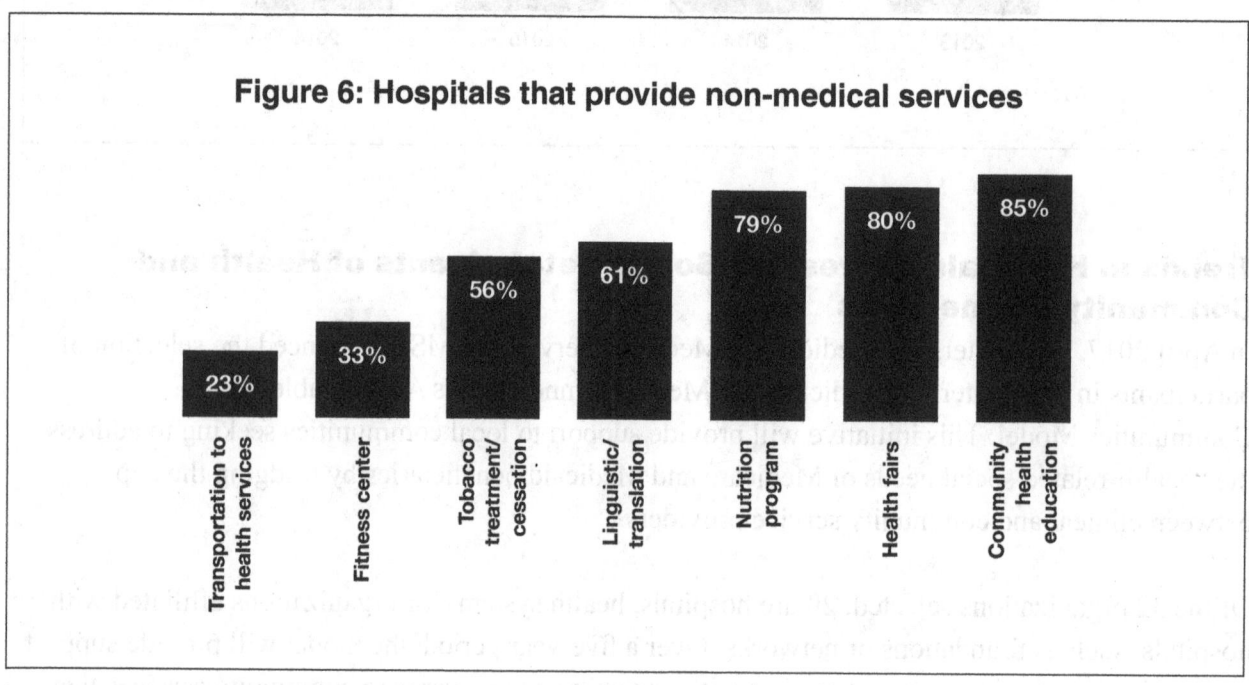

Figure 6: Hospitals that provide non-medical services

- Transportation to health services: 23%
- Fitness center: 33%
- Tobacco treatment/cessation: 56%
- Linguistic/translation: 61%
- Nutrition program: 79%
- Health fairs: 80%
- Community health education: 85%

Hospitals provide a range of additional non-medical services, although the provision of those services often varies depending on hospital type, size, or geographic location. For instance, those that offer Meals on Wheels and retirement housing or operate a retirement center to community members are disproportionately located in rural areas. Retirement housing is a facility which provides social activities to senior citizens, usually retired persons, who do not require health care but some short-term skilled nursing care may be provided. A retirement center may furnish housing and may also have acute hospital and long term care facilities, or it may arrange for acute and long term care through affiliated institutions. Although 38 percent of all hospitals are located in rural areas, 48 percent of hospitals offering Meals on Wheels are rural, and 68 percent of hospitals offering retirement housing are rural (Figure 7).[vii]

---

vi   Source: American Hospital Association, Annual Survey data 2016
vii Source: American Hospital Association, Annual Survey data 2016

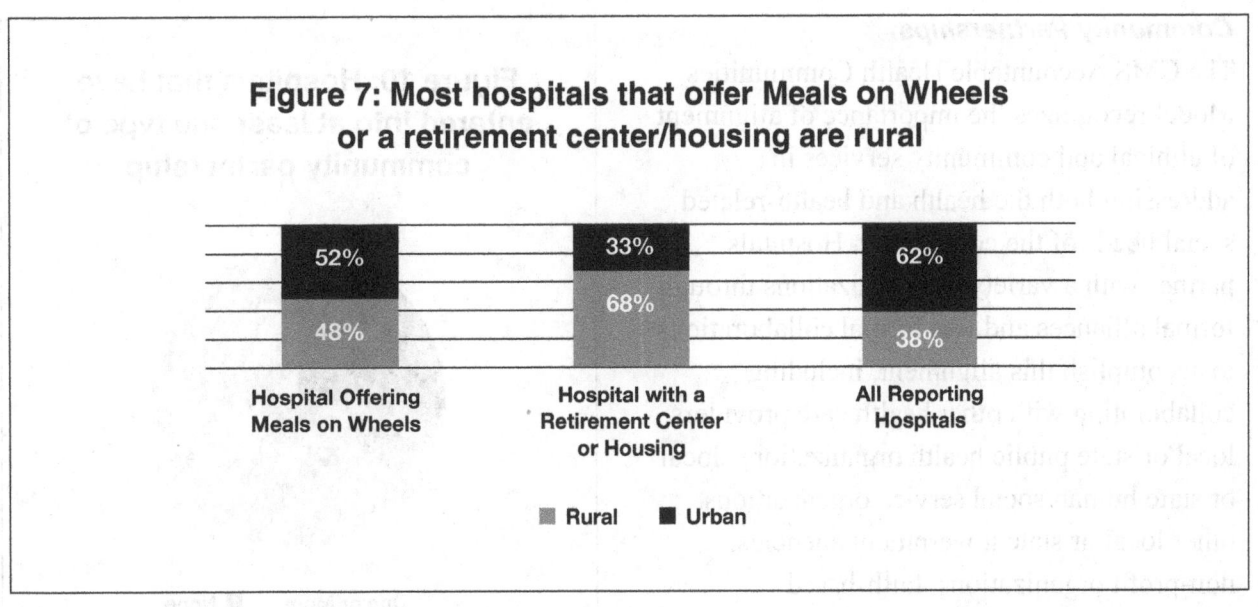

Figure 7: Most hospitals that offer Meals on Wheels or a retirement center/housing are rural

	Rural	Urban
Hospital Offering Meals on Wheels	48%	52%
Hospital with a Retirement Center or Housing	68%	33%
All Reporting Hospitals	38%	62%

Violence in communities is now commonly recognized as a public health issue. As a result, many hospitals now offer violence prevention programs, targeted either toward the workplace specifically or the community at large. In the 2016 survey, AHA began asking if hospitals offer these programs and found that 49 percent offer workplace programs (Figure 8) and 11 percent offer programs for their community (Figure 9).[viii]

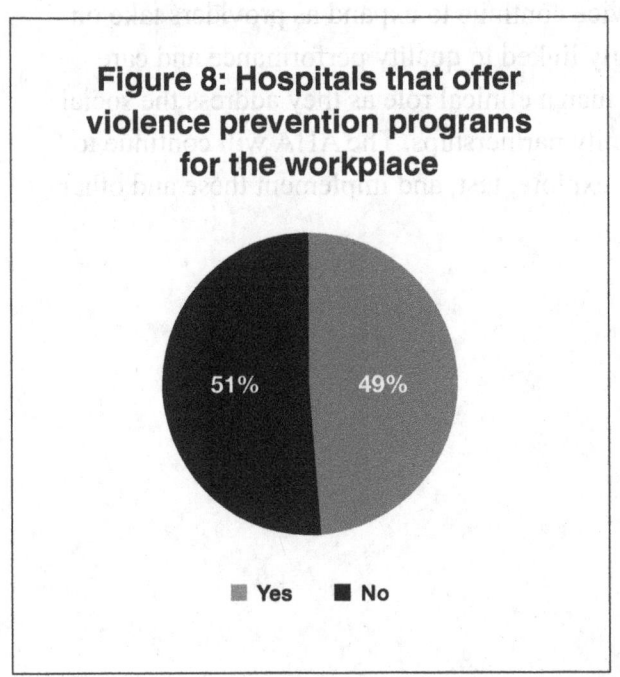

Figure 8: Hospitals that offer violence prevention programs for the workplace

Yes 49% · No 51%

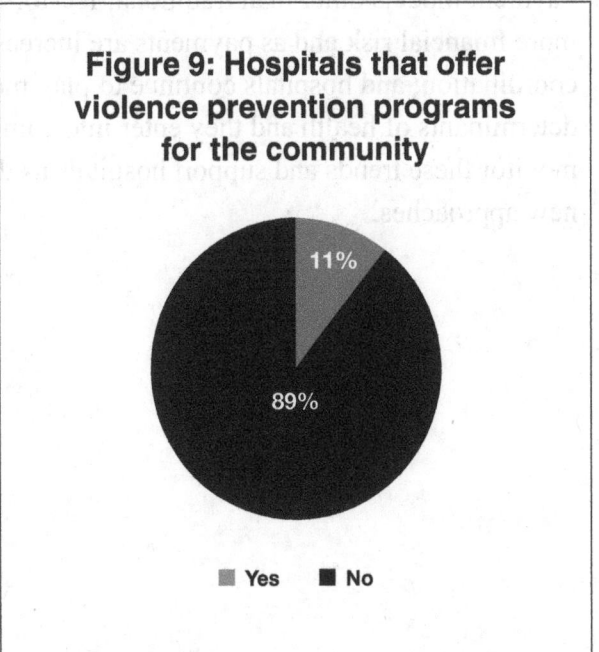

Figure 9: Hospitals that offer violence prevention programs for the community

Yes 11% · No 89%

viii Source: American Hospital Association, Annual Survey data 2016

Community Partnerships

The CMS Accountable Health Communities Model recognizes the importance of alignment of clinical and community services in addressing both the health and health-related social needs of the community. Hospitals partner with a variety of organizations through formal alliances and less formal collaborations to accomplish this alignment, including collaborating with other health care providers, local or state public health organizations, local or state human/social service organizations, other local or state government agencies, non-profit organizations, faith-based organizations, health insurance companies, schools, and local businesses or chambers of commerce. In 2016, 74 percent of hospitals reported at least one community partnership with organizations such as these (Figure 10).[ix]

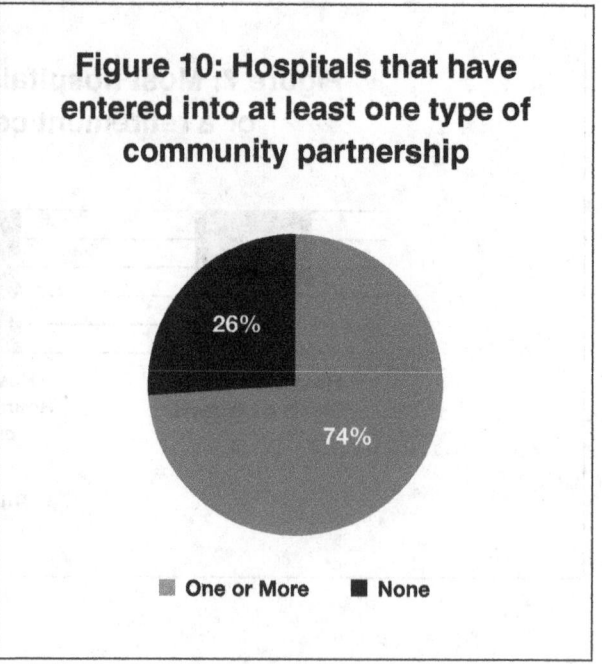

Figure 10: Hospitals that have entered into at least one type of community partnership

26%

74%

■ One or More ■ None

Conclusion

Results show that hospitals are engaged in a range of payment and delivery transformation efforts. Payment models other than traditional fee-for-service continue to expand as providers take on more financial risk and as payments are increasingly linked to quality performance and care coordination; and hospitals continue to play more than a clinical role as they address the social determinants of health and they enter into community partnerships. The AHA will continue to monitor these trends and support hospitals as they explore, test, and implement these and other new approaches.

[ix] Source: American Hospital Association, Annual Survey data 2016

How to Use this Book

For more than seven decades, *AHA Hospital Statistics*™ has reported aggregate hospital data derived from the AHA Annual Survey and is the definitive source when doing trend analysis with data by bed size category, U.S. Census Divisions, States, and Metropolitan Statistical Areas (MSAs). As the health care delivery system changes, so have the data tracked by the survey and presented in this report. Recent additions include:

- **Community health indicators** that offer readers a connection to the community for their analysis and planning: the data are broken down into beds, admissions, inpatient days, ER outpatient visits, and other indicators per 1000 population, as well as expense per capita.

- **Utilization, personnel and finance** by all MSAs in the United States.

- **Five-year trend data** on physician models, insurance products, and managed care contracts enable you to identify changes in relationships between hospitals and other health care systems and providers.

- **Tables 3 through 6 have been organized** to show breakdowns between inpatient and outpatient care to better reflect market shifts toward outpatient-centered care. Additional clarity is gained by the breakdown between total facility data (which includes nursing home type units under the control of the hospital) and hospital units (which exclude the nursing home data).

TABLE 6	**Sample State**

U.S. Registered Community Hospitals
(Nonfederal, short-term general and other special hospitals)

Overview 2012-2016

	2016	2015	2014	2013	2012
Physician Models					
Independent Practice Association	14	17	17	17	14
Group Practice without Walls	4	5	5	8	4
Open Physician-Hospital Organization	20	21	24	23	18
Closed Physician-Hospital Organization	21	17	18	17	11
Management Service Organization	14	18	20	14	9
Integrated Salary Model	35	29	30	26	24
Equity Model	4	3	4	6	3
Foundation	9	8	23	21	19
Insurance Products					
Health Maintenance Organization	20	22	23	24	19
Preferred Provider Organization	39	47	52	53	37
Indemnity Fee for Service	7	12	14	12	6
Managed Care Contracts					
Health Maintenance Organization	64	67	62	49	42
Preferred Provider Organization	97	93	92	87	72

Example of five-year trend data

- **Facilities and Services information** on more than 100 categories of hospital facilities and services in Table 7. At a glance, you can determine the number and percentage of hospitals offering a specific service such as Oncology, Palliative Care Program, Complementary Medicine, Women's Health Services and Tobacco Cessation.

- **Plus, System and Network involvement along with Group Purchasing Organizations** that demonstrate ways in which organizations are linked.

The survey instrument and the glossary

A good place to begin your analysis is the AHA Annual Survey instrument. Found on page 215, it includes the instructions, questions, and terms that were used to gather the data for fiscal year 2016. This can be extremely valuable for a clearer understanding of the data we collect and the tables presented in *AHA Hospital Statistics*.

Please also review the glossary in the back of the book. The glossary contains complete definitions for specific terms used in the tables and text of *AHA Hospital Statistics*. These definitions will clarify how terminology is being used.

As mentioned above, it is important to note that the primary focus of the most detailed data contained in *AHA Hospital Statistics* is community hospitals. As defined, community hospitals are all non-federal, short-term general and special hospitals whose facilities and services are available to the public. If the majority of a hospital's patients are admitted to units where the average length of stay is 30 days or less, a hospital may still be classified as short-term even if it includes a nursing- home-type unit. (For a more complete definition of community hospitals, please see the glossary definition, located on page 203.)

Getting the most out of *AHA Hospital Statistics*

This section of the book provides an introduction for getting the most out of your *AHA Hospital Statistics* 2018 edition. Here, you'll find a guide to the book, with insights into each table.

Equity model: An arrangement that allows established practitioners to become shareholders in a professional corporation in exchange for tangible and intangible assets of their existing practices.

Expenses: Includes all expenses for the reporting period including payroll, non-payroll, and all nonoperating expenses. *Payroll expenses* include all salaries and wages. *Non-payroll expenses* are all professional fees and those salary expenditures excluded from payroll. *Labor related expenses* are defined as payroll expenses plus employee benefits. *Non-labor related expenses* are all other non-payroll expenses. *Bad debt* has been reclassified from a "reduction in revenue" to an expense in accordance with the revised AICPA Audit Guide. However, for purposes of historical consistency, the expense total that appears throughout *AHA Hospital Statistics does not include "bad debt" as an expense item*. Note: Financial data may not add due to rounding.

Extracorporeal shock wave lithotripter (ESWL): A medical device used for treating stones in the kidney or urethra. The device disintegrates kidney stones noninvasively through the transmission of acoustic shock waves directed at the stones.

Fitness center: Provides exercise, testing, or evaluation programs and fitness activities to the community and hospital employees.

Example of Glossary definitions.

Table 1 — Historical Trends in Utilization, Personnel and Finances for Selected Years from 1946 through 2016

Table

1

Historical Trends in Utilization, Personnel, and Finances for Selected Years from 1946 through 2016

CLASSIFICATION	YEAR	HOSPITALS	BEDS (in thousands)	ADMISSIONS (in thousands)	AVERAGE DAILY CENSUS (in thousands)	ADJUSTED AVERAGE DAILY CENSUS (in thousands)
Total United States	1946	6,125	1,436	15,675	1,142	—
	1950	6,788	1,456	18,483	1,253	—
	1955	6,956	1,604	21,073	1,363	—
	1960	6,876	1,658	25,027	1,402	—
	1965	7,123	1,704	28,812	1,403	—
	1970	7,123	1,616	31,759	1,298	—
	1971	7,097	1,556	32,664	1,237	—
	1972	7,061	1,550	33,265	1,209	—
	1973	7,123	1,535	34,352	1,189	—
	1974	7,174	1,513	35,506	1,167	—
	1975	7,156	1,466	36,157	1,125	—
	1976	7,082	1,434	36,776	1,090	—
	1977	7,099	1,407	37,060	1,066	—
	1978	7,015	1,381	37,243	1,042	—
	1979	6,988	1,372	37,802	1,043	—
	1980	6,965	1,365	38,892	1,060	—
	1981	6,933	1,362	39,169	1,061	—
	1982	6,915	1,360	39,095	1,053	—
	1983	6,888	1,350	38,887	1,028	—
	1984	6,872	1,339	37,938	970	—
	1985	6,872	1,318	36,304	910	—
	1986	6,841	1,290	35,219	883	—
	1987	6,821	1,267	34,439	873	—
	1988	6,780	1,248	34,107	863	—
	1989	6,720	1,226	33,742	853	—
	1990	6,649	1,213	33,774	844	—
	1991	6,634	1,202	33,567	827	—
	1992	6,539	1,178	33,536	807	—
	1993	6,467	1,163	33,201	783	—
	1994	6,374	1,128	33,125	745	—
	1995	6,291	1,081	33,282	710	—
	1996	6,201	1,062	33,307	685	—
	1997	6,097	1,035	33,624	673	—
	1998	6,021	1,013	33,766	662	—
	1999	5,890	994	34,181	657	—
	2000	5,810	984	34,891	650	—
	2001	5,801	987	35,644	658	—
	2002	5,794	976	36,326	662	—
	2003	5,764	965	36,611	657	—
	2004	5,759	956	36,942	658	—
	2005	5,756	947	37,006	656	—

Example of Table 1

Table 1 at a Glance

This table is used to evaluate historical data and allows you to examine long-term trends in health care with data dating back more than sixty years. Table 1 reports on all AHA registered hospitals in the United States. One important note: To be considered an AHA-registered hospital, a hospital does not need to be an AHA member. Rather, the hospital must meet particular certification or satisfy a number of requirements. These Registration Requirements immediately follow this section and begin on page xxviii.

This table segments the data into various organizational structure categories. Here's a brief look at these different classifications:

- Total United States Hospitals
- Total Non-Federal Short-term and other special hospitals
- Community hospitals
- Non-government not-for-profit community hospitals
- Investor-owned (for-profit) community hospitals
- State and local government community hospitals

Table 1 also provides input on nationwide utilization, personnel and finance trends. You'll find answers to questions such as: *Over the past 25 years, what trends do I see comparing the average length of stay at government and non-government not-for-profit community hospitals and investor-owned for-profit community hospitals? or What has been the trend in outpatient visits?*

Table 2 — 2016 U.S. Registered Hospitals: Utilization, Personnel and Finances

Table 2 at a Glance

This table takes a closer look at U.S. Registered Hospitals for 2016. It offers a snapshot of utilization, personnel and finance statistics, and breaks down this information for specialty hospitals. In addition, this is the only table that outlines data on federal hospitals. You'll be able to use this table to better understand the number of beds set-up and staffed, how many personnel and trainees are on the payroll, and what the financial implications of these may be.

TABLE 3

TOTAL UNITED STATES

U.S. Registered Community Hospitals
(Nonfederal, short-term general and other special hospitals)

Utilization, Personnel, Revenue and Expenses, Community Health Indicators 2012-2016

	2016	2015	2014	2013	2012
TOTAL FACILITY (Includes Hospital and Nursing Home Units)					
Utilization - Inpatient					
Beds	839,988	853,287	862,352	872,736	902,061
Admissions	31,811,673	31,576,960	31,098,959	30,945,357	30,718,136
Inpatient Days	191,430,450	192,504,015	193,747,004	199,876,367	207,180,278
Average Length of Stay	6.0	6.1	6.2	6.5	6.7
Inpatient Surgeries	9,735,705	9,509,081	9,545,612	9,700,613	9,833,938
Births	3,726,233	3,742,191	3,723,871	3,764,698	3,809,367
HOSPITAL UNIT (Excludes Separate Nursing Home Units)					
Utilization - Inpatient					
Beds	758,186	769,505	782,504	794,502	824,969
Admissions	31,265,867	31,047,930	30,652,820	30,577,564	30,403,766
Inpatient Days	165,644,176	165,605,620	168,189,130	174,898,504	182,702,882
Average Length of Stay	5.3	5.3	5.5	5.7	6.0
Personnel					
Total Full Time	3,235,153	3,183,730	3,154,603	3,166,729	3,147,922
Total Part Time	1,213,426	1,214,232	1,153,790	1,146,082	1,122,957
Revenue and Expenses - Totals					
(Includes Inpatient and Outpatient)					
Total Net Revenue	$333,054,828,642	$322,459,942,930	$310,513,291,998	$298,519,717,355	$285,858,018,951
Total Expenses	314,709,758,455	301,905,101,393	290,128,641,153	282,372,557,487	272,840,121,437

Example of Table 3. Helps contrast acute and long-term care

Table 3 — Total United States

Table 3 at a Glance

This table provides a look at all U.S. Registered Community Hospitals, in terms of general overview with utilization by inpatient and outpatient, personnel, revenue, expenses and community health indicators. It provides a snapshot of the past five years, allowing you to track emerging trends.

This national information can be compared to local or regional trends, for benchmarking:

- Both inpatient and outpatient information is included, for better evaluation of data.

- Reporting by total facility *Includes hospital and Nursing Home Units* and hospital unit only *Excludes Separate Nursing Home Units* helps contrast acute and long-term care.

- Community health indicators can help uncover trends and help determine future facility needs.

TABLE 4 — BED SIZE CATEGORY 25-49

	2016	2015	2014	2013	2012
Total U.S. Community Hospitals in Bed Size Category 25-49	900	890	906	922	900

TABLE 4 — BED SIZE CATEGORY 100-199

	2016	2015	2014	2013	2012
Total U.S. Community Hospitals in Bed Size Category 100-199	1,304	1,289	1,338	1,324	1,331

TABLE 4 — BED SIZE CATEGORY 500 +

	2016	2015	2014	2013	2012
Total U.S. Community Hospitals in Bed Size Category 500 +	254	255	251	264	273
Location					
Hospitals Urban	251	251	247	260	270
Hospitals Rural	3	4	4	4	3
Control					
State and Local Government	42	43	48	53	56
Not for Profit	198	197	186	197	208
Investor owned	14	15	17	14	9
Physician Models					
Independent Practice Association	85	86	93	93	93
Group Practice without Walls	25	28	38	34	35
Open Physician-Hospital Organization	79	87	79	83	82
Closed Physician-Hospital Organization	53	50	61	68	53
Management Service Organization	80	93	108	90	90
Integrated Salary Model	103	97	96	97	94
Equity Model	17	17	18	17	16
Foundation	35	41	52	53	49
Insurance Products					
Health Maintenance Organization	138	130	121	115	116
Preferred Provider Organization	122	127	119	121	122
Indemnity Fee for Service	34	37	35	35	35
Managed Care Contracts					
Health Maintenance Organization	197	206	199	213	217
Preferred Provider Organization	193	202	199	215	211

Example of Table 4. Compares facilities with peers.

Table 4 — Bed Size Categories

Table 4 at a Glance

This table provides a look at all U.S. Registered Community Hospitals, broken down by bed size. The table includes general overview, utilization, personnel, and revenue and expense information. These categories of bed sizes were developed by the AHA, and have become an industry standard. By categorizing each facility into a peer group, this table provides a snapshot of the past five years allowing you to compare facilities with their peers.

U.S. CENSUS DIVISION 2: MIDDLE ATLANTIC

U.S. Registered Community Hospitals
(Nonfederal, short-term general and other special hospitals)

Utilization, Personnel, Revenue and Expenses, Community Health Indicators 2012-2016

	2016	2015	2014	2013	2012
COMMUNITY HEALTH INDICATORS PER 1000 POPULATION					
Total Population (in thousands)...	38,292	38,216	38,184	38,147	38,108
Inpatient					
Beds.........................	3.6	3.8	3.9	4.0	4.1
Admissions....................	135.8	136.7	136.2	138.3	137.4
Inpatient Days..................	963.5	988.8	1,019.0	1,093.8	1,145.0
Inpatient Surgeries	42.2	41.4	41.2	42.7	43.6
Births.........................	13.0	13.2	13.6	13.7	14.3
Outpatient					
Emergency Outpatient Visits......	367.7	362.0	363.4	379.5	360.1
Other Outpatient Visits...........	1,970.9	1,802.3	1,767.7	1,680.3	1,573.9
Total Outpatient Visits	2,338.6	2,164.3	2,131.1	2,059.8	1,934.0
Outpatient Surgeries.............	67.8	62.4	59.9	55.4	53.5
Expense per Capita (per person)....	$1,494.9	$1,462.7	$1,428.6	$1,429.8	$1,369.2

Example of Table 5. Uncovers trends to determine future facility needs.

Table 5 — U.S. Census Divisions

Table 5 at a Glance

This table provides a look at all U.S. Registered Community Hospitals, broken down by Census Division. The table includes general overview, utilization, personnel, and expenses, and community health indicator information. It provides a snapshot of the past five years, allowing you to track trends on a regional level. In addition, this allows you to compare this data to other population based health indicators, offering a more comprehensive look than the survey data alone. Community health indicators can help uncover trends and help determine future facility needs.

Table 6 — States

Table 6 at a Glance

This table provides a look at all U.S. Registered Community Hospitals, broken down by State. The table includes general overview, utilization, personnel, revenue and expenses, and community health indicator information. It provides a snapshot of the past five years, allowing you to track trends on a state level.

Note:

You can use the information in tables 3, 4, 5 and 6 to make accurate comparisons across Total U.S., Bed Size Category, Census Division and State.

Table 7 (Continued)

Table 7 — 2016 Facilities and Services in the U.S. Census Divisions and States

Table 7 at a Glance

This table examines facilities and services by both Census Division and State. A comprehensive alphabetical guide helps make each facility or service easy to find. This table will allow you to better understand what service lines are emerging and how many facilities offer a particular service in a discrete state or region.

This collection of facilities and services information data is unique to *AHA Hospital Statistics* and the list is continually growing. Recent additions include:

- Violence prevention programs for the workplace

- Violence prevention programs for the community

These new categories reflect the trends as hospitals expand their service lines to mirror the needs of their patients. For example, services such as acupuncture or massage therapy are now accounted for in the Complementary Medicine service item.

This table can answer questions such as: *What percentage of hospitals in the United States offer complementary medicine or wound management? or How are these new services distributed by state?*

CLASSIFICATION	HOSPITALS REPORTING	CHILDREN'S WELLNESS PROGRAM Number	Percent	CHIROPRACTIC SERVICES Number	Percent	COMMUNITY OUTREACH Number	Percent	COMPLEMENTARY AND ALTERNATIVE MEDICINE SERVICES Number	Percent
UNITED STATES	4,530	894	19.5	131	2.9	3,221	70.2	950	20.
COMMUNITY HOSPITALS	3,866	864	22.4	100	2.6	2,970	76.8	887	22.
CENSUS DIVISION 1, NEW ENGLAND	172	62	36.0	9	5.2	145	84.3	82	47.7
Connecticut	30	9	30.0	0	0.0	26	86.7	19	63.3
Maine	32	12	37.5	2	6.3	27	84.4	13	40.6
Massachusetts	64	25	39.1	3	4.7	52	81.3	27	42.2
New Hampshire	25	12	48.0	2	8.0	21	84.0	14	56.0
Rhode Island	10	1	10.0	1	10.0	9	90.0	3	30.0
Vermont	11	3	27.3	1	9.1	10	90.9	6	54.5
CENSUS DIVISION 2, MIDDLE ATLANTIC	404	131	32.4	20	5.0	322	79.7	140	34.7
New Jersey	62	33	53.2	2	3.2	53	85.5	31	50.0
New York	142	58	40.8	11	7.7	125	88.0	56	39.
Pennsylvania	200	40	20.0	7	3.5	144	72.0	53	
CENSUS DIVISION 3, SOUTH ATLANTIC	671	115	17.1	10	1.5	499	74.4	131	19.
Delaware	10	6	60.0	0	0.0	6	60.0	3	30.
District of Columbia	11	5	45.5	0	0.0	9	81.8	6	54.5
Florida	180	21	11.7	4	2.2	125	69.4	31	17.2
Georgia	100	9	9.0	2	2.0	70	70.0	17	17.0
Maryland	44	15	34.1	0	0.0	38	86.4	22	50.0
North Carolina	108	18	16.7	1	0.9	90	83.3	17	15.7
South Carolina	79	14	17.7	0	0.0	57	72.2	5	6.3
Virginia	84	13	15.5	2	2.4	66	78.6	26	31.
West Virginia	55	14	25.5	1	1.8	38	69.1	4	
CENSUS DIVISION 4, EAST NORTH CENTRAL	706	184	26.1	31	4.4	560	79.3	226	
Illinois	165	56	33.9	8	4.8	137	83.0	46	
Indiana	122	25	20.5	5	4.1	100	82.0	29	23.
Michigan	130	45	34.6	5	3.8	113	86.9	46	35.4
Ohio	144	29	20.1	10	6.9	123	85.4	52	36.
Wisconsin	145	30	20.7	3	2.1	87	60.0	53	36.
CENSUS DIVISION 5, EAST SOUTH CENTRAL	367	49	13.4	4	1.1	220	62.7	23	6.3
Alabama	102	9	8.8	2	2.0	55	53.9	0	0.0
Kentucky	88	14	15.9	1	1.1	64	72.7	12	13.6
Mississippi	104	17	16.3	1	1.0	64	61.5	4	
Tennessee	73	9	12.3	0	0.0	47	64.4	7	
CENSUS DIVISION 6, WEST NORTH CENTRAL	637	111	17.4	26	4.1	421	66.1	109	17.
Iowa	124	25	20.2	4	3.2	96	77.4	29	23.
Kansas	143	10	7.0	1	0.7	64	44.8	8	5.6
Minnesota	105	24	22.9	8	7.6	91	77.1	31	29.5
Missouri	143	28	19.6	6	4.2	95	66.4	24	16.8
Nebraska	54	11	20.4	0	0.0	44	81.5	7	13.0
North Dakota	26	6	23.1	6	23.1	16	61.5	6	23.
South Dakota	42	7	16.7	1	2.4	25	59.5	4	
CENSUS DIVISION 7, WEST SOUTH CENTRAL	891	94	10.5	6	0.7	471	52.9	49	
Arkansas	88	8	9.1	0	0.0	50	56.8	5	
Louisiana	95	20	21.1	1	1.1	52	54.7	8	
Oklahoma	116	9	7.8	0	0.0	60	51.7	5	
Texas	592	57	9.6	5	0.8	309	52.2	30	5
CENSUS DIVISION 8, MOUNTAIN	319	71	22.3	13	4.1	235	73.7	83	26.
Arizona	48	13	27.1	3	6.3	35	72.9	19	
Colorado	72	16	22.2	4	5.6	58	90.6	33	
Idaho	32	9	28.1	2	6.3	26	81.3	6	
Montana	57	11	19.3	2	3.5	37	64.9	10	
Nevada	26	4	15.4	2	7.7	16	61.5	3	
New Mexico	29	9	31.0	0	0.0	22	75.9	3	
Utah	35	7	20.0	0	0.0	24	68.6	6	
Wyoming	20	2	10.0	0	0.0	17	85.0	3	
CENSUS DIVISION 9, PACIFIC	423	77	18.2	12	2.8	339	79.9	108	
Alaska	15	4	26.7	1	6.7	8	53.3	2	
California	249	38	15.3	6	2.4	197	79.4	66	
Hawaii	17	6	35.3	1	5.9	14	82.4	5	
Oregon	62	12	19.4	2	3.2	56	90.3	18	
Washington	81	17	21.0	2	2.5	63	77.8	18	

Example of Table 7.

Table 8 — Utilization, Personnel and Finances in Community Hospitals by MSAs for 2016

Table 8 at a Glance

This table provides a look at all U.S. Registered Community Hospitals, broken down by Metropolitan Statistical Area (MSA). The table includes general overview, utilization, personnel, and finance information. It provides a snapshot of the past year.

Additional Resources

Again, in the back of the book you will find the comprehensive glossary and the 2016 annual survey questionnaire. The survey itself can be a valuable resource to understanding what was asked in order to gather the data in the book. This survey is also used to produce the *AHA Guide®* and AHA Annual Survey Database™.

Hospital Requirements

An institution is considered a hospital by the American Hospital Association if it is licensed as general or specialty hospital by the appropriate state agency, and accredited as a hospital by one of the following organizations: The Joint Commission; Healthcare Facilities Accreditation Program (HFAP); DNV Healthcare accreditation; Center for Improvement in Healthcare Quality accreditation; or Medicare certified as a provider of acute service under Title 18 of the Social Security Act.

Types of Hospitals

Hospitals are registered as one of four types of hospitals: general, special, rehabilitation and chronic disease, or psychiatric. The following type of hospital and special requirements for registration are employed:

General

The primary function of the institution is to provide patient services, diagnostic and therapeutic, for a variety of medical conditions. A general hospital also shall provide:

- diagnostic x-ray services with facilities and staff for a variety of procedures
- clinical laboratory service with facilities and staff for a variety of procedures and with anatomical pathology services regularly and conveniently available
- operating room service with facilities and staff.

Special

The primary function of the institution is to provide diagnostic and treatment services for patients who have specified medical conditions, both surgical and nonsurgical. A special hospital also shall provide:

- such diagnostic and treatment services as may be determined by the Executive Committee of the Board of Trustees of the American Hospital Association to be appropriate for the specified medical conditions for which medical services are provided shall be maintained in the institution with suitable facilities and staff. If such conditions do not normally require diagnostic x-ray service, laboratory service, or operating room service, and if any such services are therefore not maintained in the institution, there shall be written arrangements to make them available to patients requiring them.
- clinical laboratory services capable of providing tissue diagnosis when offering pregnancy termination services.

Rehabilitation and Chronic Disease

The primary function of the institution is to provide diagnostic and treatment services to handicapped or disabled individuals requiring restorative and adjustive services. A rehabilitation and chronic disease hospital also shall provide:

- arrangements for diagnostic x-ray services, as required, on a regular and conveniently available basis
- arrangements for clinical laboratory service, as required on a regular and conveniently available basis
- arrangements for operating room service, as required, on a regular and conveniently available basis
- a physical therapy service with suitable facilities and staff in the institution
- an occupational therapy service with suitable facilities and staff in the institution
- arrangements for psychological and social work services on a regular and conveniently available basis

- arrangements for educational and vocational services on a regular and conveniently available basis
- written arrangements with a general hospital for the transfer of patients who require medical, obstetrical, or surgical services not available in the institution.

Psychiatric

The primary function of the institution is to provide diagnostic and treatment services for patients who have psychiatric-related illnesses. A psychiatric hospital also shall provide:

- arrangements for clinical laboratory service, as required, on a regular and conveniently available basis
- arrangements for diagnostic x-ray services, as required on a regular and conveniently available basis
- psychiatric, psychological, and social work service with facilities and staff in the institution
- arrangements for electroencephalograph services, as required, on a regular and conveniently available basis.
- written arrangements with a general hospital for the transfer of patients who require medical, obstetrical, or surgical services not available in the institution.

The American Hospital Association may, at the sole discretion of the Executive Committee of the Board of Trustees, grant, deny, or withdraw the registration of an institution.

The economic climate, demographic characteristics, personnel issues, and health care financing and payment policies differ by region, state, and city across the country. *Differences in these factors must be taken into account when using the data.* In addition, the profiles of hospitals across comparison groups vary. For example, states will differ in terms of the number and percentage of hospitals by size, ownership, services provided, types of patients treated, and so forth. *Differences in these variables also must be taken into consideration when doing a comparative analysis.*

The 2018 edition of *AHA Hospital Statistics*™ draws its data from the 2016 AHA Annual Survey of Hospitals. It is the statistical complement to the 2018 edition of the *AHA Guide*®, which contains selected data about individual hospitals.

The AHA Survey was mailed to all hospitals, both AHA-registered and nonregistered, in the U.S. and its associated areas: American Samoa, Guam, the Marshall Islands, Puerto Rico, and the Virgin Islands. U.S. government hospitals located outside the U.S. were not included. Overall, the average response rate over the past five years has been approximately 83 percent.

Reporting Period

In completing the survey, hospitals were requested to report data for a full year, in accord with their fiscal year, ending in 2016. The statistical table present data reported or estimated for a 12-month period, except for data on personnel, which represent situations as they existed at the end of the reporting period.

Respondents
Data for Tables 1 and 2 include 5,534 AHA-registered hospitals in the U.S. Data on community hospitals (nonfederal, short-term general and other special hospitals) only are presented in Tables 3-6, and Table 8.

It is important to note that the AHA-registered hospitals included in *AHA Hospital Statistics* are not necessarily identical to those included in *AHA Guide*. The institutions listed in the 2018 edition of *AHA Guide* include all of those institutions CMS certified, or Joint Commission accredited as of September 2017. Tables 1-6 in *AHA Hospital Statistics* present data for AHA-registered hospitals that were in operation during the 12-month reporting period ending 2016.

Estimates

Estimates were made of data for nonreporting hospitals and for reporting hospitals that submitted incomplete AHA Annual Survey questionnaires. Estimates were not made for beds, bassinets and facilities and services. Data for beds and bassinets of nonreporting hospitals were based on the most recent information from those hospitals. (Note that in all statistical tables, whenever bed-size categories are listed, all eight categories appear, whether or not there are hospitals in every category.)

Missing revenue, expenses, admissions, births, inpatient days, surgical operations, outpatient visits, and full-time-equivalent personnel values are estimates from regression models. For all other variables the estimates were based on ratios such as per bed averages derived from data reported by hospitals similar in size, control, major service provided, length of stay, and geographical characteristics to the hospitals that did not report this information.

Tables 1–2

Table

1

Historical Trends in Utilization, Personnel, and Finances for Selected Years from 1946 through 2016

Data are for all AHA-registered hospitals in the United States. Data are estimated for nonreporting hospitals with the exception of newborn and outpatient data before 1972. Personnel data exclude residents, interns, and students from 1952 on; personnel data include full-time personnel and full-time equivalents for part-time personnel from 1954 on. As a result of the AHA Annual Survey validation process, the New York state expense data from 1976 were revised after the 1977 edition was published. The revised figures are included below. In order to provide trend data on a consistent basis, the 1970 and 1971 psychiatric and long-term data have been slightly modified. The 1982 FTE figures have been updated to provide the most accurate data possible.

CLASSIFICATION	YEAR	HOSPITALS	BEDS (in thousands)	ADMISSIONS (in thousands)	AVERAGE DAILY CENSUS (in thousands)	ADJUSTED AVERAGE DAILY CENSUS (in thousands)	AVERAGE STAY (days)	OUTPATIENT VISITS (in thousands)	NEWBORNS Bassinets	NEWBORNS Births	FTE PERSONNEL Number (in thousands)	FTE PERSONNEL Per 100 Adjusted Census	TOTAL EXPENSES Amount (In Millions of dollars)	TOTAL EXPENSES Adjusted per Inpatient Stay (dollars)	TOTAL EXPENSES Adjusted per Inpatient Day (dollars)
Total United States	1946	6,125	1,436	15,675	1,142	—	—	—	85,585	2,135,327	830	—	$1,963	—	—
	1950	6,788	1,456	18,483	1,253	—	—	—	90,101	2,742,780	1,058	—	$3,651	—	—
	1955	6,956	1,604	21,073	1,363	—	—	—	98,823	3,476,753	1,301	—	$5,594	—	—
	1960	6,876	1,658	25,027	1,402	—	—	—	102,764	3,835,735	1,598	—	$8,421	—	—
	1965	7,123	1,704	28,812	1,403	—	—	125,793	101,287	3,565,344	1,952	—	$12,948	—	—
	1970	7,123	1,616	31,759	1,298	—	—	181,370	97,128	3,537,000	2,537	—	$25,556	—	—
	1971	7,097	1,556	32,664	1,237	—	—	199,725	94,344	3,464,513	2,589	—	$28,812	—	—
	1972	7,061	1,550	33,265	1,209	—	—	219,182	92,960	3,231,875	2,671	—	$32,667	—	—
	1973	7,123	1,535	34,352	1,189	—	—	233,555	90,071	3,087,210	2,769	—	$36,290	—	—
	1974	7,174	1,513	35,506	1,167	—	—	250,481	88,269	3,043,386	2,919	—	$41,406	—	—
	1975	7,156	1,466	36,157	1,125	—	—	254,844	86,875	3,091,629	3,023	—	$48,706	—	—
	1976	7,082	1,434	36,776	1,090	—	—	270,951	85,284	3,067,063	3,108	—	$56,005	—	—
	1977	7,099	1,407	37,060	1,066	—	—	263,775	83,193	3,223,699	3,213	—	$63,630	—	—
	1978	7,015	1,381	37,243	1,042	—	—	263,606	80,650	3,250,373	3,280	—	$70,927	—	—
	1979	6,988	1,372	37,802	1,043	—	—	262,009	79,720	3,376,467	3,382	—	$79,796	—	—
	1980	6,965	1,365	38,892	1,060	—	—	262,951	79,842	3,500,043	3,492	—	$91,886	—	—
	1981	6,933	1,362	39,169	1,061	—	—	265,332	78,823	3,558,274	3,661	—	$107,146	—	—
	1982	6,915	1,360	39,095	1,053	—	—	313,667	77,998	3,615,751	3,746	—	$123,219	—	—
	1983	6,888	1,350	38,887	1,028	—	—	273,168	77,837	3,596,146	3,707	—	$136,315	—	—
	1984	6,872	1,339	37,938	970	—	—	276,566	77,845	3,563,106	3,630	—	$144,114	—	—
	1985	6,872	1,318	36,304	910	—	—	282,140	77,202	3,630,961	3,625	—	$153,327	—	—
	1986	6,841	1,290	35,219	883	—	—	294,634	76,002	3,680,178	3,647	—	$165,194	—	—
	1987	6,821	1,267	34,439	873	—	—	310,707	74,770	3,698,294	3,742	—	$178,662	—	—
	1988	6,780	1,248	34,107	863	—	—	336,208	72,568	3,794,369	3,839	—	$196,704	—	—
	1989	6,720	1,226	33,742	853	—	—	352,248	71,491	3,920,384	3,937	—	$214,886	—	—
	1990	6,649	1,213	33,774	844	—	—	368,184	70,539	4,046,704	4,063	—	$234,870	—	—
	1991	6,634	1,202	33,567	827	—	—	387,675	69,464	4,047,504	4,165	—	$258,508	—	—
	1992	6,539	1,178	33,536	807	—	—	417,874	69,052	4,007,179	4,236	—	$282,531	—	—
	1993	6,467	1,163	33,201	783	—	—	435,619	67,911	3,949,788	4,289	—	$301,538	—	—
	1994	6,374	1,128	33,125	745	—	—	453,584	67,311	3,886,667	4,270	—	$310,834	—	—
	1995	6,291	1,081	33,282	710	—	—	483,195	66,256	3,833,132	4,273	—	$320,252	—	—
	1996	6,201	1,062	33,307	685	—	—	505,455	65,138	3,790,678	4,276	—	$330,531	—	—
	1997	6,097	1,035	33,624	673	—	—	520,600	64,649	3,811,522	4,333	—	$342,334	—	—
	1998	6,021	1,013	33,766	662	—	—	545,481	63,485	3,795,212	4,407	—	$355,450	—	—
	1999	5,890	994	34,181	657	—	—	573,461	62,714	3,829,881	4,369	—	$372,933	—	—
	2000	5,810	984	34,891	650	—	—	592,673	61,915	3,940,017	4,454	—	$395,391	—	—
	2001	5,801	987	35,644	658	—	—	612,276	61,527	3,929,733	4,535	—	$426,849	—	—
	2002	5,794	976	36,326	662	—	—	640,515	62,151	3,934,421	4,610	—	$462,222	—	—
	2003	5,764	965	36,611	657	—	—	648,560	60,699	3,976,886	4,651	—	$498,104	—	—
	2004	5,759	956	36,942	658	—	—	662,131	59,660	3,965,906	4,696	—	$533,853	—	—
	2005	5,756	947	37,006	656	—	—	673,689	59,073	4,048,442	4,791	—	$570,534	—	—
	2006	5,747	947	37,189	653	—	—	690,425	58,670	4,126,598	4,907	—	$607,355	—	—
	2007	5,708	945	37,120	645	—	—	693,510	58,429	4,128,796	5,024	—	$641,124	—	—
	2008	5,815	951	37,529	649	—	—	709,960	58,133	4,109,081	5,116	—	$690,074	—	—
	2009	5,795	944	37,480	641	—	—	741,551	58,078	4,001,748	5,178	—	$726,671	—	—
	2010	5,754	942	36,915	627	—	—	750,408	57,396	3,871,751	5,184	—	$750,602	—	—
	2011	5,724	924	36,565	615	—	—	754,454	57,022	3,767,697	5,196	—	$773,547	—	—
	2012	5,723	921	36,156	600	—	—	777,961	56,693	3,754,085	5,258	—	$829,665	—	—
	2013	5,686	915	35,416	592	—	—	787,422	57,037	3,749,696	5,342	—	$859,419	—	—
	2014	5,627	902	34,879	584	—	—	802,680	56,481	3,787,573	5,314	—	$892,701	—	—
	2015	5,564	898	35,061	588	—	—	832,325	55,958	3,786,130	5,397	—	$936,532	—	—
	2016	5,534	895	35,159	589	—	—	863,654	55,774	3,761,594	5,563	—	$991,532	—	—

Table 1 (Continued)

Total nonfederal short-term general and other special

YEAR	HOSPITALS	BEDS (in thousands)	ADMISSIONS (in thousands)	AVERAGE DAILY CENSUS (in thousands)	ADJUSTED AVERAGE DAILY CENSUS (in thousands)	AVERAGE STAY (days)	OUTPATIENT VISITS (in thousands)	NEWBORNS Bassinets	NEWBORNS Births	FTE PERSONNEL Number (in thousands)	FTE PERSONNEL Per 100 Adjusted Census	TOTAL EXPENSES Amount (In Millions of dollars)	TOTAL EXPENSES Adjusted per Inpatient Stay (dollars)	TOTAL EXPENSES Adjusted per Inpatient Day (dollars)
1946	4,444	473	13,655	341	—	9.1	—	80,987	2,087,503	505	—	$1,169	—	—
1950	5,031	505	16,663	372	—	8.1	—	86,019	2,660,982	662	—	$2,120	—	—
1955	5,237	568	19,100	407	—	7.8	—	93,868	3,304,451	826	—	$3,434	—	—
1960	5,407	639	22,970	477	—	7.6	—	98,127	3,678,051	1,080	—	$5,617	—	—
1965	5,736	741	26,463	563	620	7.8	92,631	96,782	3,413,370	1,386	224	$9,147	$316.37	$40.56
1970	5,859	848	29,252	662	727	8.2	133,545	93,079	3,403,064	1,929	265	$19,560	$604.59	$73.73
1971	5,865	867	30,142	665	736	8.0	148,423	90,444	3,337,605	1,999	272	$22,400	$667.44	$83.43
1972	5,843	884	30,777	664	739	7.9	166,983	89,315	3,119,446	2,056	278	$25,549	$747.42	$94.61
1973	5,891	903	31,761	681	768	7.8	178,939	86,851	2,987,089	2,149	280	$28,496	$793.88	$101.78
1974	5,977	931	32,943	701	793	7.8	194,838	85,208	2,947,342	2,289	289	$32,751	$883.04	$113.21
1975	5,979	947	33,519	708	806	7.7	196,311	83,834	2,998,590	2,399	298	$39,110	$1,024.72	$133.08
1976	5,956	961	34,068	715	816	7.7	207,725	82,307	2,962,305	2,483	304	$45,402	$1,172.25	$152.24
1977	5,973	974	34,353	717	820	7.6	204,238	80,228	3,117,756	2,581	315	$51,832	$1,316.70	$173.25
1978	5,935	980	34,575	720	841	7.6	204,461	78,090	3,156,570	2,662	323	$58,348	$1,470.13	$193.81
1979	5,923	988	35,160	729	841	7.6	203,873	77,277	3,287,157	2,762	328	$66,184	$1,631.16	$215.75
1980	5,904	992	36,198	748	861	7.6	206,752	77,539	3,408,699	2,879	334	$76,970	$1,844.19	$244.44
1981	5,879	1,007	36,494	764	876	7.6	206,729	76,567	3,465,683	3,039	347	$90,739	$2,167.70	$283.94
1982	5,863	1,015	36,429	763	882	7.6	250,888	75,739	3,514,761	3,110	353	$105,094	$2,493.09	$326.68
1983	5,843	1,021	36,201	750	869	7.6	213,995	75,471	3,490,629	3,102	357	$116,632	$2,775.55	$368.01
1984	5,814	1,020	35,202	703	824	7.3	216,474	75,587	3,456,467	3,023	367	$123,550	$2,984.00	$409.85
1985	5,784	1,003	33,501	650	780	7.1	222,773	74,899	3,521,296	3,003	385	$130,700	$3,238.94	$459.57
1986	5,728	982	32,410	631	774	7.1	234,270	73,688	3,584,530	3,032	392	$140,907	$3,529.60	$499.19
1987	5,659	961	31,633	624	780	7.2	247,704	72,516	3,602,416	3,120	400	$152,909	$3,848.79	$536.96
1988	5,579	949	31,480	622	795	7.2	271,436	70,361	3,706,748	3,209	404	$168,941	$4,194.39	$581.08
1989	5,497	936	31,141	619	805	7.3	287,909	69,436	3,831,051	3,307	411	$185,204	$4,572.23	$630.59
1990	5,420	929	31,203	620	820	7.3	302,691	68,443	3,958,646	3,423	417	$203,927	$4,929.93	$681.52
1991	5,370	926	31,084	612	828	7.2	323,202	67,440	3,965,489	3,539	427	$225,230	$5,345.63	$745.37
1992	5,321	923	31,053	606	832	7.1	349,397	67,095	3,925,024	3,624	436	$248,318	$5,788.52	$815.99
1993	5,289	921	30,770	593	834	7.0	368,358	66,060	3,870,392	3,681	441	$266,382	$6,120.94	$874.98
1994	5,256	904	30,739	569	814	6.8	384,880	65,728	3,809,367	3,697	454	$276,148	$6,230.33	$929.65
1995	5,220	874	30,966	549	811	6.5	415,710	64,742	3,764,756	3,718	458	$286,073	$6,220.54	$966.79
1996	5,160	864	31,116	531	800	6.2	440,845	63,646	3,723,907	3,728	466	$293,920	$6,225.95	$1,005.45
1997	5,082	855	31,595	529	813	6.1	450,907	63,247	3,742,240	3,794	467	$306,088	$6,266.24	$1,031.68
1998	5,039	842	31,830	527	821	6.0	474,366	62,162	3,726,234	3,835	467	$319,035	$6,387.53	$1,064.93
1999	4,977	831	32,377	527	835	5.9	495,850	61,534	3,760,295	3,840	460	$335,405	$6,512.44	$1,101.47
2000	4,934	825	33,102	527	850	5.8	522,970	60,845	3,880,166	3,916	461	$356,757	$6,650.68	$1,147.99
2001	4,927	828	33,834	534	866	5.8	539,316	60,454	3,873,395	3,990	461	$383,911	$6,979.29	$1,216.04
2002	4,949	823	34,501	541	887	5.7	557,336	59,974	3,870,191	4,072	459	$416,791	$7,353.17	$1,288.63
2003	4,918	815	34,800	540	895	5.7	563,804	59,662	3,915,842	4,112	459	$450,403	$7,798.19	$1,378.78
2004	4,942	810	35,098	542	910	5.6	573,126	58,710	3,931,508	4,151	456	$481,517	$8,168.06	$1,449.90
2005	4,956	804	35,265	542	930	5.6	587,296	58,195	3,987,766	4,260	458	$516,172	$8,538.30	$1,521.58
2006	4,947	805	35,403	540	940	5.6	599,597	57,832	4,075,193	4,347	462	$552,276	$8,972.85	$1,610.76
2007	4,915	803	35,370	535	944	5.5	603,411	57,546	4,077,962	4,468	473	$583,550	$9,377.82	$1,694.38
2008	5,026	810	35,776	538	963	5.5	624,185	57,301	4,073,724	4,552	473	$626,823	$9,789.69	$1,780.45
2009	5,023	807	35,603	529	973	5.4	643,420	57,302	3,960,432	4,594	472	$657,242	$10,042.56	$1,851.44
2010	4,995	806	35,160	520	974	5.4	651,617	56,610	3,818,399	4,603	473	$678,254	$10,316.07	$1,908.59
2011	4,983	799	34,852	514	983	5.4	657,071	56,290	3,730,342	4,654	473	$702,822	$10,542.09	$1,959.69
2012	5,010	802	34,438	508	992	5.4	675,223	55,987	3,715,479	4,732	477	$757,213	$11,222.23	$2,089.07
2013	4,986	797	33,625	501	963	5.4	678,203	56,342	3,699,411	4,788	497	$782,360	$11,653.75	$2,155.63
2014	4,945	789	33,093	496	1,004	5.5	693,346	55,824	3,735,593	4,758	474	$809,361	$12,016.89	$2,210.78
2015	4,872	783	33,302	498	1,029	5.5	722,392	55,305	3,752,215	4,859	472	$851,782	$12,355.65	$2,269.68
2016	4,850	781	33,439	500	1,057	5.5	747,310	55,149	3,727,427	4,993	472	$903,158	$12,778.28	$2,336.94

Table 1 (Continued)

CLASSIFICATION / YEAR	HOSPITALS	BEDS (in thousands)	ADMISSIONS (in thousands)	AVERAGE DAILY CENSUS (in thousands)	ADJUSTED AVERAGE DAILY CENSUS (in thousands)	AVERAGE STAY (days)	OUTPATIENT VISITS (in thousands)	NEWBORNS Bassinets	NEWBORNS Births	FTE PERSONNEL Number (in thousands)	FTE PERSONNEL Per 100 Adjusted Census	TOTAL EXPENSES Amount (In Millions of dollars)	TOTAL EXPENSES Adjusted per Inpatient Stay (dollars)	TOTAL EXPENSES Adjusted per Inpatient Day (dollars)
Total community hospitals														
1975	5,875	942	33,435	706	798	7.7	190,672	83,829	2,998,552	2,392	300	$38,962	$1,030.34	$133.81
1976	5,857	956	33,979	713	810	7.7	201,247	82,296	2,962,216	2,475	306	$45,240	$1,176.25	$152.76
1979	5,842	984	35,099	727	833	7.6	198,778	77,266	3,287,012	2,756	331	$66,004	$1,641.67	$217.34
1980	5,830	988	36,143	747	857	7.6	202,310	77,522	3,408,482	2,873	335	$76,851	$1,851.04	$245.12
1981	5,813	1,003	36,438	763	873	7.6	202,768	76,561	3,465,401	3,033	347	$90,572	$2,171.20	$284.33
1982	5,801	1,012	36,379	762	878	7.6	248,124	75,733	3,514,457	3,103	353	$104,876	$2,500.52	$327.37
1983	5,783	1,018	36,152	749	864	7.6	210,044	75,465	3,490,254	3,096	358	$116,438	$2,789.18	$369.49
1984	5,759	1,017	35,155	702	820	7.3	211,961	75,581	3,456,308	3,017	368	$123,336	$2,995.38	$411.10
1985	5,732	1,001	33,449	649	777	7.1	218,716	74,893	3,521,135	2,997	386	$130,499	$3,244.74	$460.19
1986	5,678	978	32,379	629	770	7.1	231,912	73,682	3,584,408	3,025	393	$140,654	$3,532.51	$500.81
1987	5,611	958	31,601	622	776	7.2	245,524	72,510	3,602,296	3,114	401	$152,585	$3,850.16	$538.96
1988	5,533	947	31,453	620	787	7.2	269,129	70,325	3,706,402	3,205	407	$168,722	$4,206.73	$586.33
1989	5,455	933	31,116	618	796	7.2	285,712	69,405	3,830,615	3,303	415	$184,898	$4,587.87	$636.96
1990	5,384	927	31,181	619	813	7.2	301,329	68,412	3,958,263	3,420	421	$203,693	$4,946.68	$686.83
1991	5,342	924	31,064	611	820	7.2	322,048	67,434	3,965,396	3,535	431	$225,023	$5,359.56	$752.10
1992	5,292	921	31,034	604	827	7.1	348,522	67,089	3,924,944	3,620	437	$248,095	$5,794.43	$819.83
1993	5,261	919	30,748	592	828	7.0	366,885	66,054	3,870,376	3,677	444	$266,089	$6,132.06	$880.52
1994	5,229	902	30,718	568	812	6.7	382,924	65,722	3,809,367	3,692	455	$275,779	$6,229.83	$930.71
1995	5,194	873	30,945	548	809	6.5	414,345	64,736	3,764,698	3,714	459	$285,588	$6,215.51	$967.69
1996	5,134	862	31,099	531	799	6.2	439,863	63,640	3,723,871	3,725	466	$293,755	$6,224.94	$1,006.14
1997	5,057	853	31,577	528	811	6.1	450,140	63,241	3,742,191	3,790	467	$305,763	$6,261.93	$1,032.70
1998	5,015	840	31,812	525	819	6.0	474,193	62,156	3,726,233	3,831	468	$318,834	$6,385.99	$1,066.96
1999	4,956	830	32,359	526	833	5.9	495,346	61,528	3,760,295	3,838	461	$335,246	$6,511.72	$1,102.61
2000	4,915	824	33,089	526	849	5.8	521,404	60,839	3,880,166	3,911	461	$356,564	$6,648.82	$1,149.40
2001	4,908	826	33,814	533	865	5.7	538,480	60,448	3,873,395	3,987	461	$383,735	$6,979.53	$1,217.27
2002	4,927	821	34,478	540	886	5.7	556,404	59,974	3,870,191	4,069	459	$416,591	$7,354.60	$1,289.87
2003	4,895	813	34,783	539	894	5.7	563,186	59,662	3,915,842	4,109	460	$450,124	$7,796.41	$1,379.48
2004	4,919	808	35,086	541	909	5.6	571,569	58,710	3,931,508	4,148	456	$481,247	$8,165.55	$1,450.35
2005	4,936	802	35,239	540	929	5.6	584,429	58,195	3,987,766	4,257	458	$515,740	$8,534.90	$1,522.42
2006	4,927	803	35,378	538	939	5.6	599,553	57,832	4,075,193	4,343	463	$551,835	$8,970.31	$1,612.23
2007	4,897	801	35,346	533	943	5.5	603,300	57,546	4,077,962	4,465	474	$583,252	$9,377.17	$1,696.10
2008	5,010	808	35,761	536	962	5.5	624,098	57,301	4,073,724	4,550	473	$626,577	$9,788.25	$1,782.28
2009	5,008	806	35,527	528	970	5.4	641,953	57,282	3,959,605	4,585	472	$656,156	$10,045.15	$1,852.59
2010	4,985	805	35,149	520	973	5.4	651,424	56,610	3,818,399	4,600	473	$677,968	$10,313.44	$1,909.64
2011	4,973	797	34,843	513	982	5.4	656,079	56,290	3,730,342	4,650	473	$702,091	$10,532.52	$1,959.58
2012	4,999	801	34,422	507	991	5.4	674,971	55,987	3,715,479	4,731	477	$756,917	$11,220.70	$2,090.01
2013	4,974	796	33,609	500	962	5.4	677,951	56,342	3,699,411	4,786	497	$782,035	$11,650.90	$2,156.94
2014	4,926	787	33,067	494	1,002	5.5	693,107	55,824	3,735,593	4,755	474	$808,869	$12,015.42	$2,212.22
2015	4,862	783	33,261	497	1,027	5.5	722,121	55,305	3,752,215	4,859	473	$851,515	$12,359.32	$2,270.51
2016	4,840	780	33,425	499	1,056	5.5	747,088	55,149	3,727,427	4,991	473	$902,891	$12,777.25	$2,337.82

Table 1 (Continued)

CLASSIFICATION	YEAR	HOSPITALS	BEDS (in thousands)	ADMISSIONS (in thousands)	AVERAGE DAILY CENSUS (in thousands)	ADJUSTED AVERAGE DAILY CENSUS (in thousands)	AVERAGE STAY (days)	OUTPATIENT VISITS (in thousands)	NEWBORNS Bassinets	NEWBORNS Births	FTE PERSONNEL Number (in thousands)	FTE PERSONNEL Per 100 Adjusted Census	TOTAL EXPENSES Amount (In Millions of dollars)	TOTAL EXPENSES Adjusted per Inpatient Stay (dollars)	TOTAL EXPENSES Adjusted per Inpatient Day (dollars)
Nongovernment not-for-profit community hospitals	1975	3,339	658	23,722	510	574	7.8	131,435	57,496	2,131,057	1,712	298	$27,938	$1,040.21	$133.36
	1976	3,345	670	24,082	517	586	7.9	140,914	56,442	2,100,917	1,791	306	$32,764	$1,208.23	$152.94
	1979	3,330	690	24,874	528	603	7.7	139,565	52,859	2,308,548	1,999	332	$47,937	$1,684.40	$218.06
	1980	3,322	692	25,566	542	621	7.7	142,156	52,659	2,389,478	2,086	336	$55,780	$1,901.64	$245.74
	1981	3,340	706	25,945	555	636	7.8	143,380	52,302	2,455,033	2,213	399	$66,267	$2,225.17	$285.64
	1982	3,338	712	25,898	553	637	7.8	176,245	51,566	2,483,345	2,265	355	$76,806	$2,572.93	$330.41
	1983	3,347	718	25,827	544	629	7.7	150,839	51,649	2,465,604	2,270	362	$85,637	$2,868.80	$373.78
	1984	3,351	716	25,236	512	598	7.4	153,281	51,491	2,446,540	2,222	372	$90,814	$3,072.51	$415.04
	1985	3,349	707	24,179	476	569	7.2	158,953	51,424	2,507,288	2,216	389	$96,150	$3,307.41	$462.69
	1986	3,323	689	23,483	460	563	7.2	167,633	50,885	2,547,170	2,241	398	$103,524	$3,589.64	$503.64
	1987	3,274	673	22,937	455	566	7.2	177,413	50,133	2,557,294	2,298	406	$112,325	$3,914.23	$543.67
	1988	3,242	668	22,939	456	577	7.3	195,363	48,828	2,653,794	2,373	412	$124,703	$4,272.95	$591.13
	1989	3,220	661	22,792	455	584	7.3	209,191	48,305	2,751,426	2,454	420	$136,889	$4,649.22	$642.45
	1990	3,191	657	22,878	455	596	7.3	221,073	47,441	2,833,204	2,533	424	$150,673	$5,001.24	$692.36
	1991	3,175	656	22,964	451	603	7.2	238,204	47,229	2,845,995	2,624	435	$166,806	$5,393.30	$758.21
	1992	3,173	656	23,056	445	606	7.1	257,887	47,185	2,846,386	2,692	443	$183,793	$5,808.80	$828.44
	1993	3,154	651	22,749	432	602	6.9	270,138	46,214	2,802,164	2,711	451	$197,187	$6,177.69	$897.70
	1994	3,139	637	22,704	413	589	6.6	282,653	46,381	2,792,116	2,719	462	$204,219	$6,256.72	$950.31
	1995	3,092	610	22,557	393	578	6.4	303,851	45,198	2,725,641	2,702	468	$215,950	$6,279.17	$994.39
	1996	3,045	598	22,542	379	567	6.1	320,746	44,650	2,683,750	2,711	478	$225,287	$6,344.05	$1,042.04
	1997	3,000	591	22,905	376	575	6.0	330,215	44,484	2,698,086	2,765	481	$237,978	$6,392.74	$1,074.26
	1998	3,026	588	23,282	377	587	5.9	352,114	44,087	2,715,958	2,834	483		$6,525.68	$1,110.50
	1999	3,012	587	23,871	381	605	5.8	370,784	44,172	2,746,453	2,862	473	$251,534	$6,607.51	$1,139.89
	2000	3,003	583	24,452	382	618	5.7	393,168	43,655	2,833,615	2,919	472	$267,051	$6,717.48	$1,182.32
	2001	2,998	585	24,983	385	628	5.6	404,901	43,640	2,829,691	2,971	473	$287,250	$7,051.76	$1,255.25
	2002	3,025	582	25,425	391	646	5.6	416,910	43,241	2,820,159	3,039	471	$312,726	$7,457.84	$1,328.81
	2003	2,984	575	25,668	389	647	5.5	424,215	42,965	2,854,764	3,059	473	$337,696	$7,904.93	$1,429.62
	2004	2,967	568	25,757	388	655	5.5	430,262	41,968	2,844,617	3,077	470	$359,414	$8,266.64	$1,501.09
	2005	2,958	561	25,881	388	667	5.5	441,653	41,585	2,876,677	3,155	473	$385,993	$8,670.83	$1,585.34
	2006	2,919	559	25,798	385	671	5.4	453,501	40,888	2,905,275	3,207	478	$412,868	$9,189.58	$1,685.62
	2007	2,913	554	25,752	380	673	5.4	455,825	40,681	2,907,002	3,286	488	$436,319	$9,592.93	$1,776.06
	2008	2,923	557	25,899	380	683	5.4	469,804	40,567	2,901,854	3,340	489	$468,080	$10,080.50	$1,875.78
	2009	2,918	556	25,783	375	690	5.3	485,935	40,467	2,822,527	3,369	488	$492,853	$10,379.09	$1,956.71
	2010	2,904	556	25,532	368	691	5.3	494,178	39,946	2,750,163	3,388	490	$510,744	$10,651.81	$2,025.05
	2011	2,903	548	25,185	362	694	5.2	496,643	39,651	2,692,577	3,427	494	$528,303	$10,932.55	$2,088.05
	2012	2,894	545	24,751	354	697	5.2	512,237	39,778	2,684,600	3,477	499	$563,960	$11,563.17	$2,214.26
	2013	2,904	544	24,319	350	683	5.3	516,162	40,180	2,687,441	3,500	513	$585,470	$12,000.35	$2,288.77
	2014	2,870	535	23,742	344	704	5.3	525,424	39,497	2,707,766	3,494	496	$602,571	$12,384.99	$2,345.55
	2015	2,845	531	23,886	346	722	5.3	547,389	39,150	2,719,115	3,562	493	$635,995	$12,754.64	$2,412.87
	2016	2,849	533	24,097	349	744	5.3	568,993	39,246	2,722,575	3,681	495	$676,792	$13,182.10	$2,487.61

Table 1 (Continued)

CLASSIFICATION / YEAR	HOSPITALS	BEDS (in thousands)	ADMISSIONS (in thousands)	AVERAGE DAILY CENSUS (in thousands)	ADJUSTED AVERAGE DAILY CENSUS (in thousands)	AVERAGE STAY (days)	OUTPATIENT VISITS (in thousands)	NEWBORNS Bassinets	NEWBORNS Births	FTE PERSONNEL Number (in thousands)	FTE PERSONNEL Per 100 Adjusted Census	TOTAL EXPENSES Amount (in Millions of dollars)	TOTAL EXPENSES Adjusted per Inpatient Stay (dollars)	TOTAL EXPENSES Adjusted per Inpatient Day (dollars)
Investor-owned (for-profit) community hospitals														
1975	775	73	2,646	48	53	6.6	7,713	4,062	141,392	139	263	$2,561	$876.48	$132.80
1976	752	76	2,734	50	54	6.6	8,048	4,044	144,751	147	272	$3,085	$1,031.91	$156.35
1979	727	83	2,963	53	59	6.6	9,289	4,110	174,843	174	300	$4,820	$1,476.42	$225.87
1980	730	87	3,165	57	62	6.5	9,696	4,439	199,722	189	304	$5,847	$1,675.85	$257.12
1981	729	88	3,239	58	63	6.5	9,961	4,523	207,405	203	322	$6,856	$1,952.56	$299.02
1982	748	91	3,316	60	66	6.6	13,193	4,736	219,675	212	320	$8,177	$2,224.75	$340.03
1983	757	94	3,299	59	66	6.5	10,389	5,039	228,883	213	323	$9,208	$2,517.53	$385.42
1984	786	100	3,314	57	64	6.3	11,090	5,807	242,088	214	335	$10,251	$2,748.51	$438.30
1985	805	104	3,242	54	63	6.1	12,378	6,117	266,839	221	350	$11,486	$3,033.06	$500.48
1986	834	107	3,231	54	65	6.1	14,896	6,305	291,112	229	354	$12,987	$3,341.79	$552.40
1987	828	106	3,157	54	66	6.2	16,566	6,391	306,492	242	367	$14,067	$3,617.19	$585.01
1988	790	104	3,090	53	66	6.2	17,926	6,254	308,828	249	379	$15,545	$4,022.77	$649.33
1989	769	102	3,071	53	67	6.3	19,341	6,354	325,711	261	390	$17,240	$4,406.20	$707.90
1990	749	101	3,066	54	69	6.4	20,110	6,261	340,555	273	396	$18,822	$4,727.27	$751.55
1991	738	100	3,016	52	69	6.3	21,174	6,358	359,115	281	409	$20,516	$5,133.53	$820.19
1992	723	99	2,969	51	69	6.3	22,900	6,519	357,776	285	412	$22,496	$5,548.24	$888.73
1993	717	99	2,946	51	69	6.2	24,936	6,395	363,358	289	417	$23,077	$5,643.21	$914.39
1994	719	101	3,035	50	70	6.1	26,443	6,329	354,477	302	434	$23,445	$5,528.91	$923.90
1995	752	106	3,428	55	77	5.8	31,940	7,164	408,339	343	443	$26,653	$5,425.20	$946.99
1996	759	109	3,684	56	82	5.6	37,347	7,441	444,697	359	437	$28,385	$5,207.44	$945.49
1997	797	115	3,953	60	89	5.5	40,919	8,026	465,919	385	433	$31,179	$5,218.69	$961.96
1998	771	113	3,971	60	90	5.5	42,072	7,895	466,025	383	425	$31,732	$5,262.44	$968.00
1999	747	107	3,905	58	86	5.5	39,896	7,486	467,585	362	422	$31,179	$5,350.07	$999.03
2000	749	110	4,141	61	90	5.4	43,378	7,792	503,497	378	418	$34,969	$5,642.18	$1,057.32
2001	754	109	4,197	63	92	5.4	44,706	7,413	494,669	379	413	$37,348	$5,971.81	$1,121.31
2002	766	108	4,365	64	93	5.3	45,215	7,467	496,988	380	407	$40,082	$6,161.44	$1,180.83
2003	790	110	4,481	65	95	5.3	44,246	7,491	515,693	391	411	$43,953	$6,589.91	$1,264.50
2004	835	113	4,599	68	100	5.4	44,962	7,763	534,503	406	406	$48,971	$7,139.13	$1,362.42
2005	868	114	4,618	68	101	5.3	46,016	7,714	546,307	421	418	$51,833	$7,351.96	$1,412.74
2006	890	115	4,735	68	103	5.2	44,237	8,012	574,113	423	413	$55,030	$7,422.08	$1,471.53
2007	873	116	4,626	66	101	5.2	43,943	7,760	555,670	432	429	$56,405	$7,823.44	$1,535.98
2008	982	121	4,839	70	109	5.3	44,897	7,791	562,711	450	414	$61,762	$7,984.62	$1,555.55
2009	998	122	4,887	70	112	5.3	47,281	7,965	553,233	464	414	$64,367	$8,037.18	$1,573.64
2010	1,013	125	4,925	71	113	5.3	48,201	7,965	525,427	474	420	$67,168	$8,336.16	$1,628.90
2011	1,025	128	5,060	73	119	5.3	50,013	8,137	508,330	485	409	$70,340	$8,262.74	$1,627.65
2012	1,068	135	5,224	77	124	5.3	53,854	8,192	530,941	515	414	$79,114	$8,860.94	$1,746.85
2013	1,060	135	5,052	77	118	5.5	53,191	8,228	522,864	553	469	$81,552	$9,296.42	$1,791.20
2014	1,053	136	5,119	77	130	5.5	56,299	8,478	537,273	522	401	$85,398	$9,413.69	$1,797.74
2015	1,034	135	5,192	77	133	5.4	58,633	8,587	546,736	534	401	$88,814	$9,510.45	$1,830.67
2016	1,035	134	5,287	78	136	5.4	61,256	8,608	536,389	551	405	$94,031	$9,697.57	$1,889.09

Table 1 (Continued)

CLASSIFICATION	YEAR	HOSPITALS	BEDS (in thousands)	ADMISSIONS (in thousands)	AVERAGE DAILY CENSUS (in thousands)	ADJUSTED AVERAGE DAILY CENSUS (in thousands)	AVERAGE STAY (days)	OUTPATIENT VISITS (in thousands)	NEWBORNS Bassinets	NEWBORNS Births	FTE PERSONNEL Number (in thousands)	FTE PERSONNEL Per 100 Adjusted Census	TOTAL EXPENSES Amount (in Millions of dollars)	TOTAL EXPENSES Adjusted per Inpatient Stay (dollars)	TOTAL EXPENSES Adjusted per Inpatient Day (dollars)
State and local government community hospitals	1975	1,761	210	7,067	148	171	7.6	51,525	22,271	726,103	540	316	$8,463	$1,030.86	$135.64
	1976	1,760	210	7,163	146	170	7.5	52,286	21,810	716,548	537	315	$9,391	$1,132.50	$151.00
	1979	1,785	211	7,262	146	171	7.4	49,924	20,297	803,621	583	341	$13,247	$1,561.04	$211.89
	1980	1,778	209	7,413	149	174	7.3	50,459	20,424	819,282	598	343	$15,204	$1,750.13	$238.63
	1981	1,744	210	7,255	150	174	7.6	49,427	19,736	802,963	618	354	$17,449	$2,071.57	$274.25
	1982	1,715	210	7,165	149	175	7.6	58,685	19,431	811,437	627	320	$19,893	$2,364.09	$311.56
	1983	1,679	207	7,025	145	170	7.6	48,816	18,777	795,767	613	360	$21,593	$2,621.28	$347.56
	1984	1,622	201	6,606	133	158	7.3	47,590	18,283	767,680	581	368	$22,271	$2,823.13	$385.17
	1985	1,578	189	6,028	119	145	7.2	47,386	17,352	747,008	561	387	$22,863	$3,106.14	$432.84
	1986	1,521	182	5,665	114	142	7.4	49,383	16,492	746,126	555	391	$24,143	$3,404.69	$466.17
	1987	1,509	180	5,507	113	144	7.5	51,544	15,986	738,510	573	399	$26,192	$3,717.77	$499.33
	1988	1,501	175	5,424	112	145	7.6	55,840	15,243	743,780	583	403	$28,474	$4,033.67	$538.63
	1989	1,466	170	5,253	110	145	7.7	57,179	14,746	753,478	589	406	$30,769	$4,430.12	$582.15
	1990	1,444	169	5,236	111	148	7.7	60,146	14,710	784,504	614	415	$34,198	$4,837.76	$634.45
	1991	1,429	168	5,084	108	148	7.8	62,670	13,847	760,286	630	424	$37,701	$5,339.75	$695.89
	1992	1,396	166	5,008	108	152	7.9	67,734	13,385	720,782	643	424	$41,806	$5,870.76	$753.92
	1993	1,390	169	5,054	109	157	7.8	71,811	13,445	704,854	676	430	$45,825	$6,205.52	$799.73
	1994	1,371	164	4,979	104	154	7.6	73,828	13,012	662,774	672	438	$48,115	$6,513.39	$858.62
	1995	1,350	157	4,961	100	154	7.4	78,554	12,374	630,718	670	435	$49,322	$6,445.18	$877.85
	1996	1,330	155	4,873	96	150	7.2	81,770	11,549	595,424	654	437	$49,420	$6,418.65	$903.41
	1997	1,260	148	4,720	92	148	7.1	79,007	10,731	578,186	640	433	$49,298	$6,475.07	$913.62
	1998	1,218	139	4,559	87	142	7.0	80,008	10,174	544,250	614	433	$49,123	$6,612.23	$949.36
	1999	1,197	136	4,583	86	143	6.9	84,667	9,870	546,257	614	430	$52,534	$6,923.35	$1,006.91
	2000	1,163	131	4,496	83	140	6.7	84,858	9,392	543,054	614	438	$54,544	$7,106.05	$1,063.75
	2001	1,156	132	4,634	85	145	6.7	88,873	9,395	549,035	637	438	$59,137	$7,400.01	$1,113.79
	2002	1,136	130	4,688	84	147	6.6	94,280	9,266	553,044	651	442	$63,783	$7,772.93	$1,188.12
	2003	1,121	129	4,634	84	152	6.6	94,725	9,206	545,385	658	434	$68,475	$8,205.10	$1,237.64
	2004	1,117	128	4,730	85	154	6.5	96,345	8,979	552,388	666	431	$72,861	$8,473.18	$1,291.06
	2005	1,110	128	4,740	85	161	6.5	96,760	8,896	564,782	681	424	$77,914	$8,793.26	$1,329.64
	2006	1,119	128	4,848	86	165	6.5	101,845	8,932	595,805	713	433	$83,974	$9,147.40	$1,400.09
	2007	1,111	131	4,967	87	169	6.4	103,532	9,105	615,290	747	443	$90,528	$9,523.22	$1,472.26
	2008	1,105	131	5,023	86	170	6.3	109,398	8,943	609,159	760	446	$96,735	$9,826.94	$1,552.32
	2009	1,092	127	4,857	83	168	6.2	108,738	8,850	583,845	751	447	$98,937	$10,067.96	$1,611.31
	2010	1,068	125	4,693	80	169	6.2	109,045	8,699	542,809	738	437	$100,056	$10,283.35	$1,624.93
	2011	1,045	121	4,598	78	170	6.2	109,423	8,502	529,435	738	434	$103,448	$10,531.65	$1,666.96
	2012	1,037	120	4,447	77	170	6.3	108,880	8,017	499,938	739	435	$113,843	$11,668.15	$1,831.00
	2013	1,010	117	4,238	74	162	6.3	108,599	7,934	489,106	734	453	$115,013	$12,028.02	$1,878.21
	2014	1,003	116	4,206	73	168	6.4	111,384	7,849	490,554	739	440	$120,900	$12,601.35	$1,974.41
	2015	983	117	4,183	74	172	6.4	116,099	7,568	486,364	763	442	$126,706	$13,070.29	$2,013.32
	2016	956	113	4,041	72	176	6.5	116,839	7,295	468,463	759	432	$132,068	$13,720.11	$2,051.72

Table
2

2016 U.S. Registered Hospitals: Utilization, Personnel, and Finances

Excludes U.S.-Associated Areas, Puerto Rico, and nonregistered hospitals.

CLASSIFICATION	HOSPITALS	BEDS	ADMISSIONS	INPATIENT DAYS	ADJUSTED INPATIENT DAYS	AVERAGE DAILY CENSUS	ADJUSTED AVERAGE DAILY CENSUS	AVERAGE STAY (days)	SURGICAL OPERATIONS	OUTPATIENT VISITS Emergency	OUTPATIENT VISITS Total	NEWBORNS Bassinets	NEWBORNS Births
UNITED STATES	5,534	894,574	35,158,934	215,019,381	—	589,075	—	—	27,998,656	146,739,354	863,654,355	55,774	3,761,594
6-24 Beds	567	9,397	217,094	1,079,602	—	2,952	—	—	404,460	2,498,231	19,220,519	528	17,766
25-49	1,217	39,482	1,100,065	6,299,648	—	17,264	—	—	1,537,197	9,701,626	58,404,059	3,058	118,586
50-99	1,091	77,769	2,242,383	16,259,482	—	44,544	—	—	2,190,997	12,597,486	82,241,134	4,923	220,140
100-199	1,157	166,162	6,161,884	37,740,913	—	103,396	—	—	4,955,442	30,393,134	160,421,440	11,466	657,006
200-299	627	152,958	6,243,210	36,038,148	—	98,738	—	—	4,762,249	26,085,156	136,904,295	10,123	673,997
300-399	360	124,320	5,419,708	30,409,167	—	83,305	—	—	3,706,001	20,781,018	136,384,269	8,083	601,144
400-499	196	86,976	3,708,128	21,796,468	—	59,714	—	—	3,778,880	13,513,776	82,429,041	5,431	423,939
500 or more	319	237,510	10,066,482	65,395,953	—	179,162	—	—	7,663,430	31,168,927	223,649,598	12,162	1,049,016
Psychiatric	407	70,454	807,815	21,648,250	—	59,309	—	—	9,735	169,104	10,822,362	0	1
Hospitals	400	67,769	807,374	20,786,382	—	56,948	—	—	9,735	169,104	10,822,362	0	1
Inst. for Intellectual Disabilities	7	2,685	441	861,868	—	2,361	—	—	0	0	0	0	0
General	4,539	779,008	33,528,207	182,248,473	—	499,300	—	—	27,407,416	146,071,397	834,213,866	55,171	3,701,487
Hospitals	4,527	777,901	33,511,962	181,986,686	—	498,580	—	—	27,405,227	146,040,408	833,449,018	55,171	3,701,487
Hospital units of institutions	12	1,107	16,245	261,787	—	720	—	—	2,189	30,989	764,848	0	0
TB and other respiratory diseases	2	116	93	9,987	—	27	—	—	0	0	114,750	0	0
Obstetrics and gynecology	9	1,498	79,644	365,255	—	1,001	—	—	53,243	157,269	1,310,267	505	49,319
Eye, ear, nose and throat	4	137	1,532	5,833	—	16	—	—	64,303	48,519	874,281	0	0
Rehabilitation	201	15,700	285,994	3,974,221	—	10,887	—	—	15,407	1	6,897,434	0	0
Orthopedic	29	1,234	56,162	183,919	—	504	—	—	139,643	33,327	1,448,154	0	0
Chronic Disease	4	251	841	43,429	—	120	—	—	99	4,726	62,682	0	0
Surgical	16	447	18,176	53,157	—	146	—	—	49,007	30,606	194,179	0	0
Cancer	14	2,408	99,723	722,730	—	1,980	—	—	98,411	29,949	5,533,406	0	0
Heart	7	474	20,311	81,513	—	223	—	—	13,449	16,528	126,676	3	25
Acute long-term care hospital	280	20,198	212,934	4,863,020	—	13,317	—	—	101,324	21,836	1,181,722	95	10,762
All other	22	2,649	47,502	819,594	—	2,245	—	—	46,619	156,092	874,576	0	0
Federal	209	37,871	891,902	9,231,167	—	25,293	—	—	756,085	3,992,312	107,871,730	625	34,166
Psychiatric	10	2,821	14,722	624,920	—	1,712	—	—	3,989	14,863	3,565,381	0	0
General and other special	199	35,050	877,180	8,606,247	—	23,581	—	—	752,096	3,977,449	104,306,349	625	34,166
Nonfederal	5,325	856,703	34,267,032	205,788,214	—	563,782	—	—	27,242,571	142,747,042	755,782,625	55,149	3,727,428
Psychiatric	397	67,633	793,093	21,023,330	—	57,597	—	—	5,746	154,241	7,256,981	0	1
Hospitals	390	64,948	792,652	20,161,462	—	55,236	—	—	5,746	154,241	7,256,981	0	1
Inst. for Intellectual Disabilities	7	2,685	441	861,868	—	2,361	—	—	0	0	0	0	0
TB and other respiratory diseases	2	116	93	9,987	11,876	27	32	107.4	0	0	114,750	0	0
Long-term general and other special	76	7,614	34,410	2,204,566	2,712,290	6,040	7,418	64.1	9,598	34,922	1,101,170	0	0
Short-term general and other special	4,850	781,340	33,439,436	182,550,331	386,469,559	500,118	1,056,720	5.5	27,227,227	142,557,879	747,309,724	55,149	3,727,427
Hospital units of institutions	10	1,068	15,183	258,642	258,642	711	711	17	0	220,711	220,711	0	0
Community Hospitals	4,840	780,272	33,424,253	182,291,689	386,210,917	499,407	1,056,009	5.5	27,227,227	142,557,879	747,089,013	55,149	3,727,427
6-24 Beds	518	8,598	196,380	938,568	5,024,078	2,567	13,747	4.8	380,629	2,176,636	12,866,393	450	15,983
25-49	1,131	36,370	1,037,083	5,579,894	20,497,070	15,296	56,135	5.4	1,502,341	9,206,914	53,898,945	2,928	115,729
50-99	913	64,856	1,902,873	12,849,590	35,575,734	35,199	97,332	6.8	2,051,346	11,800,062	60,260,298	4,722	206,204
100-199	963	139,246	5,622,211	29,929,136	72,723,489	81,996	198,805	5.3	4,760,410	29,592,814	136,593,879	11,377	646,628
200-299	531	129,661	5,859,418	29,429,219	60,347,441	80,625	165,022	5	4,563,277	25,182,104	117,258,828	9,996	668,784
300-399	322	111,233	5,282,961	26,820,397	51,113,297	73,474	139,707	5.1	3,628,331	20,432,363	85,743,929	8,083	601,144
400-499	177	78,381	3,635,759	19,526,076	37,192,439	53,493	101,642	5.4	2,755,722	13,365,313	76,855,697	5,431	423,939
500 or more	285	211,927	9,887,568	57,218,809	103,737,369	156,757	283,619	5.8	7,585,171	30,801,673	203,611,044	12,162	1,049,016
Nongovernment not-for-profit	2,849	533,368	24,096,781	127,453,164	272,065,505	349,157	743,871	5.3	19,936,660	100,934,514	568,993,232	39,246	2,722,575
Investor-owned (for profit)	1,035	134,368	5,286,513	28,411,307	49,775,892	77,850	136,187	5.4	3,880,441	22,079,422	61,256,413	8,608	536,389
State and Local Government	956	112,536	4,040,959	26,427,218	64,369,520	72,400	175,951	6.5	3,410,126	19,543,943	116,839,368	7,295	468,463

Table 2 (Continued)

CLASSIFICATION	FULL-TIME EQUIVALENT PERSONNEL — Physicians and Dentists	Registered Nurses	Licensed Practical Nurses	Other Salaried Personnel	Total Personnel	FULL-TIME EQUIVALENT TRAINEES — Medical and Dental Residents	Other Trainees	Total Trainees	LABOR — Payroll (in thousands)	Employee Benefits (in thousands)	EXPENSES — Total (in thousands)	Percent of Total	Amount (in thousands)	TOTAL — Adjusted Per Admission	Adjusted Per Inpatient Day
UNITED STATES	171,606	1,589,073	99,231	3,702,972	5,562,882	121,793	14,919	136,712	$383,329,266	$103,987,450	$487,316,717	49.1	$991,531,841	—	—
6-24 Beds	2,031	16,576	3,538	57,489	79,634	25	36	61	$4,794,511	$1,392,896	$6,187,406	50.2	$12,319,622	—	—
25-49	7,511	63,107	10,128	192,489	273,235	553	703	1,256	$15,715,177	$4,104,326	$19,819,503	49.7	$39,889,787	—	—
50-99	11,533	104,093	13,150	287,603	416,379	1,253	324	1,577	$26,336,608	$6,967,378	$33,303,986	50.9	$65,388,219	—	—
100-199	23,265	252,063	19,076	602,650	897,054	7,097	2,080	9,177	$61,074,950	$16,218,427	$77,293,377	49.9	$155,024,576	—	—
200-299	26,639	255,314	16,829	596,267	895,049	11,417	2,360	13,777	$60,621,409	$16,573,999	$77,195,408	48.9	$157,798,264	—	—
300-399	19,571	224,262	10,474	466,114	720,421	10,143	1,202	11,345	$51,816,867	$13,857,441	$65,674,308	48.4	$135,730,541	—	—
400-499	16,470	167,331	6,894	372,563	563,258	15,493	1,926	17,419	$40,977,935	$11,565,620	$52,543,555	49.1	$107,091,167	—	—
500 or more	64,586	506,327	19,142	1,127,797	1,717,852	75,812	6,288	82,100	$121,991,811	$33,307,363	$155,299,174	48.8	$318,289,666	—	—
Psychiatric	4,342	26,304	5,977	143,068	179,691	422	421	843	$9,817,521	$3,448,725	$13,266,246	71.5	$18,559,044	—	—
Hospitals	4,319	26,134	5,647	136,888	172,988	422	421	843	$9,596,099	$3,346,269	$12,942,368	71.2	$18,173,166	—	—
Inst. for Intellectual Disabilities	23	170	330	6,180	6,703	0	0	0	$221,422	$102,456	$323,878	83.9	$385,878	—	—
General	160,438	1,509,294	87,740	3,399,390	5,156,862	120,074	13,017	133,091	$357,994,662	$96,519,163	$454,513,826	48.7	$934,048,172	—	—
Hospitals	160,266	1,509,058	87,566	3,397,941	5,154,831	120,072	13,015	133,087	$357,814,857	$96,460,723	$454,275,580	48.7	$933,573,532	—	—
Hospital units of institutions	172	236	174	1,449	2,031	2	2	4	$179,805	$58,440	$238,245	50.2	$474,640	—	—
TB and other respiratory diseases	156	127	25	1,413	1,721	0	19	19	$122,965	$18,220	$141,185	55.9	$252,452	—	—
Obstetrics and gynecology	148	3,544	35	5,142	8,869	61	0	61	$681,618	$176,045	$857,663	41.0	$2,089,824	—	—
Eye, ear, nose and throat	271	379	16	2,577	3,243	125	46	171	$203,646	$51,250	$254,896	45.2	$563,380	—	—
Rehabilitation	792	12,999	1,537	45,783	61,111	248	47	295	$3,472,021	$814,066	$4,286,087	56.7	$7,553,770	—	—
Orthopedic	532	2,680	144	8,253	11,609	69	5	74	$1,029,732	$276,670	$1,306,402	48.7	$2,680,442	—	—
Chronic Disease	14	137	16	844	1,011	0	0	0	$57,571	$20,538	$78,109	63.4	$123,271	—	—
Surgical	16	805	40	1,548	2,409	0	0	0	$154,086	$35,374	$189,460	31.4	$603,204	—	—
Cancer	3,759	12,286	200	45,277	61,522	763	1,360	2,123	$5,043,298	$1,450,351	$6,493,650	46.4	$13,999,835	—	—
Heart	30	926	45	1,584	2,585	0	0	0	$154,416	$40,594	$195,010	35.7	$545,741	—	—
Acute long-term care hospital	773	16,494	3,193	39,505	59,965	3	2	5	$3,672,211	$845,032	$4,517,242	54.0	$8,357,907	—	—
All other	335	3,098	263	8,588	12,284	28	2	30	$925,520	$291,422	$1,216,942	56.5	$2,154,799	—	—
Federal	31,482	81,330	18,538	247,579	378,929	8,334	4,938	13,272	$32,540,025	$9,848,330	$42,388,355	62.3	$68,050,132	—	—
Psychiatric	559	1,601	487	8,098	10,745	89	80	169	$762,700	$206,520	$969,220	69.5	$1,394,971	—	—
General and other special	30,923	79,729	18,051	239,481	368,184	8,245	4,858	13,103	$31,777,325	$9,641,810	$41,419,135	62.1	$66,655,162	—	—
Nonfederal	140,124	1,507,743	80,693	3,455,393	5,183,953	113,459	9,981	123,440	$350,789,242	$94,139,120	$444,928,362	48.2	$923,481,709	—	—
Psychiatric	3,783	24,703	5,490	134,970	168,946	333	341	674	$9,054,821	$3,242,205	$12,297,026	71.6	$17,164,073	—	—
Hospitals	3,760	24,533	5,160	128,790	162,243	333	341	674	$8,833,399	$3,139,749	$11,973,148	71.4	$16,778,195	—	—
Inst. for Intellectual Disabilities	23	170	330	6,180	6,703	0	0	0	$221,422	$102,456	$323,878	83.9	$385,878	—	—
TB and other respiratory diseases	156	127	25	1,413	1,721	0	19	19	$122,965	$18,220	$141,185	55.9	$252,452	—	—
Long-term general and other special	376	4,149	727	15,365	20,617	15	2	17	$1,389,482	$397,255	$1,786,736	61.5	$2,907,149	$228,256.57	$21,257.31
Short-term general and other special	135,809	1,478,764	74,451	3,303,645	4,992,669	113,111	9,619	122,730	$340,221,974	$90,481,441	$430,703,414	47.7	$903,158,035	$70,688.85	$1,071.84
Hospital units of institutions	116	107	107	564	894	0	0	0	$89,000	$17,800	$106,800	40.0	$267,000	$12,778.28	$1,032.31
Community Hospitals	135,693	1,478,657	74,344	3,303,081	4,991,775	113,111	9,619	122,730	$340,132,974	$90,463,641	$430,596,614	47.7	$902,891,035	$17,585.46	$2,337.82
6-24 Beds	1,410	14,770	2,790	46,129	65,099	3	16	19	$3,738,610	$951,610	$4,690,220	47.3	$9,921,428	$12,777.25	$1,974.78
25-49	6,553	59,498	9,108	176,583	251,742	306	661	967	$14,901,854	$3,846,147	$18,748,000	49.1	$38,151,187	$9,012.38	$1,861.30
50-99	6,768	86,838	8,933	230,460	332,999	819	91	910	$20,347,150	$5,150,770	$25,497,920	49.4	$51,565,187	$8,996.57	$1,449.45
100-199	16,887	226,168	14,827	517,384	775,266	4,898	491	5,389	$50,646,220	$13,263,290	$63,909,510	47.7	$134,091,394	$9,430.82	$1,843.85
200-299	18,147	230,841	10,178	509,771	768,937	8,479	673	9,152	$51,979,716	$13,644,099	$65,623,815	47.3	$138,699,721	$10,216.40	$2,298.35
300-399	14,555	211,921	7,754	423,524	657,754	9,927	908	10,835	$45,867,034	$12,145,139	$58,012,174	46.7	$124,345,120	$11,640.33	$2,432.74
400-499	14,515	161,560	5,504	346,201	527,780	14,963	1,145	16,108	$38,716,556	$10,736,906	$49,453,463	48.5	$101,971,589	$12,460.74	$2,741.73
500 or more	56,858	487,061	15,250	1,053,029	1,612,198	73,716	5,634	79,350	$113,935,833	$30,725,680	$144,661,513	47.6	$304,145,409	$14,785.32	$2,931.88
Nongovernment not-for-profit	111,945	1,085,765	45,633	2,437,730	3,681,073	82,103	7,135	89,238	$254,534,914	$66,807,283	$321,342,197	47.5	$676,791,648	$13,182.10	$2,487.61
Investor-owned (for profit)	4,931	189,026	12,273	345,171	551,401	5,137	280	5,417	$34,007,871	$7,517,591	$41,525,462	44.2	$94,031,110	$9,697.57	$1,889.09
State and Local Government	18,817	203,866	16,438	520,180	759,301	25,871	2,204	28,075	$51,590,189	$16,138,766	$67,728,955	51.3	$132,068,277	$13,720.11	$2,013.32

Total U.S.

TABLE 3

TOTAL UNITED STATES

U.S. Registered Community Hospitals
(Nonfederal, short-term general and other special hospitals)

Overview 2012–2016

	2016	2015	2014	2013	2012
TOTAL U.S. Community Hospitals	**4,840**	**4,862**	**4,926**	**4,974**	**4,999**
Bed Size Category					
6-24	518	499	486	469	462
25-49	1,131	1,146	1,168	1,186	1,192
50-99	913	916	934	959	954
100-199	963	983	1,013	995	1,012
200-299	531	535	536	571	570
300-399	322	322	328	334	348
400-499	177	177	188	183	189
500 +	285	284	273	277	272
Location					
Hospitals Urban	3,015	3,033	3,071	3,003	3,019
Hospitals Rural	1,825	1,829	1,855	1,971	1,980
Control					
State and Local Government	956	983	1,003	1,010	1,037
Not for Profit	2,849	2,845	2,870	2,904	2,894
Investor owned	1,035	1,034	1,053	1,060	1,068
Physician Models					
Independent Practice Association	499	513	483	473	496
Group Practice without Walls	153	155	195	185	165
Open Physician-Hospital Organization	566	557	578	597	620
Closed Physician-Hospital Organization	235	233	226	230	219
Management Service Organization	388	425	395	423	441
Integrated Salary Model	1,905	1,930	1,889	1,886	1,844
Equity Model	97	91	93	99	84
Foundation	289	289	284	299	269
Insurance Products					
Health Maintenance Organization	771	763	714	698	627
Preferred Provider Organization	748	724	687	676	576
Indemnity Fee for Service	301	290	271	240	210
Managed Care Contracts					
Health Maintenance Organization	2,610	2,638	2,660	2,655	2,699
Preferred Provider Organization	2,896	2,929	2,971	3,012	3,034
Affiliations					
Hospitals in a System	3,231	3,198	3,183	3,144	3,100
Hospitals in a Network	1,689	1,677	1,619	1,582	1,508
Hospitals in a Group Purchasing Organization	3,483	3,530	3,485	3,581	3,519

TABLE 3

TOTAL UNITED STATES

U.S. Registered Community Hospitals
(Nonfederal, short-term general and other special hospitals)

Utilization, Personnel, Revenue and Expenses, Community Health Indicators 2012–2016

	2016	2015	2014	2013	2012
TOTAL FACILITY (Includes Hospital and Nursing Home Units)					
Utilization - Inpatient					
Beds	780,272	782,188	786,874	795,603	800,566
Admissions	33,424,253	33,260,348	33,066,720	33,609,083	34,422,071
Inpatient Days	182,291,689	181,555,387	180,456,434	182,370,189	185,423,035
Average Length of Stay	5.5	5.5	5.5	5.4	5.4
Inpatient Surgeries	8,982,309	8,920,775	9,015,467	9,147,264	9,513,598
Births	3,727,427	3,752,215	3,735,593	3,699,411	3,715,479
Utilization - Outpatient					
Emergency Outpatient Visits	142,557,879	141,511,173	136,327,473	133,611,670	133,221,030
Other Outpatient Visits	604,531,134	580,610,215	556,779,212	544,339,450	541,750,301
Total Outpatient Visits	747,089,013	722,121,388	693,106,685	677,951,120	674,971,331
Outpatient Surgeries	18,244,918	17,588,335	17,386,061	17,418,773	17,297,633
Personnel					
Full Time RNs	1,219,425	1,187,841	1,152,496	1,120,741	1,103,906
Full Time LPNs	63,530	62,899	62,046	66,122	69,318
Part Time RNs	518,462	499,752	493,395	491,401	494,530
Part Time LPNs	21,698	21,906	22,042	24,125	25,892
Total Full Time	4,350,729	4,244,291	4,152,678	4,126,815	4,105,295
Total Part Time	1,527,530	1,465,428	1,445,935	1,453,298	1,471,619
Revenue - Inpatient					
Gross Inpatient Revenue	$1,688,296,642,474	$1,594,248,118,744	$1,490,571,905,696	$1,419,185,856,879	$1,355,940,534,641
Revenue - Outpatient					
Gross Outpatient Revenue	$1,562,939,241,185	$1,422,150,564,417	$1,286,154,215,073	$1,173,050,699,739	$1,075,704,443,658
Revenue and Expenses - Totals					
(Includes Inpatient and Outpatient)*					
Total Gross Revenue	$3,251,235,883,659	$3,016,398,683,161	$2,776,726,120,665	$2,592,236,542,201	$2,431,644,978,299
Deductions from Revenue	2,340,036,807,284	2,150,390,112,320	1,963,288,605,002	1,812,842,655,432	1,669,437,831,803
Net Patient Revenue	911,199,076,375	866,008,570,841	813,437,515,663	779,393,886,769	762,207,146,496
Other Operating Revenue	56,392,606,114	53,174,900,904	51,117,414,348	50,139,467,030	47,528,382,573
Other Nonoperating Revenue	11,408,898,787	5,637,063,784	17,720,027,270	19,765,262,658	11,599,107,141
Total Net Revenue	979,000,581,276	924,820,535,529	882,274,957,281	849,298,616,457	821,334,636,210
Total Expenses	902,891,034,769	851,514,523,144	808,869,209,436	782,035,349,979	756,916,756,696
HOSPITAL UNIT (Excludes Separate Nursing Home Units)					
Utilization - Inpatient					
Beds	738,950	738,306	744,273	748,824	751,490
Admissions	33,273,560	33,103,003	32,899,718	33,421,331	34,217,866
Inpatient Days	169,215,334	168,083,304	167,093,881	167,637,410	169,860,722
Average Length of Stay	5.1	5.1	5.1	5.0	5.0
Personnel					
Total Full Time	4,323,790	4,216,384	4,118,998	4,093,683	4,068,209
Total Part Time	1,512,960	1,449,886	1,428,488	1,435,155	1,452,480
Revenue and Expenses - Totals					
(Includes Inpatient and Outpatient)					
Total Net Revenue	$975,136,417,988	$920,646,014,445	$878,421,503,993	$845,194,660,817	$817,155,645,229
Total Expenses	899,879,056,085	848,099,878,327	805,597,791,488	778,422,090,039	753,064,177,148
COMMUNITY HEALTH INDICATORS PER 1000 POPULATION					
Total Population (in thousands)	323,128	321,419	318,857	316,129	313,914
Inpatient					
Beds	2.4	2.4	2.5	2.5	2.6
Admissions	103.4	103.5	103.7	106.3	109.7
Inpatient Days	564.1	564.9	565.9	576.9	590.7
Inpatient Surgeries	27.8	27.8	28.3	28.9	30.3
Births	11.5	11.7	11.7	11.7	11.8
Outpatient					
Emergency Outpatient Visits	441.2	440.3	427.6	422.6	424.4
Other Outpatient Visits	1870.9	1806.4	1746.2	1721.9	1725.8
Total Outpatient Visits	2312.1	2246.7	2173.7	2144.5	2150.2
Outpatient Surgeries	56.5	54.7	54.5	55.1	55.1
Expense per Capita (per person)	$2794.2	$2649.2	$2536.8	$2473.8	$2411.2

*Calculating the total margin using an aggregate average for all U.S. hospitals based on total revenue and expenses can be misleading and should be avoided. Individual hospital margins vary widely and are driven by a range of factors, including facility or system size and type; local payer mix; geographic location; patient demographics; services provided, both clinical and non-medical; and relationships and affiliations with other entities in the community.

Total U.S.

TABLE 4

BED SIZE CATEGORY 6-24

U.S. Registered Community Hospitals
(Nonfederal, short-term general and other special hospitals)

Overview 2012–2016

	2016	2015	2014	2013	2012
Total Community Hospitals in Bed Size Category 6-24	518	499	486	469	462
Location					
Hospitals Urban	149	141	143	122	120
Hospitals Rural	369	358	343	347	342
Control					
State and Local Government	193	180	170	170	176
Not for Profit	265	258	256	245	235
Investor owned	60	61	60	54	51
Physician Models					
Independent Practice Association	45	41	39	39	46
Group Practice without Walls	14	13	16	13	12
Open Physician-Hospital Organization	33	28	32	31	31
Closed Physician-Hospital Organization	17	17	9	7	8
Management Service Organization	17	16	14	14	18
Integrated Salary Model	198	195	181	163	163
Equity Model	9	4	2	8	9
Foundation	15	10	17	15	16
Insurance Products					
Health Maintenance Organization	54	48	47	48	42
Preferred Provider Organization	64	61	51	49	39
Indemnity Fee for Service	25	21	18	18	13
Managed Care Contracts					
Health Maintenance Organization	220	194	195	180	181
Preferred Provider Organization	282	256	255	247	244
Affiliations					
Hospitals in a System	239	232	221	205	207
Hospitals in a Network	164	160	147	145	133
Hospitals in a Group Purchasing Organization	354	334	329	330	317

TABLE 4

BED SIZE CATEGORY 6-24

U.S. Registered Community Hospitals
(Nonfederal, short-term general and other special hospitals)

Utilization, Personnel, Revenue and Expenses, Community Health Indicators 2012–2016

	2016	2015	2014	2013	2012
TOTAL FACILITY (Includes Hospital and Nursing Home Units)					
Utilization - Inpatient					
Beds	8,598	8,237	7,985	7,763	7,791
Admissions	196,380	196,415	185,102	189,339	197,448
Inpatient Days	938,568	895,841	884,847	862,961	879,985
Average Length of Stay	4.8	4.6	4.8	4.6	4.5
Inpatient Surgeries	44,469	44,849	41,522	38,962	41,274
Births	15,983	14,374	13,997	15,322	18,058
Utilization - Outpatient					
Emergency Outpatient Visits	2,176,636	2,115,594	1,984,350	1,955,889	1,929,787
Other Outpatient Visits	10,689,757	9,750,782	9,329,411	8,932,227	8,697,985
Total Outpatient Visits	12,866,393	11,866,376	11,313,761	10,888,116	10,627,772
Outpatient Surgeries	336,160	330,722	310,083	283,781	285,969
Personnel					
Full Time RNs	11,175	10,733	10,431	9,648	9,066
Full Time LPNs	2,332	2,290	2,157	2,258	2,044
Part Time RNs	7,186	6,885	6,172	5,692	5,508
Part Time LPNs	933	1,008	891	958	903
Total Full Time	52,134	49,725	47,948	45,873	42,797
Total Part Time	25,942	24,801	23,877	21,820	20,824
Revenue - Inpatient					
Gross Inpatient Revenue	$4,497,735,962	$4,705,789,188	$3,966,579,112	$3,397,090,171	$3,344,514,225
Revenue - Outpatient					
Gross Outpatient Revenue	$16,767,464,456	$15,119,911,738	$13,215,154,469	$11,459,413,010	$10,460,225,077
Revenue and Expenses - Totals (Includes Inpatient and Outpatient)					
Total Gross Revenue	$21,265,200,418	$19,825,700,926	$17,181,733,581	$14,856,503,181	$13,804,739,302
Deductions from Revenue	11,832,325,080	10,881,715,417	9,267,998,526	7,671,633,328	6,997,808,590
Net Patient Revenue	9,432,875,338	8,943,985,509	7,913,735,055	7,184,869,853	6,806,930,712
Other Operating Revenue	969,273,989	939,651,672	871,277,026	763,864,461	611,148,966
Other Nonoperating Revenue	139,184,495	112,066,979	174,678,558	143,595,341	154,545,670
Total Net Revenue	10,541,333,822	9,995,704,160	8,959,690,639	8,092,329,655	7,572,625,348
Total Expenses	9,921,427,569	9,256,461,309	8,412,989,501	7,609,006,694	6,984,976,928
HOSPITAL UNIT (Excludes Separate Nursing Home Units)					
Utilization - Inpatient					
Beds	8,584	8,199	7,961	7,733	7,738
Admissions	196,341	196,393	184,940	189,316	197,163
Inpatient Days	926,493	881,379	859,795	853,632	854,715
Average Length of Stay	4.7	4.5	4.6	4.5	4.3
Personnel					
Total Full Time	52,080	49,599	47,820	45,498	42,674
Total Part Time	25,913	24,696	23,786	21,381	20,730
Revenue and Expenses - Totals (Includes Inpatient and Outpatient)					
Total Net Revenue	$10,537,980,318	$9,982,356,447	$8,952,854,779	$8,086,815,684	$7,561,431,638
Total Expenses	9,919,694,944	9,249,295,710	8,407,448,861	7,606,122,912	6,979,227,864

TABLE 4

BED SIZE CATEGORY 25-49

U.S. Registered Community Hospitals
(Nonfederal, short-term general and other special hospitals)

Overview 2012–2016

	2016	2015	2014	2013	2012
Total Community Hospitals in					
Bed Size Category 25-49	**1,131**	**1,146**	**1,168**	**1,186**	**1,192**
Location					
Hospitals Urban	401	418	415	414	420
Hospitals Rural	730	728	753	772	772
Control					
State and Local Government	339	350	364	363	367
Not for Profit	570	570	569	576	574
Investor owned	222	226	235	247	251
Physician Models					
Independent Practice Association	93	93	90	87	97
Group Practice without Walls	28	26	35	29	25
Open Physician-Hospital Organization	76	68	73	72	79
Closed Physician-Hospital Organization	35	33	33	33	23
Management Service Organization	50	57	52	50	55
Integrated Salary Model	383	402	395	382	358
Equity Model	11	10	11	10	9
Foundation	42	41	43	47	44
Insurance Products					
Health Maintenance Organization	122	118	113	106	90
Preferred Provider Organization	126	122	111	114	94
Indemnity Fee for Service	56	52	46	40	31
Managed Care Contracts					
Health Maintenance Organization	485	501	509	499	502
Preferred Provider Organization	586	607	637	638	636
Affiliations					
Hospitals in a System	641	632	641	642	639
Hospitals in a Network	335	328	331	326	309
Hospitals in a Group Purchasing Organization	770	792	783	799	780

TABLE 4

BED SIZE CATEGORY 25-49

U.S. Registered Community Hospitals
(Nonfederal, short-term general and other special hospitals)

Utilization, Personnel, Revenue and Expenses, Community Health Indicators 2012–2016

	2016	2015	2014	2013	2012
TOTAL FACILITY (Includes Hospital and Nursing Home Units)					
Utilization - Inpatient					
Beds	36,370	37,020	37,559	38,039	38,338
Admissions	1,037,083	1,058,670	1,046,146	1,087,215	1,128,446
Inpatient Days	5,579,894	5,766,981	5,773,691	5,927,960	6,029,293
Average Length of Stay	5.4	5.4	5.5	5.5	5.3
Inpatient Surgeries	231,493	228,699	218,499	226,655	235,988
Births	115,729	116,542	116,655	118,178	115,996
Utilization - Outpatient					
Emergency Outpatient Visits	9,206,914	9,242,365	8,742,707	8,584,767	8,566,426
Other Outpatient Visits	44,692,031	42,613,498	39,128,261	38,868,368	38,126,632
Total Outpatient Visits	53,898,945	51,855,863	47,870,968	47,453,135	46,693,058
Outpatient Surgeries	1,270,848	1,191,786	1,176,204	1,151,191	1,147,708
Personnel					
Full Time RNs	46,091	45,262	43,863	43,974	42,864
Full Time LPNs	7,514	7,637	7,859	8,032	8,417
Part Time RNs	26,822	26,843	26,118	25,153	24,910
Part Time LPNs	3,193	3,200	3,153	3,071	3,356
Total Full Time	205,672	202,438	198,284	200,077	201,196
Total Part Time	94,093	93,189	90,117	88,138	88,578
Revenue - Inpatient					
Gross Inpatient Revenue	$31,842,164,684	$29,545,132,044	$27,689,000,672	$26,991,103,197	$26,339,586,346
Revenue - Outpatient					
Gross Outpatient Revenue	$67,993,863,430	$60,588,008,443	$54,623,143,963	$51,160,634,612	$47,719,363,855
Revenue and Expenses - Totals **(Includes Inpatient and Outpatient)**					
Total Gross Revenue	$99,836,028,114	$90,133,140,487	$82,312,144,635	$78,151,737,809	$74,058,950,201
Deductions from Revenue	62,352,824,531	54,689,234,753	49,503,831,252	46,095,620,354	42,336,288,207
Net Patient Revenue	37,483,203,583	35,443,905,734	32,808,313,383	32,056,117,455	31,722,661,994
Other Operating Revenue	3,105,429,170	3,294,711,495	2,886,287,487	2,820,302,433	2,679,807,646
Other Nonoperating Revenue	428,417,556	269,463,420	614,271,220	629,745,342	466,597,263
Total Net Revenue	41,017,050,309	39,008,080,649	36,308,872,090	35,506,165,230	34,869,066,903
Total Expenses	38,151,187,254	36,077,186,163	33,932,958,728	33,077,261,551	32,080,809,215
HOSPITAL UNIT (Excludes Separate Nursing Home Units)					
Utilization - Inpatient					
Beds	35,318	35,676	36,136	36,683	36,965
Admissions	1,035,241	1,056,069	1,043,548	1,085,021	1,126,060
Inpatient Days	5,253,850	5,353,104	5,353,884	5,481,761	5,586,318
Average Length of Stay	5.1	5.1	5.1	5.1	5.0
Personnel					
Total Full Time	204,870	201,541	197,313	199,177	200,121
Total Part Time	93,558	92,648	89,487	87,448	87,785
Revenue and Expenses - Totals **(Includes Inpatient and Outpatient)**					
Total Net Revenue	$40,936,691,482	$38,918,230,685	$36,204,291,881	$35,403,536,439	$34,771,427,302
Total Expenses	38,091,267,217	35,999,746,007	33,845,511,122	32,981,475,196	31,999,027,638

TABLE 4

BED SIZE CATEGORY 50-99

U.S. Registered Community Hospitals
(Nonfederal, short-term general and other special hospitals)

Overview 2012–2016

	2016	2015	2014	2013	2012
Total Community Hospitals in					
Bed Size Category 50-99...............................	913	916	934	959	954
Location					
Hospitals Urban	510	504	521	500	489
Hospitals Rural..	403	412	413	459	465
Control					
State and Local Government	156	168	177	184	185
Not for Profit..	458	463	467	475	470
Investor owned..	299	285	290	300	299
Physician Models					
Independent Practice Association......................	54	54	52	55	61
Group Practice without Walls..........................	17	16	22	19	21
Open Physician-Hospital Organization	82	84	88	96	98
Closed Physician-Hospital Organization.............	25	28	29	30	29
Management Service Organization.....................	45	53	47	46	49
Integrated Salary Model.................................	292	291	296	299	296
Equity Model	10	8	9	9	9
Foundation	35	36	32	35	34
Insurance Products					
Health Maintenance Organization......................	106	112	107	100	94
Preferred Provider Organization	115	116	122	110	98
Indemnity Fee for Service..............................	45	43	44	37	37
Managed Care Contracts					
Health Maintenance Organization......................	407	417	424	423	434
Preferred Provider Organization	463	467	484	505	512
Affiliations					
Hospitals in a System	617	611	620	621	604
Hospitals in a Network	233	243	251	260	254
Hospitals in a Group Purchasing Organization...	603	609	597	637	628

Bed Size Categories

TABLE 4

BED SIZE CATEGORY 50-99

U.S. Registered Community Hospitals
(Nonfederal, short-term general and other special hospitals)

Utilization, Personnel, Revenue and Expenses, Community Health Indicators 2012–2016

	2016	2015	2014	2013	2012
TOTAL FACILITY (Includes Hospital and Nursing Home Units)					
Utilization - Inpatient					
Beds	64,856	65,208	66,092	67,892	67,879
Admissions	1,902,873	1,936,728	1,925,489	2,021,449	2,017,239
Inpatient Days	12,849,590	13,146,899	13,194,044	13,639,948	13,678,515
Average Length of Stay	6.8	6.8	6.9	6.7	6.8
Inpatient Surgeries	443,403	439,953	436,457	464,612	477,962
Births	206,204	213,901	221,599	224,180	222,207
Utilization - Outpatient					
Emergency Outpatient Visits	11,800,062	11,851,263	11,661,152	11,796,586	11,275,005
Other Outpatient Visits	48,460,236	48,745,662	47,699,660	46,326,471	45,524,947
Total Outpatient Visits	60,260,298	60,596,925	59,360,812	58,123,057	56,799,952
Outpatient Surgeries	1,607,943	1,564,390	1,538,499	1,541,697	1,507,344
Personnel					
Full Time RNs	67,856	66,354	65,846	65,776	63,278
Full Time LPNs	7,413	7,004	7,039	7,803	8,560
Part Time RNs	37,962	36,659	36,268	36,146	34,249
Part Time LPNs	3,060	3,128	3,035	3,492	3,584
Total Full Time	270,595	266,856	264,580	268,350	261,529
Total Part Time	126,615	124,218	123,100	124,962	122,577
Revenue - Inpatient					
Gross Inpatient Revenue	$70,719,714,369	$65,943,736,325	$60,897,389,721	$59,688,634,837	$55,035,035,760
Revenue - Outpatient					
Gross Outpatient Revenue	$101,912,751,472	$93,966,777,896	$84,425,058,692	$78,655,991,052	$69,635,311,624
Revenue and Expenses - Totals **(Includes Inpatient and Outpatient)**					
Total Gross Revenue	$172,632,465,841	$159,910,514,221	$145,322,448,309	$138,344,625,889	$124,670,347,384
Deductions from Revenue	119,030,398,183	108,104,515,606	96,448,247,473	90,642,831,824	79,025,510,314
Net Patient Revenue	53,602,067,658	51,805,998,615	48,874,200,836	47,701,794,065	45,644,837,070
Other Operating Revenue	2,346,303,640	2,242,544,386	2,547,669,918	2,476,450,842	1,974,942,100
Other Nonoperating Revenue	989,619,635	456,799,126	1,357,720,719	780,849,538	927,504,094
Total Net Revenue	56,937,990,933	54,505,342,127	52,779,591,473	50,959,094,445	48,547,283,264
Total Expenses	51,565,187,281	49,404,788,582	47,538,778,511	46,328,180,009	43,488,785,543
HOSPITAL UNIT (Excludes Separate Nursing Home Units)					
Utilization - Inpatient					
Beds	56,984	57,062	58,022	59,427	59,055
Admissions	1,887,819	1,921,902	1,910,191	2,006,130	1,999,782
Inpatient Days	10,414,976	10,657,987	10,722,434	11,006,139	10,929,906
Average Length of Stay	5.5	5.5	5.6	5.5	5.5
Personnel					
Total Full Time	265,902	262,136	259,351	263,494	256,240
Total Part Time	123,374	120,803	119,115	121,202	118,696
Revenue and Expenses - Totals **(Includes Inpatient and Outpatient)**					
Total Net Revenue	$56,367,417,839	$53,931,360,254	$52,187,481,082	$50,396,086,960	$47,999,122,812
Total Expenses	51,136,858,785	48,958,934,895	47,084,233,054	45,871,570,407	43,042,562,713

TABLE 4

BED SIZE CATEGORY 100-199

U.S. Registered Community Hospitals
(Nonfederal, short-term general and other special hospitals)

Overview 2012–2016

	2016	2015	2014	2013	2012
Total Community Hospitals in Bed Size Category 100-199	963	983	1,013	995	1,012
Location					
Hospitals Urban	713	732	754	711	717
Hospitals Rural	250	251	259	284	295
Control					
State and Local Government	119	127	128	123	135
Not for Profit	597	600	626	621	617
Investor owned	247	256	259	251	260
Physician Models					
Independent Practice Association	88	115	102	94	97
Group Practice without Walls	29	32	41	39	36
Open Physician-Hospital Organization	128	127	147	140	142
Closed Physician-Hospital Organization	47	46	48	45	48
Management Service Organization	81	92	88	91	106
Integrated Salary Model	359	375	368	354	345
Equity Model	23	24	25	26	21
Foundation	60	65	64	71	62
Insurance Products					
Health Maintenance Organization	155	155	147	139	125
Preferred Provider Organization	142	142	147	142	122
Indemnity Fee for Service	62	60	69	55	52
Managed Care Contracts					
Health Maintenance Organization	549	565	583	567	566
Preferred Provider Organization	577	609	625	610	606
Affiliations					
Hospitals in a System	727	734	727	691	686
Hospitals in a Network	330	336	321	293	281
Hospitals in a Group Purchasing Organization	676	704	714	710	688

Bed Size Categories

TABLE 4

BED SIZE CATEGORY 100-199

U.S. Registered Community Hospitals
(Nonfederal, short-term general and other special hospitals)

Utilization, Personnel, Revenue and Expenses, Community Health Indicators 2012–2016

	2016	2015	2014	2013	2012
TOTAL FACILITY (Includes Hospital and Nursing Home Units)					
Utilization - Inpatient					
Beds	139,246	142,471	147,188	143,760	145,556
Admissions	5,622,211	5,721,983	5,849,312	5,754,158	5,920,309
Inpatient Days	29,929,136	30,338,340	30,924,198	30,164,685	30,892,477
Average Length of Stay	5.3	5.3	5.3	5.2	5.2
Inpatient Surgeries	1,372,138	1,395,213	1,495,432	1,472,473	1,546,794
Births	646,628	671,737	685,159	654,405	658,328
Utilization - Outpatient					
Emergency Outpatient Visits	29,592,814	29,891,181	28,692,743	27,201,787	27,668,989
Other Outpatient Visits	107,001,065	103,771,903	105,049,461	96,360,321	96,096,051
Total Outpatient Visits	136,593,879	133,663,084	133,742,204	123,562,108	123,765,040
Outpatient Surgeries	3,388,272	3,358,563	3,464,061	3,419,797	3,421,257
Personnel					
Full Time RNs	182,661	181,555	179,199	168,819	167,593
Full Time LPNs	12,650	12,707	12,384	12,856	13,807
Part Time RNs	87,007	87,012	89,200	85,350	85,380
Part Time LPNs	4,380	4,684	4,702	5,199	5,356
Total Full Time	647,613	641,935	652,976	618,661	622,757
Total Part Time	266,072	262,540	271,272	261,701	265,049
Revenue - Inpatient					
Gross Inpatient Revenue	$235,147,017,990	$234,427,612,582	$224,322,560,387	$206,931,061,736	$196,130,283,474
Revenue - Outpatient					
Gross Outpatient Revenue	$275,278,173,934	$256,460,573,965	$238,070,878,699	$208,345,611,345	$190,830,856,203
Revenue and Expenses - Totals					
(Includes Inpatient and Outpatient)					
Total Gross Revenue	$510,425,191,924	$490,888,186,547	$462,393,439,086	$415,276,658,664	$386,961,139,677
Deductions from Revenue	371,740,860,831	357,452,470,229	331,553,610,396	294,786,238,076	269,772,483,763
Net Patient Revenue	138,684,331,093	133,435,716,318	130,839,828,690	120,490,420,588	117,188,655,914
Other Operating Revenue	5,401,366,187	5,189,375,092	5,908,515,946	5,523,192,766	5,062,039,669
Other Nonoperating Revenue	1,583,719,408	1,103,939,862	2,283,016,011	2,575,090,869	1,638,797,895
Total Net Revenue	145,669,416,688	139,729,031,272	139,031,360,647	128,588,704,223	123,889,493,478
Total Expenses	134,091,393,666	127,915,704,973	127,400,142,442	117,726,795,452	112,758,082,370
HOSPITAL UNIT (Excludes Separate Nursing Home Units)					
Utilization - Inpatient					
Beds	127,704	130,051	135,469	131,892	132,541
Admissions	5,583,885	5,680,758	5,812,483	5,713,320	5,876,426
Inpatient Days	26,186,219	26,376,275	27,315,765	26,497,775	26,855,548
Average Length of Stay	4.7	4.6	4.7	4.6	4.6
Personnel					
Total Full Time	640,778	634,579	645,486	611,021	613,726
Total Part Time	261,938	258,034	266,626	256,801	259,764
Revenue and Expenses - Totals					
(Includes Inpatient and Outpatient)					
Total Net Revenue	$144,634,177,722	$138,680,322,398	$138,178,193,223	$127,741,585,255	$122,970,772,210
Total Expenses	133,329,301,135	127,092,370,223	126,683,059,991	116,987,799,038	111,908,745,686

TABLE **4**

BED SIZE CATEGORY 200-299

U.S. Registered Community Hospitals
(Nonfederal, short-term general and other special hospitals)

Overview 2012–2016

	2016	2015	2014	2013	2012
Total Community Hospitals in					
Bed Size Category 200-299	531	535	536	571	570
Location					
Hospitals Urban	478	475	467	486	487
Hospitals Rural	53	60	69	85	83
Control					
State and Local Government	47	49	58	57	62
Not for Profit	373	374	365	399	393
Investor owned	111	112	113	115	115
Physician Models					
Independent Practice Association......................	71	70	63	65	56
Group Practice without Walls	23	26	26	28	22
Open Physician-Hospital Organization	92	93	83	91	98
Closed Physician-Hospital Organization............	34	32	26	38	30
Management Service Organization.....................	74	70	63	73	69
Integrated Salary Model.................................	233	229	221	247	238
Equity Model	13	15	14	20	15
Foundation	46	46	40	46	34
Insurance Products					
Health Maintenance Organization.....................	108	102	92	106	90
Preferred Provider Organization	103	88	82	91	77
Indemnity Fee for Service	36	36	35	38	32
Managed Care Contracts					
Health Maintenance Organization.....................	341	345	328	358	373
Preferred Provider Organization	364	364	341	374	383
Affiliations					
Hospitals in a System	403	396	392	410	390
Hospitals in a Network.................................	219	211	190	197	185
Hospitals in a Group Purchasing Organization...	408	411	378	418	424

TABLE 4

BED SIZE CATEGORY 200-299

U.S. Registered Community Hospitals
(Nonfederal, short-term general and other special hospitals)

Utilization, Personnel, Revenue and Expenses, Community Health Indicators 2012–2016

	2016	2015	2014	2013	2012
TOTAL FACILITY (Includes Hospital and Nursing Home Units)					
Utilization - Inpatient					
Beds	129,661	131,287	131,526	140,113	139,212
Admissions	5,859,418	5,923,633	5,759,469	6,156,487	6,297,821
Inpatient Days	29,429,219	29,946,324	29,553,689	31,466,013	32,150,843
Average Length of Stay	5.0	5.1	5.1	5.1	5.1
Inpatient Surgeries	1,537,525	1,547,792	1,523,670	1,623,431	1,728,626
Births	668,784	680,565	658,373	668,891	661,428
Utilization - Outpatient					
Emergency Outpatient Visits	25,182,104	25,246,261	24,481,880	24,975,730	24,468,359
Other Outpatient Visits	92,076,724	88,218,931	81,281,901	87,945,697	87,195,255
Total Outpatient Visits	117,258,828	113,465,192	105,763,781	112,921,427	111,663,614
Outpatient Surgeries	3,025,752	2,957,311	2,838,604	2,999,018	2,963,873
Personnel					
Full Time RNs	187,461	184,861	178,755	181,464	178,938
Full Time LPNs	8,680	8,898	8,803	10,044	10,635
Part Time RNs	86,755	84,639	80,217	87,905	89,327
Part Time LPNs	2,979	3,161	3,304	3,689	4,108
Total Full Time	653,965	642,241	613,324	647,716	654,260
Total Part Time	248,250	244,793	230,745	254,023	257,126
Revenue - Inpatient					
Gross Inpatient Revenue	$285,875,299,379	$272,602,896,209	$248,302,339,484	$243,975,095,899	$240,835,907,576
Revenue - Outpatient					
Gross Outpatient Revenue	$259,426,414,323	$238,563,596,238	$211,646,176,712	$200,229,741,755	$185,911,616,840
Revenue and Expenses - Totals					
(Includes Inpatient and Outpatient)					
Total Gross Revenue	$545,301,713,702	$511,166,492,447	$459,948,516,196	$444,204,837,654	$426,747,524,416
Deductions from Revenue	403,829,128,255	374,056,488,683	335,144,597,503	316,380,880,125	300,061,387,153
Net Patient Revenue	141,472,585,447	137,110,003,764	124,803,918,693	127,823,957,529	126,686,137,263
Other Operating Revenue	7,562,208,842	7,056,549,749	6,648,909,930	6,482,336,012	5,987,888,496
Other Nonoperating Revenue	1,118,987,847	658,880,122	3,014,355,360	2,877,258,321	1,814,706,798
Total Net Revenue	150,153,782,136	144,825,433,635	134,467,183,983	137,183,551,862	134,488,732,557
Total Expenses	138,699,720,870	133,089,063,850	122,882,213,725	127,003,057,863	124,808,644,131
HOSPITAL UNIT (Excludes Separate Nursing Home Units)					
Utilization - Inpatient					
Beds	123,596	124,716	124,442	132,439	130,652
Admissions	5,829,932	5,891,131	5,722,377	6,114,738	6,248,381
Inpatient Days	27,518,496	27,868,504	27,364,700	29,079,526	29,421,703
Average Length of Stay	4.7	4.7	4.8	4.8	4.7
Personnel					
Total Full Time	649,400	637,452	606,969	642,090	647,761
Total Part Time	245,845	242,266	227,587	251,422	254,363
Revenue and Expenses - Totals					
(Includes Inpatient and Outpatient)					
Total Net Revenue	$149,567,367,680	$144,174,211,395	$133,835,590,497	$136,494,821,942	$133,703,328,242
Total Expenses	138,237,629,882	132,525,032,117	122,357,952,282	126,404,652,829	124,088,653,959

Bed Size Categories

TABLE 4

BED SIZE CATEGORY 300-399

U.S. Registered Community Hospitals
(Nonfederal, short-term general and other special hospitals)

Overview 2012–2016

	2016	2015	2014	2013	2012
Total Community Hospitals in					
Bed Size Category 300-399	322	322	328	334	348
Location					
Hospitals Urban	307	307	315	316	331
Hospitals Rural.......................................	15	15	13	18	17
Control					
State and Local Government	28	31	29	37	37
Not for Profit...	237	235	242	241	255
Investor owned.......................................	57	56	57	56	56
Physician Models					
Independent Practice Association....................	44	43	50	46	47
Group Practice without Walls........................	12	12	20	23	21
Open Physician-Hospital Organization	65	68	65	69	67
Closed Physician-Hospital Organization.............	23	18	25	25	30
Management Service Organization....................	38	38	38	48	49
Integrated Salary Model.............................	151	160	156	162	168
Equity Model	13	12	14	6	6
Foundation	32	37	36	30	30
Insurance Products					
Health Maintenance Organization....................	74	75	72	64	60
Preferred Provider Organization	68	68	62	55	47
Indemnity Fee for Service............................	30	29	22	18	14
Managed Care Contracts					
Health Maintenance Organization....................	228	234	243	247	254
Preferred Provider Organization	237	239	248	250	260
Affiliations					
Hospitals in a System.................................	249	248	239	237	241
Hospitals in a Network...............................	147	150	151	133	128
Hospitals in a Group Purchasing Organization...	255	264	276	278	278

Bed Size Categories

TABLE 4

BED SIZE CATEGORY 300-399

U.S. Registered Community Hospitals
(Nonfederal, short-term general and other special hospitals)

Utilization, Personnel, Revenue and Expenses, Community Health Indicators 2012–2016

	2016	2015	2014	2013	2012
TOTAL FACILITY (Includes Hospital and Nursing Home Units)					
Utilization - Inpatient					
Beds	111,233	111,139	112,909	115,511	120,554
Admissions	5,282,961	5,216,212	5,189,544	5,343,652	5,659,683
Inpatient Days	26,820,397	26,506,796	26,586,603	27,347,329	28,628,393
Average Length of Stay	5.1	5.1	5.1	5.1	5.1
Inpatient Surgeries	1,349,994	1,346,508	1,409,981	1,421,836	1,505,394
Births	601,144	603,326	595,162	607,340	635,069
Utilization - Outpatient					
Emergency Outpatient Visits	20,432,363	20,142,605	19,517,349	18,931,461	19,494,322
Other Outpatient Visits	65,311,566	67,292,714	66,068,055	70,815,508	74,292,746
Total Outpatient Visits	85,743,929	87,435,319	85,585,404	89,746,969	93,787,068
Outpatient Surgeries	2,278,337	2,232,805	2,225,385	2,317,170	2,419,594
Personnel					
Full Time RNs	177,633	171,244	166,905	165,887	167,220
Full Time LPNs	6,820	6,521	6,918	7,556	8,157
Part Time RNs	68,589	66,456	71,258	68,700	74,735
Part Time LPNs	1,874	1,848	2,086	2,196	2,519
Total Full Time	572,038	558,795	559,496	573,637	592,655
Total Part Time	193,117	183,762	195,367	190,809	210,937
Revenue - Inpatient					
Gross Inpatient Revenue	$276,818,178,691	$262,140,905,966	$250,071,810,658	$240,832,001,022	$230,446,967,570
Revenue - Outpatient					
Gross Outpatient Revenue	$221,679,581,604	$206,284,696,192	$187,976,265,233	$175,534,042,359	$164,159,129,172
Revenue and Expenses - Totals (Includes Inpatient and Outpatient)					
Total Gross Revenue	$498,497,760,295	$468,425,602,158	$438,048,075,891	$416,366,043,381	$394,606,096,742
Deductions from Revenue	372,343,034,144	346,860,739,151	320,458,201,969	300,900,054,698	277,863,090,524
Net Patient Revenue	126,154,726,151	121,564,863,007	117,589,873,922	115,465,988,683	116,743,006,218
Other Operating Revenue	6,401,195,912	5,884,231,965	5,996,352,921	6,912,306,120	6,414,161,778
Other Nonoperating Revenue	1,389,667,074	589,162,878	2,179,681,513	3,455,675,896	1,472,292,314
Total Net Revenue	133,945,589,137	128,038,257,850	125,765,908,356	125,833,970,699	124,629,460,310
Total Expenses	124,345,119,694	117,864,829,893	114,174,422,976	114,313,944,143	114,103,095,511
HOSPITAL UNIT (Excludes Separate Nursing Home Units)					
Utilization - Inpatient					
Beds	108,365	107,653	108,904	110,605	115,302
Admissions	5,262,769	5,194,807	5,161,239	5,311,319	5,626,701
Inpatient Days	25,951,866	25,556,899	25,374,527	25,900,164	27,018,257
Average Length of Stay	4.9	4.9	4.9	4.9	4.8
Personnel					
Total Full Time	569,982	556,228	555,223	569,603	588,298
Total Part Time	192,208	182,718	193,985	189,117	209,136
Revenue and Expenses - Totals (Includes Inpatient and Outpatient)					
Total Net Revenue	$133,595,060,239	$127,564,881,165	$125,144,792,457	$125,251,711,673	$124,094,300,216
Total Expenses	124,098,333,192	117,608,110,361	113,703,110,583	113,842,852,106	113,626,750,271

TABLE 4

BED SIZE CATEGORY 400-499

U.S. Registered Community Hospitals
(Nonfederal, short-term general and other special hospitals)

Overview 2012–2016

	2016	2015	2014	2013	2012
Total Community Hospitals in Bed Size Category 400-499	177	177	188	183	189
Location					
Hospitals Urban	174	174	185	179	186
Hospitals Rural	3	3	3	4	3
Control					
State and Local Government	24	27	31	30	29
Not for Profit	132	131	138	135	142
Investor owned	21	19	19	18	18
Physician Models					
Independent Practice Association	44	40	34	30	32
Group Practice without Walls	18	14	15	16	14
Open Physician-Hospital Organization	29	29	33	36	44
Closed Physician-Hospital Organization	16	22	20	20	16
Management Service Organization	28	34	34	35	33
Integrated Salary Model	96	92	103	98	96
Equity Model	7	6	7	7	6
Foundation	29	27	24	27	24
Insurance Products					
Health Maintenance Organization	52	54	48	44	38
Preferred Provider Organization	40	40	42	42	37
Indemnity Fee for Service	15	16	11	8	8
Managed Care Contracts					
Health Maintenance Organization	135	136	149	140	151
Preferred Provider Organization	137	139	149	144	152
Affiliations					
Hospitals in a System	132	132	141	135	137
Hospitals in a Network	98	90	85	85	88
Hospitals in a Group Purchasing Organization	155	152	162	154	159

TABLE 4

BED SIZE CATEGORY 400-499

U.S. Registered Community Hospitals
(Nonfederal, short-term general and other special hospitals)

Utilization, Personnel, Revenue and Expenses, Community Health Indicators 2012–2016

	2016	2015	2014	2013	2012
TOTAL FACILITY (Includes Hospital and Nursing Home Units)					
Utilization - Inpatient					
Beds	78,381	78,276	83,285	81,148	84,007
Admissions	3,635,759	3,623,728	3,899,412	3,750,238	3,966,019
Inpatient Days	19,526,076	19,473,188	20,633,887	20,029,447	20,755,259
Average Length of Stay	5.4	5.4	5.3	5.3	5.2
Inpatient Surgeries	1,023,758	1,010,724	1,084,572	1,038,085	1,137,327
Births	423,939	411,527	461,565	417,270	427,993
Utilization - Outpatient					
Emergency Outpatient Visits	13,365,313	12,899,493	13,464,443	12,285,620	12,993,712
Other Outpatient Visits	63,490,384	60,672,737	64,482,715	59,073,331	59,418,937
Total Outpatient Visits	76,855,697	73,572,230	77,947,158	71,358,951	72,412,649
Outpatient Surgeries	1,731,964	1,657,487	1,748,750	1,607,610	1,669,549
Personnel					
Full Time RNs	130,381	130,384	136,099	125,451	131,578
Full Time LPNs	4,685	5,331	5,063	5,246	5,571
Part Time RNs	62,368	55,114	56,071	54,284	55,526
Part Time LPNs	1,637	1,672	1,612	1,992	2,269
Total Full Time	459,454	455,341	468,458	440,221	462,528
Total Part Time	168,874	148,821	153,436	152,826	159,252
Revenue - Inpatient					
Gross Inpatient Revenue	$195,381,045,588	$180,553,181,341	$178,999,206,730	$165,377,218,755	$165,404,143,916
Revenue - Outpatient					
Gross Outpatient Revenue	$165,777,551,470	$147,175,644,365	$143,088,198,726	$125,422,311,131	$119,532,259,113
Revenue and Expenses - Totals **(Includes Inpatient and Outpatient)**					
Total Gross Revenue	$361,158,597,058	$327,728,825,706	$322,087,405,456	$290,799,529,886	$284,936,403,029
Deductions from Revenue	259,825,436,261	232,365,473,589	227,067,664,476	204,455,874,952	197,528,264,702
Net Patient Revenue	101,333,160,797	95,363,352,117	95,019,740,980	86,343,654,934	87,408,138,327
Other Operating Revenue	7,037,077,408	6,844,706,592	6,360,621,218	5,485,613,820	5,272,639,678
Other Nonoperating Revenue	1,510,800,476	629,938,259	2,149,108,579	2,567,834,662	1,325,875,743
Total Net Revenue	109,881,038,681	102,837,996,968	103,529,470,777	94,397,103,416	94,006,653,748
Total Expenses	101,971,588,975	95,428,252,524	96,135,582,660	87,818,900,913	87,804,964,580
HOSPITAL UNIT (Excludes Separate Nursing Home Units)					
Utilization - Inpatient					
Beds	75,456	75,634	80,282	77,123	80,458
Admissions	3,623,636	3,612,535	3,886,098	3,734,868	3,947,024
Inpatient Days	18,582,706	18,592,108	19,618,360	18,697,496	19,600,701
Average Length of Stay	5.1	5.1	5.0	5.0	5.0
Personnel					
Total Full Time	456,875	453,504	466,094	436,927	459,192
Total Part Time	167,786	147,860	152,150	151,242	157,372
Revenue and Expenses - Totals **(Includes Inpatient and Outpatient)**					
Total Net Revenue	$109,423,042,300	$102,416,396,046	$103,193,608,338	$93,975,576,086	$93,581,430,291
Total Expenses	101,678,240,509	95,075,355,257	95,830,792,663	87,456,206,840	87,395,944,309

Bed Size Categories

TABLE 4

BED SIZE CATEGORY 500 +

U.S. Registered Community Hospitals
(Nonfederal, short-term general and other special hospitals)

Overview 2012–2016

	2016	2015	2014	2013	2012
Total Community Hospitals in					
Bed Size Category 500 +.............................	285	284	273	277	272
Location					
Hospitals Urban	283	282	271	275	269
Hospitals Rural...	2	2	2	2	3
Control					
State and Local Government	50	51	46	46	46
Not for Profit...	217	214	207	212	208
Investor owned...	18	19	20	19	18
Physician Models					
Independent Practice Association.....................	60	57	53	57	60
Group Practice without Walls	12	16	20	18	14
Open Physician-Hospital Organization	61	60	57	62	61
Closed Physician-Hospital Organization.............	38	37	36	32	35
Management Service Organization.....................	55	65	59	66	62
Integrated Salary Model.................................	193	186	169	181	180
Equity Model	11	12	11	13	9
Foundation	30	27	28	28	25
Insurance Products					
Health Maintenance Organization.....................	100	99	88	91	88
Preferred Provider Organization	90	87	70	73	62
Indemnity Fee for Service	32	33	26	26	23
Managed Care Contracts					
Health Maintenance Organization.....................	245	246	229	241	236
Preferred Provider Organization	250	248	232	244	237
Affiliations					
Hospitals in a System	223	213	202	203	196
Hospitals in a Network.................................	163	159	143	143	130
Hospitals in a Group Purchasing Organization...	262	264	246	255	245

TABLE 4

BED SIZE CATEGORY 500 +

U.S. Registered Community Hospitals
(Nonfederal, short-term general and other special hospitals)

Utilization, Personnel, Revenue and Expenses, Community Health Indicators 2012–2016

	2016	2015	2014	2013	2012
TOTAL FACILITY (Includes Hospital and Nursing Home Units)					
Utilization - Inpatient					
Beds	211,927	208,550	200,330	201,377	197,229
Admissions	9,887,568	9,582,979	9,212,246	9,306,545	9,235,106
Inpatient Days	57,218,809	55,481,018	52,905,475	52,931,846	52,408,270
Average Length of Stay	5.8	5.8	5.7	5.7	5.7
Inpatient Surgeries	2,979,529	2,907,037	2,805,334	2,861,210	2,840,233
Births	1,049,016	1,040,243	983,083	993,825	976,400
Utilization - Outpatient					
Emergency Outpatient Visits	30,801,673	30,122,411	27,782,849	27,879,830	26,824,430
Other Outpatient Visits	172,809,371	159,543,988	143,739,748	136,017,527	132,397,748
Total Outpatient Visits	203,611,044	189,666,399	171,522,597	163,897,357	159,222,178
Outpatient Surgeries	4,605,642	4,295,271	4,084,475	4,098,509	3,882,339
Personnel					
Full Time RNs	416,167	397,448	371,398	359,722	343,369
Full Time LPNs	13,436	12,511	11,823	12,327	12,127
Part Time RNs	141,773	136,144	128,091	128,171	124,895
Part Time LPNs	3,642	3,205	3,259	3,528	3,797
Total Full Time	1,489,258	1,426,960	1,347,612	1,332,280	1,267,573
Total Part Time	404,567	383,304	358,021	359,019	347,276
Revenue - Inpatient					
Gross Inpatient Revenue	$588,015,485,811	$544,328,865,089	$496,323,018,932	$471,993,651,262	$438,404,095,774
Revenue - Outpatient					
Gross Outpatient Revenue	$454,103,440,496	$403,991,355,580	$353,109,338,579	$322,242,954,475	$287,455,681,774
Revenue and Expenses - Totals					
(Includes Inpatient and Outpatient)					
Total Gross Revenue	$1,042,118,926,307	$948,320,220,669	$849,432,357,511	$794,236,605,737	$725,859,777,548
Deductions from Revenue	739,082,799,999	665,979,474,892	593,844,453,407	551,909,522,075	495,852,998,550
Net Patient Revenue	303,036,126,308	282,340,745,777	255,587,904,104	242,327,083,662	230,006,778,998
Other Operating Revenue	23,569,750,966	21,723,129,953	19,897,779,902	19,675,400,576	19,525,754,240
Other Nonoperating Revenue	4,248,502,296	1,816,813,138	5,947,195,310	6,735,212,689	3,798,787,364
Total Net Revenue	330,854,379,570	305,880,688,868	281,432,879,316	268,737,696,927	253,331,320,602
Total Expenses	304,145,409,460	282,478,235,850	258,392,120,893	248,158,203,354	234,887,398,418
HOSPITAL UNIT (Excludes Separate Nursing Home Units)					
Utilization - Inpatient					
Beds	202,943	199,315	193,057	192,922	188,779
Admissions	9,853,937	9,549,408	9,178,842	9,266,619	9,196,329
Inpatient Days	54,380,728	52,797,048	50,484,416	50,120,917	49,593,574
Average Length of Stay	5.5	5.5	5.5	5.4	5.4
Personnel					
Total Full Time	1,483,903	1,421,345	1,340,742	1,325,873	1,260,197
Total Part Time	402,338	380,861	355,752	356,542	344,634
Revenue and Expenses - Totals					
(Includes Inpatient and Outpatient)					
Total Net Revenue	$330,074,680,408	$304,978,256,055	$280,724,691,736	$267,844,526,778	$252,473,832,518
Total Expenses	303,387,730,421	281,591,033,757	257,685,682,932	247,271,410,711	234,023,264,708

Bed Size Categories

Census Divisions

Census Division 1

New England
Connecticut, Maine, Massachusetts, New Hampshire, Rhode Island, Vermont

Census Division 2

Middle Atlantic
New Jersey, New York, Pennsylvania

Census Division 3

South Atlantic
Delaware, District of Columbia, Florida, Georgia, Maryland, North Carolina, South Carolina, Virginia, West Virginia

Census Division 4

East North Central
Illinois, Indiana, Michigan, Ohio, Wisconsin

Census Division 5

East South Central
Alabama, Kentucky, Mississippi, Tennessee

Census Division 6

West North Central
Iowa, Kansas, Minnesota, Missouri, Nebraska, North Dakota, South Dakota

Census Division 7

West South Central
Arkansas, Louisiana, Oklahoma, Texas

Census Division 8

Mountain
Arizona, Colorado, Idaho, Montana, Nevada, New Mexico, Utah, Wyoming

Census Division 9

Pacific
Alaska, California, Hawaii, Oregon, Washington

U.S. Census Divisions

TABLE 5

U.S. CENSUS DIVISION 1: NEW ENGLAND

U.S. Registered Community Hospitals
(Nonfederal, short-term general and other special hospitals)

Overview 2012–2016

	2016	2015	2014	2013	2012
Total Community Hospitals in Census Division 1, New England...............	194	195	199	203	207
Bed Size Category					
6-24..	8	9	8	7	10
25-49..	43	42	43	44	43
50-99..	43	44	45	45	47
100-199...	50	50	54	55	51
200-299...	20	19	19	23	26
300-399...	13	13	14	13	15
400-499...	6	7	5	5	4
500 +..	11	11	11	11	11
Location					
Hospitals Urban	139	140	144	146	149
Hospitals Rural..	55	55	55	57	58
Control					
State and Local Government	6	7	7	6	6
Not for Profit...	164	164	167	170	176
Investor owned..	24	24	25	27	25
Physician Models					
Independent Practice Association......................	34	34	32	34	32
Group Practice without Walls..........................	9	6	6	8	7
Open Physician-Hospital Organization	37	40	44	41	43
Closed Physician-Hospital Organization.............	7	8	9	10	12
Management Service Organization.....................	19	16	16	17	20
Integrated Salary Model................................	90	87	87	93	101
Equity Model	6	5	5	5	6
Foundation	18	15	14	12	14
Insurance Products					
Health Maintenance Organization......................	25	21	16	13	15
Preferred Provider Organization	19	15	9	9	9
Indemnity Fee for Service	9	4	3	3	4
Managed Care Contracts					
Health Maintenance Organization......................	114	111	111	116	119
Preferred Provider Organization	111	109	115	116	119
Affiliations					
Hospitals in a System	112	109	105	105	102
Hospitals in a Network..................................	78	76	79	77	75
Hospitals in a Group Purchasing Organization...	143	142	141	147	148

U.S. Census Divisions

TABLE 5

U.S. CENSUS DIVISION 1: NEW ENGLAND

U.S. Registered Community Hospitals
(Nonfederal, short-term general and other special hospitals)

Utilization, Personnel, Revenue and Expenses, Community Health Indicators 2012–2016

	2016	2015	2014	2013	2012
TOTAL FACILITY (Includes Hospital and Nursing Home Units)					
Utilization - Inpatient					
Beds	32,623	32,821	33,531	34,028	34,399
Admissions	1,567,105	1,558,931	1,540,755	1,597,809	1,608,353
Inpatient Days	8,350,338	8,378,178	8,450,523	8,611,159	8,482,806
Average Length of Stay	5.3	5.4	5.5	5.4	5.3
Inpatient Surgeries	420,910	403,326	407,432	409,361	418,336
Births	145,980	146,737	147,729	146,765	146,147
Utilization - Outpatient					
Emergency Outpatient Visits	7,187,817	7,416,637	7,027,573	7,168,129	7,131,256
Other Outpatient Visits	41,437,314	42,322,400	41,324,371	41,529,159	40,756,179
Total Outpatient Visits	48,625,131	49,739,037	48,351,944	48,697,288	47,887,435
Outpatient Surgeries	951,716	930,946	950,041	949,198	960,370
Personnel					
Full Time RNs	51,435	49,526	48,640	47,004	46,323
Full Time LPNs	1,880	1,842	1,773	1,800	1,816
Part Time RNs	42,220	41,995	41,290	40,843	41,454
Part Time LPNs	996	1,039	1,051	1,203	1,370
Total Full Time	240,968	231,656	230,443	230,028	226,202
Total Part Time	128,334	124,311	124,558	122,493	126,716
Revenue - Inpatient					
Gross Inpatient Revenue	$61,403,900,848	$59,533,307,889	$58,025,515,968	$55,981,458,810	$52,549,975,311
Revenue - Outpatient					
Gross Outpatient Revenue	$79,134,415,613	$73,345,891,999	$68,057,938,276	$64,787,872,297	$60,296,411,970
Revenue and Expenses - Totals (Includes Inpatient and Outpatient)					
Total Gross Revenue	$140,538,316,461	$132,879,199,888	$126,083,454,244	$120,769,331,107	$112,846,387,281
Deductions from Revenue	89,246,143,092	84,140,793,499	79,336,535,611	75,150,281,353	68,108,106,958
Net Patient Revenue	51,292,173,369	48,738,406,389	46,746,918,633	45,619,049,754	44,738,280,323
Other Operating Revenue	5,848,600,405	5,439,195,628	5,201,941,863	5,170,226,128	4,894,336,432
Other Nonoperating Revenue	437,716,708	1,358,993	594,068,158	1,095,149,728	464,999,614
Total Net Revenue	57,578,490,482	54,178,961,010	52,542,928,654	51,884,425,610	50,097,616,369
Total Expenses	55,525,755,312	52,145,703,452	49,846,135,493	48,855,355,041	47,321,636,263
HOSPITAL UNIT (Excludes Separate Nursing Home Units)					
Utilization - Inpatient					
Beds	31,796	31,938	32,632	33,135	33,332
Admissions	1,562,500	1,554,858	1,537,589	1,594,828	1,605,312
Inpatient Days	8,072,286	8,154,280	8,151,517	8,301,445	8,161,998
Average Length of Stay	5.2	5.2	5.3	5.2	5.1
Personnel					
Total Full Time	239,977	231,083	229,607	229,182	224,884
Total Part Time	127,612	123,814	123,749	121,946	125,777
Revenue and Expenses - Totals (Includes Inpatient and Outpatient)					
Total Net Revenue	$57,508,199,598	$54,113,824,772	$52,459,070,954	$51,788,888,807	$49,974,043,473
Total Expenses	55,453,511,737	52,083,450,646	49,758,477,399	48,773,242,820	47,206,585,210
COMMUNITY HEALTH INDICATORS PER 1000 POPULATION					
Total Population (in thousands)	14,736	14,728	14,681	14,619	14,563
Inpatient					
Beds	2.2	2.2	2.3	2.3	2.4
Admissions	106.3	105.9	105.0	109.3	110.4
Inpatient Days	566.7	568.9	575.6	589.0	582.5
Inpatient Surgeries	28.6	27.4	27.8	28.0	28.7
Births	9.9	10.0	10.1	10.0	10.0
Outpatient					
Emergency Outpatient Visits	487.8	503.6	478.7	490.3	489.7
Other Outpatient Visits	2,812.1	2,873.7	2,814.9	2,840.8	2,798.7
Total Outpatient Visits	3,299.9	3,377.3	3,293.6	3,331.1	3,288.4
Outpatient Surgeries	64.6	63.2	64.7	64.9	65.9
Expense per Capita (per person)	$3,768.2	$3,540.7	$3,395.3	$3,342.0	$3,249.5

TABLE 5

U.S. CENSUS DIVISION 2: MIDDLE ATLANTIC

U.S. Registered Community Hospitals
(Nonfederal, short-term general and other special hospitals)

Overview 2012–2016

	2016	2015	2014	2013	2012
Total Community Hospitals					
in Census Division 2, Middle Atlantic............	428	431	434	444	447
Bed Size Category					
6-24	10	10	11	10	11
25-49	41	41	35	37	36
50-99	64	65	63	63	63
100-199	111	107	109	106	107
200-299	78	80	80	90	91
300-399	43	50	52	53	52
400-499	25	21	28	27	30
500 + ...	56	57	56	58	57
Location					
Hospitals Urban	355	358	360	359	362
Hospitals Rural	73	73	74	85	85
Control					
State and Local Government	25	26	27	31	31
Not for Profit	340	341	348	353	354
Investor owned	63	64	59	60	62
Physician Models					
Independent Practice Association	71	68	63	62	61
Group Practice without Walls	18	16	16	16	17
Open Physician-Hospital Organization	45	42	38	40	42
Closed Physician-Hospital Organization	16	19	16	15	19
Management Service Organization	47	57	52	49	52
Integrated Salary Model	201	193	187	195	182
Equity Model	11	10	8	8	7
Foundation	11	13	17	17	15
Insurance Products					
Health Maintenance Organization	100	97	91	97	91
Preferred Provider Organization	58	60	57	74	65
Indemnity Fee for Service	35	46	29	40	37
Managed Care Contracts					
Health Maintenance Organization	276	276	269	281	295
Preferred Provider Organization	268	268	260	277	285
Affiliations					
Hospitals in a System	299	287	276	277	261
Hospitals in a Network	195	185	171	166	157
Hospitals in a Group Purchasing Organization...	311	309	301	335	323

TABLE **5**

U.S. CENSUS DIVISION 2: MIDDLE ATLANTIC

U.S. Registered Community Hospitals
(Nonfederal, short-term general and other special hospitals)

Utilization, Personnel, Revenue and Expenses, Community Health Indicators 2012–2016

	2016	2015	2014	2013	2012
TOTAL FACILITY (Includes Hospital and Nursing Home Units)					
Utilization - Inpatient					
Beds	110,393	110,732	113,947	116,588	117,624
Admissions	4,831,249	4,752,991	4,833,693	4,974,821	5,183,982
Inpatient Days	28,667,552	28,691,096	29,417,955	30,254,395	31,440,731
Average Length of Stay	5.9	6.0	6.1	6.1	6.1
Inpatient Surgeries	1,276,472	1,263,776	1,295,330	1,327,290	1,404,460
Births	455,921	453,441	461,201	460,691	468,787
Utilization - Outpatient					
Emergency Outpatient Visits	19,067,851	18,606,110	18,448,665	18,464,278	18,321,971
Other Outpatient Visits	93,452,968	94,006,523	92,218,023	91,471,231	92,940,002
Total Outpatient Visits	112,520,819	112,612,633	110,666,688	109,935,509	111,261,973
Outpatient Surgeries	2,741,704	2,587,835	2,609,583	2,644,536	2,604,246
Personnel					
Full Time RNs	179,348	171,066	169,247	166,205	164,025
Full Time LPNs	7,579	7,686	7,861	8,442	8,908
Part Time RNs	62,629	61,783	61,908	61,534	61,911
Part Time LPNs	2,055	2,310	2,347	2,676	2,910
Total Full Time	681,614	659,190	655,994	665,974	667,785
Total Part Time	201,760	197,054	194,911	197,905	200,851
Revenue - Inpatient					
Gross Inpatient Revenue	$270,778,787,516	$256,680,411,979	$245,751,731,763	$237,733,249,795	$232,928,664,012
Revenue - Outpatient					
Gross Outpatient Revenue	$220,988,127,280	$196,445,608,503	$181,102,970,514	$169,822,609,385	$159,129,515,739
Revenue and Expenses - Totals (Includes Inpatient and Outpatient)					
Total Gross Revenue	$491,766,914,796	$453,126,020,482	$426,854,702,277	$407,555,859,180	$392,058,179,751
Deductions from Revenue	355,938,421,940	325,922,224,898	304,781,462,214	290,276,723,196	276,630,776,133
Net Patient Revenue	135,828,492,856	127,203,795,584	122,073,240,063	117,279,135,984	115,427,403,618
Other Operating Revenue	10,044,006,841	8,761,137,239	8,866,772,815	8,770,801,527	7,842,143,044
Other Nonoperating Revenue	1,777,720,827	836,081,656	2,070,612,992	2,945,630,852	1,401,364,085
Total Net Revenue	147,650,220,524	136,801,014,479	133,010,625,870	128,995,568,363	124,670,910,747
Total Expenses	139,997,027,757	131,009,021,260	126,964,965,969	123,273,293,065	119,193,201,375
HOSPITAL UNIT (Excludes Separate Nursing Home Units)					
Utilization - Inpatient					
Beds	104,144	104,182	106,758	108,138	108,572
Admissions	4,805,618	4,725,753	4,802,392	4,936,296	5,143,373
Inpatient Days	26,566,704	26,460,408	26,989,568	27,418,799	28,351,497
Average Length of Stay	5.5	5.6	5.6	5.6	5.5
Personnel					
Total Full Time	676,795	654,267	649,963	659,374	660,600
Total Part Time	199,169	194,345	192,025	194,622	197,298
Revenue and Expenses - Totals (Includes Inpatient and Outpatient)					
Total Net Revenue	$146,940,132,501	$136,028,662,297	$132,143,884,524	$128,084,425,548	$123,724,968,154
Total Expenses	139,443,384,742	130,274,894,302	126,161,477,280	122,409,617,966	118,279,090,752
COMMUNITY HEALTH INDICATORS PER 1000 POPULATION					
Total Population (in thousands)	41,474	41,556	41,472	41,324	41,198
Inpatient					
Beds	2.7	2.7	2.7	2.8	2.9
Admissions	116.5	114.4	116.6	120.4	125.8
Inpatient Days	691.2	690.4	709.4	732.1	763.2
Inpatient Surgeries	30.8	30.4	31.2	32.1	34.1
Births	11	10.9	11.1	11.1	11.4
Outpatient					
Emergency Outpatient Visits	459.8	447.7	444.9	446.8	444.7
Other Outpatient Visits	2,253.3	2,262.1	2,223.6	2,213.5	2,255.9
Total Outpatient Visits	2,713.0	2,709.9	2,668.5	2,660.3	2,700.6
Outpatient Surgeries	66.1	62.3	62.9	64.0	63.2
Expense per Capita (per person)	$3,375.5	$3,152.6	$3,061.5	$2,983.1	$2,893.2

U.S. Census Divisions

TABLE 5

U.S. CENSUS DIVISION 3: SOUTH ATLANTIC

U.S. Registered Community Hospitals
(Nonfederal, short-term general and other special hospitals)

Overview 2012–2016

	2016	2015	2014	2013	2012
Total Community Hospitals					
in Census Division 3, South Atlantic.............	745	746	754	758	766
Bed Size Category					
6-24	30	28	29	23	22
25-49	131	133	139	142	139
50-99	147	143	139	141	138
100-199	175	180	179	175	192
200-299	97	100	104	110	109
300-399	63	58	60	64	66
400-499	39	43	41	36	37
500 + ...	63	61	63	67	63
Location					
Hospitals Urban	548	549	553	521	526
Hospitals Rural	197	197	201	237	240
Control					
State and Local Government	118	128	129	129	135
Not for Profit	410	401	399	407	403
Investor owned	217	217	226	222	228
Physician Models					
Independent Practice Association	47	56	49	48	52
Group Practice without Walls	25	25	26	30	30
Open Physician-Hospital Organization	64	64	65	69	77
Closed Physician-Hospital Organization ...	47	45	46	45	42
Management Service Organization	54	64	51	70	72
Integrated Salary Model	292	299	279	292	291
Equity Model	19	16	16	17	19
Foundation	19	17	15	15	17
Insurance Products					
Health Maintenance Organization	94	105	91	88	70
Preferred Provider Organization	109	115	94	96	73
Indemnity Fee for Service	48	43	44	37	26
Managed Care Contracts					
Health Maintenance Organization	417	405	400	414	410
Preferred Provider Organization	433	423	421	443	432
Affiliations					
Hospitals in a System	582	579	572	564	554
Hospitals in a Network	240	251	234	229	220
Hospitals in a Group Purchasing Organization...	499	512	509	525	516

TABLE 5

U.S. CENSUS DIVISION 3: SOUTH ATLANTIC

U.S. Registered Community Hospitals
(Nonfederal, short-term general and other special hospitals)

Utilization, Personnel, Revenue and Expenses, Community Health Indicators 2012–2016

	2016	2015	2014	2013	2012
TOTAL FACILITY (Includes Hospital and Nursing Home Units)					
Utilization - Inpatient					
Beds	154,298	153,526	154,927	156,366	156,937
Admissions	6,907,154	6,878,461	6,782,630	6,775,396	6,928,298
Inpatient Days	37,649,870	37,403,737	37,244,934	37,330,440	37,724,388
Average Length of Stay	5.5	5.4	5.5	5.5	5.4
Inpatient Surgeries	1,848,230	1,838,291	1,837,366	1,885,705	1,904,557
Births	716,992	711,883	689,817	688,383	690,305
Utilization - Outpatient					
Emergency Outpatient Visits	29,837,837	29,020,035	28,173,654	27,180,478	26,665,515
Other Outpatient Visits	88,725,619	80,840,291	77,490,400	76,008,760	74,855,137
Total Outpatient Visits	118,563,456	109,860,326	105,664,054	103,189,238	101,520,652
Outpatient Surgeries	3,539,327	3,436,105	3,360,000	3,402,928	3,293,896
Personnel					
Full Time RNs	246,666	243,936	236,993	229,245	226,678
Full Time LPNs	11,468	11,058	10,766	11,445	12,717
Part Time RNs	79,982	79,058	74,694	73,838	72,103
Part Time LPNs	2,930	2,951	2,822	3,227	3,438
Total Full Time	822,259	813,642	789,982	777,852	782,368
Total Part Time	228,125	227,704	213,576	211,042	209,662
Revenue - Inpatient					
Gross Inpatient Revenue	$320,894,288,384	$301,594,905,861	$278,261,148,984	$262,531,564,774	$247,143,243,581
Revenue - Outpatient					
Gross Outpatient Revenue	$287,484,214,085	$261,861,364,149	$233,116,826,117	$211,522,275,589	$191,354,643,518
Revenue and Expenses - Totals					
(Includes Inpatient and Outpatient)					
Total Gross Revenue	$608,378,502,469	$563,456,270,010	$511,377,975,101	$474,053,840,363	$438,497,887,099
Deductions from Revenue	443,793,048,706	407,547,082,638	364,940,729,770	334,573,003,794	301,779,297,485
Net Patient Revenue	164,585,453,763	155,909,187,372	146,437,245,331	139,480,836,569	136,718,589,614
Other Operating Revenue	7,183,188,984	7,101,350,109	6,500,381,754	6,380,425,184	6,785,768,283
Other Nonoperating Revenue	1,622,101,302	844,331,634	3,174,196,022	3,307,649,993	2,215,518,159
Total Net Revenue	173,390,744,049	163,854,869,115	156,111,823,107	149,168,911,746	145,719,876,056
Total Expenses	156,153,964,367	148,760,776,251	140,819,951,923	135,926,142,419	132,934,775,278
HOSPITAL UNIT (Excludes Separate Nursing Home Units)					
Utilization - Inpatient					
Beds	145,858	145,056	145,997	146,568	146,488
Admissions	6,873,871	6,845,151	6,746,808	6,734,481	6,885,814
Inpatient Days	34,944,000	34,616,596	34,371,920	34,230,779	34,334,087
Average Length of Stay	5.1	5.1	5.1	5.1	5.0
Personnel					
Total Full Time	816,312	807,461	783,227	770,841	774,599
Total Part Time	226,129	225,439	211,393	208,582	207,045
Revenue and Expenses - Totals					
(Includes Inpatient and Outpatient)					
Total Net Revenue	$172,725,568,431	$163,144,904,096	$155,327,357,125	$148,368,495,581	$144,879,731,362
Total Expenses	155,563,088,258	148,121,256,013	140,110,701,843	135,196,659,731	132,134,543,784
COMMUNITY HEALTH INDICATORS PER 1000 POPULATION					
Total Population (in thousands)	63,923	63,277	62,515	61,784	61,189
Inpatient					
Beds	2.4	2.4	2.5	2.5	2.6
Admissions	108.1	108.7	108.5	109.7	113.2
Inpatient Days	589.0	591.1	595.8	604.2	616.5
Inpatient Surgeries	28.9	29.1	29.4	30.5	31.1
Births	11.2	11.3	11.0	11.1	11.3
Outpatient					
Emergency Outpatient Visits	466.8	458.6	450.7	439.9	435.8
Other Outpatient Visits	1,388.0	1,277.6	1,239.6	1,230.2	1,223.4
Total Outpatient Visits	1,854.8	1,736.2	1,690.2	1,670.2	1,659.1
Outpatient Surgeries	55.4	54.3	53.7	55.1	53.8
Expense per Capita (per person)	$2,442.8	$2,351.0	$2,252.6	$2,200.0	$2,172.5

TABLE 5

U.S. CENSUS DIVISION 4: EAST NORTH CENTRAL

U.S. Registered Community Hospitals
(Nonfederal, short-term general and other special hospitals)

Overview 2012–2016

	2016	2015	2014	2013	2012
Total Community Hospitals					
in Census Division 4, East North Central	759	761	769	775	776
Bed Size Category					
6-24	69	66	63	59	57
25-49	194	197	197	203	204
50-99	135	137	140	148	146
100-199	155	158	171	162	161
200-299	92	89	84	90	84
300-399	47	47	45	42	55
400-499	26	25	30	30	29
500 + ...	41	42	39	41	40
Location					
Hospitals Urban	493	493	499	502	503
Hospitals Rural...................................	266	268	270	273	273
Control					
State and Local Government	77	82	86	87	90
Not for Profit..	577	576	579	587	588
Investor owned...	105	103	104	101	98
Physician Models					
Independent Practice Association.....................	57	71	72	67	71
Group Practice without Walls	28	35	41	43	27
Open Physician-Hospital Organization	171	165	162	173	162
Closed Physician-Hospital Organization............	66	56	59	57	46
Management Service Organization....................	71	68	68	74	65
Integrated Salary Model..................................	341	342	358	353	346
Equity Model	35	33	35	39	22
Foundation	43	42	47	53	40
Insurance Products					
Health Maintenance Organization.....................	167	159	161	163	152
Preferred Provider Organization	175	155	156	161	141
Indemnity Fee for Service	57	54	56	54	52
Managed Care Contracts					
Health Maintenance Organization.....................	519	530	526	519	527
Preferred Provider Organization	548	553	551	556	555
Affiliations					
Hospitals in a System	532	527	518	503	492
Hospitals in a Network	320	306	292	282	277
Hospitals in a Group Purchasing Organization...	593	598	611	613	618

TABLE 5

U.S. CENSUS DIVISION 4: EAST NORTH CENTRAL

U.S. Registered Community Hospitals
(Nonfederal, short-term general and other special hospitals)

Utilization, Personnel, Revenue and Expenses, Community Health Indicators 2012–2016

	2016	2015	2014	2013	2012
TOTAL FACILITY (Includes Hospital and Nursing Home Units)					
Utilization - Inpatient					
Beds	119,195	119,836	119,389	120,050	121,997
Admissions	5,160,744	5,183,720	5,171,957	5,309,578	5,477,164
Inpatient Days	26,008,388	26,171,518	26,063,576	26,367,306	27,190,027
Average Length of Stay	5.0	5.0	5.0	5.0	5.0
Inpatient Surgeries	1,375,157	1,372,354	1,391,133	1,415,474	1,499,944
Births	519,043	521,982	521,134	520,879	524,244
Utilization - Outpatient					
Emergency Outpatient Visits	23,336,090	23,167,411	22,166,060	21,840,082	22,161,580
Other Outpatient Visits	132,367,846	127,010,229	120,541,672	115,696,131	114,778,170
Total Outpatient Visits	155,703,936	150,177,640	142,707,732	137,536,213	136,939,750
Outpatient Surgeries	3,213,423	3,147,439	3,107,718	3,116,354	3,185,907
Personnel					
Full Time RNs	196,421	190,937	183,359	178,559	176,706
Full Time LPNs	7,360	7,186	7,142	7,894	7,987
Part Time RNs	98,683	94,627	98,575	95,846	99,210
Part Time LPNs	3,590	3,773	3,784	4,236	4,590
Total Full Time	712,516	693,333	677,119	670,958	672,905
Total Part Time	305,866	292,830	302,675	295,422	302,574
Revenue - Inpatient					
Gross Inpatient Revenue	$227,411,328,328	$216,634,732,767	$204,202,256,852	$193,599,807,491	$187,228,187,292
Revenue - Outpatient					
Gross Outpatient Revenue	$259,426,210,041	$239,660,568,035	$220,428,044,679	$200,738,677,953	$185,825,760,037
Revenue and Expenses - Totals (Includes Inpatient and Outpatient)					
Total Gross Revenue	$486,837,538,369	$456,295,300,802	$424,630,301,531	$394,338,485,444	$373,053,947,329
Deductions from Revenue	335,238,831,564	310,835,086,916	286,324,202,816	263,377,222,866	243,148,787,597
Net Patient Revenue	151,598,706,805	145,460,213,886	138,306,098,715	130,961,262,578	129,905,159,732
Other Operating Revenue	9,178,273,513	8,858,354,057	8,812,043,264	8,342,665,932	7,734,468,170
Other Nonoperating Revenue	3,090,154,654	183,387,858	3,723,265,436	3,963,965,511	2,372,671,286
Total Net Revenue	163,867,134,972	154,501,955,801	150,841,407,415	143,267,894,021	140,012,299,188
Total Expenses	148,881,102,592	141,450,901,038	135,485,952,281	130,380,820,276	128,508,223,081
HOSPITAL UNIT (Excludes Separate Nursing Home Units)					
Utilization - Inpatient					
Beds	114,978	115,137	114,725	115,570	116,777
Admissions	5,136,057	5,158,101	5,143,469	5,281,193	5,443,973
Inpatient Days	24,746,612	24,788,987	24,663,750	25,031,404	25,617,733
Average Length of Stay	4.8	4.8	4.8	4.7	4.7
Personnel					
Total Full Time	709,976	690,580	674,594	668,467	669,734
Total Part Time	304,042	290,718	300,448	293,112	299,781
Revenue and Expenses - Totals (Includes Inpatient and Outpatient)					
Total Net Revenue	$163,347,390,662	$153,998,040,195	$150,456,619,070	$142,884,583,269	$139,565,247,628
Total Expenses	148,569,589,983	141,121,944,268	135,157,396,593	130,048,404,828	128,116,255,360
COMMUNITY HEALTH INDICATORS PER 1000 POPULATION					
Total Population (in thousands)	46,756	46,787	46,739	46,662	46,567
Inpatient					
Beds	2.5	2.6	2.6	2.6	2.6
Admissions	110.4	110.8	110.7	113.8	117.6
Inpatient Days	556.3	559.4	557.6	565.1	583.9
Inpatient Surgeries	29.4	29.3	29.8	30.3	32.2
Births	11.1	11.2	11.1	11.2	11.3
Outpatient					
Emergency Outpatient Visits	499.1	495.2	474.3	468.0	475.9
Other Outpatient Visits	2,831.0	2,714.6	2,579.0	2,479.4	2,464.8
Total Outpatient Visits	3,330.1	3,209.8	3,053.3	2,947.5	2,940.7
Outpatient Surgeries	68.7	67.3	66.5	66.8	68.4
Expense per Capita (per person)	$3,184.2	$3,023.3	$2,898.8	$2,794.1	$2,759.7

TABLE 5

U.S. CENSUS DIVISION 5: EAST SOUTH CENTRAL

U.S. Registered Community Hospitals
(Nonfederal, short-term general and other special hospitals)

Overview 2012–2016

	2016	2015	2014	2013	2012
Total Community Hospitals					
in Census Division 5, East South Central......	411	414	422	432	433
Bed Size Category					
6-24	19	17	17	19	21
25-49	112	120	119	123	125
50-99	102	92	96	98	95
100-199	87	90	95	97	97
200-299	37	39	41	42	41
300-399	24	26	25	24	24
400-499	10	9	8	9	8
500 + ...	20	21	21	20	22
Location					
Hospitals Urban	197	198	202	200	200
Hospitals Rural..	214	216	220	232	233
Control					
State and Local Government	104	106	109	113	111
Not for Profit..	174	174	174	177	176
Investor owned..	133	134	139	142	146
Physician Models					
Independent Practice Association.......................	23	26	26	24	30
Group Practice without Walls.............................	6	9	8	7	7
Open Physician-Hospital Organization	39	45	47	43	45
Closed Physician-Hospital Organization............	18	13	9	8	12
Management Service Organization.....................	46	45	35	32	44
Integrated Salary Model....................................	95	108	110	112	113
Equity Model	3	4	4	4	2
Foundation	22	22	16	20	15
Insurance Products					
Health Maintenance Organization......................	39	39	37	30	26
Preferred Provider Organization	74	76	78	78	65
Indemnity Fee for Service	21	20	23	23	19
Managed Care Contracts					
Health Maintenance Organization......................	138	148	146	152	159
Preferred Provider Organization	176	180	186	184	194
Affiliations					
Hospitals in a System	292	292	297	300	295
Hospitals in a Network	101	95	97	97	89
Hospitals in a Group Purchasing Organization...	243	246	167	175	192

TABLE 5

U.S. CENSUS DIVISION 5: EAST SOUTH CENTRAL

U.S. Registered Community Hospitals
(Nonfederal, short-term general and other special hospitals)

Utilization, Personnel, Revenue and Expenses, Community Health Indicators 2012–2016

	2016	2015	2014	2013	2012
TOTAL FACILITY (Includes Hospital and Nursing Home Units)					
Utilization - Inpatient					
Beds	60,487	60,854	61,455	62,235	62,199
Admissions	2,393,807	2,358,750	2,382,356	2,419,265	2,430,269
Inpatient Days	13,556,446	13,528,462	13,251,868	13,421,013	13,150,314
Average Length of Stay	5.7	5.7	5.6	5.5	5.4
Inpatient Surgeries	671,967	651,793	668,236	676,161	728,421
Births	216,461	218,504	215,205	215,234	209,932
Utilization - Outpatient					
Emergency Outpatient Visits	10,162,137	10,228,699	9,880,646	9,732,264	9,782,661
Other Outpatient Visits	31,679,443	29,309,910	26,326,661	25,969,056	25,794,437
Total Outpatient Visits	41,841,580	39,538,609	36,207,307	35,701,320	35,577,098
Outpatient Surgeries	1,406,878	1,336,171	1,333,554	1,351,037	1,405,286
Personnel					
Full Time RNs	83,882	80,323	79,234	77,713	75,991
Full Time LPNs	5,293	5,608	5,437	6,016	6,263
Part Time RNs	29,344	26,342	23,554	24,713	25,437
Part Time LPNs	1,366	1,335	1,357	1,534	1,640
Total Full Time	274,260	269,035	269,802	267,164	266,388
Total Part Time	80,153	71,030	65,471	68,124	71,714
Revenue - Inpatient					
Gross Inpatient Revenue	$102,167,463,539	$96,404,537,971	$89,841,024,641	$85,886,311,001	$80,646,954,304
Revenue - Outpatient					
Gross Outpatient Revenue	$101,429,828,805	$93,762,795,833	$85,434,786,619	$76,616,972,839	$71,015,770,262
Revenue and Expenses - Totals					
(Includes Inpatient and Outpatient)					
Total Gross Revenue	$203,597,292,344	$190,167,333,804	$175,275,811,260	$162,503,283,840	$151,662,724,566
Deductions from Revenue	153,982,130,059	142,630,262,950	130,101,544,284	118,611,464,301	109,016,339,180
Net Patient Revenue	49,615,162,285	47,537,070,854	45,174,266,976	43,891,819,539	42,646,385,386
Other Operating Revenue	2,110,424,208	2,008,402,818	2,043,790,399	1,929,535,883	1,820,681,077
Other Nonoperating Revenue	428,383,587	267,088,480	714,113,663	758,473,581	407,005,231
Total Net Revenue	52,153,970,080	49,812,562,152	47,932,171,038	46,579,829,003	44,874,071,694
Total Expenses	47,567,158,229	45,273,765,633	44,391,934,950	42,687,366,112	41,101,364,805
HOSPITAL UNIT (Excludes Separate Nursing Home Units)					
Utilization - Inpatient					
Beds	57,280	57,098	58,048	58,109	58,411
Admissions	2,383,062	2,344,134	2,370,834	2,403,639	2,413,202
Inpatient Days	12,528,892	12,360,327	12,184,169	12,117,469	11,963,248
Average Length of Stay	5.3	5.3	5.1	5.0	5.0
Personnel					
Total Full Time	272,048	266,618	266,798	263,499	263,124
Total Part Time	79,496	70,309	64,643	66,771	70,861
Revenue and Expenses - Totals					
(Includes Inpatient and Outpatient)					
Total Net Revenue	$51,842,331,588	$49,492,603,758	$47,734,520,006	$46,303,139,122	$44,641,587,474
Total Expenses	47,337,273,426	45,025,135,657	44,227,387,246	42,457,268,955	40,885,625,657
COMMUNITY HEALTH INDICATORS PER 1000 POPULATION					
Total Population (in thousands)	18,940	18,877	18,806	18,716	18,644
Inpatient					
Beds	3.2	3.2	3.3	3.3	3.3
Admissions	126.4	125.0	126.7	129.3	130.4
Inpatient Days	715.8	716.7	704.7	717.1	705.4
Inpatient Surgeries	35.5	34.5	35.5	36.1	39.1
Births	11.4	11.6	11.4	11.5	11.3
Outpatient					
Emergency Outpatient Visits	536.5	541.9	525.4	520.0	524.7
Other Outpatient Visits	1,672.6	1,552.7	1,399.9	1,387.5	1,383.6
Total Outpatient Visits	2,209.1	2,094.6	1,925.3	1,907.5	1,908.3
Outpatient Surgeries	74.3	70.8	70.9	72.2	75.4
Expense per Capita (per person)	$2,511.4	$2,398.4	$2,360.5	$2,280.8	$2,204.6

TABLE 5

U.S. CENSUS DIVISION 6: WEST NORTH CENTRAL

U.S. Registered Community Hospitals
(Nonfederal, short-term general and other special hospitals)

Overview 2012–2016

	2016	2015	2014	2013	2012
Total Community Hospitals					
in Census Division 6, West North Central......	677	681	686	683	692
Bed Size Category					
6-24..........................	148	142	135	134	128
25-49..........................	212	215	219	212	217
50-99..........................	142	147	149	156	160
100-199..........................	87	90	95	90	97
200-299..........................	33	34	35	37	35
300-399..........................	21	21	22	24	25
400-499..........................	12	13	13	14	14
500 +..........................	22	19	18	16	16
Location					
Hospitals Urban.........................	234	238	241	224	226
Hospitals Rural.........................	443	443	445	459	466
Control					
State and Local Government.........................	221	222	227	228	233
Not for Profit.........................	403	405	403	401	405
Investor owned.........................	53	54	56	54	54
Physician Models					
Independent Practice Association.........................	42	48	55	55	63
Group Practice without Walls.........................	10	7	10	12	16
Open Physician-Hospital Organization.........................	67	64	63	68	70
Closed Physician-Hospital Organization.............	23	20	21	23	26
Management Service Organization.........................	11	12	12	12	16
Integrated Salary Model.........................	356	351	361	341	336
Equity Model.........................	4	6	6	6	7
Foundation.........................	12	12	15	18	17
Insurance Products					
Health Maintenance Organization.........................	77	75	73	68	59
Preferred Provider Organization.........................	85	84	76	67	69
Indemnity Fee for Service.........................	24	24	23	19	20
Managed Care Contracts					
Health Maintenance Organization.........................	320	322	334	312	318
Preferred Provider Organization.........................	432	434	445	433	445
Affiliations					
Hospitals in a System.........................	374	371	375	367	372
Hospitals in a Network.........................	304	302	296	291	288
Hospitals in a Group Purchasing Organization...	547	543	553	551	562

TABLE 5

U.S. CENSUS DIVISION 6: WEST NORTH CENTRAL

U.S. Registered Community Hospitals
(Nonfederal, short-term general and other special hospitals)

Utilization, Personnel, Revenue and Expenses, Community Health Indicators 2012–2016

	2016	2015	2014	2013	2012
TOTAL FACILITY (Includes Hospital and Nursing Home Units)					
Utilization - Inpatient					
Beds	65,919	66,232	66,847	67,386	68,455
Admissions	2,317,720	2,339,401	2,331,707	2,355,948	2,421,698
Inpatient Days	14,233,792	14,328,514	14,150,091	14,286,092	14,638,214
Average Length of Stay	6.1	6.1	6.1	6.1	6.0
Inpatient Surgeries	628,809	627,965	639,400	649,575	667,171
Births	268,072	269,097	270,276	267,407	268,618
Utilization - Outpatient					
Emergency Outpatient Visits	9,263,852	9,015,252	8,750,133	8,653,473	8,725,139
Other Outpatient Visits	58,398,008	54,455,594	53,611,188	51,914,260	52,156,664
Total Outpatient Visits	67,661,860	63,470,846	62,361,321	60,567,733	60,881,803
Outpatient Surgeries	1,427,908	1,397,722	1,366,852	1,356,009	1,381,534
Personnel					
Full Time RNs	85,828	84,637	82,331	81,791	78,654
Full Time LPNs	7,760	7,169	7,106	7,140	7,145
Part Time RNs	59,477	57,004	54,685	53,163	54,342
Part Time LPNs	4,047	3,948	3,947	3,944	4,109
Total Full Time	346,665	338,041	330,504	336,351	311,613
Total Part Time	176,899	168,446	161,716	161,075	164,991
Revenue - Inpatient					
Gross Inpatient Revenue	$95,128,149,809	$89,843,569,893	$85,253,852,745	$80,759,847,710	$77,970,550,986
Revenue - Outpatient					
Gross Outpatient Revenue	$109,555,993,044	$99,641,563,413	$89,991,409,306	$81,195,833,655	$76,310,450,463
Revenue and Expenses - Totals					
(Includes Inpatient and Outpatient)					
Total Gross Revenue	$204,684,142,853	$189,485,133,306	$175,245,262,051	$161,955,681,365	$154,281,001,449
Deductions from Revenue	135,163,880,888	123,927,596,908	113,156,490,271	102,735,424,002	96,278,090,518
Net Patient Revenue	69,520,261,965	65,557,536,398	62,088,771,780	59,220,257,363	58,002,910,931
Other Operating Revenue	4,061,255,388	3,927,590,370	3,689,823,992	3,513,084,143	3,444,366,586
Other Nonoperating Revenue	686,102,569	516,652,136	1,393,096,932	1,693,175,535	1,330,357,727
Total Net Revenue	74,267,619,922	70,001,778,904	67,171,692,704	64,426,517,041	62,777,635,244
Total Expenses	70,036,498,872	64,919,634,526	62,380,858,073	59,579,626,804	56,450,154,448
HOSPITAL UNIT (Excludes Separate Nursing Home Units)					
Utilization - Inpatient					
Beds	57,512	57,686	58,020	58,424	59,408
Admissions	2,302,354	2,323,006	2,311,150	2,336,928	2,400,701
Inpatient Days	11,519,878	11,621,233	11,395,728	11,484,252	11,768,543
Average Length of Stay	5.0	5.0	4.9	4.9	4.9
Personnel					
Total Full Time	342,029	333,436	325,019	330,962	305,819
Total Part Time	172,745	164,259	156,942	156,709	160,210
Revenue and Expenses - Totals					
(Includes Inpatient and Outpatient)					
Total Net Revenue	$73,666,258,975	$69,404,098,020	$66,561,154,086	$63,856,543,055	$62,194,053,711
Total Expenses	69,524,594,052	64,406,144,008	61,856,005,299	59,040,011,689	55,903,031,384
COMMUNITY HEALTH INDICATORS PER 1000 POPULATION					
Total Population (in thousands)	21,185	21,120	21,006	20,886	20,750
Inpatient					
Beds	3.1	3.1	3.2	3.2	3.3
Admissions	109.4	110.8	111.0	112.8	116.7
Inpatient Days	671.9	678.4	673.6	684.0	705.5
Inpatient Surgeries	29.7	29.7	30.4	31.1	32.2
Births	12.7	12.7	12.9	12.8	12.9
Outpatient					
Emergency Outpatient Visits	437.3	426.9	416.6	414.3	420.5
Other Outpatient Visits	2,756.5	2,578.3	2,552.2	2,485.6	2,513.6
Total Outpatient Visits	3,193.8	3,005.2	2,968.7	2,900.0	2,934.1
Outpatient Surgeries	67.4	66.2	65.1	64.9	66.6
Expense per Capita (per person)	$3,305.9	$3,073.8	$2,969.7	$2,852.7	$2,720.5

TABLE 5

U.S. CENSUS DIVISION 7: WEST SOUTH CENTRAL

U.S. Registered Community Hospitals
(Nonfederal, short-term general and other special hospitals)

Overview 2012–2016

	2016	2015	2014	2013	2012
Total Community Hospitals					
in Census Division 7, West South Central	711	714	734	746	749
Bed Size Category					
6-24	126	120	118	118	117
25-49	206	205	220	223	224
50-99	132	136	140	149	149
100-199	96	104	105	101	104
200-299	59	59	59	62	62
300-399	40	34	37	39	40
400-499	15	18	20	19	19
500 + ...	37	38	35	35	34
Location					
Hospitals Urban	432	434	444	438	439
Hospitals Rural	279	280	290	308	310
Control					
State and Local Government	190	194	195	195	206
Not for Profit	271	269	278	282	275
Investor owned	250	251	261	269	268
Physician Models					
Independent Practice Association	79	80	82	80	82
Group Practice without Walls	29	28	50	34	28
Open Physician-Hospital Organization	101	99	109	117	128
Closed Physician-Hospital Organization	27	28	38	40	38
Management Service Organization	79	81	81	83	88
Integrated Salary Model	238	249	224	228	215
Equity Model	8	6	6	10	11
Foundation	42	44	44	52	48
Insurance Products					
Health Maintenance Organization	111	108	112	104	93
Preferred Provider Organization	103	93	101	88	76
Indemnity Fee for Service	39	35	45	25	22
Managed Care Contracts					
Health Maintenance Organization	468	470	478	481	468
Preferred Provider Organization	523	532	540	559	542
Affiliations					
Hospitals in a System	442	435	449	452	451
Hospitals in a Network	204	203	206	204	193
Hospitals in a Group Purchasing Organization...	591	599	617	637	625

TABLE 5

U.S. CENSUS DIVISION 7: WEST SOUTH CENTRAL

U.S. Registered Community Hospitals
(Nonfederal, short-term general and other special hospitals)

Utilization, Personnel, Revenue and Expenses, Community Health Indicators 2012–2016

	2016	2015	2014	2013	2012
TOTAL FACILITY (Includes Hospital and Nursing Home Units)					
Utilization - Inpatient					
Beds	96,752	97,358	96,935	97,967	97,260
Admissions	3,861,630	3,844,708	3,815,555	3,852,821	3,908,065
Inpatient Days	20,957,783	20,671,761	20,297,127	20,284,467	20,396,936
Average Length of Stay	5.4	5.4	5.3	5.3	5.2
Inpatient Surgeries	1,058,697	1,062,341	1,052,155	1,055,227	1,080,738
Births	532,702	544,069	548,587	530,165	516,124
Utilization - Outpatient					
Emergency Outpatient Visits	16,851,086	16,685,491	16,436,178	16,301,738	16,269,062
Other Outpatient Visits	50,056,221	49,013,505	46,546,602	45,227,309	45,892,246
Total Outpatient Visits	66,907,307	65,698,996	62,982,780	61,529,047	62,161,308
Outpatient Surgeries	1,848,272	1,804,392	1,760,763	1,719,039	1,675,034
Personnel					
Full Time RNs	137,920	137,118	134,254	131,052	126,908
Full Time LPNs	11,919	12,239	12,312	13,147	13,783
Part Time RNs	38,430	37,068	36,642	37,846	36,330
Part Time LPNs	2,980	2,878	2,982	3,153	3,352
Total Full Time	459,746	452,589	446,541	440,358	435,758
Total Part Time	111,104	108,075	105,097	110,628	106,477
Revenue - Inpatient					
Gross Inpatient Revenue	$204,934,557,239	$190,552,050,845	$176,549,411,040	$165,441,811,098	$157,197,100,160
Revenue - Outpatient					
Gross Outpatient Revenue	$176,161,648,246	$159,295,986,535	$142,960,299,246	$129,896,699,181	$118,343,524,306
Revenue and Expenses - Totals (Includes Inpatient and Outpatient)					
Total Gross Revenue	$381,096,205,485	$349,848,037,380	$319,509,710,182	$295,338,510,279	$275,540,624,466
Deductions from Revenue	290,714,923,911	262,673,891,112	237,893,364,240	218,013,431,324	199,811,182,037
Net Patient Revenue	90,381,281,574	87,174,146,268	81,616,345,942	77,325,078,955	75,729,442,429
Other Operating Revenue	7,236,405,528	6,784,033,391	6,555,581,679	6,605,401,355	6,473,296,689
Other Nonoperating Revenue	1,336,227,918	934,255,362	2,101,925,461	1,436,996,905	1,074,127,947
Total Net Revenue	98,953,915,020	94,892,435,021	90,273,853,082	85,367,477,215	83,276,867,065
Total Expenses	89,814,664,327	84,590,653,973	80,310,161,311	77,562,496,193	74,523,034,451
HOSPITAL UNIT (Excludes Separate Nursing Home Units)					
Utilization - Inpatient					
Beds	93,366	93,923	95,357	95,923	95,188
Admissions	3,848,847	3,834,359	3,806,387	3,841,094	3,894,508
Inpatient Days	20,013,157	20,078,144	19,863,060	19,723,627	19,839,649
Average Length of Stay	5.2	5.2	5.2	5.1	5.1
Personnel					
Total Full Time	458,287	451,336	443,560	438,804	433,602
Total Part Time	110,742	107,747	103,992	110,195	106,091
Revenue and Expenses - Totals (Includes Inpatient and Outpatient)					
Total Net Revenue	$98,777,689,723	$94,678,987,140	$90,157,740,671	$85,208,123,466	$83,105,764,389
Total Expenses	89,653,519,817	84,402,200,230	80,211,596,887	77,432,447,297	74,387,874,023
COMMUNITY HEALTH INDICATORS PER 1000 POPULATION					
Total Population (in thousands)	39,456	39,029	38,451	37,884	37,425
Inpatient					
Beds	2.5	2.5	2.5	2.6	2.6
Admissions	97.9	98.5	99.2	101.7	104.4
Inpatient Days	531.2	529.6	527.9	535.4	545.0
Inpatient Surgeries	26.8	27.2	27.4	27.9	28.9
Births	13.5	13.9	14.3	14.0	13.8
Outpatient					
Emergency Outpatient Visits	427.1	427.5	427.5	430.3	434.7
Other Outpatient Visits	1,268.7	1,255.8	1,210.5	1,193.8	1,226.2
Total Outpatient Visits	1,695.7	1,683.3	1,638.0	1,624.2	1,661.0
Outpatient Surgeries	46.8	46.2	45.8	45.4	44.8
Expense per Capita (per person)	$2,276.3	$2,167.4	$2,088.6	$2,047.4	$1,991.3

U.S. Census Divisions

TABLE 5

U.S. CENSUS DIVISION 8: MOUNTAIN

U.S. Registered Community Hospitals
(Nonfederal, short-term general and other special hospitals)

Overview 2012–2016

	2016	2015	2014	2013	2012
Total Community Hospitals					
in Census Division 8, Mountain	381	384	388	390	388
Bed Size Category					
6-24	64	63	62	57	57
25-49	97	97	97	103	102
50-99	79	84	90	87	84
100-199	61	60	61	65	65
200-299	34	34	33	33	34
300-399	18	19	19	20	20
400-499	11	11	14	13	14
500 +	17	16	12	12	12
Location					
Hospitals Urban	192	195	199	193	193
Hospitals Rural	189	189	189	197	195
Control					
State and Local Government	88	88	90	90	93
Not for Profit	193	197	201	202	196
Investor owned	100	99	97	98	99
Physician Models					
Independent Practice Association	42	43	28	32	40
Group Practice without Walls	9	8	11	13	12
Open Physician-Hospital Organization	26	26	36	34	37
Closed Physician-Hospital Organization	21	29	15	14	13
Management Service Organization	17	16	20	22	21
Integrated Salary Model	152	160	154	150	148
Equity Model	4	3	4	4	4
Foundation	15	11	14	13	12
Insurance Products					
Health Maintenance Organization	49	49	51	57	55
Preferred Provider Organization	59	61	58	53	40
Indemnity Fee for Service	38	37	27	24	20
Managed Care Contracts					
Health Maintenance Organization	115	122	139	142	143
Preferred Provider Organization	146	159	185	193	190
Affiliations					
Hospitals in a System	234	236	236	234	234
Hospitals in a Network	104	108	106	107	99
Hospitals in a Group Purchasing Organization	234	246	254	268	240

TABLE 5

U.S. CENSUS DIVISION 8: MOUNTAIN

U.S. Registered Community Hospitals
(Nonfederal, short-term general and other special hospitals)

Utilization, Personnel, Revenue and Expenses, Community Health Indicators 2012–2016

	2016	2015	2014	2013	2012
TOTAL FACILITY (Includes Hospital and Nursing Home Units)					
Utilization - Inpatient					
Beds	47,589	47,734	47,180	47,322	47,501
Admissions	1,996,485	1,984,055	1,953,896	1,962,391	2,060,596
Inpatient Days	10,420,637	10,293,263	9,968,995	9,977,101	10,231,226
Average Length of Stay	5.2	5.2	5.1	5.1	5.0
Inpatient Surgeries	534,089	535,108	545,379	559,564	614,124
Births	266,519	273,082	266,986	266,237	269,841
Utilization - Outpatient					
Emergency Outpatient Visits	8,370,732	8,698,468	8,133,174	7,787,157	7,821,770
Other Outpatient Visits	38,099,708	36,525,144	34,775,370	32,829,124	32,436,477
Total Outpatient Visits	46,470,440	45,223,612	42,908,544	40,616,281	40,258,247
Outpatient Surgeries	1,093,414	1,047,207	1,028,103	1,024,797	982,976
Personnel					
Full Time RNs	77,091	75,292	73,010	69,945	66,845
Full Time LPNs	2,838	2,876	2,978	3,039	3,085
Part Time RNs	28,001	24,785	24,993	26,487	26,537
Part Time LPNs	991	950	986	1,109	1,204
Total Full Time	265,321	256,332	247,663	241,359	234,035
Total Part Time	83,529	73,944	74,968	80,434	78,088
Revenue - Inpatient					
Gross Inpatient Revenue	$110,305,261,679	$104,239,963,622	$94,555,922,887	$87,638,841,277	$83,441,071,276
Revenue - Outpatient					
Gross Outpatient Revenue	$102,667,361,374	$94,044,710,920	$82,354,172,215	$73,378,356,271	$65,655,835,782
Revenue and Expenses - Totals					
(Includes Inpatient and Outpatient)					
Total Gross Revenue	$212,972,623,053	$198,284,674,542	$176,910,095,102	$161,017,197,548	$149,096,907,058
Deductions from Revenue	155,223,915,749	144,020,307,139	126,585,492,260	113,683,233,185	102,954,441,992
Net Patient Revenue	57,748,707,304	54,264,367,403	50,324,602,842	47,333,964,363	46,142,465,066
Other Operating Revenue	2,208,071,224	2,103,829,264	2,073,527,886	2,195,077,380	1,890,523,158
Other Nonoperating Revenue	389,719,572	357,708,924	900,910,913	686,369,507	353,858,460
Total Net Revenue	60,346,498,100	56,725,905,591	53,299,041,641	50,215,411,250	48,386,846,684
Total Expenses	53,755,293,874	50,659,580,906	47,158,491,064	45,094,874,475	43,346,401,522
HOSPITAL UNIT (Excludes Separate Nursing Home Units)					
Utilization - Inpatient					
Beds	44,804	44,727	44,210	44,166	44,388
Admissions	1,990,015	1,976,808	1,946,984	1,954,560	2,052,402
Inpatient Days	9,593,210	9,394,237	9,128,451	9,030,424	9,282,591
Average Length of Stay	4.8	4.8	4.7	4.6	4.5
Personnel					
Total Full Time	263,534	254,637	245,906	239,029	232,008
Total Part Time	82,502	72,947	73,885	78,848	76,862
Revenue and Expenses - Totals					
(Includes Inpatient and Outpatient)					
Total Net Revenue	$60,126,438,161	$56,512,207,056	$53,094,299,493	$49,982,879,096	$48,172,247,901
Total Expenses	53,587,812,082	50,488,690,352	46,989,068,835	44,908,887,608	43,160,567,568
COMMUNITY HEALTH INDICATORS PER 1000 POPULATION					
Total Population (in thousands)	23,855	23,530	23,197	22,881	22,618
Inpatient					
Beds	2.0	2.0	2.0	2.1	2.1
Admissions	83.7	84.3	84.2	85.8	91.1
Inpatient Days	436.8	437.4	429.8	436.0	452.4
Inpatient Surgeries	22.4	22.7	23.5	24.5	27.2
Births	11.2	11.6	11.5	11.6	11.9
Outpatient					
Emergency Outpatient Visits	350.9	369.7	350.6	340.3	345.8
Other Outpatient Visits	1,597.1	1,552.2	1,499.1	1,434.8	1,434.1
Total Outpatient Visits	1,948.0	1,921.9	1,849.7	1,775.1	1,779.9
Outpatient Surgeries	45.8	44.5	44.3	44.8	43.5
Expense per Capita (per person)	$2,253.4	$2,152.9	$2,032.9	$1,970.8	$1,916.5

U.S. Census Divisions

TABLE 5

U.S. CENSUS DIVISION 9: PACIFIC

U.S. Registered Community Hospitals
(Nonfederal, short-term general and other special hospitals)

Overview 2012–2016

	2016	2015	2014	2013	2012
Total Community Hospitals					
in Census Division 9, Pacific	534	536	540	543	541
Bed Size Category					
6-24	44	44	43	42	39
25-49	95	96	99	99	102
50-99	69	68	72	72	72
100-199	141	144	144	144	138
200-299	81	81	81	84	88
300-399	53	54	54	55	51
400-499	33	30	29	30	34
500 +	18	19	18	17	17
Location					
Hospitals Urban	425	428	429	420	421
Hospitals Rural	109	108	111	123	120
Control					
State and Local Government	127	130	133	131	132
Not for Profit	317	318	321	325	321
Investor owned	90	88	86	87	88
Physician Models					
Independent Practice Association	104	87	76	71	65
Group Practice without Walls	19	21	27	22	21
Open Physician-Hospital Organization	16	12	14	12	16
Closed Physician-Hospital Organization	10	15	13	18	11
Management Service Organization	44	66	60	64	63
Integrated Salary Model	140	141	129	122	112
Equity Model	7	8	9	6	6
Foundation	107	113	102	99	91
Insurance Products					
Health Maintenance Organization	109	110	82	78	66
Preferred Provider Organization	66	65	58	50	38
Indemnity Fee for Service	30	27	21	15	10
Managed Care Contracts					
Health Maintenance Organization	243	254	257	238	258
Preferred Provider Organization	259	271	268	251	268
Affiliations					
Hospitals in a System	364	362	355	342	339
Hospitals in a Network	143	151	138	129	110
Hospitals in a Group Purchasing Organization	322	335	332	330	295

TABLE 5

U.S. CENSUS DIVISION 9: PACIFIC

U.S. Registered Community Hospitals
(Nonfederal, short-term general and other special hospitals)

Utilization, Personnel, Revenue and Expenses, Community Health Indicators 2012–2016

	2016	2015	2014	2013	2012
TOTAL FACILITY (Includes Hospital and Nursing Home Units)					
Utilization - Inpatient					
Beds	93,016	93,095	92,663	93,661	94,194
Admissions	4,388,359	4,359,331	4,254,171	4,361,054	4,403,646
Inpatient Days	22,446,883	22,088,858	21,611,365	21,838,216	22,168,393
Average Length of Stay	5.1	5.1	5.1	5.0	5.0
Inpatient Surgeries	1,167,978	1,165,821	1,179,036	1,168,907	1,195,847
Births	605,737	613,420	614,658	603,650	621,481
Utilization - Outpatient					
Emergency Outpatient Visits	18,480,477	18,673,070	17,311,390	16,484,071	16,342,076
Other Outpatient Visits	70,314,007	67,126,619	63,944,925	63,694,420	62,140,989
Total Outpatient Visits	88,794,484	85,799,689	81,256,315	80,178,491	78,483,065
Outpatient Surgeries	2,022,276	1,900,518	1,869,447	1,854,875	1,808,384
Personnel					
Full Time RNs	160,834	155,006	145,428	139,227	141,776
Full Time LPNs	7,433	7,235	6,671	7,199	7,614
Part Time RNs	79,696	77,090	77,054	77,131	77,206
Part Time LPNs	2,743	2,722	2,766	3,043	3,279
Total Full Time	547,380	530,473	504,630	496,771	508,241
Total Part Time	211,760	202,034	202,963	206,175	210,546
Revenue - Inpatient					
Gross Inpatient Revenue	$295,272,905,132	$278,764,637,917	$258,131,040,816	$249,612,964,923	$236,834,787,719
Revenue - Outpatient					
Gross Outpatient Revenue	$226,091,442,697	$204,092,075,030	$182,707,768,101	$165,091,402,569	$147,772,531,581
Revenue and Expenses - Totals					
(Includes Inpatient and Outpatient)					
Total Gross Revenue	$521,364,347,829	$482,856,712,947	$440,838,808,917	$414,704,353,075	$384,607,319,300
Deductions from Revenue	380,735,511,375	348,692,866,260	320,168,783,536	296,421,871,411	271,710,809,903
Net Patient Revenue	140,628,836,454	134,163,846,687	120,670,025,381	118,282,481,664	112,896,509,397
Other Operating Revenue	8,522,380,023	8,191,008,028	7,373,550,696	7,232,249,498	6,642,799,134
Other Nonoperating Revenue	1,640,771,650	1,696,198,741	3,047,837,693	3,877,851,046	1,979,204,632
Total Net Revenue	150,791,988,127	144,051,053,456	131,091,413,770	129,392,582,208	121,518,513,163
Total Expenses	141,159,569,439	132,704,486,105	121,510,758,372	118,675,375,594	113,537,965,473
HOSPITAL UNIT (Excludes Separate Nursing Home Units)					
Utilization - Inpatient					
Beds	89,212	88,559	88,526	88,791	88,926
Admissions	4,371,236	4,340,833	4,234,105	4,338,312	4,378,581
Inpatient Days	21,230,595	20,609,092	20,345,718	20,299,211	20,541,376
Average Length of Stay	4.9	4.7	4.8	4.7	4.7
Personnel					
Total Full Time	544,832	526,966	500,324	493,525	503,839
Total Part Time	210,523	200,308	201,411	204,370	208,555
Revenue and Expenses - Totals					
(Includes Inpatient and Outpatient)					
Total Net Revenue	$150,202,408,349	$143,272,687,111	$130,486,858,064	$128,717,582,873	$120,898,001,137
Total Expenses	140,746,281,988	132,176,162,851	121,125,680,106	118,155,549,145	112,990,603,410
COMMUNITY HEALTH INDICATORS PER 1000 POPULATION					
Total Population (in thousands)	52,802	52,514	51,991	51,373	50,962
Inpatient					
Beds	1.8	1.8	1.8	1.8	1.8
Admissions	83.1	83.0	81.8	84.9	86.4
Inpatient Days	425.1	420.6	415.7	425.1	435.0
Inpatient Surgeries	22.1	22.2	22.7	22.8	23.5
Births	11.5	11.7	11.8	11.8	12.2
Outpatient					
Emergency Outpatient Visits	350.0	355.6	333.0	320.9	320.7
Other Outpatient Visits	1,331.7	1,278.3	1,229.9	1,239.8	1,219.4
Total Outpatient Visits	1,681.7	1,633.8	1,562.9	1,560.7	1,540.0
Outpatient Surgeries	38.3	36.2	36.0	36.1	35.5
Expense per Capita (per person)	$2,673.4	$2,527.0	$2,337.2	$2,310.1	$2,227.9

U.S. Census Divisions

TABLE 6

ALABAMA

U.S. Registered Community Hospitals
(Nonfederal, short-term general and other special hospitals)

Overview 2012–2016

	2016	2015	2014	2013	2012
Total Community Hospitals in Alabama............	95	95	96	97	97
Bed Size Category					
6-24	5	5	5	5	7
25-49	22	25	22	24	23
50-99	25	20	22	21	21
100-199	21	23	26	25	23
200-299	8	9	8	9	10
300-399	7	6	6	6	6
400-499	2	2	2	2	2
500 + ...	5	5	5	5	5
Location					
Hospitals Urban	55	55	56	53	52
Hospitals Rural..	40	40	40	44	45
Control					
State and Local Government	39	38	40	39	38
Not for Profit...	19	20	23	24	24
Investor owned..	37	37	33	34	35
Physician Models					
Independent Practice Association....................	4	4	2	2	3
Group Practice without Walls..........................	0	0	0	0	0
Open Physician-Hospital Organization	0	5	6	6	6
Closed Physician-Hospital Organization............	5	1	0	0	4
Management Service Organization....................	5	6	3	3	11
Integrated Salary Model................................	9	9	8	9	13
Equity Model	0	0	0	0	0
Foundation	6	6	4	4	4
Insurance Products					
Health Maintenance Organization....................	4	3	4	4	2
Preferred Provider Organization	8	8	7	7	9
Indemnity Fee for Service	0	0	1	1	0
Managed Care Contracts					
Health Maintenance Organization....................	24	29	28	29	34
Preferred Provider Organization	32	34	32	33	43
Affiliations					
Hospitals in a System	62	61	61	62	61
Hospitals in a Network	12	7	8	6	8
Hospitals in a Group Purchasing Organization...	36	37	36	37	50

TABLE 6

ALABAMA

U.S. Registered Community Hospitals
(Nonfederal, short-term general and other special hospitals)

Utilization, Personnel, Revenue and Expenses, Community Health Indicators 2012–2016

	2016	2015	2014	2013	2012
TOTAL FACILITY (Includes Hospital and Nursing Home Units)					
Utilization - Inpatient					
Beds...........................	15,115	14,672	14,959	15,129	14,983
Admissions.................	630,982	616,567	632,358	641,249	650,116
Inpatient Days.............	3,556,712	3,415,658	3,335,338	3,369,852	3,235,410
Average Length of Stay	5.6	5.5	5.3	5.3	5.0
Inpatient Surgeries.............	186,179	177,093	179,858	188,370	216,437
Births........................	58,959	59,221	57,863	57,811	54,169
Utilization - Outpatient					
Emergency Outpatient Visits..............	2,204,653	2,465,545	2,347,239	2,279,572	2,349,349
Other Outpatient Visits......................	6,565,599	6,244,186	6,169,200	6,032,550	5,787,211
Total Outpatient Visits................	8,770,252	8,709,731	8,516,439	8,312,122	8,136,560
Outpatient Surgeries................	393,011	366,628	358,555	377,910	416,822
Personnel					
Full Time RNs	22,142	21,692	21,330	20,357	18,971
Full Time LPNs................	1,099	1,108	1,112	1,207	1,284
Part Time RNs................	8,380	7,939	5,856	6,329	6,450
Part Time LPNs................	319	306	284	376	423
Total Full Time................	69,328	69,071	68,620	67,282	63,711
Total Part Time................	21,726	20,171	15,991	16,854	17,393
Revenue - Inpatient					
Gross Inpatient Revenue	$26,429,929,206	$25,051,835,720	$22,806,578,952	$22,037,388,309	$21,905,302,437
Revenue - Outpatient					
Gross Outpatient Revenue	$24,523,066,659	$23,262,766,865	$20,942,673,592	$19,204,120,871	$18,451,159,730
Revenue and Expenses - Totals					
(Includes Inpatient and Outpatient)					
Total Gross Revenue........................	$50,952,995,865	$48,314,602,585	$43,749,252,544	$41,241,509,180	$40,356,462,167
Deductions from Revenue	39,705,922,745	37,619,889,142	33,567,813,199	31,119,196,377	30,849,527,537
Net Patient Revenue........................	11,247,073,120	10,694,713,443	10,181,439,345	10,122,312,803	9,506,934,630
Other Operating Revenue	668,329,250	626,073,312	613,765,569	574,099,002	530,660,281
Other Nonoperating Revenue	170,289,447	34,079,724	219,428,307	239,417,197	117,222,122
Total Net Revenue...........................	12,085,691,817	11,354,866,479	11,014,633,221	10,935,829,002	10,154,817,033
Total Expenses...............................	10,823,758,954	10,318,802,921	9,892,819,354	9,699,338,172	9,009,790,217
HOSPITAL UNIT (Excludes Separate Nursing Home Units)					
Utilization - Inpatient					
Beds..........................	14,482	14,142	14,593	14,695	14,684
Admissions.................	629,499	615,254	631,419	640,039	649,138
Inpatient Days.............	3,343,442	3,248,229	3,218,620	3,231,272	3,135,159
Average Length of Stay	5.3	5.3	5.1	5.0	4.8
Personnel					
Total Full Time...............	68,757	68,640	68,149	66,636	63,419
Total Part Time	21,563	20,036	15,913	16,433	17,324
Revenue and Expenses - Totals					
(Includes Inpatient and Outpatient)					
Total Net Revenue..............................	$12,028,635,067	$11,325,915,957	$10,995,481,060	$10,910,655,198	$10,139,471,861
Total Expenses.................................	10,782,440,528	10,282,046,047	9,877,795,683	9,676,090,169	8,994,674,312
COMMUNITY HEALTH INDICATORS PER 1000 POPULATION					
Total Population (in thousands)...........	4,863	4,859	4,849	4,834	4,822
Inpatient					
Beds..........................	3.1	3.0	3.1	3.1	3.1
Admissions.................	129.7	126.9	130.4	132.7	134.8
Inpatient Days.............	731.3	703.0	687.8	697.2	671.0
Inpatient Surgeries........	38.3	36.4	37.1	39.0	44.9
Births........................	12.1	12.2	11.9	12.0	11.2
Outpatient					
Emergency Outpatient Visits..............	453.3	507.4	484.0	471.6	487.2
Other Outpatient Visits......................	1,350.0	1,285.1	1,272.2	1,248.0	1,200.2
Total Outpatient Visits.......................	1,803.4	1,792.5	1,756.2	1,719.6	1,687.4
Outpatient Surgeries.........................	80.8	75.5	73.9	78.2	86.4
Expense per Capita (per person)........	$2,225.6	$2,123.7	$2,040.0	$2,006.6	$1,868.5

TABLE 6

ALASKA

U.S. Registered Community Hospitals
(Nonfederal, short-term general and other special hospitals)

Overview 2012–2016

	2016	2015	2014	2013	2012
Total Community Hospitals in Alaska	21	21	22	22	23
Bed Size Category					
6-24	4	4	5	5	7
25-49	7	7	7	9	8
50-99	5	5	5	3	3
100-199	3	3	3	3	3
200-299	1	1	1	1	1
300-399	0	0	0	1	1
400-499	1	1	1	0	0
500 + ...	0	0	0	0	0
Location					
Hospitals Urban	6	6	6	6	6
Hospitals Rural	15	15	16	16	17
Control					
State and Local Government	7	7	7	7	7
Not for Profit	11	11	13	13	14
Investor owned	3	3	2	2	2
Physician Models					
Independent Practice Association	2	2	1	1	1
Group Practice without Walls	1	1	0	0	0
Open Physician-Hospital Organization ...	1	1	1	1	2
Closed Physician-Hospital Organization .	1	1	0	1	1
Management Service Organization	0	0	0	0	0
Integrated Salary Model	7	7	5	4	3
Equity Model	0	0	0	0	0
Foundation	2	2	2	1	0
Insurance Products					
Health Maintenance Organization	0	0	0	0	0
Preferred Provider Organization	3	3	3	2	1
Indemnity Fee for Service	1	1	1	0	0
Managed Care Contracts					
Health Maintenance Organization	0	0	1	0	0
Preferred Provider Organization	5	6	8	4	5
Affiliations					
Hospitals in a System	7	8	8	8	8
Hospitals in a Network	2	2	2	1	2
Hospitals in a Group Purchasing Organization...	9	10	8	9	6

States

TABLE 6

ALASKA

U.S. Registered Community Hospitals
(Nonfederal, short-term general and other special hospitals)

Utilization, Personnel, Revenue and Expenses, Community Health Indicators 2012–2016

	2016	2015	2014	2013	2012
TOTAL FACILITY (Includes Hospital and Nursing Home Units)					
Utilization - Inpatient					
Beds	1,647	1,634	1,633	1,560	1,549
Admissions	51,022	52,637	53,386	57,621	56,131
Inpatient Days	384,938	378,062	376,135	376,393	341,987
Average Length of Stay	7.5	7.2	7.0	6.5	6.1
Inpatient Surgeries	18,924	13,138	14,712	13,001	15,613
Births	9,687	9,721	8,985	7,372	8,522
Utilization - Outpatient					
Emergency Outpatient Visits	342,017	324,973	303,956	257,285	290,711
Other Outpatient Visits	1,717,104	1,635,792	1,474,745	1,110,025	1,161,515
Total Outpatient Visits	2,059,121	1,960,765	1,778,701	1,367,310	1,452,226
Outpatient Surgeries	51,311	33,963	37,675	39,216	40,892
Personnel					
Full Time RNs	2,597	2,338	2,492	2,095	2,209
Full Time LPNs	120	86	129	150	145
Part Time RNs	1,165	822	862	823	893
Part Time LPNs	49	22	34	45	37
Total Full Time	10,134	8,453	9,228	8,364	8,723
Total Part Time	3,196	2,251	2,357	2,726	2,467
Revenue - Inpatient					
Gross Inpatient Revenue	$3,953,723,400	$3,489,110,219	$3,131,261,783	$2,857,156,569	$2,628,751,616
Revenue - Outpatient					
Gross Outpatient Revenue	$4,330,578,373	$3,360,897,973	$3,067,062,814	$2,965,846,524	$2,524,384,455
Revenue and Expenses - Totals					
(Includes Inpatient and Outpatient)					
Total Gross Revenue	$8,284,301,773	$6,850,008,192	$6,198,324,597	$5,823,003,093	$5,153,136,071
Deductions from Revenue	5,740,953,226	4,496,841,752	3,994,064,697	3,746,662,160	3,134,854,935
Net Patient Revenue	2,543,348,547	2,353,166,440	2,204,259,900	2,076,340,933	2,018,281,136
Other Operating Revenue	255,918,888	284,505,976	170,454,937	100,248,551	100,656,142
Other Nonoperating Revenue	44,074,181	7,386,912	31,062,392	42,606,280	33,745,177
Total Net Revenue	2,843,341,616	2,645,059,328	2,405,777,229	2,219,195,764	2,152,682,455
Total Expenses	2,291,293,712	1,963,422,824	1,932,865,572	1,824,096,637	1,765,708,752
HOSPITAL UNIT (Excludes Separate Nursing Home Units)					
Utilization - Inpatient					
Beds	1,424	1,379	1,387	1,273	1,293
Admissions	50,600	52,272	53,166	57,215	55,667
Inpatient Days	312,802	296,315	298,489	282,965	257,797
Average Length of Stay	6.2	5.7	5.6	4.9	4.6
Personnel					
Total Full Time	9,871	8,119	8,949	8,116	8,486
Total Part Time	3,042	2,108	2,259	2,596	2,371
Revenue and Expenses - Totals					
(Includes Inpatient and Outpatient)					
Total Net Revenue	$2,790,416,270	$2,596,163,699	$2,362,196,823	$2,171,602,536	$2,105,900,495
Total Expenses	2,251,240,758	1,923,795,139	1,898,027,765	1,783,712,793	1,730,733,295
COMMUNITY HEALTH INDICATORS PER 1000 POPULATION					
Total Population (in thousands)	742	738	737	735	731
Inpatient					
Beds	2.2	2.2	2.2	2.1	2.1
Admissions	68.8	71.3	72.5	78.4	76.7
Inpatient Days	518.9	512.0	510.5	512.0	467.5
Inpatient Surgeries	25.5	17.8	20.0	17.7	21.3
Births	13.1	13.2	12.2	10.0	11.7
Outpatient					
Emergency Outpatient Visits	461.0	440.1	412.6	350.0	397.4
Other Outpatient Visits	2,314.5	2,215.2	2,001.7	1,510.0	1,588.0
Total Outpatient Visits	2,775.5	2,655.3	2,414.3	1,860.0	1,985.4
Outpatient Surgeries	69.2	46.0	51.1	53.3	55.9
Expense per Capita (per person)	$3,088.4	$2,658.9	$2,623.6	$2,481.3	$2,414.0

States

TABLE 6

ARIZONA

U.S. Registered Community Hospitals
(Nonfederal, short-term general and other special hospitals)

Overview 2012–2016

	2016	2015	2014	2013	2012
Total Community Hospitals in Arizona...............	70	71	72	72	72
Bed Size Category					
6-24	6	4	5	5	5
25-49	10	12	12	13	12
50-99	14	14	16	14	15
100-199	13	15	12	13	13
200-299	10	9	11	11	10
300-399	6	6	6	5	6
400-499	6	6	5	6	5
500 + ...	5	5	5	5	6
Location					
Hospitals Urban	61	62	63	58	58
Hospitals Rural	9	9	9	14	14
Control					
State and Local Government	4	4	4	4	4
Not for Profit	41	44	46	47	46
Investor owned	25	23	22	21	22
Physician Models					
Independent Practice Association	18	19	8	6	9
Group Practice without Walls	2	1	3	2	3
Open Physician-Hospital Organization	1	0	5	4	5
Closed Physician-Hospital Organization	9	16	6	4	3
Management Service Organization	4	1	5	5	7
Integrated Salary Model	28	28	18	16	16
Equity Model	0	0	0	0	0
Foundation	1	1	1	1	1
Insurance Products					
Health Maintenance Organization	16	17	12	14	12
Preferred Provider Organization	15	16	12	8	4
Indemnity Fee for Service	14	15	4	2	0
Managed Care Contracts					
Health Maintenance Organization	9	13	24	23	26
Preferred Provider Organization	9	13	24	24	27
Affiliations					
Hospitals in a System	52	53	53	49	49
Hospitals in a Network	24	24	21	19	17
Hospitals in a Group Purchasing Organization...	35	40	40	42	37

TABLE 6

ARIZONA

U.S. Registered Community Hospitals
(Nonfederal, short-term general and other special hospitals)

Utilization, Personnel, Revenue and Expenses, Community Health Indicators 2012–2016

	2016	2015	2014	2013	2012
TOTAL FACILITY (Includes Hospital and Nursing Home Units)					
Utilization - Inpatient					
Beds	13,371	13,520	13,301	13,347	13,527
Admissions	621,129	620,447	624,898	639,279	674,808
Inpatient Days	2,989,208	2,932,887	2,864,588	2,890,733	2,977,605
Average Length of Stay	4.8	4.7	4.6	4.5	4.4
Inpatient Surgeries	161,386	159,288	177,574	187,369	216,991
Births	75,727	77,810	74,217	75,166	73,033
Utilization - Outpatient					
Emergency Outpatient Visits	2,097,304	2,299,702	2,080,313	2,066,382	2,309,621
Other Outpatient Visits	6,233,565	6,519,267	6,349,105	6,673,210	6,427,396
Total Outpatient Visits	8,330,869	8,818,969	8,429,418	8,739,592	8,737,017
Outpatient Surgeries	273,268	252,147	263,000	279,931	245,168
Personnel					
Full Time RNs	24,454	23,343	23,340	22,027	20,977
Full Time LPNs	581	513	487	577	590
Part Time RNs	6,416	4,971	4,851	5,825	6,167
Part Time LPNs	118	83	80	114	150
Total Full Time	72,502	69,621	70,075	67,017	66,940
Total Part Time	16,592	12,731	12,634	14,793	16,020
Revenue - Inpatient					
Gross Inpatient Revenue	$34,467,834,346	$31,455,255,620	$29,641,292,091	$28,048,084,817	$27,609,357,979
Revenue - Outpatient					
Gross Outpatient Revenue	$29,532,020,442	$26,772,437,712	$23,766,382,533	$21,244,955,845	$18,858,344,930
Revenue and Expenses - Totals					
(Includes Inpatient and Outpatient)					
Total Gross Revenue	$63,999,854,788	$58,227,693,332	$53,407,674,624	$49,293,040,662	$46,467,702,909
Deductions from Revenue	49,377,471,996	44,216,901,075	39,971,629,324	36,737,029,960	34,058,007,365
Net Patient Revenue	14,622,382,792	14,010,792,257	13,436,045,300	12,556,010,702	12,409,695,544
Other Operating Revenue	545,948,981	540,469,427	534,783,788	603,598,689	475,139,314
Other Nonoperating Revenue	75,508,298	49,926,612	190,853,081	139,238,418	86,412,468
Total Net Revenue	15,243,840,071	14,601,188,296	14,161,682,169	13,298,847,809	12,971,247,326
Total Expenses	14,098,473,988	13,724,478,682	12,984,716,899	12,377,784,591	12,112,683,858
HOSPITAL UNIT (Excludes Separate Nursing Home Units)					
Utilization - Inpatient					
Beds	13,293	13,418	13,199	13,252	13,401
Admissions	619,683	618,678	623,030	637,557	672,834
Inpatient Days	2,968,914	2,910,230	2,840,826	2,863,151	2,944,802
Average Length of Stay	4.8	4.7	4.6	4.5	4.4
Personnel					
Total Full Time	72,444	69,550	69,998	66,942	66,850
Total Part Time	16,580	12,715	12,618	14,777	16,010
Revenue and Expenses - Totals					
(Includes Inpatient and Outpatient)					
Total Net Revenue	$15,208,378,076	$14,566,756,483	$14,131,564,785	$13,268,304,844	$12,943,620,235
Total Expenses	14,087,165,449	13,715,394,742	12,972,257,147	12,365,050,443	12,098,532,372
COMMUNITY HEALTH INDICATORS PER 1000 POPULATION					
Total Population (in thousands)	6,931	6,828	6,731	6,627	6,553
Inpatient					
Beds	1.9	2.0	2.0	2.0	2.1
Admissions	89.6	90.9	92.8	96.5	103.0
Inpatient Days	431.3	429.5	425.6	436.2	454.4
Inpatient Surgeries	23.3	23.3	26.4	28.3	33.1
Births	10.9	11.4	11.0	11.3	11.1
Outpatient					
Emergency Outpatient Visits	302.6	336.8	309.0	311.8	352.4
Other Outpatient Visits	899.4	954.8	943.2	1,007.0	980.8
Total Outpatient Visits	1,202.0	1,291.6	1,252.2	1,318.9	1,333.2
Outpatient Surgeries	39.4	36.9	39.1	42.2	37.4
Expense per Capita (per person)	$2,034.1	$2,010.0	$1,929.0	$1,867.9	$1,848.3

States

TABLE 6

ARKANSAS

U.S. Registered Community Hospitals
(Nonfederal, short-term general and other special hospitals)

Overview 2012–2016

	2016	2015	2014	2013	2012
Total Community Hospitals in Arkansas.............	80	80	81	84	83
Bed Size Category					
6-24	5	5	6	6	5
25-49	32	30	28	31	32
50-99	14	15	18	16	14
100-199	11	13	13	15	16
200-299	8	9	8	7	7
300-399	7	5	5	6	6
400-499	1	2	2	2	2
500 + ...	2	1	1	1	1
Location					
Hospitals Urban	33	33	34	36	35
Hospitals Rural	47	47	47	48	48
Control					
State and Local Government	10	10	10	10	11
Not for Profit	50	50	49	50	49
Investor owned	20	20	22	24	23
Physician Models					
Independent Practice Association......................	6	7	5	6	6
Group Practice without Walls	4	4	3	5	5
Open Physician-Hospital Organization	20	21	23	24	23
Closed Physician-Hospital Organization............	2	4	5	6	4
Management Service Organization.....................	9	12	12	12	9
Integrated Salary Model....................................	27	28	27	29	20
Equity Model	1	1	1	1	1
Foundation	6	7	6	6	5
Insurance Products					
Health Maintenance Organization......................	12	11	15	15	14
Preferred Provider Organization	9	4	8	6	7
Indemnity Fee for Service	2	6	3	0	1
Managed Care Contracts					
Health Maintenance Organization......................	42	44	47	47	40
Preferred Provider Organization	52	58	56	64	53
Affiliations					
Hospitals in a System	45	45	45	47	46
Hospitals in a Network	27	27	28	28	22
Hospitals in a Group Purchasing Organization...	68	71	68	77	61

TABLE 6

ARKANSAS

U.S. Registered Community Hospitals
(Nonfederal, short-term general and other special hospitals)

Utilization, Personnel, Revenue and Expenses, Community Health Indicators 2012–2016

	2016	2015	2014	2013	2012
TOTAL FACILITY (Includes Hospital and Nursing Home Units)					
Utilization - Inpatient					
Beds..	9,419	9,381	9,284	9,452	9,417
Admissions.......................................	352,722	351,022	344,635	352,362	352,752
Inpatient Days..................................	1,810,494	1,822,868	1,768,146	1,817,099	1,845,443
Average Length of Stay	5.1	5.2	5.1	5.2	5.2
Inpatient Surgeries...........................	90,214	91,308	92,169	95,834	101,156
Births...	35,864	36,206	35,407	36,313	35,421
Utilization - Outpatient					
Emergency Outpatient Visits..............	1,503,862	1,485,473	1,351,198	1,438,617	1,382,183
Other Outpatient Visits......................	4,500,019	4,113,628	3,727,703	3,674,902	3,743,252
Total Outpatient Visits	6,003,881	5,599,101	5,078,901	5,113,519	5,125,435
Outpatient Surgeries.........................	191,297	189,031	172,975	174,981	174,095
Personnel					
Full Time RNs...................................	12,412	12,511	12,022	11,915	11,964
Full Time LPNs.................................	1,430	1,437	1,534	1,579	1,587
Part Time RNs..................................	3,577	3,578	3,492	3,353	3,576
Part Time LPNs................................	370	349	411	384	455
Total Full Time	41,651	41,071	39,819	39,095	40,286
Total Part Time	10,341	10,374	10,813	9,459	10,397
Revenue - Inpatient					
Gross Inpatient Revenue	$12,173,773,449	$11,456,007,960	$10,809,965,954	$10,391,798,234	$9,975,710,168
Revenue - Outpatient					
Gross Outpatient Revenue	$12,711,824,469	$11,798,345,545	$10,398,394,815	$9,513,953,822	$8,663,764,850
Revenue and Expenses - Totals					
(Includes Inpatient and Outpatient)					
Total Gross Revenue.........................	$24,885,597,918	$23,254,353,505	$21,208,360,769	$19,905,752,056	$18,639,475,018
Deductions from Revenue	18,081,615,173	16,788,731,845	15,305,292,104	14,135,092,803	12,820,230,814
Net Patient Revenue.........................	6,803,982,745	6,465,621,660	5,903,068,665	5,770,659,253	5,819,244,204
Other Operating Revenue..................	306,420,462	249,634,077	308,493,708	269,134,329	256,162,838
Other Nonoperating Revenue............	82,382,236	41,704,386	98,329,834	87,213,991	85,908,563
Total Net Revenue............................	7,192,785,443	6,756,960,123	6,309,892,207	6,127,007,573	6,161,315,605
Total Expenses................................	6,639,743,345	6,299,543,986	5,976,998,987	5,917,263,241	5,759,240,612
HOSPITAL UNIT (Excludes Separate Nursing Home Units)					
Utilization - Inpatient					
Beds..	9,111	9,013	8,916	9,176	9,200
Admissions.......................................	352,097	350,416	344,078	351,947	351,712
Inpatient Days..................................	1,719,909	1,721,874	1,666,480	1,738,385	1,774,671
Average Length of Stay	4.9	4.9	4.8	4.9	5.0
Personnel					
Total Full Time	41,472	40,860	39,591	38,944	40,123
Total Part Time	10,315	10,316	10,762	9,429	10,347
Revenue and Expenses - Totals					
(Includes Inpatient and Outpatient)					
Total Net Revenue............................	$7,173,248,383	$6,736,135,406	$6,289,224,053	$6,113,021,586	$6,148,169,295
Total Expenses................................	6,625,459,005	6,282,772,880	5,963,566,360	5,907,194,626	5,749,516,565
COMMUNITY HEALTH INDICATORS PER 1000 POPULATION					
Total Population (in thousands)...........	2,988	2,978	2,966	2,959	2,949
Inpatient					
Beds..	3.2	3.1	3.1	3.2	3.2
Admissions.......................................	118.0	117.9	116.2	119.1	119.6
Inpatient Days..................................	605.9	612.1	596.1	614.0	625.8
Inpatient Surgeries...........................	30.2	30.7	31.1	32.4	34.3
Births...	12.0	12.2	11.9	12.3	12.0
Outpatient					
Emergency Outpatient Visits..............	503.3	498.8	455.5	486.1	468.7
Other Outpatient Visits......................	1,505.9	1,381.2	1,256.7	1,241.8	1,269.3
Total Outpatient Visits	2,009.2	1,880.0	1,712.2	1,727.9	1,737.9
Outpatient Surgeries.........................	64.0	63.5	58.3	59.1	59.0
Expense per Capita (per person)........	$2,222.0	$2,115.2	$2,014.9	$1,999.5	$1,952.9

States

TABLE 6

CALIFORNIA

U.S. Registered Community Hospitals
(Nonfederal, short-term general and other special hospitals)

Overview 2012–2016

	2016	2015	2014	2013	2012
Total Community Hospitals in California	**341**	**342**	**344**	**347**	**349**
Bed Size Category					
6-24	11	12	13	13	11
25-49	37	37	38	40	44
50-99	40	39	41	39	40
100-199	107	108	110	109	105
200-299	64	65	61	64	67
300-399	44	44	47	47	44
400-499	25	24	22	22	25
500 + ...	13	13	12	13	13
Location					
Hospitals Urban	311	312	313	316	318
Hospitals Rural	30	30	31	31	31
Control					
State and Local Government	62	63	64	63	66
Not for Profit	201	203	205	207	206
Investor owned	78	76	75	77	77
Physician Models					
Independent Practice Association	90	72	64	58	51
Group Practice without Walls	13	12	18	13	10
Open Physician-Hospital Organization	6	4	6	5	4
Closed Physician-Hospital Organization	3	7	7	9	4
Management Service Organization	31	52	48	52	46
Integrated Salary Model	30	27	22	22	20
Equity Model	7	8	8	3	2
Foundation	103	109	98	91	83
Insurance Products					
Health Maintenance Organization	78	79	57	54	47
Preferred Provider Organization	27	28	25	20	18
Indemnity Fee for Service	16	19	13	9	8
Managed Care Contracts					
Health Maintenance Organization	154	167	162	156	168
Preferred Provider Organization	149	162	152	149	161
Affiliations					
Hospitals in a System	248	244	240	231	231
Hospitals in a Network	68	78	68	70	60
Hospitals in a Group Purchasing Organization...	191	205	198	199	174

States

TABLE 6

CALIFORNIA

U.S. Registered Community Hospitals
(Nonfederal, short-term general and other special hospitals)

Utilization, Personnel, Revenue and Expenses, Community Health Indicators 2012–2016

	2016	2015	2014	2013	2012
TOTAL FACILITY (Includes Hospital and Nursing Home Units)					
Utilization - Inpatient					
Beds	70,082	70,059	69,441	70,326	71,004
Admissions	3,298,740	3,261,143	3,184,754	3,255,312	3,304,230
Inpatient Days	16,955,615	16,672,906	16,332,640	16,482,984	16,919,921
Average Length of Stay	5.1	5.1	5.1	5.1	5.1
Inpatient Surgeries	822,724	830,688	842,538	835,298	867,839
Births	450,858	460,483	471,877	465,752	482,313
Utilization - Outpatient					
Emergency Outpatient Visits	13,420,209	13,648,026	12,693,166	12,088,159	11,859,123
Other Outpatient Visits	45,095,987	43,353,360	41,446,336	41,724,982	40,365,732
Total Outpatient Visits	58,516,196	57,001,386	54,139,502	53,813,141	52,224,855
Outpatient Surgeries	1,342,597	1,308,191	1,268,052	1,276,491	1,249,704
Personnel					
Full Time RNs	117,998	114,451	108,875	103,849	106,195
Full Time LPNs	5,865	5,795	5,498	5,860	6,108
Part Time RNs	59,515	56,311	55,360	54,052	55,861
Part Time LPNs	2,143	2,107	2,185	2,328	2,574
Total Full Time	390,936	382,165	364,859	359,887	370,238
Total Part Time	153,572	146,152	142,568	140,888	147,910
Revenue - Inpatient					
Gross Inpatient Revenue	$241,339,116,455	$227,715,963,815	$211,960,077,263	$205,071,437,854	$194,710,241,465
Revenue - Outpatient					
Gross Outpatient Revenue	$171,915,121,813	$154,745,128,565	$138,248,440,989	$123,867,181,756	$110,355,399,582
Revenue and Expenses - Totals					
(Includes Inpatient and Outpatient)					
Total Gross Revenue	$413,254,238,268	$382,461,092,380	$350,208,518,252	$328,938,605,193	$305,065,641,047
Deductions from Revenue	310,362,396,081	284,460,183,305	262,312,721,357	242,255,300,320	222,641,523,180
Net Patient Revenue	102,891,842,187	98,000,909,075	87,895,796,895	86,683,304,873	82,424,117,867
Other Operating Revenue	6,198,218,670	5,852,728,905	5,434,043,994	5,417,248,967	4,935,487,999
Other Nonoperating Revenue	1,243,041,811	1,319,108,887	2,565,342,915	3,336,499,298	1,579,522,303
Total Net Revenue	110,333,102,668	105,172,746,867	95,895,183,804	95,437,053,138	88,939,128,169
Total Expenses	102,994,932,244	96,957,154,301	88,682,388,820	86,710,652,989	83,074,054,310
HOSPITAL UNIT (Excludes Separate Nursing Home Units)					
Utilization - Inpatient					
Beds	66,887	66,435	66,026	66,388	66,826
Admissions	3,283,753	3,245,180	3,166,923	3,235,117	3,281,803
Inpatient Days	15,926,478	15,497,913	15,283,783	15,256,633	15,596,063
Average Length of Stay	4.9	4.8	4.8	4.7	4.8
Personnel					
Total Full Time	388,989	379,548	361,224	357,289	366,919
Total Part Time	152,722	144,866	141,348	139,433	146,283
Revenue and Expenses - Totals					
(Includes Inpatient and Outpatient)					
Total Net Revenue	$109,863,778,405	$104,526,211,040	$95,394,711,281	$94,867,298,781	$88,462,119,698
Total Expenses	102,675,578,472	96,542,664,741	88,386,060,683	86,290,640,782	82,671,685,266
COMMUNITY HEALTH INDICATORS PER 1000 POPULATION					
Total Population (in thousands)	39,250	39,145	38,803	38,333	38,041
Inpatient					
Beds	1.8	1.8	1.8	1.8	1.9
Admissions	84.0	83.3	82.1	84.9	86.9
Inpatient Days	432.0	425.9	420.9	430.0	444.8
Inpatient Surgeries	21.0	21.2	21.7	21.8	22.8
Births	11.5	11.8	12.2	12.2	12.7
Outpatient					
Emergency Outpatient Visits	341.9	348.7	327.1	315.3	311.7
Other Outpatient Visits	1,148.9	1,107.5	1,068.1	1,088.5	1,061.1
Total Outpatient Visits	1,490.9	1,456.2	1,395.3	1,403.9	1,372.8
Outpatient Surgeries	34.2	33.4	32.7	33.3	32.9
Expense per Capita (per person)	$2,624.1	$2,476.9	$2,285.5	$2,262.1	$2,183.8

States

TABLE **6**

COLORADO

U.S. Registered Community Hospitals
(Nonfederal, short-term general and other special hospitals)

Overview 2012–2016

	2016	2015	2014	2013	2012
Total Community Hospitals in Colorado	79	81	82	82	82
Bed Size Category					
6-24	13	15	13	12	12
25-49	20	21	19	20	22
50-99	16	16	19	19	17
100-199	10	10	12	13	12
200-299	8	7	7	6	7
300-399	5	5	5	7	6
400-499	4	4	6	4	6
500 +	3	3	1	1	0
Location					
Hospitals Urban	41	43	44	44	44
Hospitals Rural	38	38	38	38	38
Control					
State and Local Government	24	25	25	25	26
Not for Profit	40	39	40	40	39
Investor owned	15	17	17	17	17
Physician Models					
Independent Practice Association	13	12	10	10	10
Group Practice without Walls	2	2	2	3	3
Open Physician-Hospital Organization	8	8	12	11	11
Closed Physician-Hospital Organization	5	4	2	3	3
Management Service Organization	4	4	4	4	4
Integrated Salary Model	38	42	41	40	40
Equity Model	1	1	1	1	1
Foundation	4	2	2	3	3
Insurance Products					
Health Maintenance Organization	4	3	4	7	9
Preferred Provider Organization	2	1	3	4	3
Indemnity Fee for Service	1	0	0	0	1
Managed Care Contracts					
Health Maintenance Organization	39	39	43	46	44
Preferred Provider Organization	41	44	48	55	51
Affiliations					
Hospitals in a System	47	50	48	48	47
Hospitals in a Network	17	17	18	20	19
Hospitals in a Group Purchasing Organization	58	58	60	61	54

TABLE 6

COLORADO

U.S. Registered Community Hospitals
(Nonfederal, short-term general and other special hospitals)

Utilization, Personnel, Revenue and Expenses, Community Health Indicators 2012–2016

	2016	2015	2014	2013	2012
TOTAL FACILITY (Includes Hospital and Nursing Home Units)					
Utilization - Inpatient					
Beds	10,680	10,455	10,521	10,301	10,244
Admissions	424,472	423,796	413,537	407,432	444,430
Inpatient Days	2,192,792	2,160,039	2,142,076	2,147,937	2,253,793
Average Length of Stay	5.2	5.1	5.2	5.3	5.1
Inpatient Surgeries	130,834	126,275	124,426	122,685	134,849
Births	60,876	62,074	60,944	56,439	58,253
Utilization - Outpatient					
Emergency Outpatient Visits	2,008,376	2,055,371	1,909,887	1,875,842	1,818,858
Other Outpatient Visits	7,043,717	6,754,214	6,596,461	6,904,552	7,139,929
Total Outpatient Visits	9,052,093	8,809,585	8,506,348	8,780,394	8,958,787
Outpatient Surgeries	249,395	245,241	240,077	237,551	232,063
Personnel					
Full Time RNs	17,475	16,807	16,610	15,466	15,678
Full Time LPNs	480	533	557	479	479
Part Time RNs	7,323	6,485	6,491	6,711	6,456
Part Time LPNs	202	187	175	184	191
Total Full Time	59,140	57,002	56,284	54,760	54,125
Total Part Time	21,932	18,584	18,694	20,369	17,930
Revenue - Inpatient					
Gross Inpatient Revenue	$30,403,278,222	$28,705,502,613	$25,459,592,142	$23,145,163,295	$22,263,097,740
Revenue - Outpatient					
Gross Outpatient Revenue	$26,870,184,586	$25,472,511,351	$22,116,867,040	$20,071,791,832	$18,360,253,142
Revenue and Expenses - Totals					
(Includes Inpatient and Outpatient)					
Total Gross Revenue	$57,273,462,808	$54,178,013,964	$47,576,459,182	$43,216,955,127	$40,623,350,882
Deductions from Revenue	42,759,913,305	40,315,428,774	34,750,591,784	31,041,601,067	28,720,794,917
Net Patient Revenue	14,513,549,503	13,862,585,190	12,825,867,398	12,175,354,060	11,902,555,965
Other Operating Revenue	621,963,321	549,724,630	575,219,037	601,507,479	559,939,985
Other Nonoperating Revenue	143,591,795	139,210,024	316,257,846	289,329,393	156,458,722
Total Net Revenue	15,279,104,619	14,551,519,844	13,717,344,281	13,066,190,932	12,618,954,672
Total Expenses	13,247,938,107	12,624,852,753	11,972,904,688	11,468,752,081	10,941,848,898
HOSPITAL UNIT (Excludes Separate Nursing Home Units)					
Utilization - Inpatient					
Beds	10,085	9,861	9,923	9,561	9,663
Admissions	423,108	422,081	412,005	405,640	442,623
Inpatient Days	2,013,190	1,983,055	1,982,226	1,924,396	2,067,062
Average Length of Stay	4.8	4.7	4.8	4.7	4.7
Personnel					
Total Full Time	58,756	56,643	55,945	54,115	53,774
Total Part Time	21,782	18,441	18,519	19,867	17,727
Revenue and Expenses - Totals					
(Includes Inpatient and Outpatient)					
Total Net Revenue	$15,234,072,440	$14,509,582,676	$13,686,549,446	$13,018,522,807	$12,577,500,290
Total Expenses	13,206,864,260	12,583,192,054	11,943,486,056	11,416,084,053	10,898,966,203
COMMUNITY HEALTH INDICATORS PER 1000 POPULATION					
Total Population (in thousands)	5,541	5,457	5,356	5,268	5,188
Inpatient					
Beds	1.9	1.9	2.0	2.0	2.0
Admissions	76.6	77.7	77.2	77.3	85.7
Inpatient Days	395.8	395.9	399.9	407.7	434.5
Inpatient Surgeries	23.6	23.1	23.2	23.3	26.0
Births	11.0	11.4	11.4	10.7	11.2
Outpatient					
Emergency Outpatient Visits	362.5	376.7	356.6	356.1	350.6
Other Outpatient Visits	1,271.3	1,237.8	1,231.6	1,310.6	1,376.4
Total Outpatient Visits	1,633.8	1,614.5	1,588.2	1,666.6	1,727.0
Outpatient Surgeries	45.0	44.9	44.8	45.1	44.7
Expense per Capita (per person)	$2,391.1	$2,313.7	$2,235.5	$2,176.9	$2,109.2

TABLE 6

CONNECTICUT

U.S. Registered Community Hospitals
(Nonfederal, short-term general and other special hospitals)

Overview 2012–2016

	2016	2015	2014	2013	2012
Total Community Hospitals in Connecticut........	32	32	32	33	34
Bed Size Category					
6-24	0	0	0	0	0
25-49	3	3	3	3	2
50-99	8	8	8	8	9
100-199	12	11	11	12	10
200-299	2	2	2	2	4
300-399	3	3	4	4	5
400-499	1	2	1	1	1
500 + ...	3	3	3	3	3
Location					
Hospitals Urban	30	30	30	28	29
Hospitals Rural	2	2	2	5	5
Control					
State and Local Government	1	1	1	1	1
Not for Profit	30	30	30	31	32
Investor owned	1	1	1	1	1
Physician Models					
Independent Practice Association	6	5	6	8	7
Group Practice without Walls	1	0	0	2	0
Open Physician-Hospital Organization	6	6	7	6	5
Closed Physician-Hospital Organization.........	0	1	1	3	4
Management Service Organization.................	4	3	3	3	6
Integrated Salary Model	14	12	13	16	17
Equity Model	4	4	4	4	4
Foundation	13	11	10	8	8
Insurance Products					
Health Maintenance Organization..................	0	1	0	0	0
Preferred Provider Organization	1	1	0	0	1
Indemnity Fee for Service	0	1	0	0	0
Managed Care Contracts					
Health Maintenance Organization..................	22	19	18	20	24
Preferred Provider Organization	22	19	18	20	24
Affiliations					
Hospitals in a System	20	19	16	17	18
Hospitals in a Network	18	14	17	16	12
Hospitals in a Group Purchasing Organization...	25	24	24	26	25

TABLE **6**

CONNECTICUT

U.S. Registered Community Hospitals
(Nonfederal, short-term general and other special hospitals)

Utilization, Personnel, Revenue and Expenses, Community Health Indicators 2012–2016

	2016	2015	2014	2013	2012
TOTAL FACILITY (Includes Hospital and Nursing Home Units)					
Utilization - Inpatient					
Beds	7,278	7,531	7,806	7,811	8,120
Admissions	375,154	377,150	376,644	391,394	378,130
Inpatient Days	1,951,522	2,008,771	2,091,854	2,144,945	2,053,559
Average Length of Stay	5.2	5.3	5.6	5.5	5.4
Inpatient Surgeries	111,590	102,747	103,981	105,579	99,309
Births	36,478	36,680	36,730	36,851	35,891
Utilization - Outpatient					
Emergency Outpatient Visits	1,671,516	1,663,519	1,587,150	1,626,044	1,643,476
Other Outpatient Visits	7,644,309	7,239,266	6,900,412	7,648,981	7,342,754
Total Outpatient Visits	9,315,825	8,902,785	8,487,562	9,275,025	8,986,230
Outpatient Surgeries	220,046	209,981	214,675	217,602	216,262
Personnel					
Full Time RNs	11,502	11,070	10,250	10,664	10,989
Full Time LPNs	224	225	239	240	261
Part Time RNs	8,256	7,884	7,420	6,924	7,221
Part Time LPNs	142	148	166	190	221
Total Full Time	45,080	43,638	43,917	44,827	44,994
Total Part Time	25,222	22,897	22,315	20,843	22,084
Revenue - Inpatient					
Gross Inpatient Revenue	$16,384,469,099	$16,472,383,493	$16,003,371,951	$15,912,651,412	$14,329,380,117
Revenue - Outpatient					
Gross Outpatient Revenue	$18,392,571,010	$17,231,977,464	$16,409,353,871	$15,494,331,680	$13,501,775,551
Revenue and Expenses - Totals					
(Includes Inpatient and Outpatient)					
Total Gross Revenue	$34,777,040,109	$33,704,360,957	$32,412,725,822	$31,406,983,092	$27,831,155,668
Deductions from Revenue	23,650,482,376	22,907,056,578	21,993,137,480	21,131,372,170	18,019,019,740
Net Patient Revenue	11,126,557,733	10,797,304,379	10,419,588,342	10,275,610,922	9,812,135,928
Other Operating Revenue	620,331,081	507,484,212	485,957,179	567,209,554	562,656,610
Other Nonoperating Revenue	219,500,367	-14,004,628	168,117,622	234,905,027	123,095,744
Total Net Revenue	11,966,389,181	11,290,783,963	11,073,663,143	11,077,725,503	10,497,888,282
Total Expenses	11,386,587,495	10,833,514,095	10,341,323,608	10,399,557,016	9,795,239,002
HOSPITAL UNIT (Excludes Separate Nursing Home Units)					
Utilization - Inpatient					
Beds	7,174	7,427	7,588	7,599	7,777
Admissions	374,812	376,759	375,481	390,412	377,468
Inpatient Days	1,914,811	1,972,229	2,017,478	2,069,739	1,973,687
Average Length of Stay	5.1	5.2	5.4	5.3	5.2
Personnel					
Total Full Time	45,012	43,557	43,765	44,665	44,726
Total Part Time	25,152	22,803	22,239	20,672	21,876
Revenue and Expenses - Totals					
(Includes Inpatient and Outpatient)					
Total Net Revenue	$11,953,471,349	$11,277,901,563	$11,049,447,956	$11,043,626,112	$10,439,662,013
Total Expenses	11,377,360,293	10,824,084,611	10,314,425,719	10,376,600,813	9,741,183,887
COMMUNITY HEALTH INDICATORS PER 1000 POPULATION					
Total Population (in thousands)	3,576	3,591	3,597	3,596	3,590
Inpatient					
Beds	2.0	2.1	2.2	2.2	2.3
Admissions	104.9	105.0	104.7	108.8	105.3
Inpatient Days	545.7	559.4	581.6	596.5	572.0
Inpatient Surgeries	31.2	28.6	28.9	29.4	27.7
Births	10.2	10.2	10.2	10.2	10.0
Outpatient					
Emergency Outpatient Visits	467.4	463.3	441.3	452.2	457.7
Other Outpatient Visits	2,137.4	2,016.0	1,918.6	2,127.0	2,045.1
Total Outpatient Visits	2,604.8	2,479.3	2,359.8	2,579.2	2,502.9
Outpatient Surgeries	61.5	58.5	59.7	60.5	60.2
Expense per Capita (per person)	$3,183.8	$3,016.9	$2,875.2	$2,891.9	$2,728.2

States

TABLE 6

DELAWARE

U.S. Registered Community Hospitals
(Nonfederal, short-term general and other special hospitals)

Overview 2012–2016

	2016	2015	2014	2013	2012
Total Community Hospitals in Delaware	7	7	7	7	7
Bed Size Category					
6-24	0	0	0	0	0
25-49	1	1	1	1	1
50-99	1	1	1	1	1
100-199	2	2	2	2	2
200-299	1	1	1	1	1
300-399	1	1	1	1	1
400-499	0	0	0	0	0
500 +	1	1	1	1	1
Location					
Hospitals Urban	7	7	7	5	5
Hospitals Rural	0	0	0	2	2
Control					
State and Local Government	0	0	0	0	0
Not for Profit	6	6	6	6	6
Investor owned	1	1	1	1	1
Physician Models					
Independent Practice Association	0	0	1	0	0
Group Practice without Walls	1	1	1	1	0
Open Physician-Hospital Organization	0	0	0	0	0
Closed Physician-Hospital Organization	0	0	0	0	0
Management Service Organization	0	0	0	0	0
Integrated Salary Model	3	2	2	1	1
Equity Model	0	0	0	0	0
Foundation	1	1	1	1	1
Insurance Products					
Health Maintenance Organization	1	1	0	0	0
Preferred Provider Organization	1	1	0	0	0
Indemnity Fee for Service	1	1	0	0	0
Managed Care Contracts					
Health Maintenance Organization	5	5	4	3	3
Preferred Provider Organization	5	5	4	3	3
Affiliations					
Hospitals in a System	4	4	4	4	4
Hospitals in a Network	1	0	0	0	0
Hospitals in a Group Purchasing Organization	6	6	6	5	5

TABLE 6

DELAWARE

U.S. Registered Community Hospitals
(Nonfederal, short-term general and other special hospitals)

Utilization, Personnel, Revenue and Expenses, Community Health Indicators 2012–2016

	2016	2015	2014	2013	2012
TOTAL FACILITY (Includes Hospital and Nursing Home Units)					
Utilization - Inpatient					
Beds	2,059	2,106	2,053	2,034	1,998
Admissions	100,716	106,139	105,109	104,769	104,803
Inpatient Days	519,070	567,289	557,672	538,590	526,678
Average Length of Stay	5.2	5.3	5.3	5.1	5.0
Inpatient Surgeries	29,481	32,640	33,278	31,227	32,163
Births	11,430	11,269	11,201	11,037	11,358
Utilization - Outpatient					
Emergency Outpatient Visits	469,403	463,845	451,296	441,756	437,706
Other Outpatient Visits	1,710,846	1,787,677	1,656,267	1,648,654	1,653,598
Total Outpatient Visits	2,180,249	2,251,522	2,107,563	2,090,410	2,091,304
Outpatient Surgeries	60,646	64,599	62,667	63,281	64,243
Personnel					
Full Time RNs	4,443	4,424	4,258	4,156	3,997
Full Time LPNs	118	119	131	134	142
Part Time RNs	2,118	2,229	2,076	2,082	2,166
Part Time LPNs	38	43	136	123	118
Total Full Time	16,675	16,428	15,712	15,155	15,421
Total Part Time	5,952	6,177	5,971	5,682	5,918
Revenue - Inpatient					
Gross Inpatient Revenue	$3,947,910,339	$3,785,257,174	$3,558,726,356	$3,299,554,275	$3,097,560,492
Revenue - Outpatient					
Gross Outpatient Revenue	$3,856,305,152	$3,578,655,796	$3,223,470,034	$2,900,967,707	$2,677,941,719
Revenue and Expenses - Totals					
(Includes Inpatient and Outpatient)					
Total Gross Revenue	$7,804,215,491	$7,363,912,970	$6,782,196,390	$6,200,521,982	$5,775,502,211
Deductions from Revenue	4,386,738,942	4,088,740,893	3,736,411,693	3,349,882,012	3,063,219,162
Net Patient Revenue	3,417,476,549	3,275,172,077	3,045,784,697	2,850,639,970	2,712,283,049
Other Operating Revenue	121,878,449	112,919,384	126,674,850	110,674,336	118,067,679
Other Nonoperating Revenue	-23,074,370	48,098,253	185,293,240	136,656,471	17,706,306
Total Net Revenue	3,516,280,628	3,436,189,714	3,357,752,787	3,097,970,777	2,848,057,034
Total Expenses	3,246,810,925	3,130,591,165	2,946,252,827	2,744,800,158	2,662,272,646
HOSPITAL UNIT (Excludes Separate Nursing Home Units)					
Utilization - Inpatient					
Beds	2,059	2,106	2,053	2,034	1,998
Admissions	100,716	106,139	105,109	104,769	104,803
Inpatient Days	519,070	567,289	557,672	538,590	526,678
Average Length of Stay	5.2	5.3	5.3	5.1	5.0
Personnel					
Total Full Time	16,675	16,428	15,712	15,155	15,421
Total Part Time	5,952	6,177	5,971	5,682	5,918
Revenue and Expenses - Totals					
(Includes Inpatient and Outpatient)					
Total Net Revenue	$3,516,280,628	$3,436,189,714	$3,357,752,787	$3,097,970,777	$2,848,057,034
Total Expenses	3,246,810,925	3,130,591,165	2,946,252,827	2,744,800,158	2,662,272,646
COMMUNITY HEALTH INDICATORS PER 1000 POPULATION					
Total Population (in thousands)	952	946	936	926	917
Inpatient					
Beds	2.2	2.2	2.2	2.2	2.2
Admissions	105.8	112.2	112.3	113.2	114.3
Inpatient Days	545.2	599.7	596.0	581.8	574.3
Inpatient Surgeries	31.0	34.5	35.6	33.7	35.1
Births	12.0	11.9	12.0	11.9	12.4
Outpatient					
Emergency Outpatient Visits	493.0	490.4	482.4	477.2	477.3
Other Outpatient Visits	1,797.0	1,889.9	1,770.2	1,780.9	1,803.1
Total Outpatient Visits	2,290.0	2,380.2	2,252.6	2,258.1	2,280.4
Outpatient Surgeries	63.7	68.3	67.0	68.4	70.1
Expense per Capita (per person)	$3,410.3	$3,309.5	$3,149.0	$2,965.0	$2,903.0

States

TABLE 6

DISTRICT OF COLUMBIA

U.S. Registered Community Hospitals
(Nonfederal, short-term general and other special hospitals)

Overview 2012–2016

	2016	2015	2014	2013	2012
Total Community Hospitals in District of Columbia	11	11	11	11	11
Bed Size Category					
6-24	0	0	0	0	0
25-49	0	0	0	0	0
50-99	1	1	1	1	1
100-199	3	2	2	2	2
200-299	1	2	2	2	2
300-399	3	3	4	4	4
400-499	2	2	1	0	0
500 +	1	1	1	2	2
Location					
Hospitals Urban	11	11	11	11	11
Hospitals Rural	0	0	0	0	0
Control					
State and Local Government	0	0	0	1	1
Not for Profit	8	8	8	7	7
Investor owned	3	3	3	3	3
Physician Models					
Independent Practice Association	1	1	0	1	3
Group Practice without Walls	1	2	1	2	4
Open Physician-Hospital Organization	1	1	0	0	0
Closed Physician-Hospital Organization	2	2	2	2	3
Management Service Organization	3	3	0	1	3
Integrated Salary Model	6	6	4	4	5
Equity Model	0	0	0	0	0
Foundation	0	0	0	1	1
Insurance Products					
Health Maintenance Organization	3	4	4	4	5
Preferred Provider Organization	0	1	1	1	4
Indemnity Fee for Service	0	1	1	1	0
Managed Care Contracts					
Health Maintenance Organization	6	5	7	7	8
Preferred Provider Organization	6	5	6	7	7
Affiliations					
Hospitals in a System	8	8	8	8	8
Hospitals in a Network	0	0	1	2	1
Hospitals in a Group Purchasing Organization	5	6	7	9	9

TABLE 6

DISTRICT OF COLUMBIA

U.S. Registered Community Hospitals
(Nonfederal, short-term general and other special hospitals)

Utilization, Personnel, Revenue and Expenses, Community Health Indicators 2012–2016

	2016	2015	2014	2013	2012
TOTAL FACILITY (Includes Hospital and Nursing Home Units)					
Utilization - Inpatient					
Beds	3,449	3,590	3,542	3,609	3,617
Admissions	126,578	129,047	127,293	132,633	132,539
Inpatient Days	948,524	950,661	924,407	946,679	933,177
Average Length of Stay	7.5	7.4	7.3	7.1	7.0
Inpatient Surgeries	37,194	37,098	40,866	43,045	39,163
Births	14,725	13,139	13,689	13,718	13,783
Utilization - Outpatient					
Emergency Outpatient Visits	476,259	496,827	497,658	482,319	499,154
Other Outpatient Visits	2,129,340	2,251,154	2,155,117	2,095,979	1,961,067
Total Outpatient Visits	2,605,599	2,747,981	2,652,775	2,578,298	2,460,221
Outpatient Surgeries	65,550	63,068	66,333	72,560	66,622
Personnel					
Full Time RNs	6,278	6,294	6,097	5,930	5,647
Full Time LPNs	172	200	236	190	249
Part Time RNs	1,672	1,453	1,416	1,544	1,318
Part Time LPNs	33	36	57	27	38
Total Full Time	23,369	23,215	22,603	23,125	22,972
Total Part Time	4,553	4,481	4,350	3,984	3,313
Revenue - Inpatient					
Gross Inpatient Revenue	$8,407,719,505	$8,076,303,894	$7,521,916,741	$7,091,366,429	$6,515,832,670
Revenue - Outpatient					
Gross Outpatient Revenue	$5,626,000,810	$5,437,986,154	$4,731,589,184	$4,311,322,460	$3,968,228,093
Revenue and Expenses - Totals					
(Includes Inpatient and Outpatient)					
Total Gross Revenue	$14,033,720,315	$13,514,290,048	$12,253,505,925	$11,402,688,889	$10,484,060,763
Deductions from Revenue	9,464,321,731	9,162,113,899	8,288,747,229	7,509,944,561	6,640,686,593
Net Patient Revenue	4,569,398,584	4,352,176,149	3,964,758,696	3,892,744,328	3,843,374,170
Other Operating Revenue	288,482,386	298,773,643	267,439,583	300,528,852	299,523,683
Other Nonoperating Revenue	-1,681,270	30,835,705	124,213,686	118,719,257	-15,527,022
Total Net Revenue	4,856,199,700	4,681,785,497	4,356,411,965	4,311,992,437	4,127,370,831
Total Expenses	4,503,224,661	4,252,693,489	4,112,356,988	3,946,217,682	3,937,620,808
HOSPITAL UNIT (Excludes Separate Nursing Home Units)					
Utilization - Inpatient					
Beds	3,161	3,218	3,125	3,192	3,200
Admissions	125,103	128,394	125,602	130,885	130,696
Inpatient Days	846,819	823,863	782,484	802,846	791,242
Average Length of Stay	6.8	6.4	6.2	6.1	6.1
Personnel					
Total Full Time	23,308	23,079	22,285	23,026	22,602
Total Part Time	4,528	4,438	4,205	3,968	3,241
Revenue and Expenses - Totals					
(Includes Inpatient and Outpatient)					
Total Net Revenue	$4,820,039,291	$4,642,415,151	$4,306,684,083	$4,286,006,742	$4,074,614,436
Total Expenses	4,493,486,091	4,220,791,003	4,072,559,344	3,922,587,203	3,890,891,777
COMMUNITY HEALTH INDICATORS PER 1000 POPULATION					
Total Population (in thousands)	681	672	659	646	632
Inpatient					
Beds	5.1	5.3	5.4	5.6	5.7
Admissions	185.8	192.0	193.2	205.2	209.6
Inpatient Days	1,392.5	1,414.2	1,403.0	1,464.4	1,475.8
Inpatient Surgeries	54.6	55.2	62.0	66.6	61.9
Births	21.6	19.5	20.8	21.2	21.8
Outpatient					
Emergency Outpatient Visits	699.2	739.1	755.3	746.1	789.4
Other Outpatient Visits	3,126.0	3,348.8	3,270.8	3,242.3	3,101.4
Total Outpatient Visits	3,825.2	4,087.9	4,026.1	3,988.4	3,890.8
Outpatient Surgeries	96.2	93.8	100.7	112.2	105.4
Expense per Capita (per person)	$6,611.0	$6,326.3	$6,241.3	$6,104.5	$6,227.2

States

TABLE 6

FLORIDA

U.S. Registered Community Hospitals
(Nonfederal, short-term general and other special hospitals)

Overview 2012–2016

	2016	2015	2014	2013	2012
Total Community Hospitals in Florida...............	210	210	211	212	216
Bed Size Category					
6-24	7	5	4	3	4
25-49	19	21	22	24	23
50-99	41	41	40	40	39
100-199	48	49	50	50	55
200-299	37	38	36	37	37
300-399	25	23	24	24	25
400-499	13	14	13	11	10
500 + ...	20	19	22	23	23
Location					
Hospitals Urban	188	188	189	182	186
Hospitals Rural	22	22	22	30	30
Control					
State and Local Government	24	23	23	24	24
Not for Profit	78	79	79	79	80
Investor owned	108	108	109	109	112
Physician Models					
Independent Practice Association	5	5	3	3	3
Group Practice without Walls	4	4	5	7	6
Open Physician-Hospital Organization	19	16	15	15	19
Closed Physician-Hospital Organization	5	4	4	4	2
Management Service Organization	8	11	10	22	15
Integrated Salary Model	68	65	61	71	66
Equity Model	1	0	0	0	0
Foundation	2	0	1	1	2
Insurance Products					
Health Maintenance Organization	14	15	15	19	14
Preferred Provider Organization	17	18	13	15	7
Indemnity Fee for Service	11	12	8	8	4
Managed Care Contracts					
Health Maintenance Organization	103	96	104	107	100
Preferred Provider Organization	101	95	101	104	100
Affiliations					
Hospitals in a System	177	175	174	175	176
Hospitals in a Network	57	59	52	51	48
Hospitals in a Group Purchasing Organization...	114	112	116	112	113

TABLE 6

FLORIDA

U.S. Registered Community Hospitals
(Nonfederal, short-term general and other special hospitals)

Utilization, Personnel, Revenue and Expenses, Community Health Indicators 2012–2016

	2016	2015	2014	2013	2012
TOTAL FACILITY (Includes Hospital and Nursing Home Units)					
Utilization - Inpatient					
Beds	53,708	53,019	53,489	53,198	53,785
Admissions	2,543,053	2,511,751	2,473,183	2,407,117	2,472,181
Inpatient Days	12,753,577	12,545,929	12,310,835	12,063,283	12,372,261
Average Length of Stay	5.0	5.0	5.0	5.0	5.0
Inpatient Surgeries	618,227	604,156	591,885	602,806	610,533
Births	217,309	210,362	196,237	198,157	196,681
Utilization - Outpatient					
Emergency Outpatient Visits	9,417,424	9,054,011	9,063,174	8,436,473	8,126,914
Other Outpatient Visits	16,957,973	17,101,751	16,532,903	15,558,477	15,367,371
Total Outpatient Visits	26,375,397	26,155,762	25,596,077	23,994,950	23,494,285
Outpatient Surgeries	884,650	853,309	836,401	837,962	800,782
Personnel					
Full Time RNs	80,799	79,414	75,406	72,327	74,829
Full Time LPNs	2,868	2,828	2,785	3,041	3,495
Part Time RNs	21,663	22,102	19,981	20,562	18,183
Part Time LPNs	810	826	736	836	885
Total Full Time	249,929	246,067	234,719	229,333	239,356
Total Part Time	61,087	63,436	57,735	58,340	55,168
Revenue - Inpatient					
Gross Inpatient Revenue	$145,467,021,024	$134,062,068,432	$120,899,048,988	$113,515,265,844	$106,765,072,734
Revenue - Outpatient					
Gross Outpatient Revenue	$107,595,419,335	$96,489,480,868	$85,284,740,554	$77,113,649,369	$70,527,318,626
Revenue and Expenses - Totals					
(Includes Inpatient and Outpatient)					
Total Gross Revenue	$253,062,440,359	$230,551,549,300	$206,183,789,542	$190,628,915,213	$177,292,391,360
Deductions from Revenue	202,035,663,472	182,356,265,448	160,812,813,895	148,060,768,748	135,271,195,802
Net Patient Revenue	51,026,776,887	48,195,283,852	45,370,975,647	42,568,146,465	42,021,195,558
Other Operating Revenue	2,414,644,644	2,486,724,609	2,263,801,087	2,224,603,404	2,402,722,300
Other Nonoperating Revenue	774,499,594	386,579,354	714,150,459	681,074,241	498,972,173
Total Net Revenue	54,215,921,125	51,068,587,815	48,348,927,193	45,473,824,110	44,922,890,031
Total Expenses	47,056,719,067	45,563,477,611	42,851,681,447	41,035,030,196	40,816,430,398
HOSPITAL UNIT (Excludes Separate Nursing Home Units)					
Utilization - Inpatient					
Beds	52,823	52,016	52,496	52,204	52,723
Admissions	2,538,287	2,506,439	2,467,786	2,401,783	2,465,633
Inpatient Days	12,472,272	12,225,861	11,981,943	11,737,932	12,021,523
Average Length of Stay	4.9	4.9	4.9	4.9	4.9
Personnel					
Total Full Time	248,936	245,061	233,358	228,398	238,286
Total Part Time	60,806	63,107	57,444	58,061	54,951
Revenue and Expenses - Totals					
(Includes Inpatient and Outpatient)					
Total Net Revenue	$54,128,698,196	$50,942,840,873	$48,243,102,108	$45,368,763,076	$44,817,002,142
Total Expenses	46,955,065,641	45,432,435,940	42,734,599,088	40,928,021,253	40,697,886,032
COMMUNITY HEALTH INDICATORS PER 1000 POPULATION					
Total Population (in thousands)	20,612	20,271	19,893	19,553	19,318
Inpatient					
Beds	2.6	2.6	2.7	2.7	2.8
Admissions	123.4	123.9	124.3	123.1	128.0
Inpatient Days	618.7	618.9	618.8	617.0	640.5
Inpatient Surgeries	30.0	29.8	29.8	30.8	31.6
Births	10.5	10.4	9.9	10.1	10.2
Outpatient					
Emergency Outpatient Visits	456.9	446.6	455.6	431.5	420.7
Other Outpatient Visits	822.7	843.6	831.1	795.7	795.5
Total Outpatient Visits	1,279.6	1,290.3	1,286.7	1,227.2	1,216.2
Outpatient Surgeries	42.9	42.1	42.0	42.9	41.5
Expense per Capita (per person)	$2,282.9	$2,247.7	$2,154.1	$2,098.7	$2,112.9

States

TABLE 6

GEORGIA

U.S. Registered Community Hospitals
(Nonfederal, short-term general and other special hospitals)

Overview 2012–2016

	2016	2015	2014	2013	2012
Total Community Hospitals in Georgia	141	141	142	144	148
Bed Size Category					
6-24	5	5	3	4	4
25-49	38	37	41	40	38
50-99	23	23	22	25	25
100-199	35	36	35	33	39
200-299	12	12	14	15	18
300-399	10	9	9	8	6
400-499	6	7	7	9	10
500 + ...	12	12	11	10	8
Location					
Hospitals Urban	85	85	85	84	86
Hospitals Rural	56	56	57	60	62
Control					
State and Local Government	40	48	47	46	49
Not for Profit	76	67	64	67	66
Investor owned	25	26	31	31	33
Physician Models					
Independent Practice Association	8	12	10	8	5
Group Practice without Walls	0	1	3	0	0
Open Physician-Hospital Organization	8	8	9	12	12
Closed Physician-Hospital Organization	16	17	18	18	18
Management Service Organization	3	3	3	5	7
Integrated Salary Model	39	42	34	34	35
Equity Model	2	2	2	2	2
Foundation	2	2	3	5	3
Insurance Products					
Health Maintenance Organization	4	7	11	7	6
Preferred Provider Organization	7	10	11	10	8
Indemnity Fee for Service	2	2	2	2	2
Managed Care Contracts					
Health Maintenance Organization	62	62	64	67	67
Preferred Provider Organization	65	65	69	74	72
Affiliations					
Hospitals in a System	87	86	84	81	78
Hospitals in a Network	37	43	38	38	36
Hospitals in a Group Purchasing Organization...	75	76	78	83	76

TABLE 6

GEORGIA

U.S. Registered Community Hospitals
(Nonfederal, short-term general and other special hospitals)

Utilization, Personnel, Revenue and Expenses, Community Health Indicators 2012–2016

	2016	2015	2014	2013	2012
TOTAL FACILITY (Includes Hospital and Nursing Home Units)					
Utilization - Inpatient					
Beds	24,758	24,507	24,479	24,729	24,657
Admissions	980,496	967,694	941,742	947,299	953,817
Inpatient Days	6,197,094	6,120,557	6,140,718	6,034,948	5,970,497
Average Length of Stay	6.3	6.3	6.5	6.4	6.3
Inpatient Surgeries	258,708	255,344	255,921	259,747	257,747
Births	123,918	125,173	121,828	119,564	119,564
Utilization - Outpatient					
Emergency Outpatient Visits	4,611,446	4,383,403	4,114,916	4,221,105	4,153,101
Other Outpatient Visits	14,230,952	12,329,171	11,345,271	11,801,504	10,881,116
Total Outpatient Visits	18,842,398	16,712,574	15,460,187	16,022,609	15,034,217
Outpatient Surgeries	480,363	467,737	458,180	467,792	474,453
Personnel					
Full Time RNs	35,059	35,038	34,129	32,648	31,786
Full Time LPNs	2,495	2,358	2,317	2,359	2,866
Part Time RNs	11,413	10,782	10,269	9,376	9,066
Part Time LPNs	671	642	561	628	591
Total Full Time	124,300	120,736	117,568	114,844	111,769
Total Part Time	33,473	31,762	29,727	27,612	26,565
Revenue - Inpatient					
Gross Inpatient Revenue	$43,551,568,422	$41,748,486,003	$38,624,004,575	$36,086,097,252	$32,638,245,514
Revenue - Outpatient					
Gross Outpatient Revenue	$41,371,423,432	$38,559,320,810	$34,584,791,447	$31,192,879,578	$26,952,133,432
Revenue and Expenses - Totals					
(Includes Inpatient and Outpatient)					
Total Gross Revenue	$84,922,991,854	$80,307,806,813	$73,208,796,022	$67,278,976,830	$59,590,378,946
Deductions from Revenue	61,278,323,530	57,865,930,136	52,515,635,482	47,570,657,745	41,286,051,494
Net Patient Revenue	23,644,668,324	22,441,876,677	20,693,160,540	19,708,319,085	18,304,327,452
Other Operating Revenue	1,154,309,784	1,041,324,596	933,337,513	938,355,641	896,928,314
Other Nonoperating Revenue	11,264,347	154,571,394	492,130,104	591,589,397	313,593,866
Total Net Revenue	24,810,242,455	23,637,772,667	22,118,628,157	21,238,264,123	19,514,849,632
Total Expenses	23,013,231,110	21,494,965,992	19,975,006,680	19,519,696,158	17,663,914,623
HOSPITAL UNIT (Excludes Separate Nursing Home Units)					
Utilization - Inpatient					
Beds	21,767	21,584	21,623	21,808	21,695
Admissions	973,533	961,067	936,020	939,876	947,058
Inpatient Days	5,208,088	5,107,608	5,203,686	5,145,091	4,988,750
Average Length of Stay	5.3	5.3	5.6	5.5	5.3
Personnel					
Total Full Time	122,395	118,589	115,697	113,000	109,799
Total Part Time	33,083	31,187	29,400	27,296	26,140
Revenue and Expenses - Totals					
(Includes Inpatient and Outpatient)					
Total Net Revenue	$24,640,410,232	$23,449,564,419	$21,950,548,763	$21,061,224,646	$19,343,288,346
Total Expenses	22,857,743,576	21,327,791,868	19,831,945,852	19,365,889,564	17,517,267,271
COMMUNITY HEALTH INDICATORS PER 1000 POPULATION					
Total Population (in thousands)	10,310	10,215	10,097	9,992	9,920
Inpatient					
Beds	2.4	2.4	2.4	2.5	2.5
Admissions	95.1	94.7	93.3	94.8	96.2
Inpatient Days	601.1	599.2	608.2	604.0	601.9
Inpatient Surgeries	25.1	25.0	25.3	26.0	26.0
Births	12.0	12.3	12.1	12.0	12.1
Outpatient					
Emergency Outpatient Visits	447.3	429.1	407.5	422.4	418.7
Other Outpatient Visits	1,380.3	1,207.0	1,123.6	1,181.1	1,096.9
Total Outpatient Visits	1,827.5	1,636.1	1,531.1	1,603.5	1,515.6
Outpatient Surgeries	46.6	45.8	45.4	46.8	47.8
Expense per Capita (per person)	$2,232.0	$2,104.3	$1,978.2	$1,953.5	$1,780.6

States

TABLE 6

HAWAII

U.S. Registered Community Hospitals
(Nonfederal, short-term general and other special hospitals)

Overview 2012–2016

	2016	2015	2014	2013	2012
Total Community Hospitals in Hawaii	23	24	25	25	24
Bed Size Category					
6-24	6	6	6	6	5
25-49	3	3	3	3	3
50-99	5	5	6	6	6
100-199	6	7	5	5	5
200-299	2	2	4	4	4
300-399	0	0	0	0	0
400-499	0	0	0	1	1
500 + ...	1	1	1	0	0
Location					
Hospitals Urban	15	16	16	12	12
Hospitals Rural	8	8	9	13	12
Control					
State and Local Government	6	9	10	9	10
Not for Profit	17	15	15	16	14
Investor owned	0	0	0	0	0
Physician Models					
Independent Practice Association	2	2	1	2	2
Group Practice without Walls	0	0	0	0	0
Open Physician-Hospital Organization	4	2	3	2	2
Closed Physician-Hospital Organization	2	2	2	2	3
Management Service Organization	0	0	0	0	0
Integrated Salary Model	6	7	7	6	9
Equity Model	0	0	0	0	0
Foundation	1	0	0	0	0
Insurance Products					
Health Maintenance Organization	2	1	1	1	1
Preferred Provider Organization	1	0	0	0	0
Indemnity Fee for Service	1	0	0	0	0
Managed Care Contracts					
Health Maintenance Organization	12	13	13	12	14
Preferred Provider Organization	12	13	12	12	14
Affiliations					
Hospitals in a System	19	20	21	20	19
Hospitals in a Network	7	6	8	4	3
Hospitals in a Group Purchasing Organization...	13	16	14	13	15

TABLE 6

HAWAII

U.S. Registered Community Hospitals
(Nonfederal, short-term general and other special hospitals)

Utilization, Personnel, Revenue and Expenses, Community Health Indicators 2012–2016

	2016	2015	2014	2013	2012
TOTAL FACILITY (Includes Hospital and Nursing Home Units)					
Utilization - Inpatient					
Beds	2,488	2,645	2,861	2,817	2,803
Admissions	110,104	110,061	109,311	110,374	109,270
Inpatient Days	703,010	717,607	749,201	760,960	745,956
Average Length of Stay	6.4	6.5	6.9	6.9	6.8
Inpatient Surgeries	29,232	30,138	26,095	26,137	27,141
Births	18,495	17,140	10,626	10,229	11,085
Utilization - Outpatient					
Emergency Outpatient Visits	468,601	487,500	432,641	401,191	399,437
Other Outpatient Visits	2,107,180	1,962,647	1,858,155	1,752,696	1,635,223
Total Outpatient Visits	2,575,781	2,450,147	2,290,796	2,153,887	2,034,660
Outpatient Surgeries	58,636	56,872	51,497	47,416	48,246
Personnel					
Full Time RNs	4,510	4,331	4,331	4,045	3,863
Full Time LPNs	170	198	196	221	253
Part Time RNs	1,413	1,487	1,362	963	867
Part Time LPNs	48	43	47	37	46
Total Full Time	15,310	15,195	15,011	14,561	15,008
Total Part Time	3,973	4,007	3,762	2,660	3,143
Revenue - Inpatient					
Gross Inpatient Revenue	$4,781,623,649	$4,577,583,888	$4,181,164,838	$4,009,282,994	$4,003,578,286
Revenue - Outpatient					
Gross Outpatient Revenue	$4,718,970,176	$4,190,277,597	$3,730,384,969	$3,536,452,224	$3,523,042,969
Revenue and Expenses - Totals					
(Includes Inpatient and Outpatient)					
Total Gross Revenue	$9,500,593,825	$8,767,861,485	$7,911,549,807	$7,545,735,218	$7,526,621,255
Deductions from Revenue	6,134,403,356	5,555,573,283	5,025,528,223	4,709,531,039	4,871,561,656
Net Patient Revenue	3,366,190,469	3,212,288,202	2,886,021,584	2,836,204,179	2,655,059,599
Other Operating Revenue	217,984,188	233,450,364	208,715,461	208,314,941	202,568,356
Other Nonoperating Revenue	30,217,539	54,891,387	63,534,103	132,431,586	35,719,144
Total Net Revenue	3,614,392,196	3,500,629,953	3,158,271,148	3,176,950,706	2,893,347,099
Total Expenses	3,556,186,542	3,350,489,890	3,148,443,424	2,917,345,070	2,855,849,784
HOSPITAL UNIT (Excludes Separate Nursing Home Units)					
Utilization - Inpatient					
Beds	2,360	2,320	2,630	2,523	2,355
Admissions	109,558	108,928	108,182	108,687	107,534
Inpatient Days	671,095	610,787	680,962	660,686	644,358
Average Length of Stay	6.1	5.6	6.3	6.1	6.0
Personnel					
Total Full Time	15,265	14,918	14,838	14,355	14,408
Total Part Time	3,953	3,953	3,729	2,623	3,077
Revenue and Expenses - Totals					
(Includes Inpatient and Outpatient)					
Total Net Revenue	$3,596,598,513	$3,450,094,108	$3,125,503,974	$3,149,956,310	$2,828,961,559
Total Expenses	3,543,403,181	3,306,636,383	3,120,902,400	2,886,933,350	2,775,697,478
COMMUNITY HEALTH INDICATORS PER 1000 POPULATION					
Total Population (in thousands)	1,429	1,432	1,420	1,404	1,392
Inpatient					
Beds	1.7	1.8	2.0	2.0	2.0
Admissions	77.1	76.9	77.0	78.6	78.5
Inpatient Days	492.1	501.3	527.8	542.0	535.8
Inpatient Surgeries	20.5	21.1	18.4	18.6	19.5
Births	12.9	12.0	7.5	7.3	8.0
Outpatient					
Emergency Outpatient Visits	328.0	340.5	304.8	285.7	286.9
Other Outpatient Visits	1,475.0	1,370.9	1,309.0	1,248.3	1,174.5
Total Outpatient Visits	1,803.1	1,711.5	1,613.7	1,534.0	1,461.4
Outpatient Surgeries	41.0	39.7	36.3	33.8	34.7
Expense per Capita (per person)	$2,489.4	$2,340.4	$2,217.9	$2,077.8	$2,051.2

TABLE 6

IDAHO

U.S. Registered Community Hospitals
(Nonfederal, short-term general and other special hospitals)

Overview 2012–2016

	2016	2015	2014	2013	2012
Total Community Hospitals in Idaho	40	40	40	40	40
Bed Size Category					
6-24	14	12	12	12	11
25-49	10	11	11	10	13
50-99	8	9	9	9	7
100-199	3	3	3	4	5
200-299	3	2	2	2	1
300-399	1	2	2	2	2
400-499	0	0	0	0	0
500 +	1	1	1	1	1
Location					
Hospitals Urban	14	14	14	14	14
Hospitals Rural	26	26	26	26	26
Control					
State and Local Government	18	18	19	18	19
Not for Profit	17	17	16	17	16
Investor owned	5	5	5	5	5
Physician Models					
Independent Practice Association	1	1	1	1	4
Group Practice without Walls	0	0	0	0	0
Open Physician-Hospital Organization	6	5	6	6	10
Closed Physician-Hospital Organization	1	2	3	1	1
Management Service Organization	0	1	0	0	0
Integrated Salary Model	13	13	14	14	15
Equity Model	1	1	1	1	1
Foundation	1	2	2	1	1
Insurance Products					
Health Maintenance Organization	1	1	1	1	0
Preferred Provider Organization	2	2	3	2	2
Indemnity Fee for Service	1	1	2	1	1
Managed Care Contracts					
Health Maintenance Organization	12	11	12	12	14
Preferred Provider Organization	17	14	19	17	17
Affiliations					
Hospitals in a System	21	21	21	20	21
Hospitals in a Network	12	13	10	9	10
Hospitals in a Group Purchasing Organization	25	23	23	24	26

TABLE 6

IDAHO

U.S. Registered Community Hospitals
(Nonfederal, short-term general and other special hospitals)

Utilization, Personnel, Revenue and Expenses, Community Health Indicators 2012–2016

	2016	2015	2014	2013	2012
TOTAL FACILITY (Includes Hospital and Nursing Home Units)					
Utilization - Inpatient					
Beds	3,296	3,333	3,311	3,355	3,305
Admissions	130,266	128,634	121,728	126,164	123,794
Inpatient Days	654,000	624,322	593,788	609,999	611,785
Average Length of Stay	5.0	4.9	4.9	4.8	4.9
Inpatient Surgeries	36,187	35,664	35,856	36,416	40,313
Births	19,192	20,122	19,845	19,285	20,117
Utilization - Outpatient					
Emergency Outpatient Visits	668,997	676,265	627,163	590,382	543,272
Other Outpatient Visits	4,836,534	5,133,017	4,577,820	4,187,775	3,807,298
Total Outpatient Visits	5,505,531	5,809,282	5,204,983	4,778,157	4,350,570
Outpatient Surgeries	91,434	88,587	86,554	76,661	81,915
Personnel					
Full Time RNs	5,415	5,510	5,076	4,878	4,651
Full Time LPNs	462	453	438	448	443
Part Time RNs	2,281	2,444	2,583	2,688	2,418
Part Time LPNs	165	165	189	201	193
Total Full Time	25,966	25,147	23,357	22,143	20,340
Total Part Time	7,731	8,194	8,861	8,840	8,192
Revenue - Inpatient					
Gross Inpatient Revenue	$5,628,637,883	$5,103,598,447	$4,648,452,893	$4,216,564,570	$3,543,382,140
Revenue - Outpatient					
Gross Outpatient Revenue	$6,802,035,679	$6,092,495,488	$5,438,016,219	$4,739,814,434	$4,029,848,296
Revenue and Expenses - Totals					
(Includes Inpatient and Outpatient)					
Total Gross Revenue	$12,430,673,562	$11,196,093,935	$10,086,469,112	$8,956,379,004	$7,573,230,436
Deductions from Revenue	7,720,679,365	6,850,280,506	6,053,377,363	5,257,575,535	4,057,678,208
Net Patient Revenue	4,709,994,197	4,345,813,429	4,033,091,749	3,698,803,469	3,515,552,228
Other Operating Revenue	142,699,588	135,272,070	125,368,316	149,063,415	116,996,412
Other Nonoperating Revenue	29,484,197	14,727,710	56,565,814	38,229,484	17,730,950
Total Net Revenue	4,882,177,982	4,495,813,209	4,215,025,879	3,886,096,368	3,650,279,590
Total Expenses	4,455,756,852	4,093,530,211	3,792,866,699	3,549,202,960	3,127,967,915
HOSPITAL UNIT (Excludes Separate Nursing Home Units)					
Utilization - Inpatient					
Beds	3,091	3,088	3,136	3,087	3,041
Admissions	129,866	128,166	121,467	125,217	122,840
Inpatient Days	595,313	559,858	543,992	536,798	536,537
Average Length of Stay	4.6	4.4	4.5	4.3	4.4
Personnel					
Total Full Time	25,843	24,997	23,228	21,912	20,159
Total Part Time	7,659	8,076	8,761	8,716	8,074
Revenue and Expenses - Totals					
(Includes Inpatient and Outpatient)					
Total Net Revenue	$4,863,651,769	$4,478,203,471	$4,202,706,609	$3,858,606,336	$3,630,538,385
Total Expenses	4,443,911,938	4,080,873,555	3,779,790,525	3,530,094,122	3,117,054,550
COMMUNITY HEALTH INDICATORS PER 1000 POPULATION					
Total Population (in thousands)	1,683	1,655	1,634	1,612	1,596
Inpatient					
Beds	2.0	2.0	2.0	2.1	2.1
Admissions	77.4	77.7	74.5	78.3	77.6
Inpatient Days	388.6	377.2	363.3	378.4	383.4
Inpatient Surgeries	21.5	21.6	21.9	22.6	25.3
Births	11.4	12.2	12.1	12.0	12.6
Outpatient					
Emergency Outpatient Visits	397.5	408.6	383.7	366.2	340.5
Other Outpatient Visits	2,873.5	3,101.7	2,800.8	2,597.7	2,385.9
Total Outpatient Visits	3,271.0	3,510.3	3,184.5	2,963.9	2,726.4
Outpatient Surgeries	54.3	53.5	53.0	47.6	51.3
Expense per Capita (per person)	$2,647.3	$2,473.5	$2,320.6	$2,201.6	$1,960.2

States

TABLE **6**

ILLINOIS

U.S. Registered Community Hospitals
(Nonfederal, short-term general and other special hospitals)

Overview 2012–2016

	2016	2015	2014	2013	2012
Total Community Hospitals in Illinois	188	188	189	189	188
Bed Size Category					
6-24	14	16	14	13	12
25-49	35	35	36	37	38
50-99	31	29	29	29	27
100-199	49	49	55	54	53
200-299	29	29	25	25	22
300-399	15	16	16	17	20
400-499	7	6	6	6	9
500 + ...	8	8	8	8	7
Location					
Hospitals Urban	130	130	130	125	124
Hospitals Rural	58	58	59	64	64
Control					
State and Local Government	23	24	24	23	24
Not for Profit	144	143	144	146	144
Investor owned	21	21	21	20	20
Physician Models					
Independent Practice Association	23	31	26	24	26
Group Practice without Walls	4	10	10	12	8
Open Physician-Hospital Organization	54	53	53	56	46
Closed Physician-Hospital Organization	12	10	10	11	9
Management Service Organization	21	17	19	19	21
Integrated Salary Model	70	72	74	71	63
Equity Model	4	4	4	5	3
Foundation	8	8	9	10	8
Insurance Products					
Health Maintenance Organization	24	21	23	25	21
Preferred Provider Organization	14	15	15	17	13
Indemnity Fee for Service	6	7	7	6	4
Managed Care Contracts					
Health Maintenance Organization	124	128	123	120	122
Preferred Provider Organization	138	139	135	136	137
Affiliations					
Hospitals in a System	125	125	120	118	114
Hospitals in a Network	76	70	67	58	52
Hospitals in a Group Purchasing Organization...	143	149	151	149	145

States

TABLE 6

ILLINOIS

U.S. Registered Community Hospitals
(Nonfederal, short-term general and other special hospitals)

Utilization, Personnel, Revenue and Expenses, Community Health Indicators 2012–2016

	2016	2015	2014	2013	2012
TOTAL FACILITY (Includes Hospital and Nursing Home Units)					
Utilization - Inpatient					
Beds	31,805	31,823	31,573	31,745	32,662
Admissions	1,374,759	1,385,953	1,380,085	1,426,848	1,484,155
Inpatient Days	6,889,705	6,827,990	6,841,826	6,865,573	7,190,230
Average Length of Stay	5.0	4.9	5.0	4.8	4.8
Inpatient Surgeries	347,458	354,815	360,213	368,428	376,684
Births	146,341	148,744	147,464	146,392	150,234
Utilization - Outpatient					
Emergency Outpatient Visits	5,516,659	5,556,422	5,273,213	5,252,340	5,422,193
Other Outpatient Visits	32,536,797	32,014,417	28,160,509	27,556,186	27,694,668
Total Outpatient Visits	38,053,456	37,570,839	33,433,722	32,808,526	33,116,861
Outpatient Surgeries	739,804	755,329	736,891	743,687	728,808
Personnel					
Full Time RNs	50,348	49,064	47,039	46,160	44,894
Full Time LPNs	1,432	1,448	1,468	1,679	1,684
Part Time RNs	21,808	23,064	23,887	21,818	23,656
Part Time LPNs	512	529	558	633	690
Total Full Time	176,472	173,895	170,080	168,524	168,745
Total Part Time	69,922	72,077	75,417	70,370	72,684
Revenue - Inpatient					
Gross Inpatient Revenue	$65,186,844,391	$61,802,651,499	$59,479,867,913	$55,496,665,893	$54,040,034,827
Revenue - Outpatient					
Gross Outpatient Revenue	$72,354,495,169	$67,143,188,040	$62,657,072,479	$55,220,592,255	$51,085,072,799
Revenue and Expenses - Totals					
(Includes Inpatient and Outpatient)					
Total Gross Revenue	$137,541,339,560	$128,945,839,539	$122,136,940,392	$110,717,258,148	$105,125,107,626
Deductions from Revenue	99,536,570,720	92,652,197,929	86,861,936,578	78,196,471,517	73,249,630,932
Net Patient Revenue	38,004,768,840	36,293,641,610	35,275,003,814	32,520,786,631	31,875,476,694
Other Operating Revenue	1,829,822,163	2,137,345,481	2,092,681,737	2,131,938,656	1,930,010,171
Other Nonoperating Revenue	1,722,471,524	163,550,113	1,406,842,660	1,098,662,582	597,357,110
Total Net Revenue	41,557,062,527	38,594,537,204	38,774,528,211	35,751,387,869	34,402,843,975
Total Expenses	37,012,400,899	35,872,183,416	35,123,918,794	32,752,851,815	31,914,764,033
HOSPITAL UNIT (Excludes Separate Nursing Home Units)					
Utilization - Inpatient					
Beds	30,800	30,729	30,374	30,716	31,431
Admissions	1,366,225	1,377,209	1,369,430	1,417,171	1,471,741
Inpatient Days	6,619,365	6,549,361	6,547,258	6,623,180	6,891,159
Average Length of Stay	4.8	4.8	4.8	4.7	4.7
Personnel					
Total Full Time	176,018	173,327	169,603	167,903	168,056
Total Part Time	69,607	71,658	75,033	69,892	72,171
Revenue and Expenses - Totals					
(Includes Inpatient and Outpatient)					
Total Net Revenue	$41,345,981,599	$38,393,201,864	$38,682,715,068	$35,673,229,824	$34,307,140,177
Total Expenses	36,918,137,788	35,779,914,464	35,048,528,192	32,686,336,226	31,835,376,910
COMMUNITY HEALTH INDICATORS PER 1000 POPULATION					
Total Population (in thousands)	12,802	12,860	12,881	12,882	12,875
Inpatient					
Beds	2.5	2.5	2.5	2.5	2.5
Admissions	107.4	107.8	107.1	110.8	115.3
Inpatient Days	538.2	530.9	531.2	533.0	558.5
Inpatient Surgeries	27.1	27.6	28.0	28.6	29.3
Births	11.4	11.6	11.4	11.4	11.7
Outpatient					
Emergency Outpatient Visits	430.9	432.1	409.4	407.7	421.1
Other Outpatient Visits	2,541.6	2,489.5	2,186.3	2,139.1	2,151.0
Total Outpatient Visits	2,972.6	2,921.5	2,595.7	2,546.8	2,572.1
Outpatient Surgeries	57.8	58.7	57.2	57.7	56.6
Expense per Capita (per person)	$2,891.2	$2,789.4	$2,726.9	$2,542.5	$2,478.8

States

TABLE 6

INDIANA

U.S. Registered Community Hospitals
(Nonfederal, short-term general and other special hospitals)

Overview 2012–2016

	2016	2015	2014	2013	2012
Total Community Hospitals in Indiana	119	120	121	123	124
Bed Size Category					
6-24	8	7	8	6	6
25-49	39	41	40	42	40
50-99	22	22	23	26	28
100-199	23	23	26	23	24
200-299	13	12	9	12	11
300-399	4	4	4	3	5
400-499	5	5	6	6	4
500 + ...	5	6	5	5	6
Location					
Hospitals Urban	78	78	79	83	84
Hospitals Rural	41	42	42	40	40
Control					
State and Local Government	26	27	30	30	30
Not for Profit	68	68	67	68	69
Investor owned	25	25	24	25	25
Physician Models					
Independent Practice Association	8	7	7	5	7
Group Practice without Walls	5	6	4	4	5
Open Physician-Hospital Organization	20	18	19	23	21
Closed Physician-Hospital Organization	4	4	5	5	8
Management Service Organization	6	7	8	9	7
Integrated Salary Model	59	61	62	61	58
Equity Model	2	2	4	4	3
Foundation	5	4	6	6	4
Insurance Products					
Health Maintenance Organization	38	38	34	31	28
Preferred Provider Organization	31	28	28	35	29
Indemnity Fee for Service	8	8	7	9	9
Managed Care Contracts					
Health Maintenance Organization	68	74	72	64	64
Preferred Provider Organization	80	81	82	78	76
Affiliations					
Hospitals in a System	86	87	87	86	85
Hospitals in a Network	45	44	48	45	42
Hospitals in a Group Purchasing Organization...	95	91	95	96	92

TABLE 6

INDIANA

U.S. Registered Community Hospitals
(Nonfederal, short-term general and other special hospitals)

Utilization, Personnel, Revenue and Expenses, Community Health Indicators 2012–2016

	2016	2015	2014	2013	2012
TOTAL FACILITY (Includes Hospital and Nursing Home Units)					
Utilization - Inpatient					
Beds.................................	16,947	17,326	17,193	17,264	17,556
Admissions.........................	669,044	672,370	681,537	701,743	731,046
Inpatient Days....................	3,502,421	3,582,895	3,567,957	3,653,922	3,739,056
Average Length of Stay........	5.2	5.3	5.2	5.2	5.1
Inpatient Surgeries..............	181,819	175,529	180,347	186,776	200,708
Births................................	72,730	71,805	72,348	71,984	73,460
Utilization - Outpatient					
Emergency Outpatient Visits....	3,316,584	3,357,931	3,261,594	3,129,456	3,207,214
Other Outpatient Visits.........	17,110,362	16,096,087	15,922,420	15,270,100	14,711,090
Total Outpatient Visits.........	20,426,946	19,454,018	19,184,014	18,399,556	17,918,304
Outpatient Surgeries............	427,134	403,271	402,487	420,844	441,917
Personnel					
Full Time RNs....................	23,038	22,867	22,750	23,370	23,611
Full Time LPNs..................	1,107	1,207	1,283	1,468	1,536
Part Time RNs...................	15,118	13,111	13,871	14,311	14,379
Part Time LPNs.................	547	561	619	711	722
Total Full Time..................	88,060	86,907	86,732	87,286	88,265
Total Part Time..................	42,424	38,274	41,307	41,032	41,617
Revenue - Inpatient					
Gross Inpatient Revenue..........	$32,268,597,293	$30,478,063,917	$28,291,483,706	$26,593,801,942	$26,099,729,709
Revenue - Outpatient					
Gross Outpatient Revenue........	$36,959,751,198	$33,470,699,258	$30,389,753,127	$28,186,114,204	$26,487,465,316
Revenue and Expenses - Totals					
(Includes Inpatient and Outpatient)					
Total Gross Revenue.............	$69,228,348,491	$63,948,763,175	$58,681,236,833	$54,779,916,146	$52,587,195,025
Deductions from Revenue	48,047,934,472	43,619,240,443	38,981,153,394	36,132,735,438	33,296,640,742
Net Patient Revenue.............	21,180,414,019	20,329,522,732	19,700,083,439	18,647,180,708	19,290,554,283
Other Operating Revenue........	1,716,659,183	1,468,183,472	1,263,877,365	1,042,257,524	1,104,200,980
Other Nonoperating Revenue....	404,857,815	-36,961,288	475,251,971	607,370,565	439,930,085
Total Net Revenue...............	23,301,931,017	21,760,744,916	21,439,212,775	20,296,808,797	20,834,685,348
Total Expenses..................	20,473,531,919	18,765,776,017	18,019,558,162	17,893,508,316	17,926,526,564
HOSPITAL UNIT (Excludes Separate Nursing Home Units)					
Utilization - Inpatient					
Beds.................................	16,197	16,287	16,445	16,552	16,911
Admissions.........................	666,163	669,283	678,617	698,347	726,693
Inpatient Days....................	3,303,806	3,307,741	3,351,720	3,442,577	3,569,377
Average Length of Stay........	5.0	4.9	4.9	4.9	4.9
Personnel					
Total Full Time..................	87,703	86,200	86,234	86,819	87,873
Total Part Time..................	42,066	37,797	40,871	40,642	41,296
Revenue and Expenses - Totals					
(Includes Inpatient and Outpatient)					
Total Net Revenue...............	$23,239,280,569	$21,672,420,917	$21,372,452,682	$20,233,420,523	$20,781,574,841
Total Expenses..................	20,433,508,703	18,698,338,078	17,965,282,386	17,841,711,211	17,894,880,475
COMMUNITY HEALTH INDICATORS PER 1000 POPULATION					
Total Population (in thousands)..........	6,633	6,620	6,597	6,571	6,537
Inpatient					
Beds.................................	2.6	2.6	2.6	2.6	2.7
Admissions.........................	100.9	101.6	103.3	106.8	111.8
Inpatient Days....................	528.0	541.2	540.9	556.1	572.0
Inpatient Surgeries..............	27.4	26.5	27.3	28.4	30.7
Births................................	11.0	10.8	11.0	11.0	11.2
Outpatient					
Emergency Outpatient Visits..............	500.0	507.3	494.4	476.3	490.6
Other Outpatient Visits.........	2,579.6	2,431.6	2,413.6	2,323.9	2,250.3
Total Outpatient Visits.........	3,079.6	2,938.8	2,908.1	2,800.2	2,740.9
Outpatient Surgeries............	64.4	60.9	61.0	64.0	67.6
Expense per Capita (per person).........	$3,086.6	$2,834.8	$2,731.5	$2,723.1	$2,742.2

States

TABLE 6   IOWA

U.S. Registered Community Hospitals
(Nonfederal, short-term general and other special hospitals)

Overview 2012–2016

	2016	2015	2014	2013	2012
Total Community Hospitals in Iowa	117	118	118	118	118
Bed Size Category					
6-24	24	21	21	20	19
25-49	48	51	50	49	48
50-99	20	22	23	26	26
100-199	11	10	10	9	11
200-299	7	7	7	6	6
300-399	4	4	4	5	5
400-499	0	0	0	1	1
500 +	3	3	3	2	2
Location					
Hospitals Urban	34	35	35	34	34
Hospitals Rural	83	83	83	84	84
Control					
State and Local Government	58	59	59	59	59
Not for Profit	57	57	57	57	57
Investor owned	2	2	2	2	2
Physician Models					
Independent Practice Association	8	10	13	13	14
Group Practice without Walls	2	2	3	5	5
Open Physician-Hospital Organization	17	17	18	20	19
Closed Physician-Hospital Organization	11	10	10	11	11
Management Service Organization	6	7	7	8	8
Integrated Salary Model	77	77	76	77	76
Equity Model	1	1	1	1	1
Foundation	3	3	3	4	3
Insurance Products					
Health Maintenance Organization	19	20	19	14	10
Preferred Provider Organization	20	20	17	15	12
Indemnity Fee for Service	6	6	5	3	4
Managed Care Contracts					
Health Maintenance Organization	75	74	77	75	75
Preferred Provider Organization	90	92	95	95	95
Affiliations					
Hospitals in a System	76	73	73	70	69
Hospitals in a Network	81	80	78	79	79
Hospitals in a Group Purchasing Organization	116	118	117	117	116

TABLE 6

IOWA

U.S. Registered Community Hospitals
(Nonfederal, short-term general and other special hospitals)

Utilization, Personnel, Revenue and Expenses, Community Health Indicators 2012–2016

	2016	2015	2014	2013	2012
TOTAL FACILITY (Includes Hospital and Nursing Home Units)					
Utilization - Inpatient					
Beds...	9,536	9,592	9,740	9,839	9,962
Admissions.....................................	314,865	324,964	318,999	326,593	336,765
Inpatient Days................................	1,926,274	1,973,257	1,958,693	2,001,590	2,022,552
Average Length of Stay	6.1	6.1	6.1	6.1	6.0
Inpatient Surgeries.........................	82,456	79,852	79,279	80,936	84,008
Births...	39,034	39,100	39,101	38,344	37,967
Utilization - Outpatient					
Emergency Outpatient Visits..............	1,369,607	1,363,799	1,290,755	1,292,810	1,297,129
Other Outpatient Visits....................	10,066,760	9,692,797	9,501,854	9,316,036	9,318,536
Total Outpatient Visits	11,436,367	11,056,596	10,792,609	10,608,846	10,615,665
Outpatient Surgeries.......................	254,174	255,548	250,088	247,077	253,460
Personnel					
Full Time RNs	12,842	12,380	11,977	11,653	11,208
Full Time LPNs................................	759	742	738	702	761
Part Time RNs.................................	6,766	6,441	6,502	6,734	6,913
Part Time LPNs...............................	518	519	505	497	563
Total Full Time	47,872	46,707	45,734	45,507	44,797
Total Part Time	22,900	21,619	22,084	22,560	23,460
Revenue - Inpatient					
Gross Inpatient Revenue	$10,186,069,754	$9,765,982,515	$9,132,937,528	$8,806,484,946	$8,408,565,148
Revenue - Outpatient					
Gross Outpatient Revenue	$14,161,466,846	$12,979,201,679	$11,904,002,918	$10,917,710,660	$10,161,337,605
Revenue and Expenses - Totals					
(Includes Inpatient and Outpatient)					
Total Gross Revenue........................	$24,347,536,600	$22,745,184,194	$21,036,940,446	$19,724,195,606	$18,569,902,753
Deductions from Revenue	15,631,835,494	14,403,224,839	13,223,158,549	12,194,888,808	11,074,628,171
Net Patient Revenue.........................	8,715,701,106	8,341,959,355	7,813,781,897	7,529,306,798	7,495,274,582
Other Operating Revenue..................	712,536,063	667,628,847	642,979,756	620,140,454	591,931,420
Other Nonoperating Revenue............	146,949,242	140,063,075	306,092,900	292,293,006	149,767,795
Total Net Revenue............................	9,575,186,411	9,149,651,277	8,762,854,553	8,441,740,258	8,236,973,797
Total Expenses................................	8,991,715,429	8,465,354,745	8,129,893,480	7,832,928,280	7,709,621,525
HOSPITAL UNIT (Excludes Separate Nursing Home Units)					
Utilization - Inpatient					
Beds...	7,970	8,014	8,123	8,153	8,275
Admissions.....................................	312,045	321,912	315,816	323,713	332,949
Inpatient Days................................	1,432,661	1,474,488	1,445,672	1,482,642	1,501,406
Average Length of Stay	4.6	4.6	4.6	4.6	4.5
Personnel					
Total Full Time	47,150	45,985	44,921	44,714	44,073
Total Part Time	22,119	20,850	21,305	21,781	22,722
Revenue and Expenses - Totals					
(Includes Inpatient and Outpatient)					
Total Net Revenue............................	$9,484,666,194	$9,063,804,737	$8,673,877,088	$8,349,001,790	$8,147,277,912
Total Expenses................................	8,917,489,464	8,392,829,019	8,055,771,463	7,756,011,550	7,631,417,462
COMMUNITY HEALTH INDICATORS PER 1000 POPULATION					
Total Population (in thousands)...........	3,135	3,124	3,107	3,090	3,074
Inpatient					
Beds...	3.0	3.1	3.1	3.2	3.2
Admissions.....................................	100.4	104.0	102.7	105.7	109.5
Inpatient Days................................	614.5	631.7	630.4	647.7	657.9
Inpatient Surgeries.........................	26.3	25.6	25.5	26.2	27.3
Births...	12.5	12.5	12.6	12.4	12.4
Outpatient					
Emergency Outpatient Visits..............	436.9	436.6	415.4	418.3	421.9
Other Outpatient Visits....................	3,211.4	3,102.8	3,058.1	3,014.5	3,031.2
Total Outpatient Visits	3,648.3	3,539.4	3,473.5	3,432.8	3,453.2
Outpatient Surgeries.......................	81.1	81.8	80.5	79.9	82.4
Expense per Capita (per person).........	$2,868.5	$2,709.9	$2,616.5	$2,534.6	$2,507.9

States

TABLE 6

KANSAS

U.S. Registered Community Hospitals
(Nonfederal, short-term general and other special hospitals)

Overview 2012–2016

	2016	2015	2014	2013	2012
Total Community Hospitals in Kansas...............	131	131	133	130	131
Bed Size Category					
6-24	26	24	21	21	20
25-49	53	53	54	49	49
50-99	29	30	32	35	37
100-199	13	14	16	16	16
200-299	5	5	5	4	4
300-399	1	2	1	2	2
400-499	1	0	1	0	0
500 + ...	3	3	3	3	3
Location					
Hospitals Urban	36	36	37	34	34
Hospitals Rural	95	95	96	96	97
Control					
State and Local Government	61	63	64	61	61
Not for Profit	52	51	51	51	53
Investor owned	18	17	18	18	17
Physician Models					
Independent Practice Association......................	7	9	9	10	13
Group Practice without Walls..........................	3	3	3	3	4
Open Physician-Hospital Organization	8	9	8	11	12
Closed Physician-Hospital Organization.............	0	0	0	1	2
Management Service Organization.....................	0	0	0	1	2
Integrated Salary Model.................................	86	84	85	79	79
Equity Model	1	1	1	1	2
Foundation	4	3	3	4	5
Insurance Products					
Health Maintenance Organization......................	2	2	1	2	2
Preferred Provider Organization	5	6	5	5	7
Indemnity Fee for Service	0	0	0	1	3
Managed Care Contracts					
Health Maintenance Organization......................	56	58	59	57	56
Preferred Provider Organization	106	109	110	109	112
Affiliations					
Hospitals in a System	54	53	52	53	56
Hospitals in a Network	74	78	80	80	79
Hospitals in a Group Purchasing Organization...	120	126	129	129	128

TABLE 6

KANSAS

U.S. Registered Community Hospitals
(Nonfederal, short-term general and other special hospitals)

Utilization, Personnel, Revenue and Expenses, Community Health Indicators 2012–2016

	2016	2015	2014	2013	2012
TOTAL FACILITY (Includes Hospital and Nursing Home Units)					
Utilization - Inpatient					
Beds	9,656	9,822	10,028	9,998	10,127
Admissions	300,573	297,399	296,085	289,696	296,267
Inpatient Days	1,919,932	1,908,209	1,891,620	1,899,716	1,915,826
Average Length of Stay	6.4	6.4	6.4	6.6	6.5
Inpatient Surgeries	68,445	67,460	69,380	71,156	73,240
Births	37,712	38,065	38,189	37,311	38,623
Utilization - Outpatient					
Emergency Outpatient Visits	1,207,379	1,211,169	1,174,104	1,127,551	1,114,026
Other Outpatient Visits	6,476,457	6,091,924	5,982,336	5,962,793	6,179,011
Total Outpatient Visits	7,683,836	7,303,093	7,156,440	7,090,344	7,293,037
Outpatient Surgeries	164,132	161,047	160,208	156,088	166,253
Personnel					
Full Time RNs	12,951	11,995	11,919	12,146	11,619
Full Time LPNs	1,185	1,008	1,005	1,036	1,009
Part Time RNs	5,239	5,126	4,743	4,861	4,917
Part Time LPNs	341	380	356	389	405
Total Full Time	43,869	41,106	40,854	40,892	40,129
Total Part Time	16,989	15,279	14,165	14,722	14,838
Revenue - Inpatient					
Gross Inpatient Revenue	$13,458,172,903	$12,478,999,660	$11,791,354,318	$10,790,044,124	$10,396,751,854
Revenue - Outpatient					
Gross Outpatient Revenue	$14,929,186,007	$13,355,791,768	$11,935,261,119	$10,497,568,428	$10,046,165,626
Revenue and Expenses - Totals					
(Includes Inpatient and Outpatient)					
Total Gross Revenue	$28,387,358,910	$25,834,791,428	$23,726,615,437	$21,287,612,552	$20,442,917,480
Deductions from Revenue	20,350,953,568	18,341,965,456	16,686,914,957	14,616,689,279	13,766,315,018
Net Patient Revenue	8,036,405,342	7,492,825,972	7,039,700,480	6,670,923,273	6,676,602,462
Other Operating Revenue	415,499,923	409,625,627	345,399,844	288,774,222	284,943,541
Other Nonoperating Revenue	69,394,334	1,419,933	161,037,772	171,234,302	160,005,906
Total Net Revenue	8,521,299,599	7,903,871,532	7,546,138,096	7,130,931,797	7,121,551,909
Total Expenses	7,848,855,906	7,316,594,359	6,954,230,448	6,616,602,126	6,513,729,367
HOSPITAL UNIT (Excludes Separate Nursing Home Units)					
Utilization - Inpatient					
Beds	8,368	8,421	8,505	8,440	8,568
Admissions	298,953	295,432	293,840	287,249	293,835
Inpatient Days	1,468,978	1,484,906	1,435,936	1,426,105	1,440,628
Average Length of Stay	4.9	5.0	4.9	5.0	4.9
Personnel					
Total Full Time	42,944	40,176	39,789	39,877	39,007
Total Part Time	16,513	14,770	13,677	14,237	14,268
Revenue and Expenses - Totals					
(Includes Inpatient and Outpatient)					
Total Net Revenue	$8,448,107,345	$7,824,768,422	$7,464,308,710	$7,047,938,513	$7,040,162,578
Total Expenses	7,789,382,212	7,249,246,278	6,881,820,540	6,548,127,097	6,440,417,821
COMMUNITY HEALTH INDICATORS PER 1000 POPULATION					
Total Population (in thousands)	2,907	2,912	2,904	2,894	2,886
Inpatient					
Beds	3.3	3.4	3.5	3.5	3.5
Admissions	103.4	102.1	102.0	100.1	102.7
Inpatient Days	660.4	655.4	651.4	656.4	663.9
Inpatient Surgeries	23.5	23.2	23.9	24.6	25.4
Births	13.0	13.1	13.2	12.9	13.4
Outpatient					
Emergency Outpatient Visits	415.3	416.0	404.3	389.6	386.0
Other Outpatient Visits	2,227.7	2,092.3	2,060.0	2,060.4	2,141.1
Total Outpatient Visits	2,643.0	2,508.2	2,464.3	2,450.1	2,527.1
Outpatient Surgeries	56.5	55.3	55.2	53.9	57.6
Expense per Capita (per person)	$2,699.7	$2,512.9	$2,394.7	$2,286.4	$2,257.1

States

TABLE 6

KENTUCKY

U.S. Registered Community Hospitals
(Nonfederal, short-term general and other special hospitals)

Overview 2012–2016

	2016	2015	2014	2013	2012
Total Community Hospitals in Kentucky............	103	103	104	106	106
Bed Size Category					
6-24..	3	2	2	3	3
25-49..	33	34	34	35	36
50-99..	20	20	21	19	19
100-199..	23	23	23	26	25
200-299..	11	9	11	10	10
300-399..	9	11	9	9	9
400-499..	1	1	3	2	0
500 +..	3	3	1	2	4
Location					
Hospitals Urban..	41	41	41	43	43
Hospitals Rural...	62	62	63	63	63
Control					
State and Local Government.....................	9	11	11	11	12
Not for Profit..	73	74	72	75	74
Investor owned..	21	18	21	20	20
Physician Models					
Independent Practice Association.............	2	3	4	3	6
Group Practice without Walls....................	1	1	1	1	1
Open Physician-Hospital Organization......	6	6	5	5	6
Closed Physician-Hospital Organization....	4	4	0	1	1
Management Service Organization............	11	11	9	9	10
Integrated Salary Model...........................	37	42	41	40	44
Equity Model..	0	0	0	0	0
Foundation..	3	4	1	2	2
Insurance Products					
Health Maintenance Organization.............	13	15	10	6	7
Preferred Provider Organization...............	16	18	13	10	7
Indemnity Fee for Service........................	5	6	2	4	3
Managed Care Contracts					
Health Maintenance Organization.............	46	49	44	41	43
Preferred Provider Organization...............	50	54	55	42	44
Affiliations					
Hospitals in a System..............................	82	83	81	80	80
Hospitals in a Network.............................	33	31	30	28	24
Hospitals in a Group Purchasing Organization...	69	73	71	70	74

TABLE 6

KENTUCKY

U.S. Registered Community Hospitals
(Nonfederal, short-term general and other special hospitals)

Utilization, Personnel, Revenue and Expenses, Community Health Indicators 2012–2016

	2016	2015	2014	2013	2012
TOTAL FACILITY (Includes Hospital and Nursing Home Units)					
Utilization - Inpatient					
Beds	13,978	14,108	13,994	14,021	14,180
Admissions	560,235	556,186	558,430	578,841	572,294
Inpatient Days	3,055,410	3,052,078	2,975,806	3,026,582	2,908,461
Average Length of Stay	5.5	5.5	5.3	5.2	5.1
Inpatient Surgeries	160,807	149,476	159,471	159,628	166,885
Births	55,003	53,551	52,786	54,263	53,538
Utilization - Outpatient					
Emergency Outpatient Visits	2,596,349	2,501,247	2,332,013	2,279,740	2,404,826
Other Outpatient Visits	11,252,154	10,505,860	8,443,852	8,241,623	8,166,103
Total Outpatient Visits	13,848,503	13,007,107	10,775,865	10,521,363	10,570,929
Outpatient Surgeries	378,555	368,498	361,098	368,971	371,089
Personnel					
Full Time RNs	20,529	19,175	18,505	18,551	18,672
Full Time LPNs	1,071	1,384	1,116	1,243	1,290
Part Time RNs	7,030	6,967	6,825	6,624	6,093
Part Time LPNs	222	279	247	261	268
Total Full Time	66,674	65,760	61,865	62,625	64,131
Total Part Time	19,318	19,772	18,717	19,000	17,391
Revenue - Inpatient					
Gross Inpatient Revenue	$23,567,484,478	$21,338,595,640	$19,807,874,013	$18,199,474,364	$16,779,961,324
Revenue - Outpatient					
Gross Outpatient Revenue	$25,892,182,594	$23,737,778,365	$22,184,632,530	$18,314,577,975	$16,724,256,215
Revenue and Expenses - Totals					
(Includes Inpatient and Outpatient)					
Total Gross Revenue	$49,459,667,072	$45,076,374,005	$41,992,506,543	$36,514,052,339	$33,504,217,539
Deductions from Revenue	36,478,752,646	32,772,462,590	30,206,766,007	25,507,901,441	22,702,995,327
Net Patient Revenue	12,980,914,426	12,303,911,415	11,785,740,536	11,006,150,898	10,801,222,212
Other Operating Revenue	520,487,548	486,494,218	534,897,827	407,398,136	406,456,390
Other Nonoperating Revenue	71,765,524	28,080,493	168,148,966	237,296,737	56,938,657
Total Net Revenue	13,573,167,498	12,818,486,126	12,488,787,329	11,650,845,771	11,264,617,259
Total Expenses	12,661,868,743	11,683,172,808	11,788,394,914	10,884,059,289	10,400,750,170
HOSPITAL UNIT (Excludes Separate Nursing Home Units)					
Utilization - Inpatient					
Beds	13,553	13,497	13,542	13,319	13,573
Admissions	555,353	549,588	553,728	572,724	564,937
Inpatient Days	2,942,210	2,879,266	2,856,932	2,818,046	2,743,755
Average Length of Stay	5.3	5.2	5.2	4.9	4.9
Personnel					
Total Full Time	66,301	65,172	61,414	61,903	63,588
Total Part Time	19,216	19,613	18,576	18,769	17,221
Revenue and Expenses - Totals					
(Includes Inpatient and Outpatient)					
Total Net Revenue	$13,495,766,996	$12,730,586,085	$12,437,772,106	$11,593,715,843	$11,207,210,342
Total Expenses	12,609,626,199	11,623,609,799	11,746,322,153	10,817,318,399	10,337,675,256
COMMUNITY HEALTH INDICATORS PER 1000 POPULATION					
Total Population (in thousands)	4,437	4,425	4,413	4,395	4,380
Inpatient					
Beds	3.2	3.2	3.2	3.2	3.2
Admissions	126.3	125.7	126.5	131.7	130.6
Inpatient Days	688.6	689.7	674.3	688.6	664.0
Inpatient Surgeries	36.2	33.8	36.1	36.3	38.1
Births	12.4	12.1	12.0	12.3	12.2
Outpatient					
Emergency Outpatient Visits	585.2	565.2	528.4	518.7	549.0
Other Outpatient Visits	2,536.0	2,374.2	1,913.2	1,875.1	1,864.2
Total Outpatient Visits	3,121.2	2,939.4	2,441.6	2,393.8	2,413.2
Outpatient Surgeries	85.3	83.3	81.8	83.9	84.7
Expense per Capita (per person)	$2,853.7	$2,640.2	$2,671.0	$2,476.3	$2,374.4

States

TABLE **6**

LOUISIANA

U.S. Registered Community Hospitals
(Nonfederal, short-term general and other special hospitals)

Overview 2012–2016

	2016	2015	2014	2013	2012
Total Community Hospitals in Louisiana............	118	120	122	122	124
Bed Size Category					
6-24..	19	18	16	17	17
25-49..	37	39	41	38	38
50-99..	22	22	20	24	25
100-199...	18	19	21	19	20
200-299...	12	12	12	10	10
300-399...	5	4	6	7	7
400-499...	2	2	3	4	4
500 +..	3	4	3	3	3
Location					
Hospitals Urban	80	82	84	74	77
Hospitals Rural...	38	38	38	48	47
Control					
State and Local Government	42	44	45	44	49
Not for Profit..	45	43	41	41	38
Investor owned...	31	33	36	37	37
Physician Models					
Independent Practice Association......................	7	7	8	6	5
Group Practice without Walls............................	3	3	5	4	3
Open Physician-Hospital Organization	9	7	8	8	10
Closed Physician-Hospital Organization............	3	3	3	5	5
Management Service Organization.....................	7	8	7	7	8
Integrated Salary Model..................................	32	35	31	25	28
Equity Model	0	0	0	1	1
Foundation	2	3	2	5	4
Insurance Products					
Health Maintenance Organization......................	5	5	6	8	6
Preferred Provider Organization	8	8	9	7	7
Indemnity Fee for Service	3	3	4	2	3
Managed Care Contracts					
Health Maintenance Organization......................	44	43	40	44	45
Preferred Provider Organization	48	47	43	48	51
Affiliations					
Hospitals in a System	63	64	63	59	57
Hospitals in a Network.....................................	25	27	22	20	22
Hospitals in a Group Purchasing Organization...	59	61	58	59	62

TABLE 6

LOUISIANA

U.S. Registered Community Hospitals
(Nonfederal, short-term general and other special hospitals)

Utilization, Personnel, Revenue and Expenses, Community Health Indicators 2012–2016

	2016	2015	2014	2013	2012
TOTAL FACILITY (Includes Hospital and Nursing Home Units)					
Utilization - Inpatient					
Beds	14,052	14,216	15,076	15,550	15,204
Admissions	548,316	552,342	561,930	565,779	582,425
Inpatient Days	3,012,767	3,057,319	3,077,460	3,073,041	3,138,473
Average Length of Stay	5.5	5.5	5.5	5.4	5.4
Inpatient Surgeries	157,620	147,835	145,240	138,430	142,744
Births	60,923	66,029	70,969	64,083	60,736
Utilization - Outpatient					
Emergency Outpatient Visits	2,853,225	2,677,500	2,739,120	2,587,672	2,539,449
Other Outpatient Visits	8,760,613	9,457,113	7,994,071	7,076,596	7,011,868
Total Outpatient Visits	11,613,838	12,134,613	10,733,191	9,664,268	9,551,317
Outpatient Surgeries	288,590	266,555	265,642	263,440	253,503
Personnel					
Full Time RNs	19,939	20,085	20,041	18,917	18,885
Full Time LPNs	2,653	2,779	2,644	2,668	2,829
Part Time RNs	7,665	7,724	7,212	6,792	5,624
Part Time LPNs	720	762	909	905	728
Total Full Time	71,991	71,250	72,928	71,050	70,723
Total Part Time	22,119	22,575	21,384	21,073	17,577
Revenue - Inpatient					
Gross Inpatient Revenue	$22,679,087,663	$21,059,595,083	$20,532,002,034	$19,263,175,093	$18,651,353,386
Revenue - Outpatient					
Gross Outpatient Revenue	$23,391,542,818	$21,310,915,092	$19,353,422,874	$17,447,605,153	$15,579,961,189
Revenue and Expenses - Totals					
(Includes Inpatient and Outpatient)					
Total Gross Revenue	$46,070,630,481	$42,370,510,175	$39,885,424,908	$36,710,780,246	$34,231,314,575
Deductions from Revenue	33,921,107,033	30,578,707,526	28,916,804,408	26,304,382,131	24,308,385,152
Net Patient Revenue	12,149,523,448	11,791,802,649	10,968,620,500	10,406,398,115	9,922,929,423
Other Operating Revenue	1,016,896,798	799,145,785	694,606,495	683,792,470	650,768,859
Other Nonoperating Revenue	79,682,551	41,289,716	260,144,885	167,277,594	118,810,348
Total Net Revenue	13,246,102,797	12,632,238,150	11,923,371,880	11,257,468,179	10,692,508,630
Total Expenses	12,493,815,000	11,676,829,432	11,224,972,279	10,689,977,269	10,146,975,702
HOSPITAL UNIT (Excludes Separate Nursing Home Units)					
Utilization - Inpatient					
Beds	13,540	13,718	14,530	14,850	14,552
Admissions	546,207	550,224	560,304	563,829	580,792
Inpatient Days	2,825,191	2,916,671	2,920,175	2,895,780	3,001,522
Average Length of Stay	5.2	5.3	5.2	5.1	5.2
Personnel					
Total Full Time	71,723	70,858	71,239	70,604	69,836
Total Part Time	22,005	22,463	20,585	20,881	17,416
Revenue and Expenses - Totals					
(Includes Inpatient and Outpatient)					
Total Net Revenue	$13,212,299,338	$12,601,123,200	$11,897,431,139	$11,211,808,807	$10,660,949,288
Total Expenses	12,465,897,380	11,650,696,847	11,203,169,688	10,646,734,797	10,112,917,995
COMMUNITY HEALTH INDICATORS PER 1000 POPULATION					
Total Population (in thousands)	4,682	4,671	4,650	4,625	4,602
Inpatient					
Beds	3.0	3.0	3.2	3.4	3.3
Admissions	117.1	118.3	120.9	122.3	126.6
Inpatient Days	643.5	654.6	661.9	664.4	682.0
Inpatient Surgeries	33.7	31.7	31.2	29.9	31.0
Births	13.0	14.1	15.3	13.9	13.2
Outpatient					
Emergency Outpatient Visits	609.4	573.3	589.1	559.4	551.8
Other Outpatient Visits	1,871.3	2,024.8	1,719.3	1,529.9	1,523.7
Total Outpatient Visits	2,480.7	2,598.0	2,308.4	2,089.4	2,075.5
Outpatient Surgeries	61.6	57.1	57.1	57.0	55.1
Expense per Capita (per person)	$2,668.7	$2,500.0	$2,414.1	$2,311.1	$2,205.0

States

TABLE 6

MAINE

U.S. Registered Community Hospitals
(Nonfederal, short-term general and other special hospitals)

Overview 2012–2016

	2016	2015	2014	2013	2012
Total Community Hospitals in Maine	34	34	35	35	37
Bed Size Category					
6-24	3	3	2	1	2
25-49	14	15	16	17	17
50-99	8	7	8	7	8
100-199	5	5	6	6	7
200-299	1	1	1	2	1
300-399	2	2	1	1	1
400-499	0	0	0	0	0
500 +	1	1	1	1	1
Location					
Hospitals Urban	13	13	14	14	15
Hospitals Rural	21	21	21	21	22
Control					
State and Local Government	2	3	2	2	2
Not for Profit	31	30	32	32	34
Investor owned	1	1	1	1	1
Physician Models					
Independent Practice Association	3	3	0	0	2
Group Practice without Walls	2	1	0	1	2
Open Physician-Hospital Organization	7	7	9	8	9
Closed Physician-Hospital Organization	3	3	3	2	3
Management Service Organization	3	2	2	2	3
Integrated Salary Model	14	13	13	17	22
Equity Model	0	0	0	0	1
Foundation	0	0	0	0	1
Insurance Products					
Health Maintenance Organization	0	0	4	4	3
Preferred Provider Organization	1	2	4	4	3
Indemnity Fee for Service	0	0	1	1	0
Managed Care Contracts					
Health Maintenance Organization	15	15	15	19	21
Preferred Provider Organization	15	17	18	21	23
Affiliations					
Hospitals in a System	22	22	18	18	20
Hospitals in a Network	12	15	16	17	18
Hospitals in a Group Purchasing Organization	28	29	26	28	32

TABLE 6

MAINE

U.S. Registered Community Hospitals
(Nonfederal, short-term general and other special hospitals)

Utilization, Personnel, Revenue and Expenses, Community Health Indicators 2012–2016

	2016	2015	2014	2013	2012
TOTAL FACILITY (Includes Hospital and Nursing Home Units)					
Utilization - Inpatient					
Beds	3,397	3,478	3,379	3,474	3,523
Admissions	135,281	137,950	135,001	139,976	142,159
Inpatient Days	851,357	816,880	772,923	782,150	783,992
Average Length of Stay	6.3	5.9	5.7	5.6	5.5
Inpatient Surgeries	40,697	39,339	39,374	40,786	42,816
Births	12,524	11,798	11,495	11,687	11,224
Utilization - Outpatient					
Emergency Outpatient Visits	678,948	964,240	771,696	795,374	790,258
Other Outpatient Visits	5,271,196	6,239,268	7,063,404	6,358,880	5,387,237
Total Outpatient Visits	5,950,144	7,203,508	7,835,100	7,154,254	6,177,495
Outpatient Surgeries	108,801	105,713	112,626	103,239	117,491
Personnel					
Full Time RNs	5,762	6,119	5,779	5,509	5,229
Full Time LPNs	269	335	255	242	190
Part Time RNs	2,945	3,511	3,944	3,503	3,884
Part Time LPNs	106	141	121	118	149
Total Full Time	27,178	26,456	25,520	24,591	23,343
Total Part Time	10,927	11,607	12,346	11,034	12,446
Revenue - Inpatient					
Gross Inpatient Revenue	$4,429,901,617	$4,571,897,264	$4,059,334,894	$3,801,387,888	$3,743,957,102
Revenue - Outpatient					
Gross Outpatient Revenue	$6,500,678,123	$6,083,795,956	$5,658,735,515	$5,272,970,618	$5,068,158,029
Revenue and Expenses - Totals					
(Includes Inpatient and Outpatient)					
Total Gross Revenue	$10,930,579,740	$10,655,693,220	$9,718,070,409	$9,074,358,506	$8,812,115,131
Deductions from Revenue	5,972,381,386	5,991,204,223	5,323,172,816	4,805,408,453	4,477,604,537
Net Patient Revenue	4,958,198,354	4,664,488,997	4,394,897,593	4,268,950,053	4,334,510,594
Other Operating Revenue	409,506,843	344,974,562	322,528,528	307,982,903	257,362,641
Other Nonoperating Revenue	39,795,272	16,792,277	107,159,154	85,107,098	52,339,735
Total Net Revenue	5,407,500,469	5,026,255,836	4,824,585,275	4,662,040,054	4,644,212,970
Total Expenses	5,281,349,738	4,912,530,828	4,635,468,221	4,501,336,652	4,421,717,517
HOSPITAL UNIT (Excludes Separate Nursing Home Units)					
Utilization - Inpatient					
Beds	2,901	2,984	2,983	3,078	3,109
Admissions	131,949	135,289	134,085	139,093	141,049
Inpatient Days	677,182	714,550	638,945	646,155	645,365
Average Length of Stay	5.1	5.3	4.8	4.6	4.6
Personnel					
Total Full Time	26,427	26,139	24,953	24,087	22,538
Total Part Time	10,396	11,351	11,679	10,755	11,898
Revenue and Expenses - Totals					
(Includes Inpatient and Outpatient)					
Total Net Revenue	$5,372,226,471	$4,998,768,917	$4,791,979,724	$4,629,095,790	$4,608,434,715
Total Expenses	5,243,064,736	4,886,600,125	4,601,902,809	4,470,359,564	4,389,756,790
COMMUNITY HEALTH INDICATORS PER 1000 POPULATION					
Total Population (in thousands)	1,331	1,329	1,330	1,328	1,329
Inpatient					
Beds	2.6	2.6	2.5	2.6	2.7
Admissions	101.6	103.8	101.5	105.4	107.0
Inpatient Days	639.4	614.5	581.1	588.8	589.8
Inpatient Surgeries	30.6	29.6	29.6	30.7	32.2
Births	9.4	8.9	8.6	8.8	8.4
Outpatient					
Emergency Outpatient Visits	509.9	725.4	580.2	598.8	594.5
Other Outpatient Visits	3,958.9	4,693.6	5,310.5	4,787.2	4,053.0
Total Outpatient Visits	4,468.8	5,418.9	5,890.7	5,386.0	4,647.6
Outpatient Surgeries	81.7	79.5	84.7	77.7	88.4
Expense per Capita (per person)	$3,966.5	$3,695.5	$3,485.1	$3,388.8	$3,326.6

TABLE 6

MARYLAND

U.S. Registered Community Hospitals
(Nonfederal, short-term general and other special hospitals)

Overview 2012–2016

	2016	2015	2014	2013	2012
Total Community Hospitals in Maryland.............	50	50	50	50	50
Bed Size Category					
6-24..	0	0	0	0	0
25-49..	4	4	3	3	3
50-99..	8	7	9	9	8
100-199..	14	14	12	9	11
200-299..	9	10	12	14	11
300-399..	8	7	6	8	9
400-499..	5	6	6	4	6
500 +..	2	2	2	3	2
Location					
Hospitals Urban	46	46	46	44	44
Hospitals Rural..	4	4	4	6	6
Control					
State and Local Government	0	0	0	0	0
Not for Profit..	49	49	49	49	48
Investor owned	1	1	1	1	2
Physician Models					
Independent Practice Association.......................	3	7	6	9	12
Group Practice without Walls.............................	4	4	3	6	8
Open Physician-Hospital Organization	7	6	6	5	6
Closed Physician-Hospital Organization.............	7	7	9	9	9
Management Service Organization......................	7	10	5	10	14
Integrated Salary Model.....................................	28	31	30	31	32
Equity Model	2	1	2	3	4
Foundation	3	6	6	5	6
Insurance Products					
Health Maintenance Organization......................	20	20	18	18	16
Preferred Provider Organization	10	8	8	10	13
Indemnity Fee for Service	4	5	4	5	5
Managed Care Contracts					
Health Maintenance Organization......................	28	28	27	29	31
Preferred Provider Organization	28	28	27	29	30
Affiliations					
Hospitals in a System	36	35	35	35	35
Hospitals in a Network......................................	13	18	14	16	16
Hospitals in a Group Purchasing Organization...	36	42	36	41	42

TABLE 6

MARYLAND

U.S. Registered Community Hospitals
(Nonfederal, short-term general and other special hospitals)

Utilization, Personnel, Revenue and Expenses, Community Health Indicators 2012–2016

	2016	2015	2014	2013	2012
TOTAL FACILITY (Includes Hospital and Nursing Home Units)					
Utilization - Inpatient					
Beds	11,547	11,778	12,027	12,392	12,271
Admissions	584,519	593,976	609,185	628,485	659,128
Inpatient Days	3,009,310	3,041,811	3,067,846	3,165,089	3,230,567
Average Length of Stay	5.1	5.1	5.0	5.0	4.9
Inpatient Surgeries	168,249	171,174	176,580	182,075	193,816
Births	66,271	67,409	65,730	66,699	67,554
Utilization - Outpatient					
Emergency Outpatient Visits	2,492,585	2,471,206	2,341,061	2,542,407	2,552,154
Other Outpatient Visits	10,293,308	6,935,809	6,671,728	6,879,374	7,244,174
Total Outpatient Visits	12,785,893	9,407,015	9,012,789	9,421,781	9,796,328
Outpatient Surgeries	361,728	349,762	352,010	355,688	348,264
Personnel					
Full Time RNs	21,158	20,735	21,205	19,966	19,382
Full Time LPNs	389	414	420	434	502
Part Time RNs	8,982	8,234	8,779	8,383	8,776
Part Time LPNs	155	157	160	212	241
Total Full Time	75,476	74,559	78,634	75,810	75,558
Total Part Time	28,475	27,036	27,551	25,681	28,069
Revenue - Inpatient					
Gross Inpatient Revenue	$12,212,486,677	$12,904,106,612	$11,825,919,787	$10,661,965,230	$11,340,693,112
Revenue - Outpatient					
Gross Outpatient Revenue	$10,755,713,411	$11,327,811,621	$9,739,331,110	$8,799,199,791	$8,221,461,005
Revenue and Expenses - Totals					
(Includes Inpatient and Outpatient)					
Total Gross Revenue	$22,968,200,088	$24,231,918,233	$21,565,250,897	$19,461,165,021	$19,562,154,117
Deductions from Revenue	7,811,966,297	9,585,576,596	7,462,716,486	5,848,369,205	5,814,859,991
Net Patient Revenue	15,156,233,791	14,646,341,637	14,102,534,411	13,612,795,816	13,747,294,126
Other Operating Revenue	891,475,771	790,139,930	745,533,295	720,549,006	587,505,820
Other Nonoperating Revenue	-114,116,391	-19,397,372	432,996,623	258,822,436	16,735,289
Total Net Revenue	15,933,593,171	15,417,084,195	15,281,064,329	14,592,167,258	14,351,535,235
Total Expenses	15,583,580,031	14,778,269,734	14,187,741,189	13,836,110,822	13,808,394,036
HOSPITAL UNIT (Excludes Separate Nursing Home Units)					
Utilization - Inpatient					
Beds	11,316	11,453	11,725	11,614	11,503
Admissions	581,984	590,808	605,304	621,936	653,062
Inpatient Days	2,948,025	2,946,453	2,976,468	2,926,235	3,003,853
Average Length of Stay	5.1	5.0	4.9	4.7	4.6
Personnel					
Total Full Time	75,316	74,289	78,206	75,010	74,873
Total Part Time	28,341	26,889	27,297	25,282	27,724
Revenue and Expenses - Totals					
(Includes Inpatient and Outpatient)					
Total Net Revenue	$15,908,510,446	$15,381,581,055	$15,213,654,834	$14,477,831,557	$14,246,938,190
Total Expenses	15,560,002,631	14,743,238,139	14,129,417,337	13,728,619,619	13,710,327,354
COMMUNITY HEALTH INDICATORS PER 1000 POPULATION					
Total Population (in thousands)	6,016	6,006	5,976	5,929	5,885
Inpatient					
Beds	1.9	2.0	2.0	2.1	2.1
Admissions	97.2	98.9	101.9	106.0	112.0
Inpatient Days	500.2	506.4	513.3	533.8	549.0
Inpatient Surgeries	28.0	28.5	29.5	30.7	32.9
Births	11.0	11.2	11.0	11.2	11.5
Outpatient					
Emergency Outpatient Visits	414.3	411.4	391.7	428.8	433.7
Other Outpatient Visits	1,710.9	1,154.7	1,116.3	1,160.3	1,231.0
Total Outpatient Visits	2,125.2	1,566.2	1,508.1	1,589.2	1,664.8
Outpatient Surgeries	60.1	58.2	58.9	60.0	59.2
Expense per Capita (per person)	$2,590.2	$2,460.4	$2,374.0	$2,333.7	$2,346.5

States

TABLE 6

MASSACHUSETTS

U.S. Registered Community Hospitals
(Nonfederal, short-term general and other special hospitals)

Overview 2012–2016

	2016	2015	2014	2013	2012
Total Community Hospitals in Massachusetts	75	76	79	82	83
Bed Size Category					
6-24	3	4	4	4	5
25-49	7	7	7	7	8
50-99	16	17	17	18	19
100-199	22	22	25	25	22
200-299	11	10	10	13	14
300-399	7	7	8	6	7
400-499	3	3	2	3	2
500 +	6	6	6	6	6
Location					
Hospitals Urban	72	73	76	80	81
Hospitals Rural	3	3	3	2	2
Control					
State and Local Government	3	3	4	3	3
Not for Profit	55	56	57	59	61
Investor owned	17	17	18	20	19
Physician Models					
Independent Practice Association	18	19	19	19	17
Group Practice without Walls	3	2	2	1	2
Open Physician-Hospital Organization	19	18	17	17	18
Closed Physician-Hospital Organization	4	4	5	5	5
Management Service Organization	8	9	9	9	9
Integrated Salary Model	32	33	32	30	31
Equity Model	1	1	1	1	1
Foundation	1	2	2	2	3
Insurance Products					
Health Maintenance Organization	16	14	9	7	9
Preferred Provider Organization	11	10	5	4	4
Indemnity Fee for Service	5	3	2	1	2
Managed Care Contracts					
Health Maintenance Organization	46	48	50	48	47
Preferred Provider Organization	46	46	49	47	45
Affiliations					
Hospitals in a System	51	50	53	52	51
Hospitals in a Network	28	28	26	24	24
Hospitals in a Group Purchasing Organization	51	50	52	50	50

TABLE 6

MASSACHUSETTS

U.S. Registered Community Hospitals
(Nonfederal, short-term general and other special hospitals)

Utilization, Personnel, Revenue and Expenses, Community Health Indicators 2012–2016

	2016	2015	2014	2013	2012
TOTAL FACILITY (Includes Hospital and Nursing Home Units)					
Utilization - Inpatient					
Beds	15,678	15,518	16,060	16,483	16,233
Admissions	766,005	761,288	754,971	787,003	802,312
Inpatient Days	4,043,067	4,041,254	4,116,984	4,181,114	4,130,110
Average Length of Stay	5.3	5.3	5.5	5.3	5.1
Inpatient Surgeries	192,325	187,701	190,086	188,191	197,450
Births	67,394	67,950	69,068	68,965	70,702
Utilization - Outpatient					
Emergency Outpatient Visits	3,318,069	3,243,961	3,186,679	3,221,445	3,164,871
Other Outpatient Visits	19,534,152	19,523,290	18,768,118	18,876,709	19,349,547
Total Outpatient Visits	22,852,221	22,767,251	21,954,797	22,098,154	22,514,418
Outpatient Surgeries	431,641	427,884	425,225	426,553	421,694
Personnel					
Full Time RNs	23,839	22,119	22,686	21,855	21,137
Full Time LPNs	827	768	798	835	868
Part Time RNs	23,355	23,284	22,458	23,005	22,948
Part Time LPNs	513	498	526	641	708
Total Full Time	120,150	114,424	114,832	115,714	113,291
Total Part Time	68,887	66,944	67,176	67,465	69,520
Revenue - Inpatient					
Gross Inpatient Revenue	$29,930,619,531	$28,091,059,841	$27,543,954,703	$26,147,419,070	$25,212,735,967
Revenue - Outpatient					
Gross Outpatient Revenue	$36,550,161,403	$33,667,937,536	$30,741,997,367	$29,745,996,654	$28,198,949,623
Revenue and Expenses - Totals					
(Includes Inpatient and Outpatient)					
Total Gross Revenue	$66,480,780,934	$61,758,997,377	$58,285,952,070	$55,893,415,724	$53,411,685,590
Deductions from Revenue	41,765,745,156	38,372,046,941	35,818,774,175	34,008,609,464	31,738,657,662
Net Patient Revenue	24,715,035,778	23,386,950,436	22,467,177,895	21,884,806,260	21,673,027,928
Other Operating Revenue	4,147,254,188	3,946,891,242	3,805,293,934	3,772,351,494	3,570,796,587
Other Nonoperating Revenue	154,742,280	13,810,837	157,175,096	600,472,377	158,781,349
Total Net Revenue	29,017,032,246	27,347,652,515	26,429,646,925	26,257,630,131	25,402,605,864
Total Expenses	28,226,012,758	26,370,800,309	25,349,887,484	24,670,533,446	24,080,576,139
HOSPITAL UNIT (Excludes Separate Nursing Home Units)					
Utilization - Inpatient					
Beds	15,649	15,489	16,031	16,454	16,204
Admissions	765,408	760,661	754,338	786,315	801,583
Inpatient Days	4,035,010	4,033,008	4,108,438	4,172,412	4,121,270
Average Length of Stay	5.3	5.3	5.4	5.3	5.1
Personnel					
Total Full Time	120,141	114,417	114,826	115,708	113,273
Total Part Time	68,873	66,927	67,161	67,446	69,452
Revenue and Expenses - Totals					
(Includes Inpatient and Outpatient)					
Total Net Revenue	$29,012,915,401	$27,343,283,662	$26,425,067,104	$26,252,955,720	$25,397,992,218
Total Expenses	28,220,703,861	26,365,473,316	25,344,892,287	24,665,183,716	24,075,430,900
COMMUNITY HEALTH INDICATORS PER 1000 POPULATION					
Total Population (in thousands)	6,812	6,794	6,745	6,693	6,646
Inpatient					
Beds	2.3	2.3	2.4	2.5	2.4
Admissions	112.5	112.0	111.9	117.6	120.7
Inpatient Days	593.5	594.8	610.3	624.7	621.4
Inpatient Surgeries	28.2	27.6	28.2	28.1	29.7
Births	9.9	10.0	10.2	10.3	10.6
Outpatient					
Emergency Outpatient Visits	487.1	477.4	472.4	481.3	476.2
Other Outpatient Visits	2,867.7	2,873.4	2,782.4	2,820.4	2,911.4
Total Outpatient Visits	3,354.8	3,350.9	3,254.8	3,301.8	3,387.6
Outpatient Surgeries	63.4	63.0	63.0	63.7	63.4
Expense per Capita (per person)	$4,143.7	$3,881.2	$3,758.1	$3,686.1	$3,623.2

States

TABLE 6

MICHIGAN

U.S. Registered Community Hospitals
(Nonfederal, short-term general and other special hospitals)

Overview 2012–2016

	2016	2015	2014	2013	2012
Total Community Hospitals in Michigan	146	147	148	151	151
Bed Size Category					
6-24	14	13	12	13	12
25-49	43	44	42	44	46
50-99	27	30	32	32	29
100-199	21	19	21	19	20
200-299	9	11	12	15	15
300-399	13	12	11	10	11
400-499	8	8	8	6	7
500 + ...	11	10	10	12	11
Location					
Hospitals Urban	92	92	93	93	93
Hospitals Rural	54	55	55	58	58
Control					
State and Local Government	10	12	12	14	15
Not for Profit	110	111	111	114	114
Investor owned	26	24	25	23	22
Physician Models					
Independent Practice Association	3	8	11	12	14
Group Practice without Walls	3	7	8	8	8
Open Physician-Hospital Organization	47	39	42	40	45
Closed Physician-Hospital Organization	21	19	15	16	11
Management Service Organization	6	8	9	13	16
Integrated Salary Model	89	85	89	88	85
Equity Model	2	1	1	1	1
Foundation	6	7	6	6	6
Insurance Products					
Health Maintenance Organization	47	42	42	40	38
Preferred Provider Organization	39	34	32	28	27
Indemnity Fee for Service	13	10	12	8	10
Managed Care Contracts					
Health Maintenance Organization	101	98	101	100	102
Preferred Provider Organization	102	99	103	102	104
Affiliations					
Hospitals in a System	110	109	106	100	96
Hospitals in a Network	65	60	63	58	62
Hospitals in a Group Purchasing Organization...	112	108	116	116	119

TABLE 6

MICHIGAN

U.S. Registered Community Hospitals
(Nonfederal, short-term general and other special hospitals)

Utilization, Personnel, Revenue and Expenses, Community Health Indicators 2012–2016

	2016	2015	2014	2013	2012
TOTAL FACILITY (Includes Hospital and Nursing Home Units)					
Utilization - Inpatient					
Beds	24,924	24,723	24,398	25,059	25,100
Admissions	1,159,341	1,167,500	1,125,043	1,158,802	1,182,541
Inpatient Days	5,802,970	5,870,291	5,730,883	5,912,166	6,037,474
Average Length of Stay	5.0	5.0	5.1	5.1	5.1
Inpatient Surgeries	309,796	306,288	310,581	315,259	325,219
Births	106,510	107,136	106,127	107,429	106,525
Utilization - Outpatient					
Emergency Outpatient Visits	5,157,734	5,007,114	4,814,596	4,875,899	4,781,685
Other Outpatient Visits	32,275,034	30,689,232	29,132,989	27,692,597	28,037,761
Total Outpatient Visits	37,432,768	35,696,346	33,947,585	32,568,496	32,819,446
Outpatient Surgeries	680,673	657,116	680,084	674,583	678,329
Personnel					
Full Time RNs	43,576	42,175	41,409	38,800	38,759
Full Time LPNs	1,526	1,315	1,264	1,341	1,270
Part Time RNs	18,747	18,452	19,049	18,723	19,313
Part Time LPNs	714	685	709	796	748
Total Full Time	159,904	153,744	149,877	144,269	146,597
Total Part Time	62,701	59,161	61,585	61,716	63,422
Revenue - Inpatient					
Gross Inpatient Revenue	$41,408,403,971	$39,277,867,357	$36,289,771,030	$35,163,188,185	$34,248,317,962
Revenue - Outpatient					
Gross Outpatient Revenue	$45,924,845,258	$42,346,825,089	$38,763,168,547	$36,798,222,853	$34,632,987,398
Revenue and Expenses - Totals					
(Includes Inpatient and Outpatient)					
Total Gross Revenue	$87,333,249,229	$81,624,692,446	$75,052,939,577	$71,961,411,038	$68,881,305,360
Deductions from Revenue	56,354,481,482	52,418,895,696	47,734,916,913	45,245,940,980	41,938,126,634
Net Patient Revenue	30,978,767,747	29,205,796,750	27,318,022,664	26,715,470,058	26,943,178,726
Other Operating Revenue	1,418,180,280	1,345,541,708	1,388,381,837	1,525,618,772	1,306,714,292
Other Nonoperating Revenue	228,176,258	54,970,733	715,274,398	551,058,172	242,121,301
Total Net Revenue	32,625,124,285	30,606,309,191	29,421,678,899	28,792,147,002	28,492,014,319
Total Expenses	30,657,065,188	28,980,606,436	27,710,262,310	27,272,388,730	27,293,081,777
HOSPITAL UNIT (Excludes Separate Nursing Home Units)					
Utilization - Inpatient					
Beds	24,032	23,830	23,451	24,121	23,759
Admissions	1,155,583	1,163,393	1,120,926	1,154,598	1,177,789
Inpatient Days	5,515,461	5,570,796	5,411,436	5,605,462	5,600,603
Average Length of Stay	4.8	4.8	4.8	4.9	4.8
Personnel					
Total Full Time	159,124	152,979	149,252	143,689	145,517
Total Part Time	62,308	58,587	60,932	61,162	62,504
Revenue and Expenses - Totals					
(Includes Inpatient and Outpatient)					
Total Net Revenue	$32,532,225,154	$30,513,274,384	$29,323,229,916	$28,697,947,450	$28,374,005,103
Total Expenses	30,597,673,030	28,913,507,675	27,628,458,974	27,200,999,172	27,190,001,432
COMMUNITY HEALTH INDICATORS PER 1000 POPULATION					
Total Population (in thousands)	9,928	9,923	9,910	9,896	9,883
Inpatient					
Beds	2.5	2.5	2.5	2.5	2.5
Admissions	116.8	117.7	113.5	117.1	119.6
Inpatient Days	584.5	591.6	578.3	597.5	610.9
Inpatient Surgeries	31.2	30.9	31.3	31.9	32.9
Births	10.7	10.8	10.7	10.9	10.8
Outpatient					
Emergency Outpatient Visits	519.5	504.6	485.8	492.7	483.8
Other Outpatient Visits	3,250.8	3,092.9	2,939.8	2,798.5	2,836.9
Total Outpatient Visits	3,770.3	3,597.5	3,425.6	3,291.2	3,320.7
Outpatient Surgeries	68.6	66.2	68.6	68.2	68.6
Expense per Capita (per person)	$3,087.8	$2,920.7	$2,796.2	$2,756.0	$2,761.5

States

TABLE 6

MINNESOTA

U.S. Registered Community Hospitals
(Nonfederal, short-term general and other special hospitals)

Overview 2012–2016

	2016	2015	2014	2013	2012
Total Community Hospitals in Minnesota..........	129	130	131	131	133
Bed Size Category					
6-24..	27	24	21	21	21
25-49..	33	33	35	34	32
50-99..	30	33	34	35	37
100-199...	24	25	26	25	26
200-299...	2	3	3	4	4
300-399...	4	4	5	6	7
400-499...	6	5	4	3	3
500 +..	3	3	3	3	3
Location					
Hospitals Urban	53	54	55	49	51
Hospitals Rural..	76	76	76	82	82
Control					
State and Local Government........................	32	31	33	36	37
Not for Profit..	97	99	98	95	95
Investor owned..	0	0	0	0	1
Physician Models					
Independent Practice Association.....................	9	10	10	11	10
Group Practice without Walls........................	1	1	1	2	2
Open Physician-Hospital Organization	6	6	7	9	8
Closed Physician-Hospital Organization...........	2	2	2	2	2
Management Service Organization....................	1	2	2	1	2
Integrated Salary Model................................	59	61	62	61	56
Equity Model	0	1	1	1	0
Foundation	0	0	1	1	1
Insurance Products					
Health Maintenance Organization....................	22	21	22	19	19
Preferred Provider Organization	24	22	23	19	19
Indemnity Fee for Service..............................	6	6	7	6	5
Managed Care Contracts					
Health Maintenance Organization....................	52	50	56	47	44
Preferred Provider Organization	58	56	61	55	49
Affiliations					
Hospitals in a System...................................	83	84	85	81	82
Hospitals in a Network..................................	31	29	29	31	30
Hospitals in a Group Purchasing Organization...	92	91	94	92	90

TABLE 6

MINNESOTA

U.S. Registered Community Hospitals
(Nonfederal, short-term general and other special hospitals)

Utilization, Personnel, Revenue and Expenses, Community Health Indicators 2012–2016

	2016	2015	2014	2013	2012
TOTAL FACILITY (Includes Hospital and Nursing Home Units)					
Utilization - Inpatient					
Beds	14,277	14,393	14,562	14,781	14,895
Admissions	546,613	547,399	548,360	562,035	583,142
Inpatient Days	3,319,384	3,357,517	3,346,653	3,395,406	3,479,304
Average Length of Stay	6.1	6.1	6.1	6.0	6.0
Inpatient Surgeries	174,253	173,157	175,793	181,758	166,285
Births	67,449	67,081	66,960	67,898	64,001
Utilization - Outpatient					
Emergency Outpatient Visits	2,019,387	1,961,075	1,946,061	1,933,651	1,898,093
Other Outpatient Visits	11,499,803	10,278,747	10,023,292	9,732,473	9,532,070
Total Outpatient Visits	13,519,190	12,239,822	11,969,353	11,666,124	11,430,163
Outpatient Surgeries	335,648	335,562	322,191	322,895	302,985
Personnel					
Full Time RNs	12,678	13,120	12,942	12,220	11,693
Full Time LPNs	1,579	1,554	1,492	1,559	1,538
Part Time RNs	27,073	25,092	23,902	22,010	20,586
Part Time LPNs	1,679	1,615	1,681	1,666	1,524
Total Full Time	83,523	83,073	80,627	83,940	62,967
Total Part Time	71,017	66,846	64,045	61,875	57,938
Revenue - Inpatient					
Gross Inpatient Revenue	$23,766,111,231	$22,441,151,417	$21,280,123,954	$20,263,141,343	$19,494,970,283
Revenue - Outpatient					
Gross Outpatient Revenue	$24,607,182,442	$22,431,972,337	$20,107,877,258	$18,010,747,799	$17,426,213,830
Revenue and Expenses - Totals					
(Includes Inpatient and Outpatient)					
Total Gross Revenue	$48,373,293,673	$44,873,123,754	$41,388,001,212	$38,273,889,142	$36,921,184,113
Deductions from Revenue	29,987,533,574	27,385,010,912	24,738,287,806	22,240,528,284	21,566,323,331
Net Patient Revenue	18,385,760,099	17,488,112,842	16,649,713,406	16,033,360,858	15,354,860,782
Other Operating Revenue	974,290,684	879,946,693	857,887,159	797,395,199	736,968,011
Other Nonoperating Revenue	60,420,818	85,927,538	285,082,518	285,377,987	105,178,701
Total Net Revenue	19,420,471,601	18,453,987,073	17,792,683,083	17,116,134,044	16,197,007,494
Total Expenses	18,651,840,870	17,156,049,679	16,528,924,367	15,886,275,897	15,069,347,845
HOSPITAL UNIT (Excludes Separate Nursing Home Units)					
Utilization - Inpatient					
Beds	12,144	12,098	12,428	12,773	12,798
Admissions	542,848	543,432	544,181	558,324	579,267
Inpatient Days	2,622,349	2,602,118	2,631,904	2,749,985	2,790,444
Average Length of Stay	4.8	4.8	4.8	4.9	4.8
Personnel					
Total Full Time	82,582	82,103	79,565	82,892	61,780
Total Part Time	69,419	65,186	62,199	60,139	56,197
Revenue and Expenses - Totals					
(Includes Inpatient and Outpatient)					
Total Net Revenue	$19,238,547,023	$18,281,872,718	$17,618,940,851	$16,969,593,334	$16,055,142,778
Total Expenses	18,485,511,994	16,999,260,248	16,384,436,397	15,749,642,682	14,927,729,599
COMMUNITY HEALTH INDICATORS PER 1000 POPULATION					
Total Population (in thousands)	5,520	5,490	5,457	5,420	5,379
Inpatient					
Beds	2.6	2.6	2.7	2.7	2.8
Admissions	99.0	99.7	100.5	103.7	108.4
Inpatient Days	601.3	611.6	613.3	626.4	646.8
Inpatient Surgeries	31.6	31.5	32.2	33.5	30.9
Births	12.2	12.2	12.3	12.5	11.9
Outpatient					
Emergency Outpatient Visits	365.8	357.2	356.6	356.7	352.9
Other Outpatient Visits	2,083.3	1,872.4	1,836.7	1,795.5	1,772.0
Total Outpatient Visits	2,449.1	2,229.6	2,193.3	2,152.3	2,124.9
Outpatient Surgeries	60.8	61.1	59.0	59.6	56.3
Expense per Capita (per person)	$3,379.0	$3,125.2	$3,028.8	$2,930.8	$2,801.4

States

TABLE 6

MISSISSIPPI

U.S. Registered Community Hospitals
(Nonfederal, short-term general and other special hospitals)

Overview 2012–2016

	2016	2015	2014	2013	2012
Total Community Hospitals in Mississippi	93	95	97	99	98
Bed Size Category					
6-24	4	3	2	2	2
25-49	30	32	33	32	32
50-99	23	22	22	25	24
100-199	20	20	21	22	23
200-299	6	8	10	10	8
300-399	3	3	2	1	2
400-499	3	3	2	3	3
500 + ...	4	4	5	4	4
Location					
Hospitals Urban	26	26	27	28	28
Hospitals Rural	67	69	70	71	70
Control					
State and Local Government	38	39	39	41	40
Not for Profit	31	29	29	29	29
Investor owned	24	27	29	29	29
Physician Models					
Independent Practice Association	6	6	6	5	5
Group Practice without Walls	2	2	2	2	2
Open Physician-Hospital Organization	16	16	20	15	16
Closed Physician-Hospital Organization ...	3	4	4	4	3
Management Service Organization	13	11	8	8	9
Integrated Salary Model	21	24	25	29	26
Equity Model	0	1	2	1	2
Foundation	5	4	7	8	7
Insurance Products					
Health Maintenance Organization	10	9	9	8	8
Preferred Provider Organization	28	28	35	37	36
Indemnity Fee for Service	7	6	10	8	9
Managed Care Contracts					
Health Maintenance Organization	21	22	23	26	26
Preferred Provider Organization	42	39	42	46	45
Affiliations					
Hospitals in a System	49	51	53	51	47
Hospitals in a Network	27	27	25	26	26
Hospitals in a Group Purchasing Organization...	86	82	1	2	0

TABLE 6

MISSISSIPPI

U.S. Registered Community Hospitals
(Nonfederal, short-term general and other special hospitals)

Utilization, Personnel, Revenue and Expenses, Community Health Indicators 2012–2016

	2016	2015	2014	2013	2012
TOTAL FACILITY (Includes Hospital and Nursing Home Units)					
Utilization - Inpatient					
Beds...	12,032	12,240	12,471	12,826	12,882
Admissions.................................	378,550	358,505	373,189	380,059	384,078
Inpatient Days............................	2,447,098	2,483,397	2,511,963	2,499,123	2,505,846
Average Length of Stay	6.5	6.9	6.7	6.6	6.5
Inpatient Surgeries.....................	94,135	96,550	97,278	100,878	104,043
Births...	35,787	37,108	37,543	36,911	37,565
Utilization - Outpatient					
Emergency Outpatient Visits..............	1,814,490	1,769,678	1,796,073	1,794,793	1,767,684
Other Outpatient Visits...............	4,241,961	3,739,085	3,205,427	3,160,783	3,321,143
Total Outpatient Visits................	6,056,451	5,508,763	5,001,500	4,955,576	5,088,827
Outpatient Surgeries..................	184,931	175,584	180,721	173,872	169,096
Personnel					
Full Time RNs	12,780	12,874	12,307	12,265	12,179
Full Time LPNs..........................	1,214	1,255	1,236	1,427	1,437
Part Time RNs............................	4,791	4,353	4,113	4,134	3,784
Part Time LPNs..........................	287	316	375	379	339
Total Full Time...........................	46,706	47,461	46,299	46,669	46,695
Total Part Time	13,069	12,202	12,124	11,989	11,755
Revenue - Inpatient					
Gross Inpatient Revenue	$14,944,863,371	$14,214,172,663	$14,133,584,691	$13,886,931,276	$12,982,460,621
Revenue - Outpatient					
Gross Outpatient Revenue	$15,786,159,174	$14,024,937,283	$12,952,432,101	$12,199,680,887	$11,618,451,746
Revenue and Expenses - Totals					
(Includes Inpatient and Outpatient)					
Total Gross Revenue......................	$30,731,022,545	$28,239,109,946	$27,086,016,792	$26,086,612,163	$24,600,912,367
Deductions from Revenue	23,083,709,411	20,830,266,436	19,927,771,753	18,961,333,700	17,485,118,401
Net Patient Revenue...................	7,647,313,134	7,408,843,510	7,158,245,039	7,125,278,463	7,115,793,966
Other Operating Revenue	317,736,196	299,447,552	322,055,646	316,465,170	336,578,667
Other Nonoperating Revenue	71,554,976	82,105,898	109,916,744	122,250,060	124,396,684
Total Net Revenue......................	8,036,604,306	7,790,396,960	7,590,217,429	7,563,993,693	7,576,769,317
Total Expenses...........................	7,206,410,015	7,225,388,181	7,188,316,628	7,101,439,812	6,982,689,683
HOSPITAL UNIT (Excludes Separate Nursing Home Units)					
Utilization - Inpatient					
Beds...	10,447	10,714	10,858	11,037	11,102
Admissions.................................	377,655	357,520	372,154	378,968	383,020
Inpatient Days............................	1,903,032	1,959,302	1,966,719	1,896,950	1,906,203
Average Length of Stay	5.0	5.5	5.3	5.0	5.0
Personnel					
Total Full Time...........................	45,932	46,768	45,036	45,233	45,222
Total Part Time	12,735	11,898	11,661	11,496	11,330
Revenue and Expenses - Totals					
(Includes Inpatient and Outpatient)					
Total Net Revenue......................	$7,907,083,995	$7,667,528,694	$7,527,130,297	$7,460,470,583	$7,501,877,310
Total Expenses...........................	7,112,964,142	7,146,552,141	7,140,037,508	7,040,309,114	6,920,499,818
COMMUNITY HEALTH INDICATORS PER 1000 POPULATION					
Total Population (in thousands)..........	2,989	2,992	2,994	2,991	2,985
Inpatient					
Beds...	4.0	4.1	4.2	4.3	4.3
Admissions.................................	126.7	119.8	124.6	127.1	128.7
Inpatient Days............................	818.8	829.9	839.0	835.5	839.5
Inpatient Surgeries.....................	31.5	32.3	32.5	33.7	34.9
Births...	12.0	12.4	12.5	12.3	12.6
Outpatient					
Emergency Outpatient Visits..............	607.1	591.4	599.9	600.0	592.2
Other Outpatient Visits...............	1,419.3	1,249.6	1,070.6	1,056.7	1,112.6
Total Outpatient Visits................	2,026.4	1,841.0	1,670.5	1,656.7	1,704.8
Outpatient Surgeries..................	61.9	58.7	60.4	58.1	56.6
Expense per Capita (per person).........	$2,411.2	$2,414.6	$2,400.8	$2,374.1	$2,339.3

States

TABLE **6**

MISSOURI

U.S. Registered Community Hospitals
(Nonfederal, short-term general and other special hospitals)

Overview 2012–2016

	2016	2015	2014	2013	2012
Total Community Hospitals in Missouri.............	119	121	122	123	123
Bed Size Category					
6-24	12	12	10	11	9
25-49	34	35	38	38	39
50-99	21	21	19	19	20
100-199	21	24	26	25	25
200-299	12	10	10	11	11
300-399	7	7	7	7	7
400-499	3	5	6	6	6
500 + ...	9	7	6	6	6
Location					
Hospitals Urban	69	71	71	70	70
Hospitals Rural..	50	50	51	53	53
Control					
State and Local Government	30	30	31	32	34
Not for Profit...	65	65	65	65	64
Investor owned..	24	26	26	26	25
Physician Models					
Independent Practice Association..............	11	10	11	8	8
Group Practice without Walls	0	0	0	0	0
Open Physician-Hospital Organization	15	14	14	15	15
Closed Physician-Hospital Organization.....	5	4	5	6	6
Management Service Organization.............	0	0	0	0	0
Integrated Salary Model...........................	76	71	75	70	66
Equity Model	1	1	1	1	1
Foundation	2	1	3	4	2
Insurance Products					
Health Maintenance Organization.............	16	12	12	11	11
Preferred Provider Organization	14	11	10	10	10
Indemnity Fee for Service	6	4	5	3	2
Managed Care Contracts					
Health Maintenance Organization.............	97	97	97	97	99
Preferred Provider Organization	103	103	105	107	105
Affiliations					
Hospitals in a System	75	75	77	77	77
Hospitals in a Network	55	53	47	39	38
Hospitals in a Group Purchasing Organization...	119	117	120	122	121

TABLE 6

MISSOURI

U.S. Registered Community Hospitals
(Nonfederal, short-term general and other special hospitals)

Utilization, Personnel, Revenue and Expenses, Community Health Indicators 2012–2016

	2016	2015	2014	2013	2012
TOTAL FACILITY (Includes Hospital and Nursing Home Units)					
Utilization - Inpatient					
Beds	18,575	18,615	18,613	18,899	19,032
Admissions	770,748	784,290	779,774	781,070	799,256
Inpatient Days	4,090,544	4,107,971	4,057,997	4,060,151	4,120,318
Average Length of Stay	5.3	5.2	5.2	5.2	5.2
Inpatient Surgeries	192,833	194,981	196,360	199,770	206,215
Births	73,188	73,498	74,548	74,688	75,301
Utilization - Outpatient					
Emergency Outpatient Visits	3,139,087	3,108,239	2,975,892	2,987,268	3,042,008
Other Outpatient Visits	21,222,530	20,026,094	19,055,501	18,856,989	18,024,433
Total Outpatient Visits	24,361,617	23,134,333	22,031,393	21,844,257	21,066,441
Outpatient Surgeries	397,782	382,782	380,551	385,614	382,699
Personnel					
Full Time RNs	30,707	30,348	29,757	28,943	27,597
Full Time LPNs	2,423	2,373	2,429	2,377	2,375
Part Time RNs	10,996	11,359	10,962	11,212	12,913
Part Time LPNs	540	535	528	555	664
Total Full Time	109,626	106,437	104,705	104,194	102,089
Total Part Time	34,018	34,185	32,984	33,507	38,730
Revenue - Inpatient					
Gross Inpatient Revenue	$32,523,745,717	$30,959,437,887	$29,539,049,363	$27,966,288,581	$27,122,625,962
Revenue - Outpatient					
Gross Outpatient Revenue	$36,558,004,173	$33,041,134,406	$30,066,527,678	$27,913,913,149	$26,031,861,914
Revenue and Expenses - Totals					
(Includes Inpatient and Outpatient)					
Total Gross Revenue	$69,081,749,890	$64,000,572,293	$59,605,577,041	$55,880,201,730	$53,154,487,876
Deductions from Revenue	48,136,858,189	44,162,427,882	40,798,547,659	37,726,886,672	35,362,416,605
Net Patient Revenue	20,944,891,701	19,838,144,411	18,807,029,382	18,153,315,058	17,792,071,271
Other Operating Revenue	1,231,314,006	1,248,433,494	1,104,602,991	1,154,601,122	1,281,736,177
Other Nonoperating Revenue	292,011,651	237,425,463	382,421,126	665,919,682	794,602,472
Total Net Revenue	22,468,217,358	21,324,003,368	20,294,053,499	19,973,835,862	19,868,409,920
Total Expenses	21,355,922,273	20,150,390,956	19,367,868,494	18,734,464,777	17,024,103,374
HOSPITAL UNIT (Excludes Separate Nursing Home Units)					
Utilization - Inpatient					
Beds	17,645	17,646	17,650	17,904	18,035
Admissions	766,491	779,555	772,501	775,368	793,155
Inpatient Days	3,846,510	3,845,995	3,769,911	3,767,287	3,822,166
Average Length of Stay	5.0	4.9	4.9	4.9	4.8
Personnel					
Total Full Time	108,937	105,658	103,901	103,345	101,135
Total Part Time	33,699	33,856	32,534	33,091	38,172
Revenue and Expenses - Totals					
(Includes Inpatient and Outpatient)					
Total Net Revenue	$22,399,298,332	$21,240,147,610	$20,205,003,962	$19,902,552,926	$19,777,379,107
Total Expenses	21,294,439,429	20,075,372,457	19,304,920,800	18,659,708,181	16,948,096,420
COMMUNITY HEALTH INDICATORS PER 1000 POPULATION					
Total Population (in thousands)	6,093	6,084	6,064	6,044	6,022
Inpatient					
Beds	3.0	3.1	3.1	3.1	3.2
Admissions	126.5	128.9	128.6	129.2	132.7
Inpatient Days	671.4	675.2	669.2	671.7	684.2
Inpatient Surgeries	31.6	32.0	32.4	33.1	34.2
Births	12.0	12.1	12.3	12.4	12.5
Outpatient					
Emergency Outpatient Visits	515.2	510.9	490.8	494.2	505.2
Other Outpatient Visits	3,483.1	3,291.8	3,142.6	3,119.9	2,993.1
Total Outpatient Visits	3,998.3	3,802.7	3,633.4	3,614.1	3,498.3
Outpatient Surgeries	65.3	62.9	62.8	63.8	63.6
Expense per Capita (per person)	$3,505.0	$3,312.2	$3,194.1	$3,099.6	$2,827.0

States

TABLE 6

MONTANA

U.S. Registered Community Hospitals
(Nonfederal, short-term general and other special hospitals)

Overview 2012–2016

	2016	2015	2014	2013	2012
Total Community Hospitals in Montana	50	50	50	50	48
Bed Size Category					
6-24	11	10	11	9	10
25-49	17	15	14	16	13
50-99	13	16	16	16	15
100-199	5	5	6	6	7
200-299	2	2	1	1	1
300-399	0	1	1	1	1
400-499	1	0	1	1	1
500 +	1	1	0	0	0
Location					
Hospitals Urban	6	6	6	6	6
Hospitals Rural	44	44	44	44	42
Control					
State and Local Government	7	8	8	9	10
Not for Profit	39	39	41	40	37
Investor owned	4	3	1	1	1
Physician Models					
Independent Practice Association	2	1	2	5	4
Group Practice without Walls	2	2	2	5	4
Open Physician-Hospital Organization	2	4	4	4	4
Closed Physician-Hospital Organization	1	1	0	1	1
Management Service Organization	2	3	4	6	5
Integrated Salary Model	28	28	32	30	28
Equity Model	0	0	1	1	1
Foundation	5	3	6	6	6
Insurance Products					
Health Maintenance Organization	3	2	3	2	2
Preferred Provider Organization	13	13	13	9	9
Indemnity Fee for Service	4	4	5	3	4
Managed Care Contracts					
Health Maintenance Organization	14	11	11	7	8
Preferred Provider Organization	30	27	31	26	27
Affiliations					
Hospitals in a System	12	12	11	11	11
Hospitals in a Network	23	23	23	23	23
Hospitals in a Group Purchasing Organization	41	42	42	45	40

TABLE 6

MONTANA

U.S. Registered Community Hospitals
(Nonfederal, short-term general and other special hospitals)

Utilization, Personnel, Revenue and Expenses, Community Health Indicators 2012–2016

	2016	2015	2014	2013	2012
TOTAL FACILITY (Includes Hospital and Nursing Home Units)					
Utilization - Inpatient					
Beds	3,644	3,799	3,685	3,722	3,710
Admissions	93,184	94,043	92,687	95,321	93,423
Inpatient Days	781,200	839,109	800,383	820,251	809,199
Average Length of Stay	8.4	8.9	8.6	8.6	8.7
Inpatient Surgeries	28,054	27,587	27,976	28,116	27,627
Births	10,933	11,561	10,613	10,245	10,191
Utilization - Outpatient					
Emergency Outpatient Visits	421,448	413,742	373,953	376,845	366,756
Other Outpatient Visits	3,534,065	3,234,191	3,108,414	3,386,696	3,218,282
Total Outpatient Visits	3,955,513	3,647,933	3,482,367	3,763,541	3,585,038
Outpatient Surgeries	62,170	58,095	55,309	52,787	48,788
Personnel					
Full Time RNs	3,557	3,579	3,374	3,304	3,191
Full Time LPNs	334	404	519	491	486
Part Time RNs	2,642	2,194	1,961	2,052	2,047
Part Time LPNs	209	208	219	238	280
Total Full Time	17,378	16,763	16,486	15,919	15,720
Total Part Time	9,635	7,832	7,698	8,209	7,743
Revenue - Inpatient					
Gross Inpatient Revenue	$3,147,502,582	$2,897,071,002	$2,513,809,538	$2,454,369,080	$2,279,133,191
Revenue - Outpatient					
Gross Outpatient Revenue	$4,323,446,869	$3,902,496,332	$3,520,042,567	$3,397,775,194	$2,990,024,968
Revenue and Expenses - Totals (Includes Inpatient and Outpatient)					
Total Gross Revenue	$7,470,949,451	$6,799,567,334	$6,033,852,105	$5,852,144,274	$5,269,158,159
Deductions from Revenue	4,136,690,971	3,593,503,008	3,096,468,098	3,015,777,016	2,595,587,712
Net Patient Revenue	3,334,258,480	3,206,064,326	2,937,384,007	2,836,367,258	2,673,570,447
Other Operating Revenue	174,272,958	135,427,864	143,190,912	155,924,250	110,280,462
Other Nonoperating Revenue	42,429,263	51,038,645	110,042,762	71,944,698	22,151,981
Total Net Revenue	3,550,960,701	3,392,530,835	3,190,617,681	3,064,236,206	2,806,002,890
Total Expenses	3,278,884,240	3,049,703,007	2,855,454,234	2,874,246,551	2,660,995,740
HOSPITAL UNIT (Excludes Separate Nursing Home Units)					
Utilization - Inpatient					
Beds	2,544	2,591	2,418	2,424	2,403
Admissions	91,502	92,348	90,949	93,268	91,325
Inpatient Days	471,211	473,132	435,698	426,085	410,312
Average Length of Stay	5.1	5.1	4.8	4.6	4.5
Personnel					
Total Full Time	16,661	16,095	15,739	15,182	14,970
Total Part Time	9,014	7,314	7,115	7,616	7,213
Revenue and Expenses - Totals (Includes Inpatient and Outpatient)					
Total Net Revenue	$3,486,877,534	$3,322,780,417	$3,114,852,318	$2,986,335,907	$2,733,592,548
Total Expenses	3,218,669,605	2,986,935,030	2,787,516,329	2,812,268,630	2,591,928,424
COMMUNITY HEALTH INDICATORS PER 1000 POPULATION					
Total Population (in thousands)	1,043	1,033	1,024	1,015	1,005
Inpatient					
Beds	3.5	3.7	3.6	3.7	3.7
Admissions	89.4	91.0	90.6	93.9	92.9
Inpatient Days	749.3	812.3	781.9	808.0	805.1
Inpatient Surgeries	26.9	26.7	27.3	27.7	27.5
Births	10.5	11.2	10.4	10.1	10.1
Outpatient					
Emergency Outpatient Visits	404.3	400.5	365.3	371.2	364.9
Other Outpatient Visits	3,389.9	3,131.0	3,036.8	3,336.1	3,201.8
Total Outpatient Visits	3,794.2	3,531.6	3,402.1	3,707.3	3,566.7
Outpatient Surgeries	59.6	56.2	54.0	52.0	48.5
Expense per Capita (per person)	$3,145.2	$2,952.4	$2,789.7	$2,831.3	$2,647.4

States

TABLE 6

NEBRASKA

U.S. Registered Community Hospitals
(Nonfederal, short-term general and other special hospitals)

Overview 2012–2016

	2016	2015	2014	2013	2012
Total Community Hospitals in Nebraska.............	88	88	89	87	89
Bed Size Category					
6-24	29	28	27	26	26
25-49	23	23	23	21	21
50-99	18	19	20	21	22
100-199	10	9	9	7	10
200-299	3	4	5	7	5
300-399	3	3	4	4	3
400-499	0	0	0	0	2
500 + ...	2	2	1	1	0
Location					
Hospitals Urban	22	22	23	18	18
Hospitals Rural	66	66	66	69	71
Control					
State and Local Government	36	35	36	36	38
Not for Profit	49	50	49	49	49
Investor owned	3	3	4	2	2
Physician Models					
Independent Practice Association	4	5	5	4	6
Group Practice without Walls	0	0	1	1	2
Open Physician-Hospital Organization	18	14	12	11	11
Closed Physician-Hospital Organization............	3	3	2	2	2
Management Service Organization.....................	3	2	2	2	2
Integrated Salary Model.....................................	22	23	25	20	24
Equity Model	1	1	0	0	0
Foundation	0	1	2	2	2
Insurance Products					
Health Maintenance Organization......................	1	2	2	4	2
Preferred Provider Organization	7	10	6	4	7
Indemnity Fee for Service	1	1	0	0	1
Managed Care Contracts					
Health Maintenance Organization......................	12	13	15	14	16
Preferred Provider Organization	39	38	35	32	43
Affiliations					
Hospitals in a System	28	28	30	28	29
Hospitals in a Network	33	32	31	30	30
Hospitals in a Group Purchasing Organization...	47	45	37	36	42

TABLE 6

NEBRASKA

U.S. Registered Community Hospitals
(Nonfederal, short-term general and other special hospitals)

Utilization, Personnel, Revenue and Expenses, Community Health Indicators 2012–2016

	2016	2015	2014	2013	2012
TOTAL FACILITY (Includes Hospital and Nursing Home Units)					
Utilization - Inpatient					
Beds	6,540	6,625	6,674	6,784	6,997
Admissions	192,539	193,135	195,869	199,933	205,065
Inpatient Days	1,281,265	1,299,608	1,331,045	1,335,733	1,411,707
Average Length of Stay	6.7	6.7	6.8	6.7	6.9
Inpatient Surgeries	59,901	62,954	67,043	60,205	81,170
Births	25,223	26,263	26,037	25,323	25,859
Utilization - Outpatient					
Emergency Outpatient Visits	824,722	715,084	706,923	692,717	671,332
Other Outpatient Visits	4,334,928	3,957,161	3,867,470	4,066,743	4,556,326
Total Outpatient Visits	5,159,650	4,672,245	4,574,393	4,759,460	5,227,658
Outpatient Surgeries	137,480	128,122	124,786	119,958	130,932
Personnel					
Full Time RNs	8,067	8,290	7,861	8,332	8,429
Full Time LPNs	654	611	571	617	681
Part Time RNs	4,302	3,839	3,950	3,878	4,274
Part Time LPNs	336	269	275	296	388
Total Full Time	29,370	29,308	27,336	28,467	29,039
Total Part Time	14,893	13,340	12,701	12,462	13,789
Revenue - Inpatient					
Gross Inpatient Revenue	$7,517,884,432	$7,298,558,037	$7,188,591,726	$6,714,985,216	$6,600,070,735
Revenue - Outpatient					
Gross Outpatient Revenue	$8,731,242,590	$7,806,383,994	$7,542,831,120	$6,650,376,967	$6,127,521,502
Revenue and Expenses - Totals (Includes Inpatient and Outpatient)					
Total Gross Revenue	$16,249,127,022	$15,104,942,031	$14,731,422,846	$13,365,362,183	$12,727,592,237
Deductions from Revenue	10,065,988,026	9,442,863,394	9,077,024,900	8,104,547,928	7,443,134,120
Net Patient Revenue	6,183,138,996	5,662,078,637	5,654,397,946	5,260,814,255	5,284,458,117
Other Operating Revenue	326,114,531	332,963,149	319,076,285	314,198,761	276,960,199
Other Nonoperating Revenue	83,152,066	17,487,088	135,583,028	175,886,117	61,823,105
Total Net Revenue	6,592,405,593	6,012,528,874	6,109,057,259	5,750,899,133	5,623,241,421
Total Expenses	5,924,356,169	5,269,358,793	5,246,493,342	4,870,429,742	4,972,245,644
HOSPITAL UNIT (Excludes Separate Nursing Home Units)					
Utilization - Inpatient					
Beds	5,792	5,986	5,782	5,921	5,979
Admissions	191,638	192,388	194,041	197,813	202,588
Inpatient Days	1,053,914	1,101,480	1,094,583	1,074,406	1,097,274
Average Length of Stay	5.5	5.7	5.6	5.4	5.4
Personnel					
Total Full Time	28,941	28,918	26,847	27,928	28,349
Total Part Time	14,613	13,117	12,315	12,190	13,362
Revenue and Expenses - Totals (Includes Inpatient and Outpatient)					
Total Net Revenue	$6,549,495,673	$5,975,561,535	$6,053,452,583	$5,689,097,400	$5,554,405,718
Total Expenses	5,890,624,235	5,238,548,687	5,187,610,294	4,798,846,323	4,897,073,033
COMMUNITY HEALTH INDICATORS PER 1000 POPULATION					
Total Population (in thousands)	1,907	1,896	1,882	1,869	1,856
Inpatient					
Beds	3.4	3.5	3.5	3.6	3.8
Admissions	101.0	101.9	104.1	107.0	110.5
Inpatient Days	671.8	685.4	707.4	714.9	760.8
Inpatient Surgeries	31.4	33.2	35.6	32.2	43.7
Births	13.2	13.9	13.8	13.6	13.9
Outpatient					
Emergency Outpatient Visits	432.4	377.1	375.7	370.7	361.8
Other Outpatient Visits	2,273.0	2,086.9	2,055.5	2,176.5	2,455.5
Total Outpatient Visits	2,705.5	2,464.0	2,431.2	2,547.2	2,817.3
Outpatient Surgeries	72.1	67.6	66.3	64.2	70.6
Expense per Capita (per person)	$3,106.4	$2,778.9	$2,788.5	$2,606.6	$2,679.7

States

TABLE 6

NEVADA

U.S. Registered Community Hospitals
(Nonfederal, short-term general and other special hospitals)

Overview 2012–2016

	2016	2015	2014	2013	2012
Total Community Hospitals in Nevada	36	36	37	38	38
Bed Size Category					
6-24	5	6	6	5	5
25-49	5	5	6	7	6
50-99	10	9	9	10	11
100-199	6	6	7	7	7
200-299	3	4	3	3	4
300-399	4	3	3	3	2
400-499	0	0	0	0	0
500 + ...	3	3	3	3	3
Location					
Hospitals Urban	26	26	27	27	27
Hospitals Rural	10	10	10	11	11
Control					
State and Local Government	6	5	6	6	6
Not for Profit...	12	13	12	12	12
Investor owned...	18	18	19	20	20
Physician Models					
Independent Practice Association......................	1	1	0	1	4
Group Practice without Walls...........................	0	1	1	1	0
Open Physician-Hospital Organization	1	2	2	3	1
Closed Physician-Hospital Organization............	1	1	1	2	2
Management Service Organization....................	4	4	2	2	1
Integrated Salary Model..................................	10	9	9	8	9
Equity Model	0	0	0	0	0
Foundation	0	0	1	1	0
Insurance Products					
Health Maintenance Organization......................	6	6	6	7	6
Preferred Provider Organization	6	6	6	7	6
Indemnity Fee for Service	6	6	6	6	6
Managed Care Contracts					
Health Maintenance Organization......................	14	16	15	16	17
Preferred Provider Organization	14	16	15	16	17
Affiliations					
Hospitals in a System	26	26	27	27	27
Hospitals in a Network	5	6	4	6	6
Hospitals in a Group Purchasing Organization...	13	16	17	21	18

TABLE 6

NEVADA

U.S. Registered Community Hospitals
(Nonfederal, short-term general and other special hospitals)

Utilization, Personnel, Revenue and Expenses, Community Health Indicators 2012–2016

	2016	2015	2014	2013	2012
TOTAL FACILITY (Includes Hospital and Nursing Home Units)					
Utilization - Inpatient					
Beds..	5,662	5,532	5,549	5,655	5,504
Admissions....................................	269,741	261,480	256,223	253,822	260,781
Inpatient Days...............................	1,540,521	1,498,077	1,398,303	1,384,938	1,361,402
Average Length of Stay	5.7	5.7	5.5	5.5	5.2
Inpatient Surgeries........................	50,079	58,556	56,353	62,098	63,184
Births..	24,282	25,041	23,860	28,592	26,384
Utilization - Outpatient					
Emergency Outpatient Visits..........	905,556	960,933	909,831	928,562	865,371
Other Outpatient Visits..................	2,365,317	2,052,550	2,067,141	1,697,472	2,045,456
Total Outpatient Visits	3,270,873	3,013,483	2,976,972	2,626,034	2,910,827
Outpatient Surgeries......................	95,529	95,218	91,475	88,318	88,694
Personnel					
Full Time RNs	7,702	8,010	7,662	7,796	6,951
Full Time LPNs.............................	287	248	276	312	322
Part Time RNs..............................	1,886	2,028	1,860	1,900	1,816
Part Time LPNs.............................	56	67	57	72	69
Total Full Time	23,430	23,630	22,654	22,786	21,297
Total Part Time	5,394	5,961	5,296	5,264	4,899
Revenue - Inpatient					
Gross Inpatient Revenue	$15,383,438,308	$15,928,383,247	$14,249,565,398	$13,752,019,901	$12,294,975,694
Revenue - Outpatient					
Gross Outpatient Revenue	$11,652,126,211	$10,653,440,520	$9,280,344,629	$8,132,111,085	$6,990,158,850
Revenue and Expenses - Totals					
(Includes Inpatient and Outpatient)					
Total Gross Revenue......................	$27,035,564,519	$26,581,823,767	$23,529,910,027	$21,884,130,986	$19,285,134,544
Deductions from Revenue	21,567,840,750	21,387,678,975	18,729,674,504	17,304,616,909	15,017,726,173
Net Patient Revenue......................	5,467,723,769	5,194,144,792	4,800,235,523	4,579,514,077	4,267,408,371
Other Operating Revenue...............	174,494,678	169,214,952	154,396,930	151,926,188	102,905,260
Other Nonoperating Revenue..........	35,122,756	34,733,755	52,723,747	28,598,769	35,498,438
Total Net Revenue.........................	5,677,341,203	5,398,093,499	5,007,356,200	4,760,039,034	4,405,812,069
Total Expenses.............................	5,316,360,076	4,936,440,717	4,538,309,153	4,407,998,320	4,199,882,893
HOSPITAL UNIT (Excludes Separate Nursing Home Units)					
Utilization - Inpatient					
Beds..	5,546	5,469	5,549	5,655	5,479
Admissions....................................	269,640	261,460	256,223	253,822	260,768
Inpatient Days...............................	1,508,771	1,478,297	1,398,303	1,384,938	1,354,258
Average Length of Stay	5.6	5.7	5.5	5.5	5.2
Personnel					
Total Full Time	23,371	23,607	22,654	22,786	21,284
Total Part Time	5,367	5,949	5,296	5,264	4,899
Revenue and Expenses - Totals					
(Includes Inpatient and Outpatient)					
Total Net Revenue.........................	$5,670,335,528	$5,396,161,276	$5,007,356,200	$4,760,039,034	$4,403,869,456
Total Expenses.............................	5,311,539,046	4,934,443,491	4,538,309,153	4,407,998,320	4,198,988,696
COMMUNITY HEALTH INDICATORS PER 1000 POPULATION					
Total Population (in thousands)...........	2,940	2,891	2,839	2,790	2,759
Inpatient					
Beds..	1.9	1.9	2.0	2.0	2.0
Admissions....................................	91.7	90.5	90.2	91.0	94.5
Inpatient Days...............................	524.0	518.2	492.5	496.4	493.5
Inpatient Surgeries........................	17.0	20.3	19.8	22.3	22.9
Births..	8.3	8.7	8.4	10.2	9.6
Outpatient					
Emergency Outpatient Visits..............	308.0	332.4	320.5	332.8	313.7
Other Outpatient Visits..................	804.5	710.0	728.1	608.4	741.4
Total Outpatient Visits	1,112.5	1,042.4	1,048.6	941.2	1,055.1
Outpatient Surgeries......................	32.5	32.9	32.2	31.7	32.1
Expense per Capita (per person)........	$1,808.3	$1,707.6	$1,598.5	$1,579.9	$1,522.3

States

TABLE 6

NEW HAMPSHIRE

U.S. Registered Community Hospitals
(Nonfederal, short-term general and other special hospitals)

Overview 2012–2016

	2016	2015	2014	2013	2012
Total Community Hospitals in New Hampshire..	28	28	28	28	28
Bed Size Category					
6-24	1	1	1	1	1
25-49	11	10	10	10	10
50-99	6	7	7	7	7
100-199	6	6	6	6	6
200-299	3	3	3	3	3
300-399	0	0	0	1	1
400-499	1	1	1	0	0
500 +	0	0	0	0	0
Location					
Hospitals Urban	11	11	11	11	11
Hospitals Rural	17	17	17	17	17
Control					
State and Local Government	0	0	0	0	0
Not for Profit	24	24	24	24	24
Investor owned	4	4	4	4	4
Physician Models					
Independent Practice Association	2	2	2	2	2
Group Practice without Walls	2	2	2	2	2
Open Physician-Hospital Organization	4	4	4	4	4
Closed Physician-Hospital Organization	0	0	0	0	0
Management Service Organization	0	0	0	0	0
Integrated Salary Model	20	20	18	19	19
Equity Model	0	0	0	0	0
Foundation	0	0	0	0	0
Insurance Products					
Health Maintenance Organization	8	5	2	0	0
Preferred Provider Organization	6	2	0	0	0
Indemnity Fee for Service	4	0	0	0	0
Managed Care Contracts					
Health Maintenance Organization	17	19	18	19	19
Preferred Provider Organization	16	18	17	18	18
Affiliations					
Hospitals in a System	8	7	7	7	6
Hospitals in a Network	12	12	13	11	12
Hospitals in a Group Purchasing Organization...	24	23	22	24	25

TABLE 6

NEW HAMPSHIRE

U.S. Registered Community Hospitals
(Nonfederal, short-term general and other special hospitals)

Utilization, Personnel, Revenue and Expenses, Community Health Indicators 2012–2016

	2016	2015	2014	2013	2012
TOTAL FACILITY (Includes Hospital and Nursing Home Units)					
Utilization - Inpatient					
Beds	2,792	2,819	2,839	2,809	2,831
Admissions	124,840	120,080	117,327	119,566	119,814
Inpatient Days	654,451	651,556	630,685	628,043	627,784
Average Length of Stay	5.2	5.4	5.4	5.3	5.2
Inpatient Surgeries	34,031	33,616	34,546	32,881	33,606
Births	13,017	13,485	13,516	12,664	12,035
Utilization - Outpatient					
Emergency Outpatient Visits	653,672	670,738	644,075	700,141	652,190
Other Outpatient Visits	4,589,175	4,732,025	4,265,408	4,346,816	4,330,937
Total Outpatient Visits	5,242,847	5,402,763	4,909,483	5,046,957	4,983,127
Outpatient Surgeries	86,929	85,009	85,589	89,108	90,715
Personnel					
Full Time RNs	5,247	5,164	4,982	4,648	4,460
Full Time LPNs	310	265	254	283	278
Part Time RNs	2,747	2,666	2,926	2,889	3,068
Part Time LPNs	79	81	96	111	128
Total Full Time	24,027	23,186	22,877	21,980	21,736
Total Part Time	9,049	9,131	9,680	10,181	10,229
Revenue - Inpatient					
Gross Inpatient Revenue	$4,868,308,563	$4,681,725,519	$4,989,417,217	$4,696,146,268	$4,263,267,285
Revenue - Outpatient					
Gross Outpatient Revenue	$8,756,510,168	$7,960,187,285	$7,220,073,530	$6,733,412,770	$6,315,255,279
Revenue and Expenses - Totals					
(Includes Inpatient and Outpatient)					
Total Gross Revenue	$13,624,818,731	$12,641,912,804	$12,209,490,747	$11,429,559,038	$10,578,522,564
Deductions from Revenue	8,668,511,254	8,085,622,586	7,808,011,257	7,139,588,921	6,389,949,615
Net Patient Revenue	4,956,307,477	4,556,290,218	4,401,479,490	4,289,970,117	4,188,572,949
Other Operating Revenue	240,104,568	210,402,508	197,582,231	165,027,209	172,037,917
Other Nonoperating Revenue	6,673,937	3,370,504	123,495,316	87,925,169	65,319,726
Total Net Revenue	5,203,085,982	4,770,063,230	4,722,557,037	4,542,922,495	4,425,930,592
Total Expenses	4,814,609,303	4,465,458,316	4,250,644,036	4,089,847,120	4,024,997,567
HOSPITAL UNIT (Excludes Separate Nursing Home Units)					
Utilization - Inpatient					
Beds	2,747	2,716	2,736	2,706	2,728
Admissions	124,825	119,988	117,253	119,473	119,684
Inpatient Days	638,304	618,237	595,536	592,762	592,483
Average Length of Stay	5.1	5.2	5.1	5.0	5.0
Personnel					
Total Full Time	24,003	23,135	22,817	21,933	21,685
Total Part Time	9,034	9,104	9,646	10,159	10,202
Revenue and Expenses - Totals					
(Includes Inpatient and Outpatient)					
Total Net Revenue	$5,199,781,022	$4,763,300,694	$4,715,825,712	$4,535,848,627	$4,417,200,764
Total Expenses	4,812,487,558	4,459,583,467	4,244,135,217	4,083,503,383	4,017,253,998
COMMUNITY HEALTH INDICATORS PER 1000 POPULATION					
Total Population (in thousands)	1,335	1,331	1,327	1,323	1,321
Inpatient					
Beds	2.1	2.1	2.1	2.1	2.1
Admissions	93.5	90.2	88.4	90.3	90.7
Inpatient Days	490.3	489.7	475.3	474.5	475.3
Inpatient Surgeries	25.5	25.3	26.0	24.8	25.4
Births	9.8	10.1	10.2	9.6	9.1
Outpatient					
Emergency Outpatient Visits	489.7	504.1	485.4	529.0	493.8
Other Outpatient Visits	3,438.1	3,556.3	3,214.8	3,284.4	3,279.2
Total Outpatient Visits	3,927.8	4,060.4	3,700.2	3,813.5	3,773.0
Outpatient Surgeries	65.1	63.9	64.5	67.3	68.7
Expense per Capita (per person)	$3,607.0	$3,356.0	$3,203.6	$3,090.3	$3,047.6

States

TABLE 6

NEW JERSEY

U.S. Registered Community Hospitals
(Nonfederal, short-term general and other special hospitals)

Overview 2012–2016

	2016	2015	2014	2013	2012
Total Community Hospitals in New Jersey.........	75	75	75	77	77
Bed Size Category					
6-24	0	0	0	0	0
25-49	3	2	2	2	2
50-99	9	9	8	9	9
100-199	21	21	23	19	20
200-299	11	12	11	16	17
300-399	16	17	16	15	12
400-499	5	4	6	7	9
500 + ...	10	10	9	9	8
Location					
Hospitals Urban	75	75	75	77	77
Hospitals Rural...	0	0	0	0	0
Control					
State and Local Government	1	1	2	4	3
Not for Profit...	58	59	59	60	60
Investor owned...	16	15	14	13	14
Physician Models					
Independent Practice Association.....................	13	12	11	12	11
Group Practice without Walls...........................	10	5	4	4	5
Open Physician-Hospital Organization	9	9	5	5	5
Closed Physician-Hospital Organization............	5	6	6	5	3
Management Service Organization....................	16	19	18	15	13
Integrated Salary Model..................................	35	37	39	38	27
Equity Model	5	3	3	3	3
Foundation	8	9	10	8	8
Insurance Products					
Health Maintenance Organization.....................	14	13	12	17	12
Preferred Provider Organization	7	9	8	19	14
Indemnity Fee for Service	4	6	5	11	5
Managed Care Contracts					
Health Maintenance Organization.....................	48	48	47	47	49
Preferred Provider Organization	47	48	47	48	49
Affiliations					
Hospitals in a System	56	55	53	54	47
Hospitals in a Network.....................................	37	34	32	32	30
Hospitals in a Group Purchasing Organization...	51	54	57	59	54

TABLE 6

NEW JERSEY

U.S. Registered Community Hospitals
(Nonfederal, short-term general and other special hospitals)

Utilization, Personnel, Revenue and Expenses, Community Health Indicators 2012–2016

	2016	2015	2014	2013	2012
TOTAL FACILITY (Includes Hospital and Nursing Home Units)					
Utilization - Inpatient					
Beds	20,711	20,555	20,517	21,348	21,162
Admissions	989,292	962,684	970,436	1,005,271	1,047,545
Inpatient Days	4,859,232	4,961,832	5,015,867	5,173,783	5,370,619
Average Length of Stay	4.9	5.2	5.2	5.1	5.1
Inpatient Surgeries	227,583	232,716	231,329	237,735	243,512
Births	96,894	98,558	99,550	99,416	101,599
Utilization - Outpatient					
Emergency Outpatient Visits	3,696,748	3,489,161	3,613,702	3,584,950	3,703,899
Other Outpatient Visits	10,801,883	12,522,533	11,875,594	12,009,026	11,883,599
Total Outpatient Visits	14,498,631	16,011,694	15,489,296	15,593,976	15,587,498
Outpatient Surgeries	351,117	363,954	356,709	361,755	381,289
Personnel					
Full Time RNs	31,009	29,262	27,204	27,680	27,979
Full Time LPNs	693	624	597	692	763
Part Time RNs	13,216	13,465	13,504	13,141	13,111
Part Time LPNs	235	216	236	240	294
Total Full Time	107,087	102,763	99,374	100,545	101,341
Total Part Time	43,321	41,230	42,432	40,840	42,586
Revenue - Inpatient					
Gross Inpatient Revenue	$61,028,049,595	$59,523,515,691	$59,549,833,885	$59,880,957,599	$58,452,281,514
Revenue - Outpatient					
Gross Outpatient Revenue	$41,618,707,213	$39,023,961,252	$36,553,897,644	$34,166,641,289	$31,284,903,340
Revenue and Expenses - Totals					
(Includes Inpatient and Outpatient)					
Total Gross Revenue	$102,646,756,808	$98,547,476,943	$96,103,731,529	$94,047,598,888	$89,737,184,854
Deductions from Revenue	80,088,003,146	77,071,917,496	75,732,520,919	74,483,147,229	70,204,451,132
Net Patient Revenue	22,558,753,662	21,475,559,447	20,371,210,610	19,564,451,659	19,532,733,722
Other Operating Revenue	1,549,924,421	1,428,661,579	1,390,647,332	1,399,525,038	1,217,574,869
Other Nonoperating Revenue	434,361,719	-11,707,244	230,925,324	561,510,820	398,816,960
Total Net Revenue	24,543,039,802	22,892,513,782	21,992,783,266	21,525,487,517	21,149,125,551
Total Expenses	22,539,689,953	21,504,636,526	20,672,554,704	20,199,975,055	19,790,864,680
HOSPITAL UNIT (Excludes Separate Nursing Home Units)					
Utilization - Inpatient					
Beds	20,320	20,311	20,133	20,929	20,632
Admissions	986,239	959,543	967,029	1,001,500	1,043,187
Inpatient Days	4,729,811	4,882,010	4,892,006	5,037,093	5,189,878
Average Length of Stay	4.8	5.1	5.1	5.0	5.0
Personnel					
Total Full Time	106,619	102,564	99,061	100,231	100,839
Total Part Time	43,100	41,136	42,211	40,689	42,335
Revenue and Expenses - Totals					
(Includes Inpatient and Outpatient)					
Total Net Revenue	$24,490,060,255	$22,854,228,096	$21,947,697,784	$21,472,958,854	$21,088,046,402
Total Expenses	22,501,909,034	21,480,255,186	20,638,686,308	20,160,424,322	19,740,490,336
COMMUNITY HEALTH INDICATORS PER 1000 POPULATION					
Total Population (in thousands)	8,944	8,958	8,938	8,899	8,865
Inpatient					
Beds	2.3	2.3	2.3	2.4	2.4
Admissions	110.6	107.5	108.6	113.0	118.2
Inpatient Days	543.3	553.9	561.2	581.4	605.9
Inpatient Surgeries	25.4	26.0	25.9	26.7	27.5
Births	10.8	11.0	11.1	11.2	11.5
Outpatient					
Emergency Outpatient Visits	413.3	389.5	404.3	402.8	417.8
Other Outpatient Visits	1,207.7	1,397.9	1,328.6	1,349.4	1,340.6
Total Outpatient Visits	1,621.0	1,787.4	1,732.9	1,752.3	1,758.4
Outpatient Surgeries	39.3	40.6	39.9	40.6	43.0
Expense per Capita (per person)	$2,520.0	$2,400.6	$2,312.8	$2,269.8	$2,232.6

States

TABLE 6

NEW MEXICO

U.S. Registered Community Hospitals
(Nonfederal, short-term general and other special hospitals)

Overview 2012–2016

	2016	2015	2014	2013	2012
Total Community Hospitals in New Mexico	36	36	37	37	37
Bed Size Category					
6-24	3	4	4	4	5
25-49	13	11	11	11	9
50-99	9	11	12	10	10
100-199	7	5	5	6	6
200-299	2	3	3	4	5
300-399	0	0	0	0	0
400-499	0	0	1	1	1
500 + ...	2	2	1	1	1
Location					
Hospitals Urban	13	13	14	14	14
Hospitals Rural	23	23	23	23	23
Control					
State and Local Government	6	6	6	6	6
Not for Profit	14	14	15	15	15
Investor owned	16	16	16	16	16
Physician Models					
Independent Practice Association	2	2	3	3	3
Group Practice without Walls	0	0	0	0	0
Open Physician-Hospital Organization	4	4	3	2	4
Closed Physician-Hospital Organization	0	0	0	0	0
Management Service Organization	0	1	1	1	0
Integrated Salary Model	9	10	12	15	11
Equity Model	0	0	0	0	0
Foundation	0	0	0	0	0
Insurance Products					
Health Maintenance Organization	6	7	8	8	8
Preferred Provider Organization	6	7	8	8	6
Indemnity Fee for Service	6	7	8	8	4
Managed Care Contracts					
Health Maintenance Organization	10	11	16	18	16
Preferred Provider Organization	11	13	18	18	16
Affiliations					
Hospitals in a System	27	25	27	29	29
Hospitals in a Network	9	12	12	11	11
Hospitals in a Group Purchasing Organization ...	19	21	24	24	22

TABLE 6

NEW MEXICO

U.S. Registered Community Hospitals
(Nonfederal, short-term general and other special hospitals)

Utilization, Personnel, Revenue and Expenses, Community Health Indicators 2012–2016

	2016	2015	2014	2013	2012
TOTAL FACILITY (Includes Hospital and Nursing Home Units)					
Utilization - Inpatient					
Beds	3,798	3,938	3,771	3,806	4,076
Admissions	177,167	176,606	174,429	166,307	177,744
Inpatient Days	854,001	857,245	819,119	771,150	850,391
Average Length of Stay	4.8	4.9	4.7	4.6	4.8
Inpatient Surgeries	44,882	44,422	40,142	43,384	47,292
Births	20,145	22,537	22,664	22,252	23,924
Utilization - Outpatient					
Emergency Outpatient Visits	1,032,462	1,019,566	953,949	826,885	793,582
Other Outpatient Visits	5,609,178	4,985,742	4,698,796	3,657,027	3,361,978
Total Outpatient Visits	6,641,640	6,005,308	5,652,745	4,483,912	4,155,560
Outpatient Surgeries	103,869	100,042	79,654	89,154	92,264
Personnel					
Full Time RNs	7,073	7,004	6,441	6,330	6,326
Full Time LPNs	280	312	309	327	353
Part Time RNs	2,450	2,244	2,418	2,221	2,254
Part Time LPNs	108	98	104	109	100
Total Full Time	24,524	24,854	21,683	21,883	21,672
Total Part Time	7,207	6,875	6,745	6,755	6,526
Revenue - Inpatient					
Gross Inpatient Revenue	$8,100,174,346	$7,944,000,369	$6,839,112,627	$6,186,832,999	$6,068,430,416
Revenue - Outpatient					
Gross Outpatient Revenue	$9,997,098,802	$8,973,267,901	$7,317,852,735	$6,581,129,820	$6,116,116,964
Revenue and Expenses - Totals					
(Includes Inpatient and Outpatient)					
Total Gross Revenue	$18,097,273,148	$16,917,268,270	$14,156,965,362	$12,767,962,819	$12,184,547,380
Deductions from Revenue	12,365,302,181	11,788,761,428	9,903,703,375	8,697,316,188	8,059,915,659
Net Patient Revenue	5,731,970,967	5,128,506,842	4,253,261,987	4,070,646,631	4,124,631,721
Other Operating Revenue	248,602,725	259,585,795	246,751,305	220,599,613	229,495,765
Other Nonoperating Revenue	29,251,256	40,983,598	84,752,165	55,758,352	21,327,949
Total Net Revenue	6,009,824,948	5,429,076,235	4,584,765,457	4,347,004,596	4,375,455,435
Total Expenses	5,291,810,444	4,752,424,709	4,087,540,556	3,818,356,732	4,003,331,871
HOSPITAL UNIT (Excludes Separate Nursing Home Units)					
Utilization - Inpatient					
Beds	3,798	3,938	3,719	3,806	4,076
Admissions	177,167	176,606	174,406	166,307	177,744
Inpatient Days	854,001	857,245	809,549	771,150	850,391
Average Length of Stay	4.8	4.9	4.6	4.6	4.8
Personnel					
Total Full Time	24,524	24,854	21,656	21,695	21,499
Total Part Time	7,207	6,875	6,744	6,644	6,433
Revenue and Expenses - Totals					
(Includes Inpatient and Outpatient)					
Total Net Revenue	$6,009,824,948	$5,429,076,235	$4,579,619,544	$4,347,004,596	$4,375,455,435
Total Expenses	5,291,810,444	4,752,424,709	4,084,228,633	3,818,356,732	4,003,331,871
COMMUNITY HEALTH INDICATORS PER 1000 POPULATION					
Total Population (in thousands)	2,081	2,085	2,086	2,085	2,086
Inpatient					
Beds	1.8	1.9	1.8	1.8	2.0
Admissions	85.1	84.7	83.6	79.8	85.2
Inpatient Days	410.4	411.1	392.8	369.8	407.8
Inpatient Surgeries	21.6	21.3	19.2	20.8	22.7
Births	9.7	10.8	10.9	10.7	11.5
Outpatient					
Emergency Outpatient Visits	496.1	489.0	457.4	396.5	380.5
Other Outpatient Visits	2,695.4	2,391.1	2,253.0	1,753.7	1,612.0
Total Outpatient Visits	3,191.5	2,880.1	2,710.4	2,150.3	1,992.6
Outpatient Surgeries	49.9	48.0	38.2	42.8	44.2
Expense per Capita (per person)	$2,542.9	$2,279.2	$1,959.9	$1,831.1	$1,919.6

States

TABLE 6

NEW YORK

U.S. Registered Community Hospitals
(Nonfederal, short-term general and other special hospitals)

Overview 2012–2016

	2016	2015	2014	2013	2012
Total Community Hospitals in New York	169	170	174	177	178
Bed Size Category					
6-24	8	8	7	7	7
25-49	10	10	8	7	7
50-99	17	17	19	17	16
100-199	42	40	40	40	40
200-299	36	38	36	40	39
300-399	12	13	18	20	22
400-499	14	12	13	12	12
500 +	30	32	33	34	35
Location					
Hospitals Urban	134	135	138	139	140
Hospitals Rural	35	35	36	38	38
Control					
State and Local Government	23	24	24	25	26
Not for Profit	146	146	150	152	152
Investor owned	0	0	0	0	0
Physician Models					
Independent Practice Association	46	47	42	39	38
Group Practice without Walls	4	7	7	6	7
Open Physician-Hospital Organization	14	14	12	12	15
Closed Physician-Hospital Organization	5	7	5	7	13
Management Service Organization	14	22	18	13	16
Integrated Salary Model	86	80	77	83	77
Equity Model	1	1	1	1	1
Foundation	1	2	4	5	3
Insurance Products					
Health Maintenance Organization	45	49	49	48	42
Preferred Provider Organization	14	23	20	25	13
Indemnity Fee for Service	9	21	6	10	9
Managed Care Contracts					
Health Maintenance Organization	105	105	106	109	114
Preferred Provider Organization	98	99	99	105	108
Affiliations					
Hospitals in a System	104	96	95	94	87
Hospitals in a Network	90	89	80	78	75
Hospitals in a Group Purchasing Organization	125	128	127	129	128

TABLE 6

NEW YORK

U.S. Registered Community Hospitals
(Nonfederal, short-term general and other special hospitals)

Utilization, Personnel, Revenue and Expenses, Community Health Indicators 2012–2016

	2016	2015	2014	2013	2012
TOTAL FACILITY (Includes Hospital and Nursing Home Units)					
Utilization - Inpatient					
Beds.........................	52,550	52,829	55,306	56,270	57,148
Admissions..................	2,275,571	2,215,696	2,278,459	2,331,678	2,444,350
Inpatient Days.............	15,242,826	15,083,125	15,678,478	15,933,416	16,783,079
Average Length of Stay	6.7	6.8	6.9	6.8	6.9
Inpatient Surgeries........	586,743	569,541	594,891	599,625	615,646
Births......................	226,884	225,215	231,715	232,325	232,967
Utilization - Outpatient					
Emergency Outpatient Visits....	9,053,118	8,628,081	8,589,335	8,616,225	8,379,030
Other Outpatient Visits..........	48,616,430	48,837,800	48,413,762	47,693,175	48,264,808
Total Outpatient Visits	57,669,548	57,465,881	57,003,097	56,309,400	56,643,838
Outpatient Surgeries	1,465,369	1,314,186	1,369,867	1,374,086	1,309,661
Personnel					
Full Time RNs	90,001	84,754	85,835	82,755	80,336
Full Time LPNs.............	4,601	4,857	5,000	5,133	5,110
Part Time RNs.............	25,457	23,788	23,457	23,281	23,613
Part Time LPNs............	1,043	1,240	1,176	1,358	1,389
Total Full Time	364,980	348,457	349,101	358,347	354,362
Total Part Time	89,021	85,557	81,095	84,342	84,860
Revenue - Inpatient					
Gross Inpatient Revenue	$116,369,414,632	$106,722,067,474	$102,292,546,309	$93,765,207,434	$91,398,462,566
Revenue - Outpatient					
Gross Outpatient Revenue	$90,424,171,557	$78,079,787,648	$73,697,207,463	$68,815,204,133	$62,547,461,326
Revenue and Expenses - Totals					
(Includes Inpatient and Outpatient)					
Total Gross Revenue..........	$206,793,586,189	$184,801,855,122	$175,989,753,772	$162,580,411,567	$153,945,923,892
Deductions from Revenue	136,427,250,153	120,115,286,581	113,311,427,323	103,028,887,067	95,942,060,347
Net Patient Revenue...........	70,366,336,036	64,686,568,541	62,678,326,449	59,551,524,500	58,003,863,545
Other Operating Revenue.......	6,253,410,953	5,122,998,193	5,421,095,659	5,362,994,107	4,732,632,403
Other Nonoperating Revenue	1,235,828,598	505,591,214	963,360,033	1,788,296,692	758,391,592
Total Net Revenue.............	77,855,575,587	70,315,157,948	69,062,782,141	66,702,815,299	63,494,887,540
Total Expenses...............	75,132,634,052	68,883,519,133	67,346,714,902	64,889,138,257	62,122,860,564
HOSPITAL UNIT (Excludes Separate Nursing Home Units)					
Utilization - Inpatient					
Beds.........................	48,002	47,625	49,734	50,184	50,458
Admissions..................	2,264,710	2,202,889	2,263,824	2,314,517	2,426,083
Inpatient Days.............	13,679,240	13,277,363	13,756,529	13,831,403	14,420,693
Average Length of Stay	6.0	6.0	6.1	6.0	5.9
Personnel					
Total Full Time	361,389	344,421	344,290	353,126	348,723
Total Part Time	87,070	83,319	78,942	81,870	82,206
Revenue and Expenses - Totals					
(Includes Inpatient and Outpatient)					
Total Net Revenue.............	$77,328,216,630	$69,708,680,223	$68,375,734,988	$66,062,124,750	$62,830,487,679
Total Expenses...............	74,709,589,875	68,307,607,626	66,689,194,014	64,249,125,162	61,440,662,596
COMMUNITY HEALTH INDICATORS PER 1000 POPULATION					
Total Population (in thousands)..........	19,745	19,796	19,746	19,651	19,570
Inpatient					
Beds.........................	2.7	2.7	2.8	2.9	2.9
Admissions..................	115.2	111.9	115.4	118.7	124.9
Inpatient Days.............	772.0	761.9	794.0	810.8	857.6
Inpatient Surgeries.........	29.7	28.8	30.1	30.5	31.5
Births......................	11.5	11.4	11.7	11.8	11.9
Outpatient					
Emergency Outpatient Visits....	458.5	435.9	435.0	438.5	428.2
Other Outpatient Visits........	2,462.2	2,467.1	2,451.8	2,427.0	2,466.2
Total Outpatient Visits	2,920.7	2,902.9	2,886.8	2,865.5	2,894.4
Outpatient Surgeries	74.2	66.4	69.4	69.9	66.9
Expense per Capita (per person)........	$3,805.1	$3,479.7	$3,410.6	$3,302.1	$3,174.4

TABLE 6

NORTH CAROLINA

U.S. Registered Community Hospitals
(Nonfederal, short-term general and other special hospitals)

Overview 2012–2016

	2016	2015	2014	2013	2012
Total Community Hospitals in North Carolina....	112	113	116	117	118
Bed Size Category					
6-24	5	5	7	5	5
25-49	22	23	24	25	26
50-99	27	26	24	23	22
100-199	29	30	30	30	31
200-299	10	10	11	12	12
300-399	4	4	5	7	8
400-499	3	3	3	2	1
500 +	12	12	12	13	13
Location					
Hospitals Urban	64	65	67	60	61
Hospitals Rural	48	48	49	57	57
Control					
State and Local Government	28	27	28	28	30
Not for Profit	65	67	68	72	72
Investor owned	19	19	20	17	16
Physician Models					
Independent Practice Association	5	8	7	8	8
Group Practice without Walls	5	4	3	3	2
Open Physician-Hospital Organization	7	8	7	9	9
Closed Physician-Hospital Organization	5	5	5	5	5
Management Service Organization	15	16	16	15	14
Integrated Salary Model	58	60	61	61	60
Equity Model	0	0	0	1	2
Foundation	2	2	1	1	2
Insurance Products					
Health Maintenance Organization	7	9	3	4	5
Preferred Provider Organization	25	22	17	19	14
Indemnity Fee for Service	4	4	2	2	2
Managed Care Contracts					
Health Maintenance Organization	70	73	72	70	75
Preferred Provider Organization	78	80	80	81	83
Affiliations					
Hospitals in a System	98	102	100	99	95
Hospitals in a Network	49	48	47	45	46
Hospitals in a Group Purchasing Organization...	88	93	95	96	99

TABLE 6

NORTH CAROLINA

U.S. Registered Community Hospitals
(Nonfederal, short-term general and other special hospitals)

Utilization, Personnel, Revenue and Expenses, Community Health Indicators 2012–2016

	2016	2015	2014	2013	2012
TOTAL FACILITY (Includes Hospital and Nursing Home Units)					
Utilization - Inpatient					
Beds	21,791	21,586	22,034	22,617	22,708
Admissions	1,006,097	1,005,230	995,842	1,011,304	1,027,640
Inpatient Days	5,472,055	5,457,178	5,496,740	5,730,722	5,726,216
Average Length of Stay	5.4	5.4	5.5	5.7	5.6
Inpatient Surgeries	280,107	280,021	277,123	278,068	281,357
Births	115,681	116,273	114,799	112,844	114,140
Utilization - Outpatient					
Emergency Outpatient Visits	4,922,026	4,817,883	4,661,360	4,689,431	4,636,192
Other Outpatient Visits	15,784,692	15,074,189	15,004,635	14,969,949	15,094,661
Total Outpatient Visits	20,706,718	19,892,072	19,665,995	19,659,380	19,730,853
Outpatient Surgeries	588,117	562,929	548,249	555,407	549,918
Personnel					
Full Time RNs	41,172	40,502	40,257	40,181	39,539
Full Time LPNs	1,366	1,363	1,373	1,532	1,454
Part Time RNs	13,095	14,329	13,863	13,150	13,727
Part Time LPNs	309	327	325	381	395
Total Full Time	138,299	140,479	138,906	138,355	138,663
Total Part Time	35,936	37,501	37,571	36,141	36,991
Revenue - Inpatient					
Gross Inpatient Revenue	$39,916,873,454	$38,057,166,396	$35,672,703,965	$34,091,849,676	$32,277,023,087
Revenue - Outpatient					
Gross Outpatient Revenue	$47,116,545,234	$42,376,004,261	$38,064,010,629	$34,470,700,452	$31,543,420,298
Revenue and Expenses - Totals					
(Includes Inpatient and Outpatient)					
Total Gross Revenue	$87,033,418,688	$80,433,170,657	$73,736,714,594	$68,562,550,128	$63,820,443,385
Deductions from Revenue	59,502,716,310	54,531,637,899	50,072,141,483	45,661,471,693	40,976,435,538
Net Patient Revenue	27,530,702,378	25,901,532,758	23,664,573,111	22,901,078,435	22,844,007,847
Other Operating Revenue	905,684,782	874,590,303	843,853,426	855,996,247	1,376,765,805
Other Nonoperating Revenue	489,754,195	70,175,039	493,237,081	551,411,198	664,882,512
Total Net Revenue	28,926,141,355	26,846,298,100	25,001,663,618	24,308,485,880	24,885,656,164
Total Expenses	25,492,417,229	24,427,020,445	23,206,884,777	22,436,224,717	22,659,692,061
HOSPITAL UNIT (Excludes Separate Nursing Home Units)					
Utilization - Inpatient					
Beds	20,505	20,524	20,591	21,092	20,823
Admissions	1,000,112	999,700	989,690	1,004,965	1,020,541
Inpatient Days	5,080,039	5,122,212	5,043,706	5,244,404	5,135,293
Average Length of Stay	5.1	5.1	5.1	5.2	5.0
Personnel					
Total Full Time	137,549	139,687	137,996	137,327	137,311
Total Part Time	35,588	37,111	37,156	35,653	36,455
Revenue and Expenses - Totals					
(Includes Inpatient and Outpatient)					
Total Net Revenue	$28,841,378,529	$26,766,730,274	$24,899,363,204	$24,201,100,219	$24,752,345,760
Total Expenses	25,409,477,718	24,359,616,065	23,109,433,313	22,329,567,069	22,524,391,595
COMMUNITY HEALTH INDICATORS PER 1000 POPULATION					
Total Population (in thousands)	10,147	10,043	9,944	9,848	9,752
Inpatient					
Beds	2.1	2.1	2.2	2.3	2.3
Admissions	99.2	100.1	100.1	102.7	105.4
Inpatient Days	539.3	543.4	552.8	581.9	587.2
Inpatient Surgeries	27.6	27.9	27.9	28.2	28.9
Births	11.4	11.6	11.5	11.5	11.7
Outpatient					
Emergency Outpatient Visits	485.1	479.7	468.8	476.2	475.4
Other Outpatient Visits	1,555.6	1,501.0	1,508.9	1,520.1	1,547.8
Total Outpatient Visits	2,040.7	1,980.7	1,977.7	1,996.3	2,023.2
Outpatient Surgeries	58.0	56.1	55.1	56.4	56.4
Expense per Capita (per person)	$2,512.4	$2,432.3	$2,333.8	$2,278.2	$2,323.6

States

TABLE 6

NORTH DAKOTA

U.S. Registered Community Hospitals
(Nonfederal, short-term general and other special hospitals)

Overview 2012–2016

	2016	2015	2014	2013	2012
Total Community Hospitals in North Dakota	40	40	40	40	44
Bed Size Category					
6-24	12	14	16	15	14
25-49	10	10	9	10	15
50-99	11	9	8	9	8
100-199	2	2	2	1	2
200-299	2	3	3	3	3
300-399	1	0	0	0	0
400-499	1	1	1	2	1
500 + ...	1	1	1	0	1
Location					
Hospitals Urban	8	8	8	8	8
Hospitals Rural	32	32	32	32	36
Control					
State and Local Government	0	0	0	0	0
Not for Profit	38	38	38	38	41
Investor owned	2	2	2	2	3
Physician Models					
Independent Practice Association	0	1	1	2	3
Group Practice without Walls	1	0	0	0	1
Open Physician-Hospital Organization	1	2	2	1	2
Closed Physician-Hospital Organization	0	0	0	0	0
Management Service Organization	0	0	0	0	0
Integrated Salary Model	11	10	11	10	10
Equity Model	0	0	0	0	0
Foundation	2	2	1	1	1
Insurance Products					
Health Maintenance Organization	5	4	4	4	2
Preferred Provider Organization	5	5	4	4	2
Indemnity Fee for Service	1	0	0	0	0
Managed Care Contracts					
Health Maintenance Organization	6	7	5	0	1
Preferred Provider Organization	11	13	12	10	10
Affiliations					
Hospitals in a System	19	19	19	19	20
Hospitals in a Network	8	8	9	9	9
Hospitals in a Group Purchasing Organization...	19	17	21	19	22

TABLE 6

NORTH DAKOTA

U.S. Registered Community Hospitals
(Nonfederal, short-term general and other special hospitals)

Utilization, Personnel, Revenue and Expenses, Community Health Indicators 2012–2016

	2016	2015	2014	2013	2012
TOTAL FACILITY (Includes Hospital and Nursing Home Units)					
Utilization - Inpatient					
Beds....................	3,260	3,183	3,144	2,924	3,254
Admissions...........	90,877	92,352	92,692	94,743	92,940
Inpatient Days.......	701,386	666,539	644,992	658,748	727,855
Average Length of Stay.....	7.7	7.2	7.0	7.0	7.8
Inpatient Surgeries........	25,612	26,043	27,107	27,930	26,617
Births..................	13,137	13,109	12,561	11,061	14,625
Utilization - Outpatient					
Emergency Outpatient Visits..............	371,089	385,322	360,374	328,299	419,652
Other Outpatient Visits.....	2,273,123	2,267,225	2,159,913	2,007,191	2,566,926
Total Outpatient Visits........	2,644,212	2,652,547	2,520,287	2,335,490	2,986,578
Outpatient Surgeries..........	78,048	76,448	76,723	73,072	68,599
Personnel					
Full Time RNs........	4,100	3,715	3,320	3,701	3,651
Full Time LPNs.......	795	540	558	509	514
Part Time RNs........	2,634	2,736	2,562	2,579	2,791
Part Time LPNs.......	444	456	462	413	441
Total Full Time.......	15,967	14,792	15,290	16,391	16,049
Total Part Time.......	8,946	8,934	8,980	8,850	9,429
Revenue - Inpatient					
Gross Inpatient Revenue..............	$3,533,156,153	$2,756,294,460	$2,706,066,510	$2,807,963,590	$2,688,456,061
Revenue - Outpatient					
Gross Outpatient Revenue...............	$5,218,580,430	$4,961,154,801	$4,252,502,194	$3,905,959,216	$3,413,782,975
Revenue and Expenses - Totals					
(Includes Inpatient and Outpatient)					
Total Gross Revenue..............	$8,751,736,583	$7,717,449,261	$6,958,568,704	$6,713,922,806	$6,102,239,036
Deductions from Revenue.................	5,001,324,621	4,281,622,247	3,822,990,720	3,821,510,799	3,415,592,851
Net Patient Revenue...........	3,750,411,962	3,435,827,014	3,135,577,984	2,892,412,007	2,686,646,185
Other Operating Revenue...........	184,634,957	195,835,576	231,190,503	161,549,912	125,508,307
Other Nonoperating Revenue...........	22,168,901	16,523,124	26,912,185	28,978,906	24,882,062
Total Net Revenue...........	3,957,215,820	3,648,185,714	3,393,680,672	3,082,940,825	2,837,036,554
Total Expenses.............	3,764,650,593	3,394,209,261	3,186,530,035	2,966,838,008	2,666,135,816
HOSPITAL UNIT (Excludes Separate Nursing Home Units)					
Utilization - Inpatient					
Beds....................	2,755	2,682	2,674	2,422	2,906
Admissions...........	90,062	91,487	91,882	93,845	91,966
Inpatient Days.......	531,621	504,193	494,750	495,592	613,301
Average Length of Stay.....	5.9	5.5	5.4	5.3	6.7
Personnel					
Total Full Time.......	15,722	14,550	14,779	16,134	15,785
Total Part Time.......	8,821	8,729	8,693	8,700	9,268
Revenue and Expenses - Totals					
(Includes Inpatient and Outpatient)					
Total Net Revenue...........	$3,904,906,417	$3,595,128,392	$3,355,550,091	$3,051,733,992	$2,813,596,727
Total Expenses.............	3,726,681,439	3,355,476,243	3,147,793,319	2,925,639,027	2,647,960,716
COMMUNITY HEALTH INDICATORS PER 1000 POPULATION					
Total Population (in thousands)..........	758	757	739	723	700
Inpatient					
Beds....................	4.3	4.2	4.3	4.0	4.7
Admissions...........	119.9	122.0	125.3	131.0	132.8
Inpatient Days.......	925.4	880.6	872.2	910.6	1,040.3
Inpatient Surgeries........	33.8	34.4	36.7	38.6	38.0
Births..................	17.3	17.3	17.0	15.3	20.9
Outpatient					
Emergency Outpatient Visits..............	489.6	509.1	487.3	453.8	599.8
Other Outpatient Visits.....	2,999.0	2,995.3	2,920.8	2,774.7	3,669.0
Total Outpatient Visits........	3,488.6	3,504.4	3,408.2	3,228.5	4,268.8
Outpatient Surgeries..........	103.0	101.0	103.8	101.0	98.1
Expense per Capita (per person).........	$4,966.9	$4,484.2	$4,309.1	$4,101.3	$3,810.8

States

TABLE 6

OHIO

U.S. Registered Community Hospitals
(Nonfederal, short-term general and other special hospitals)

Overview 2012–2016

	2016	2015	2014	2013	2012
Total Community Hospitals in Ohio....................	179	179	182	183	185
Bed Size Category					
6-24	6	7	7	4	6
25-49	48	45	45	48	47
50-99	25	25	25	29	29
100-199	39	44	45	44	44
200-299	30	25	28	26	25
300-399	11	12	10	8	12
400-499	6	6	9	11	9
500 + ...	14	15	13	13	13
Location					
Hospitals Urban	123	123	125	128	130
Hospitals Rural	56	56	57	55	55
Control					
State and Local Government	16	17	18	18	19
Not for Profit	136	135	136	138	140
Investor owned	27	27	28	27	26
Physician Models					
Independent Practice Association	16	18	21	18	13
Group Practice without Walls	16	12	18	18	6
Open Physician-Hospital Organization	44	49	42	46	44
Closed Physician-Hospital Organization	25	21	24	21	15
Management Service Organization	34	34	30	32	19
Integrated Salary Model	76	72	82	79	78
Equity Model	13	14	17	18	8
Foundation	22	21	24	29	20
Insurance Products					
Health Maintenance Organization	27	25	28	24	24
Preferred Provider Organization	49	37	37	36	31
Indemnity Fee for Service	12	13	12	13	10
Managed Care Contracts					
Health Maintenance Organization	111	113	112	115	121
Preferred Provider Organization	113	117	112	118	117
Affiliations					
Hospitals in a System	127	126	125	123	122
Hospitals in a Network	79	79	72	76	77
Hospitals in a Group Purchasing Organization...	121	126	124	128	136

TABLE 6

OHIO

U.S. Registered Community Hospitals
(Nonfederal, short-term general and other special hospitals)

Utilization, Personnel, Revenue and Expenses, Community Health Indicators 2012–2016

	2016	2015	2014	2013	2012
TOTAL FACILITY (Includes Hospital and Nursing Home Units)					
Utilization - Inpatient					
Beds	33,277	33,487	33,566	33,222	33,659
Admissions	1,427,555	1,420,265	1,433,894	1,455,817	1,501,183
Inpatient Days	7,164,552	7,152,242	7,168,533	7,126,702	7,367,870
Average Length of Stay	5.0	5.0	5.0	4.9	4.9
Inpatient Surgeries	363,998	366,505	370,741	372,371	383,187
Births	129,240	129,784	130,762	130,476	128,393
Utilization - Outpatient					
Emergency Outpatient Visits	6,972,256	6,811,790	6,616,818	6,484,063	6,578,749
Other Outpatient Visits	34,221,915	32,948,620	32,244,279	30,776,656	30,377,613
Total Outpatient Visits	41,194,171	39,760,410	38,861,097	37,260,719	36,956,362
Outpatient Surgeries	882,788	863,870	830,099	822,722	810,268
Personnel					
Full Time RNs	60,636	59,956	56,208	54,669	54,347
Full Time LPNs	2,659	2,559	2,586	2,789	2,960
Part Time RNs	27,139	24,890	25,888	25,029	25,890
Part Time LPNs	1,234	1,361	1,311	1,407	1,785
Total Full Time	216,667	211,270	206,879	206,245	205,576
Total Part Time	81,704	77,191	76,520	72,993	76,463
Revenue - Inpatient					
Gross Inpatient Revenue	$67,887,572,081	$64,998,337,594	$61,289,688,782	$58,384,380,015	$55,828,522,139
Revenue - Outpatient					
Gross Outpatient Revenue	$73,688,560,600	$68,772,748,086	$63,819,780,250	$58,206,812,939	$52,981,694,494
Revenue and Expenses - Totals (Includes Inpatient and Outpatient)					
Total Gross Revenue	$141,576,132,681	$133,771,085,680	$125,109,469,032	$116,591,192,954	$108,810,216,633
Deductions from Revenue	99,321,737,490	92,824,738,019	86,231,176,288	79,710,922,376	73,204,925,076
Net Patient Revenue	42,254,395,191	40,946,347,661	38,878,292,744	36,880,270,578	35,605,291,557
Other Operating Revenue	3,170,935,461	3,075,257,904	3,104,508,063	2,927,044,680	2,642,307,155
Other Nonoperating Revenue	571,561,227	-129,032,751	680,756,807	1,250,816,674	770,720,233
Total Net Revenue	45,996,891,879	43,892,572,814	42,663,557,614	41,058,131,932	39,018,318,945
Total Expenses	42,234,369,933	40,163,569,928	38,332,807,975	37,050,070,738	35,772,141,755
HOSPITAL UNIT (Excludes Separate Nursing Home Units)					
Utilization - Inpatient					
Beds	32,639	32,836	32,896	32,570	32,901
Admissions	1,420,145	1,412,717	1,425,516	1,447,101	1,491,784
Inpatient Days	6,953,381	6,938,350	6,948,319	6,909,524	7,117,086
Average Length of Stay	4.9	4.9	4.9	4.8	4.8
Personnel					
Total Full Time	216,136	210,832	206,404	205,768	205,033
Total Part Time	81,322	76,910	76,205	72,650	76,040
Revenue and Expenses - Totals (Includes Inpatient and Outpatient)					
Total Net Revenue	$45,924,264,949	$43,830,375,531	$42,603,477,149	$40,990,936,895	$38,920,461,713
Total Expenses	42,175,178,712	40,106,104,202	38,277,821,356	36,986,993,669	35,672,905,913
COMMUNITY HEALTH INDICATORS PER 1000 POPULATION					
Total Population (in thousands)	11,614	11,613	11,594	11,571	11,544
Inpatient					
Beds	2.9	2.9	2.9	2.9	2.9
Admissions	122.9	122.3	123.7	125.8	130.0
Inpatient Days	616.9	615.9	618.3	615.9	638.2
Inpatient Surgeries	31.3	31.6	32.0	32.2	33.2
Births	11.1	11.2	11.3	11.3	11.1
Outpatient					
Emergency Outpatient Visits	600.3	586.5	570.7	560.4	569.9
Other Outpatient Visits	2,946.5	2,837.1	2,781.1	2,659.9	2,631.4
Total Outpatient Visits	3,546.8	3,423.7	3,351.8	3,220.2	3,201.3
Outpatient Surgeries	76.0	74.4	71.6	71.1	70.2
Expense per Capita (per person)	$3,636.4	$3,458.4	$3,306.2	$3,202.0	$3,098.7

TABLE 6

OKLAHOMA

U.S. Registered Community Hospitals
(Nonfederal, short-term general and other special hospitals)

Overview 2012–2016

	2016	2015	2014	2013	2012
Total Community Hospitals in Oklahoma	110	110	114	116	117
Bed Size Category					
6-24	26	26	23	21	21
25-49	40	40	43	46	47
50-99	19	19	23	23	23
100-199	13	12	11	12	13
200-299	2	3	4	4	3
300-399	4	4	4	4	4
400-499	0	0	0	0	0
500 +	6	6	6	6	6
Location					
Hospitals Urban	50	50	49	51	51
Hospitals Rural	60	60	65	65	66
Control					
State and Local Government	38	40	38	38	40
Not for Profit	35	33	36	37	37
Investor owned	37	37	40	41	40
Physician Models					
Independent Practice Association	14	12	14	14	13
Group Practice without Walls	6	6	8	6	5
Open Physician-Hospital Organization	7	9	9	10	12
Closed Physician-Hospital Organization	4	5	5	3	3
Management Service Organization	9	11	9	9	9
Integrated Salary Model	47	54	54	52	52
Equity Model	1	0	0	1	1
Foundation	2	1	1	1	2
Insurance Products					
Health Maintenance Organization	13	13	13	13	13
Preferred Provider Organization	11	13	12	14	12
Indemnity Fee for Service	8	8	6	5	5
Managed Care Contracts					
Health Maintenance Organization	53	53	55	53	52
Preferred Provider Organization	70	72	78	77	76
Affiliations					
Hospitals in a System	67	63	63	63	65
Hospitals in a Network	41	40	40	39	33
Hospitals in a Group Purchasing Organization	76	77	88	93	95

TABLE 6

OKLAHOMA

U.S. Registered Community Hospitals
(Nonfederal, short-term general and other special hospitals)

Utilization, Personnel, Revenue and Expenses, Community Health Indicators 2012–2016

	2016	2015	2014	2013	2012
TOTAL FACILITY (Includes Hospital and Nursing Home Units)					
Utilization - Inpatient					
Beds	11,167	11,109	11,240	11,365	11,349
Admissions	396,764	392,580	393,816	412,225	424,024
Inpatient Days	2,205,360	2,153,248	2,172,592	2,221,235	2,242,204
Average Length of Stay	5.6	5.5	5.5	5.4	5.3
Inpatient Surgeries	98,748	97,675	99,213	102,141	107,089
Births	52,663	48,485	51,509	52,910	50,107
Utilization - Outpatient					
Emergency Outpatient Visits	1,829,289	1,871,693	1,856,987	1,871,330	1,908,047
Other Outpatient Visits	4,730,026	4,306,098	4,508,176	4,741,807	4,866,096
Total Outpatient Visits	6,559,315	6,177,791	6,365,163	6,613,137	6,774,143
Outpatient Surgeries	233,348	226,063	225,422	221,650	223,225
Personnel					
Full Time RNs	12,975	12,750	12,937	13,018	12,313
Full Time LPNs	1,423	1,427	1,524	1,642	1,688
Part Time RNs	4,033	3,864	4,228	3,531	4,277
Part Time LPNs	376	347	357	383	495
Total Full Time	44,189	43,925	45,097	46,292	46,426
Total Part Time	12,650	12,454	12,602	11,446	13,623
Revenue - Inpatient					
Gross Inpatient Revenue	$19,297,588,653	$17,044,756,661	$15,334,379,316	$14,505,192,200	$14,248,526,243
Revenue - Outpatient					
Gross Outpatient Revenue	$17,313,994,526	$15,676,101,665	$14,429,955,582	$13,122,142,376	$11,878,040,440
Revenue and Expenses - Totals					
(Includes Inpatient and Outpatient)					
Total Gross Revenue	$36,611,583,179	$32,720,858,326	$29,764,334,898	$27,627,334,576	$26,126,566,683
Deductions from Revenue	27,747,271,867	24,054,668,319	21,514,817,782	19,789,608,584	18,251,141,886
Net Patient Revenue	8,864,311,312	8,666,190,007	8,249,517,116	7,837,725,992	7,875,424,797
Other Operating Revenue	299,392,974	295,455,124	322,344,777	288,772,295	264,973,762
Other Nonoperating Revenue	34,053,635	82,917,369	199,331,969	244,751,865	27,381,522
Total Net Revenue	9,197,757,921	9,044,562,500	8,771,193,862	8,371,250,152	8,167,780,081
Total Expenses	8,470,169,172	8,276,760,096	7,888,228,952	7,684,078,335	7,462,798,181
HOSPITAL UNIT (Excludes Separate Nursing Home Units)					
Utilization - Inpatient					
Beds	10,876	10,896	10,997	11,095	11,086
Admissions	395,896	392,108	393,467	411,403	422,856
Inpatient Days	2,114,364	2,091,061	2,100,133	2,143,080	2,164,883
Average Length of Stay	5.3	5.3	5.3	5.2	5.1
Personnel					
Total Full Time	43,937	43,696	44,868	46,006	46,159
Total Part Time	12,606	12,396	12,524	11,382	13,555
Revenue and Expenses - Totals					
(Includes Inpatient and Outpatient)					
Total Net Revenue	$9,182,130,355	$9,034,220,106	$8,760,512,983	$8,358,970,765	$8,133,239,746
Total Expenses	8,453,877,878	8,267,963,632	7,880,119,990	7,672,845,200	7,451,915,559
COMMUNITY HEALTH INDICATORS PER 1000 POPULATION					
Total Population (in thousands)	3,924	3,911	3,878	3,851	3,815
Inpatient					
Beds	2.8	2.8	2.9	3.0	3.0
Admissions	101.1	100.4	101.5	107.1	111.2
Inpatient Days	562.1	550.5	560.2	576.9	587.8
Inpatient Surgeries	25.2	25.0	25.6	26.5	28.1
Births	13.4	12.4	13.3	13.7	13.1
Outpatient					
Emergency Outpatient Visits	466.2	478.5	478.8	486.0	500.2
Other Outpatient Visits	1,205.5	1,100.9	1,162.5	1,231.5	1,275.6
Total Outpatient Visits	1,671.8	1,579.5	1,641.3	1,717.4	1,775.7
Outpatient Surgeries	59.5	57.8	58.1	57.6	58.5
Expense per Capita (per person)	$2,158.8	$2,116.1	$2,034.1	$1,995.6	$1,956.3

States

TABLE **6**

OREGON

U.S. Registered Community Hospitals
(Nonfederal, short-term general and other special hospitals)

Overview 2012–2016

	2016	2015	2014	2013	2012
Total Community Hospitals in Oregon	59	59	59	59	58
Bed Size Category					
6-24	13	12	9	9	8
25-49	20	21	23	20	20
50-99	4	4	5	8	9
100-199	11	11	11	11	10
200-299	3	3	4	4	4
300-399	3	3	2	2	2
400-499	4	3	3	3	3
500 + ...	1	2	2	2	2
Location					
Hospitals Urban	33	33	33	30	30
Hospitals Rural	26	26	26	29	28
Control					
State and Local Government	11	11	12	12	11
Not for Profit..	46	46	45	45	45
Investor owned	2	2	2	2	2
Physician Models					
Independent Practice Association...........	9	9	9	9	10
Group Practice without Walls	3	5	6	7	8
Open Physician-Hospital Organization ...	3	3	2	2	5
Closed Physician-Hospital Organization............	2	4	3	6	2
Management Service Organization..........	11	12	11	10	14
Integrated Salary Model........................	53	55	54	54	41
Equity Model	0	0	0	0	1
Foundation	1	2	2	1	4
Insurance Products					
Health Maintenance Organization..........	21	22	18	19	14
Preferred Provider Organization	22	22	20	19	10
Indemnity Fee for Service	10	5	5	5	0
Managed Care Contracts					
Health Maintenance Organization..........	41	40	40	39	38
Preferred Provider Organization	55	55	55	52	49
Affiliations					
Hospitals in a System	42	41	41	41	41
Hospitals in a Network	30	30	31	30	28
Hospitals in a Group Purchasing Organization...	58	58	58	58	56

TABLE 6

OREGON

U.S. Registered Community Hospitals
(Nonfederal, short-term general and other special hospitals)

Utilization, Personnel, Revenue and Expenses, Community Health Indicators 2012–2016

	2016	2015	2014	2013	2012
TOTAL FACILITY (Includes Hospital and Nursing Home Units)					
Utilization - Inpatient					
Beds	6,673	6,760	6,740	6,778	6,706
Admissions	337,535	342,408	330,065	337,228	336,677
Inpatient Days	1,508,241	1,505,041	1,441,975	1,454,053	1,429,092
Average Length of Stay	4.5	4.4	4.4	4.3	4.2
Inpatient Surgeries	122,380	120,095	120,327	123,905	119,276
Births	42,705	42,905	42,741	42,393	43,472
Utilization - Outpatient					
Emergency Outpatient Visits	1,565,520	1,540,170	1,440,808	1,399,434	1,402,280
Other Outpatient Visits	9,892,670	9,320,659	9,364,637	8,986,321	8,402,499
Total Outpatient Visits	11,458,190	10,860,829	10,805,445	10,385,755	9,804,779
Outpatient Surgeries	206,355	199,275	190,460	192,524	203,622
Personnel					
Full Time RNs	12,609	11,920	11,213	10,997	10,528
Full Time LPNs	138	137	143	142	162
Part Time RNs	7,758	7,102	7,567	7,165	7,366
Part Time LPNs	85	74	81	88	113
Total Full Time	44,248	42,678	41,277	39,732	38,512
Total Part Time	20,736	18,580	19,498	18,834	19,732
Revenue - Inpatient					
Gross Inpatient Revenue	$12,575,789,582	$11,773,880,264	$10,984,589,849	$10,304,742,501	$9,763,893,851
Revenue - Outpatient					
Gross Outpatient Revenue	$13,324,763,530	$11,937,261,521	$10,661,166,352	$9,695,486,581	$9,057,121,305
Revenue and Expenses - Totals					
(Includes Inpatient and Outpatient)					
Total Gross Revenue	$25,900,553,112	$23,711,141,785	$21,645,756,201	$20,000,229,082	$18,821,015,156
Deductions from Revenue	14,678,260,551	13,090,695,353	11,907,313,288	10,889,922,069	9,946,369,291
Net Patient Revenue	11,222,292,561	10,620,446,432	9,738,442,913	9,110,307,013	8,874,645,865
Other Operating Revenue	708,151,974	686,223,294	551,197,366	486,233,283	431,506,659
Other Nonoperating Revenue	100,467,573	252,643,812	145,430,882	116,357,557	120,073,921
Total Net Revenue	12,030,912,108	11,559,313,538	10,435,071,161	9,712,897,853	9,426,226,445
Total Expenses	11,398,930,401	10,660,827,864	9,956,534,588	9,358,601,796	9,102,609,637
HOSPITAL UNIT (Excludes Separate Nursing Home Units)					
Utilization - Inpatient					
Beds	6,644	6,709	6,659	6,610	6,538
Admissions	337,522	342,378	329,951	337,095	336,526
Inpatient Days	1,500,867	1,489,548	1,418,598	1,412,321	1,387,370
Average Length of Stay	4.4	4.4	4.3	4.2	4.1
Personnel					
Total Full Time	44,224	42,641	41,232	39,667	38,416
Total Part Time	20,724	18,546	19,458	18,780	19,687
Revenue and Expenses - Totals					
(Includes Inpatient and Outpatient)					
Total Net Revenue	$12,029,472,329	$11,556,607,268	$10,429,237,256	$9,702,942,089	$9,416,990,860
Total Expenses	11,396,773,036	10,657,954,568	9,951,469,324	9,350,034,260	9,094,089,019
COMMUNITY HEALTH INDICATORS PER 1000 POPULATION					
Total Population (in thousands)	4,093	4,029	3,970	3,930	3,899
Inpatient					
Beds	1.6	1.7	1.7	1.7	1.7
Admissions	82.5	85.0	83.1	85.8	86.3
Inpatient Days	368.5	373.6	363.2	370.0	366.5
Inpatient Surgeries	29.9	29.8	30.3	31.5	30.6
Births	10.4	10.6	10.8	10.8	11.1
Outpatient					
Emergency Outpatient Visits	382.4	382.3	362.9	356.1	359.6
Other Outpatient Visits	2,416.7	2,313.4	2,358.7	2,286.6	2,154.8
Total Outpatient Visits	2,799.1	2,695.7	2,721.6	2,642.6	2,514.5
Outpatient Surgeries	50.4	49.5	48.0	49.0	52.2
Expense per Capita (per person)	$2,784.7	$2,646.0	$2,507.8	$2,381.3	$2,334.4

States

TABLE 6

PENNSYLVANIA

U.S. Registered Community Hospitals
(Nonfederal, short-term general and other special hospitals)

Overview 2012–2016

	2016	2015	2014	2013	2012
Total Community Hospitals in Pennsylvania......	184	186	185	190	192
Bed Size Category					
6-24	2	2	4	3	4
25-49	28	29	25	28	27
50-99	38	39	36	37	38
100-199	48	46	46	47	47
200-299	31	30	33	34	35
300-399	15	20	18	18	18
400-499	6	5	9	8	9
500 + ...	16	15	14	15	14
Location					
Hospitals Urban	146	148	147	143	145
Hospitals Rural	38	38	38	47	47
Control					
State and Local Government	1	1	1	2	2
Not for Profit	136	136	139	141	142
Investor owned	47	49	45	47	48
Physician Models					
Independent Practice Association......	12	9	10	11	12
Group Practice without Walls.............	4	4	5	6	5
Open Physician-Hospital Organization	22	19	21	23	22
Closed Physician-Hospital Organization............	6	6	5	3	3
Management Service Organization......	17	16	16	21	23
Integrated Salary Model....................	80	76	71	74	78
Equity Model	5	6	4	4	3
Foundation	2	2	3	4	4
Insurance Products					
Health Maintenance Organization......	41	35	30	32	37
Preferred Provider Organization	37	28	29	30	38
Indemnity Fee for Service	22	19	18	19	23
Managed Care Contracts					
Health Maintenance Organization......	123	123	116	125	132
Preferred Provider Organization	123	121	114	124	128
Affiliations					
Hospitals in a System	139	136	128	129	127
Hospitals in a Network	68	62	59	56	52
Hospitals in a Group Purchasing Organization...	135	127	117	147	141

TABLE **6**

PENNSYLVANIA

U.S. Registered Community Hospitals
(Nonfederal, short-term general and other special hospitals)

Utilization, Personnel, Revenue and Expenses, Community Health Indicators 2012–2016

	2016	2015	2014	2013	2012
TOTAL FACILITY (Includes Hospital and Nursing Home Units)					
Utilization - Inpatient					
Beds	37,132	37,348	38,124	38,970	39,314
Admissions	1,566,386	1,574,611	1,584,798	1,637,872	1,692,087
Inpatient Days	8,565,494	8,646,139	8,723,610	9,147,196	9,287,033
Average Length of Stay	5.5	5.5	5.5	5.6	5.5
Inpatient Surgeries	462,146	461,519	469,110	489,930	545,302
Births	132,143	129,668	129,936	128,950	134,221
Utilization - Outpatient					
Emergency Outpatient Visits	6,317,985	6,488,868	6,245,628	6,263,103	6,239,042
Other Outpatient Visits	34,034,655	32,646,190	31,928,667	31,769,030	32,791,595
Total Outpatient Visits	40,352,640	39,135,058	38,174,295	38,032,133	39,030,637
Outpatient Surgeries	925,218	909,695	883,007	908,695	913,296
Personnel					
Full Time RNs	58,338	57,050	56,208	55,770	55,710
Full Time LPNs	2,285	2,205	2,264	2,617	3,035
Part Time RNs	23,956	24,530	24,947	25,112	25,187
Part Time LPNs	777	854	935	1,078	1,227
Total Full Time	209,547	207,970	207,519	207,082	212,082
Total Part Time	69,418	70,267	71,384	72,723	73,405
Revenue - Inpatient					
Gross Inpatient Revenue	$93,381,323,289	$90,434,828,814	$83,909,351,569	$84,087,084,762	$83,077,919,932
Revenue - Outpatient					
Gross Outpatient Revenue	$88,945,248,510	$79,341,859,603	$70,851,865,407	$66,840,763,963	$65,297,151,073
Revenue and Expenses - Totals					
(Includes Inpatient and Outpatient)					
Total Gross Revenue	$182,326,571,799	$169,776,688,417	$154,761,216,976	$150,927,848,725	$148,375,071,005
Deductions from Revenue	139,423,168,641	128,735,020,821	115,737,513,972	112,764,688,900	110,484,264,654
Net Patient Revenue	42,903,403,158	41,041,667,596	39,023,703,004	38,163,159,825	37,890,806,351
Other Operating Revenue	2,240,671,467	2,209,477,467	2,055,029,824	2,008,282,382	1,891,935,772
Other Nonoperating Revenue	107,530,510	342,197,686	876,327,635	595,823,340	244,155,533
Total Net Revenue	45,251,605,135	43,593,342,749	41,955,060,463	40,767,265,547	40,026,897,656
Total Expenses	42,324,703,752	40,620,865,601	38,945,696,363	38,184,179,753	37,279,476,131
HOSPITAL UNIT (Excludes Separate Nursing Home Units)					
Utilization - Inpatient					
Beds	35,822	36,246	36,891	37,025	37,482
Admissions	1,554,669	1,563,321	1,571,539	1,620,279	1,674,103
Inpatient Days	8,157,653	8,301,035	8,341,033	8,550,303	8,740,926
Average Length of Stay	5.2	5.3	5.3	5.3	5.2
Personnel					
Total Full Time	208,787	207,282	206,612	206,017	211,038
Total Part Time	68,999	69,890	70,872	72,063	72,757
Revenue and Expenses - Totals					
(Includes Inpatient and Outpatient)					
Total Net Revenue	$45,121,855,616	$43,465,753,978	$41,820,451,752	$40,549,341,944	$39,806,434,073
Total Expenses	42,231,885,833	40,487,031,490	38,833,596,958	38,000,068,482	37,097,937,820
COMMUNITY HEALTH INDICATORS PER 1000 POPULATION					
Total Population (in thousands)	12,784	12,803	12,787	12,774	12,764
Inpatient					
Beds	2.9	2.9	3.0	3.1	3.1
Admissions	122.5	123.0	123.9	128.2	132.6
Inpatient Days	670.0	675.3	682.2	716.1	727.6
Inpatient Surgeries	36.1	36.0	36.7	38.4	42.7
Births	10.3	10.1	10.2	10.1	10.5
Outpatient					
Emergency Outpatient Visits	494.2	506.8	488.4	490.3	488.8
Other Outpatient Visits	2,662.2	2,550.0	2,496.9	2,487.0	2,569.2
Total Outpatient Visits	3,156.4	3,056.8	2,985.4	2,977.4	3,058.0
Outpatient Surgeries	72.4	71.1	69.1	71.1	71.6
Expense per Capita (per person)	$3,310.7	$3,172.9	$3,045.7	$2,989.3	$2,920.8

States

TABLE 6

RHODE ISLAND

U.S. Registered Community Hospitals
(Nonfederal, short-term general and other special hospitals)

Overview 2012–2016

	2016	2015	2014	2013	2012
Total Community Hospitals in Rhode Island	11	11	11	11	11
Bed Size Category					
6-24	0	0	0	0	0
25-49	1	0	0	0	0
50-99	2	2	2	2	1
100-199	4	5	5	5	5
200-299	2	2	2	2	3
300-399	1	1	1	1	1
400-499	0	0	0	0	0
500 + ...	1	1	1	1	1
Location					
Hospitals Urban	11	11	11	11	11
Hospitals Rural	0	0	0	0	0
Control					
State and Local Government	0	0	0	0	0
Not for Profit	10	10	10	10	11
Investor owned	1	1	1	1	0
Physician Models					
Independent Practice Association	5	5	5	5	4
Group Practice without Walls	0	0	1	1	1
Open Physician-Hospital Organization	0	4	5	5	4
Closed Physician-Hospital Organization	0	0	0	0	0
Management Service Organization	4	2	2	3	2
Integrated Salary Model	6	5	6	6	6
Equity Model	1	0	0	0	0
Foundation	4	2	2	2	2
Insurance Products					
Health Maintenance Organization	1	1	1	1	1
Preferred Provider Organization	0	0	0	0	0
Indemnity Fee for Service	0	0	0	0	0
Managed Care Contracts					
Health Maintenance Organization	7	6	6	7	6
Preferred Provider Organization	6	6	8	7	6
Affiliations					
Hospitals in a System	10	10	10	10	6
Hospitals in a Network	5	4	4	5	4
Hospitals in a Group Purchasing Organization...	7	7	7	8	6

TABLE 6

RHODE ISLAND

U.S. Registered Community Hospitals
(Nonfederal, short-term general and other special hospitals)

Utilization, Personnel, Revenue and Expenses, Community Health Indicators 2012–2016

	2016	2015	2014	2013	2012
TOTAL FACILITY (Includes Hospital and Nursing Home Units)					
Utilization - Inpatient					
Beds	2,237	2,269	2,247	2,250	2,461
Admissions	115,978	114,768	110,848	111,406	117,051
Inpatient Days	553,379	566,962	549,575	571,352	580,207
Average Length of Stay	4.8	4.9	5.0	5.1	5.0
Inpatient Surgeries	29,475	27,987	27,265	29,139	32,119
Births	11,283	11,349	11,363	11,352	11,045
Utilization - Outpatient					
Emergency Outpatient Visits	547,657	546,113	510,907	522,861	578,431
Other Outpatient Visits	1,813,161	1,755,673	1,509,583	1,518,166	1,605,322
Total Outpatient Visits	2,360,818	2,301,786	2,020,490	2,041,027	2,183,753
Outpatient Surgeries	65,860	64,721	66,310	66,445	67,537
Personnel					
Full Time RNs	2,854	2,858	2,724	2,322	2,656
Full Time LPNs	66	62	54	50	71
Part Time RNs	3,173	2,869	2,935	2,876	2,780
Part Time LPNs	46	47	45	52	60
Total Full Time	12,601	12,599	12,271	12,542	12,871
Total Part Time	9,159	8,383	8,356	8,313	7,847
Revenue - Inpatient					
Gross Inpatient Revenue	$4,219,298,393	$4,207,269,720	$4,054,821,275	$3,987,915,217	$3,911,358,415
Revenue - Outpatient					
Gross Outpatient Revenue	$5,156,269,206	$4,772,658,215	$4,583,059,093	$4,343,532,799	$4,210,401,437
Revenue and Expenses - Totals					
(Includes Inpatient and Outpatient)					
Total Gross Revenue	$9,375,567,599	$8,979,927,935	$8,637,880,368	$8,331,448,016	$8,121,759,852
Deductions from Revenue	6,138,499,500	5,863,197,368	5,682,487,354	5,499,978,376	5,309,722,108
Net Patient Revenue	3,237,068,099	3,116,730,567	2,955,393,014	2,831,469,640	2,812,037,744
Other Operating Revenue	270,254,917	267,972,554	250,712,004	255,547,838	259,567,063
Other Nonoperating Revenue	-16,293,602	-1,683,828	10,550,939	18,026,453	26,181,940
Total Net Revenue	3,491,029,414	3,383,019,293	3,216,655,957	3,105,043,931	3,097,786,747
Total Expenses	3,502,432,176	3,360,655,796	3,167,662,418	3,151,478,325	3,067,815,218
HOSPITAL UNIT (Excludes Separate Nursing Home Units)					
Utilization - Inpatient					
Beds	2,237	2,269	2,247	2,250	2,461
Admissions	115,978	114,768	110,848	111,406	117,051
Inpatient Days	553,379	566,962	549,575	571,352	580,207
Average Length of Stay	4.8	4.9	5.0	5.1	5.0
Personnel					
Total Full Time	12,601	12,599	12,271	12,542	12,871
Total Part Time	9,159	8,383	8,356	8,313	7,847
Revenue and Expenses - Totals					
(Includes Inpatient and Outpatient)					
Total Net Revenue	$3,491,029,414	$3,383,019,293	$3,216,655,957	$3,105,043,931	$3,097,786,747
Total Expenses	3,502,432,176	3,360,655,796	3,167,662,418	3,151,478,325	3,067,815,218
COMMUNITY HEALTH INDICATORS PER 1000 POPULATION					
Total Population (in thousands)	1,056	1,056	1,055	1,052	1,050
Inpatient					
Beds	2.1	2.1	2.1	2.1	2.3
Admissions	109.8	108.7	105.1	105.9	111.4
Inpatient Days	523.8	536.7	520.8	543.4	552.4
Inpatient Surgeries	27.9	26.5	25.8	27.7	30.6
Births	10.7	10.7	10.8	10.8	10.5
Outpatient					
Emergency Outpatient Visits	518.4	517.0	484.2	497.2	550.7
Other Outpatient Visits	1,716.3	1,662.1	1,430.6	1,443.8	1,528.5
Total Outpatient Visits	2,234.7	2,179.1	1,914.8	1,941.0	2,079.2
Outpatient Surgeries	62.3	61.3	62.8	63.2	64.3
Expense per Capita (per person)	$3,315.4	$3,181.5	$3,002.0	$2,997.1	$2,920.9

States

TABLE **6**

SOUTH CAROLINA

U.S. Registered Community Hospitals
(Nonfederal, short-term general and other special hospitals)

Overview 2012–2016

	2016	2015	2014	2013	2012
Total Community Hospitals in South Carolina ...	68	68	70	69	67
Bed Size Category					
6-24	1	2	5	2	1
25-49	16	15	15	16	16
50-99	16	16	15	13	13
100-199	13	13	13	14	14
200-299	8	9	8	9	9
300-399	4	3	4	5	6
400-499	5	6	6	5	4
500 + ...	5	4	4	5	4
Location					
Hospitals Urban	54	54	54	45	43
Hospitals Rural	14	14	16	24	24
Control					
State and Local Government	15	19	19	18	18
Not for Profit	29	27	27	28	26
Investor owned	24	22	24	23	23
Physician Models					
Independent Practice Association	8	8	6	6	6
Group Practice without Walls	0	0	0	1	1
Open Physician-Hospital Organization	3	3	3	3	5
Closed Physician-Hospital Organization	5	5	3	3	2
Management Service Organization	0	0	0	1	1
Integrated Salary Model	17	16	19	19	20
Equity Model	5	4	2	2	2
Foundation	6	5	1	0	0
Insurance Products					
Health Maintenance Organization	13	17	12	4	1
Preferred Provider Organization	9	14	11	3	6
Indemnity Fee for Service	7	8	6	0	0
Managed Care Contracts					
Health Maintenance Organization	50	48	42	42	40
Preferred Provider Organization	49	48	44	43	40
Affiliations					
Hospitals in a System	56	56	54	51	50
Hospitals in a Network	24	22	20	13	12
Hospitals in a Group Purchasing Organization...	64	62	61	61	55

TABLE 6

SOUTH CAROLINA

U.S. Registered Community Hospitals
(Nonfederal, short-term general and other special hospitals)

Utilization, Personnel, Revenue and Expenses, Community Health Indicators 2012–2016

	2016	2015	2014	2013	2012
TOTAL FACILITY (Includes Hospital and Nursing Home Units)					
Utilization - Inpatient					
Beds	12,299	12,263	12,228	12,758	12,539
Admissions	523,640	522,422	498,690	498,344	506,072
Inpatient Days	2,800,574	2,809,843	2,784,918	2,864,513	2,861,439
Average Length of Stay	5.3	5.4	5.6	5.7	5.7
Inpatient Surgeries	179,421	183,355	177,731	194,834	197,921
Births	53,735	54,587	53,437	52,388	53,353
Utilization - Outpatient					
Emergency Outpatient Visits	2,543,747	2,470,621	2,217,906	1,575,728	1,435,010
Other Outpatient Visits	6,887,039	5,790,736	5,317,945	5,134,748	5,114,768
Total Outpatient Visits	9,430,786	8,261,357	7,535,851	6,710,476	6,549,778
Outpatient Surgeries	327,141	314,241	308,003	317,318	309,250
Personnel					
Full Time RNs	20,453	20,324	19,603	18,693	17,934
Full Time LPNs	715	587	650	722	775
Part Time RNs	5,864	5,178	4,900	4,641	4,652
Part Time LPNs	194	140	162	174	227
Total Full Time	65,846	63,968	61,512	60,317	60,411
Total Part Time	15,701	14,504	13,638	13,327	13,579
Revenue - Inpatient					
Gross Inpatient Revenue	$24,316,896,697	$23,042,804,405	$21,965,206,597	$21,575,477,093	$20,007,919,363
Revenue - Outpatient					
Gross Outpatient Revenue	$24,183,655,122	$21,158,257,947	$18,535,025,990	$17,600,043,070	$15,551,458,526
Revenue and Expenses - Totals					
(Includes Inpatient and Outpatient)					
Total Gross Revenue	$48,500,551,819	$44,201,062,352	$40,500,232,587	$39,175,520,163	$35,559,377,889
Deductions from Revenue	36,190,553,627	32,817,496,916	29,269,848,157	28,456,657,258	25,246,098,981
Net Patient Revenue	12,309,998,192	11,383,565,436	11,230,384,430	10,718,862,905	10,313,278,908
Other Operating Revenue	332,967,924	491,023,067	379,328,304	321,252,507	308,030,013
Other Nonoperating Revenue	225,852,643	121,981,450	249,266,110	293,338,530	277,725,354
Total Net Revenue	12,868,818,759	11,996,569,953	11,858,978,844	11,333,453,942	10,899,034,275
Total Expenses	11,486,589,733	10,607,759,498	10,299,166,490	10,033,330,821	9,729,644,756
HOSPITAL UNIT (Excludes Separate Nursing Home Units)					
Utilization - Inpatient					
Beds	11,891	11,858	11,696	12,027	11,656
Admissions	520,807	519,856	495,088	495,189	502,923
Inpatient Days	2,677,732	2,680,778	2,628,598	2,653,359	2,585,730
Average Length of Stay	5.1	5.2	5.3	5.4	5.1
Personnel					
Total Full Time	65,442	63,637	61,091	59,621	59,664
Total Part Time	15,546	14,373	13,495	13,133	13,328
Revenue and Expenses - Totals					
(Includes Inpatient and Outpatient)					
Total Net Revenue	$12,803,556,782	$11,958,331,155	$11,759,944,896	$11,269,144,355	$10,842,235,748
Total Expenses	11,432,588,620	10,564,643,928	10,216,436,727	9,974,428,391	9,666,217,448
COMMUNITY HEALTH INDICATORS PER 1000 POPULATION					
Total Population (in thousands)	4,961	4,896	4,832	4,775	4,724
Inpatient					
Beds	2.5	2.5	2.5	2.7	2.7
Admissions	105.5	106.7	103.2	104.4	107.1
Inpatient Days	564.5	573.9	576.3	599.9	605.8
Inpatient Surgeries	36.2	37.4	36.8	40.8	41.9
Births	10.8	11.1	11.1	11.0	11.3
Outpatient					
Emergency Outpatient Visits	512.7	504.6	459.0	330.0	303.8
Other Outpatient Visits	1,388.2	1,182.7	1,100.5	1,075.4	1,082.8
Total Outpatient Visits	1,900.9	1,687.3	1,559.4	1,405.4	1,386.6
Outpatient Surgeries	65.9	64.2	63.7	66.5	65.5
Expense per Capita (per person)	$2,315.3	$2,166.6	$2,131.2	$2,101.3	$2,059.7

States

TABLE 6

SOUTH DAKOTA

U.S. Registered Community Hospitals
(Nonfederal, short-term general and other special hospitals)

Overview 2012–2016

	2016	2015	2014	2013	2012
Total Community Hospitals in South Dakota	53	53	53	54	54
Bed Size Category					
6-24..	18	19	19	20	19
25-49..	11	10	10	11	13
50-99..	13	13	13	11	10
100-199..	6	6	6	7	7
200-299..	2	2	2	2	2
300-399..	1	1	1	0	1
400-499..	1	2	1	2	1
500 +...	1	0	1	1	1
Location					
Hospitals Urban	12	12	12	11	11
Hospitals Rural...	41	41	41	43	43
Control					
State and Local Government	4	4	4	4	4
Not for Profit..	45	45	45	46	46
Investor owned...	4	4	4	4	4
Physician Models					
Independent Practice Association......................	3	3	6	7	9
Group Practice without Walls...........................	3	1	2	1	2
Open Physician-Hospital Organization	2	2	2	1	3
Closed Physician-Hospital Organization............	2	1	2	1	3
Management Service Organization....................	1	1	1	0	2
Integrated Salary Model..................................	25	25	27	24	25
Equity Model	0	1	2	2	3
Foundation	1	2	2	2	3
Insurance Products					
Health Maintenance Organization.....................	12	14	13	14	13
Preferred Provider Organization	10	10	11	10	12
Indemnity Fee for Service	4	7	6	6	5
Managed Care Contracts					
Health Maintenance Organization.....................	22	23	25	22	27
Preferred Provider Organization	25	23	27	25	31
Affiliations					
Hospitals in a System	39	39	39	39	39
Hospitals in a Network....................................	22	22	22	23	23
Hospitals in a Group Purchasing Organization...	34	29	35	36	43

TABLE 6

SOUTH DAKOTA

U.S. Registered Community Hospitals
(Nonfederal, short-term general and other special hospitals)

Utilization, Personnel, Revenue and Expenses, Community Health Indicators 2012–2016

	2016	2015	2014	2013	2012
TOTAL FACILITY (Includes Hospital and Nursing Home Units)					
Utilization - Inpatient					
Beds	4,075	4,002	4,086	4,161	4,188
Admissions	101,505	99,862	99,928	101,878	108,263
Inpatient Days	995,007	1,015,413	919,091	934,748	960,652
Average Length of Stay	9.8	10.2	9.2	9.2	8.9
Inpatient Surgeries	25,309	23,518	24,438	27,820	29,636
Births	12,329	11,981	12,880	12,782	12,242
Utilization - Outpatient					
Emergency Outpatient Visits	332,581	270,564	296,024	291,177	282,899
Other Outpatient Visits	2,524,407	2,141,646	3,020,822	1,972,035	1,979,362
Total Outpatient Visits	2,856,988	2,412,210	3,316,846	2,263,212	2,262,261
Outpatient Surgeries	60,644	58,213	52,305	51,305	76,606
Personnel					
Full Time RNs	4,483	4,789	4,555	4,796	4,457
Full Time LPNs	365	341	313	340	267
Part Time RNs	2,467	2,411	2,064	1,889	1,948
Part Time LPNs	189	174	140	128	124
Total Full Time	16,438	16,618	15,958	16,960	16,543
Total Part Time	8,136	8,243	6,757	7,099	6,807
Revenue - Inpatient					
Gross Inpatient Revenue	$4,143,009,619	$4,143,145,917	$3,615,729,346	$3,410,939,910	$3,259,110,943
Revenue - Outpatient					
Gross Outpatient Revenue	$5,350,330,556	$5,065,924,428	$4,182,407,019	$3,299,557,436	$3,103,567,011
Revenue and Expenses - Totals					
(Includes Inpatient and Outpatient)					
Total Gross Revenue	$9,493,340,175	$9,209,070,345	$7,798,136,365	$6,710,497,346	$6,362,677,954
Deductions from Revenue	5,989,387,416	5,910,482,178	4,809,565,680	4,030,372,232	3,649,680,422
Net Patient Revenue	3,503,952,759	3,298,588,167	2,988,570,685	2,680,125,114	2,712,997,532
Other Operating Revenue	216,865,224	193,156,984	188,687,454	176,424,473	146,318,931
Other Nonoperating Revenue	12,005,557	17,805,915	95,967,403	73,485,535	34,097,686
Total Net Revenue	3,732,823,540	3,509,551,066	3,273,225,542	2,930,035,122	2,893,414,149
Total Expenses	3,499,157,632	3,167,676,733	2,966,917,907	2,672,087,974	2,494,970,877
HOSPITAL UNIT (Excludes Separate Nursing Home Units)					
Utilization - Inpatient					
Beds	2,838	2,839	2,858	2,811	2,847
Admissions	100,317	98,800	98,889	100,616	106,941
Inpatient Days	563,845	608,053	522,972	488,235	503,324
Average Length of Stay	5.6	6.2	5.3	4.9	4.7
Personnel					
Total Full Time	15,753	16,046	15,217	16,072	15,690
Total Part Time	7,561	7,751	6,219	6,571	6,221
Revenue and Expenses - Totals					
(Includes Inpatient and Outpatient)					
Total Net Revenue	$3,641,237,991	$3,422,814,606	$3,190,020,801	$2,846,625,100	$2,806,088,891
Total Expenses	3,420,465,279	3,095,411,076	2,893,652,486	2,602,036,829	2,410,336,333
COMMUNITY HEALTH INDICATORS PER 1000 POPULATION					
Total Population (in thousands)	865	858	853	845	833
Inpatient					
Beds	4.7	4.7	4.8	4.9	5.0
Admissions	117.3	116.3	117.1	120.6	129.9
Inpatient Days	1,149.7	1,182.8	1,077.3	1,106.4	1,152.8
Inpatient Surgeries	29.2	27.4	28.6	32.9	35.6
Births	14.2	14.0	15.1	15.1	14.7
Outpatient					
Emergency Outpatient Visits	384.3	315.2	347.0	344.6	339.5
Other Outpatient Visits	2,916.9	2,494.7	3,540.7	2,334.1	2,375.2
Total Outpatient Visits	3,301.1	2,809.9	3,887.7	2,678.7	2,714.6
Outpatient Surgeries	70.1	67.8	61.3	60.7	91.9
Expense per Capita (per person)	$4,043.1	$3,689.9	$3,477.5	$3,162.7	$2,993.9

TABLE 6

TENNESSEE

U.S. Registered Community Hospitals
(Nonfederal, short-term general and other special hospitals)

Overview 2012–2016

	2016	2015	2014	2013	2012
Total Community Hospitals in Tennessee..........	120	121	125	130	132
Bed Size Category					
6-24	7	7	8	9	9
25-49	27	29	30	32	34
50-99	34	30	31	33	31
100-199	23	24	25	24	26
200-299	12	13	12	13	13
300-399	5	6	8	8	7
400-499	4	3	1	2	3
500 + ...	8	9	10	9	9
Location					
Hospitals Urban	75	76	78	76	77
Hospitals Rural	45	45	47	54	55
Control					
State and Local Government	18	18	19	22	21
Not for Profit	51	51	50	49	49
Investor owned	51	52	56	59	62
Physician Models					
Independent Practice Association.....................	11	13	14	14	16
Group Practice without Walls	3	6	5	4	4
Open Physician-Hospital Organization	17	18	16	17	17
Closed Physician-Hospital Organization...........	6	4	5	3	4
Management Service Organization....................	17	17	15	12	14
Integrated Salary Model...................................	28	33	36	34	30
Equity Model	3	3	2	3	0
Foundation	8	8	4	6	2
Insurance Products					
Health Maintenance Organization.....................	12	12	14	12	9
Preferred Provider Organization	22	22	23	24	13
Indemnity Fee for Service	9	8	10	10	7
Managed Care Contracts					
Health Maintenance Organization.....................	47	48	51	56	56
Preferred Provider Organization	52	53	57	63	62
Affiliations					
Hospitals in a System	99	97	102	107	107
Hospitals in a Network	29	30	34	37	31
Hospitals in a Group Purchasing Organization...	52	54	59	66	68

TABLE 6

TENNESSEE

U.S. Registered Community Hospitals
(Nonfederal, short-term general and other special hospitals)

Utilization, Personnel, Revenue and Expenses, Community Health Indicators 2012–2016

	2016	2015	2014	2013	2012
TOTAL FACILITY (Includes Hospital and Nursing Home Units)					
Utilization - Inpatient					
Beds	19,362	19,834	20,031	20,259	20,154
Admissions	824,040	827,492	818,379	819,116	823,781
Inpatient Days	4,497,226	4,577,329	4,428,761	4,525,456	4,500,597
Average Length of Stay	5.5	5.5	5.4	5.5	5.5
Inpatient Surgeries	230,846	228,674	231,629	227,285	241,056
Births	66,712	68,624	67,013	66,249	64,660
Utilization - Outpatient					
Emergency Outpatient Visits	3,546,645	3,492,229	3,405,321	3,378,159	3,260,802
Other Outpatient Visits	9,619,729	8,820,779	8,508,182	8,534,100	8,519,980
Total Outpatient Visits	13,166,374	12,313,008	11,913,503	11,912,259	11,780,782
Outpatient Surgeries	450,381	425,461	433,180	430,284	448,279
Personnel					
Full Time RNs	28,431	26,582	27,092	26,540	26,169
Full Time LPNs	1,909	1,861	1,973	2,139	2,252
Part Time RNs	9,143	7,083	6,760	7,626	9,110
Part Time LPNs	538	434	451	518	610
Total Full Time	91,552	86,743	93,018	90,588	91,851
Total Part Time	26,040	18,885	18,639	20,281	25,175
Revenue - Inpatient					
Gross Inpatient Revenue	$37,225,186,484	$35,799,933,948	$33,092,986,985	$31,762,517,052	$28,979,229,922
Revenue - Outpatient					
Gross Outpatient Revenue	$35,228,420,378	$32,737,313,320	$29,355,048,396	$26,898,593,106	$24,221,902,571
Revenue and Expenses - Totals					
(Includes Inpatient and Outpatient)					
Total Gross Revenue	$72,453,606,862	$68,537,247,268	$62,448,035,381	$58,661,110,158	$53,201,132,493
Deductions from Revenue	54,713,745,257	51,407,644,782	46,399,193,325	43,023,032,783	37,978,697,915
Net Patient Revenue	17,739,861,605	17,129,602,486	16,048,842,056	15,638,077,375	15,222,434,578
Other Operating Revenue	603,871,214	596,387,736	573,071,357	631,573,575	546,985,739
Other Nonoperating Revenue	114,773,640	122,822,365	216,619,646	159,509,587	108,447,768
Total Net Revenue	18,458,506,459	17,848,812,587	16,838,533,059	16,429,160,537	15,877,868,085
Total Expenses	16,875,120,517	16,046,401,723	15,522,404,054	15,002,528,839	14,708,134,735
HOSPITAL UNIT (Excludes Separate Nursing Home Units)					
Utilization - Inpatient					
Beds	18,798	18,745	19,055	19,058	19,052
Admissions	820,555	821,772	813,533	811,908	816,107
Inpatient Days	4,340,208	4,273,530	4,141,898	4,171,201	4,178,131
Average Length of Stay	5.3	5.2	5.1	5.1	5.1
Personnel					
Total Full Time	91,058	86,038	92,199	89,727	90,895
Total Part Time	25,982	18,762	18,493	20,073	24,986
Revenue and Expenses - Totals					
(Includes Inpatient and Outpatient)					
Total Net Revenue	$18,410,845,530	$17,768,573,022	$16,774,136,543	$16,338,297,498	$15,793,027,961
Total Expenses	16,832,242,557	15,972,927,670	15,463,231,902	14,923,551,273	14,632,776,271
COMMUNITY HEALTH INDICATORS PER 1000 POPULATION					
Total Population (in thousands)	6,651	6,600	6,549	6,496	6,456
Inpatient					
Beds	2.9	3.0	3.1	3.1	3.1
Admissions	123.9	125.4	125.0	126.1	127.6
Inpatient Days	676.2	693.5	676.2	696.7	697.1
Inpatient Surgeries	34.7	34.6	35.4	35.0	37.3
Births	10.0	10.4	10.2	10.2	10.0
Outpatient					
Emergency Outpatient Visits	533.2	529.1	519.9	520.0	505.1
Other Outpatient Visits	1,446.3	1,336.4	1,299.1	1,313.8	1,319.6
Total Outpatient Visits	1,979.6	1,865.5	1,819.0	1,833.8	1,824.7
Outpatient Surgeries	67.7	64.5	66.1	66.2	69.4
Expense per Capita (per person)	$2,537.2	$2,431.2	$2,370.1	$2,309.5	$2,278.1

TABLE **6**

TEXAS

U.S. Registered Community Hospitals
(Nonfederal, short-term general and other special hospitals)

Overview 2012–2016

	2016	2015	2014	2013	2012
Total Community Hospitals in Texas	**403**	**404**	**417**	**424**	**425**
Bed Size Category					
6-24	76	71	73	74	74
25-49	97	96	108	108	107
50-99	77	80	79	86	87
100-199	54	60	60	55	55
200-299	37	35	35	41	42
300-399	24	21	22	22	23
400-499	12	14	15	13	13
500 + ...	26	27	25	25	24
Location					
Hospitals Urban	269	269	277	277	276
Hospitals Rural	134	135	140	147	149
Control					
State and Local Government	100	100	102	103	106
Not for Profit	141	143	152	154	151
Investor owned	162	161	163	167	168
Physician Models					
Independent Practice Association	52	54	55	54	58
Group Practice without Walls	16	15	34	19	15
Open Physician-Hospital Organization	65	62	69	75	83
Closed Physician-Hospital Organization	18	16	25	26	26
Management Service Organization	54	50	53	55	62
Integrated Salary Model	132	132	112	122	115
Equity Model	6	5	5	7	8
Foundation	32	33	35	40	37
Insurance Products					
Health Maintenance Organization	81	79	78	68	60
Preferred Provider Organization	75	68	72	61	50
Indemnity Fee for Service	26	18	32	18	13
Managed Care Contracts					
Health Maintenance Organization	329	330	336	337	331
Preferred Provider Organization	353	355	363	370	362
Affiliations					
Hospitals in a System	267	263	278	283	283
Hospitals in a Network	111	109	116	117	116
Hospitals in a Group Purchasing Organization...	388	390	403	408	407

TABLE **6**

TEXAS

U.S. Registered Community Hospitals
(Nonfederal, short-term general and other special hospitals)

Utilization, Personnel, Revenue and Expenses, Community Health Indicators 2012–2016

	2016	2015	2014	2013	2012
TOTAL FACILITY (Includes Hospital and Nursing Home Units)					
Utilization - Inpatient					
Beds	62,114	62,652	61,335	61,600	61,290
Admissions	2,563,828	2,548,764	2,515,174	2,522,455	2,548,864
Inpatient Days	13,929,162	13,638,326	13,278,929	13,173,092	13,170,816
Average Length of Stay	5.4	5.4	5.3	5.2	5.2
Inpatient Surgeries	712,115	725,523	715,533	718,822	729,749
Births	383,252	393,349	390,702	376,859	369,860
Utilization - Outpatient					
Emergency Outpatient Visits	10,664,710	10,650,825	10,488,873	10,404,119	10,439,383
Other Outpatient Visits	32,065,563	31,136,666	30,316,652	29,734,004	30,271,030
Total Outpatient Visits	42,730,273	41,787,491	40,805,525	40,138,123	40,710,413
Outpatient Surgeries	1,135,037	1,122,743	1,096,724	1,058,968	1,024,211
Personnel					
Full Time RNs	92,594	91,772	89,254	87,202	83,746
Full Time LPNs	6,413	6,596	6,610	7,258	7,679
Part Time RNs	23,155	21,902	21,710	24,170	22,853
Part Time LPNs	1,514	1,420	1,305	1,481	1,674
Total Full Time	301,915	296,343	288,697	283,921	278,323
Total Part Time	65,994	62,672	60,298	68,650	64,880
Revenue - Inpatient					
Gross Inpatient Revenue	$150,784,107,474	$140,991,691,141	$129,873,063,736	$121,281,645,571	$114,321,510,363
Revenue - Outpatient					
Gross Outpatient Revenue	$122,744,286,433	$110,510,624,233	$98,778,525,975	$89,812,997,830	$82,221,757,827
Revenue and Expenses - Totals					
(Includes Inpatient and Outpatient)					
Total Gross Revenue	$273,528,393,907	$251,502,315,374	$228,651,589,607	$211,094,643,401	$196,543,268,190
Deductions from Revenue	210,964,929,838	191,251,783,422	172,156,449,946	157,784,347,806	144,431,424,185
Net Patient Revenue	62,563,464,069	60,250,531,952	56,495,139,661	53,310,295,595	52,111,844,005
Other Operating Revenue	5,613,695,294	5,439,798,405	5,230,136,699	5,363,702,261	5,301,391,230
Other Nonoperating Revenue	1,140,109,496	768,343,891	1,544,118,773	937,753,455	842,027,514
Total Net Revenue	69,317,268,859	66,458,674,248	63,269,395,133	59,611,751,311	58,255,262,749
Total Expenses	62,210,936,810	58,337,520,459	55,219,961,093	53,271,177,348	51,154,019,956
HOSPITAL UNIT (Excludes Separate Nursing Home Units)					
Utilization - Inpatient					
Beds	59,839	60,296	60,914	60,802	60,350
Admissions	2,554,647	2,541,611	2,508,538	2,513,915	2,539,148
Inpatient Days	13,353,693	13,348,538	13,176,272	12,946,382	12,898,573
Average Length of Stay	5.2	5.3	5.3	5.1	5.1
Personnel					
Total Full Time	301,155	295,922	287,862	283,250	277,484
Total Part Time	65,816	62,572	60,121	68,503	64,773
Revenue and Expenses - Totals					
(Includes Inpatient and Outpatient)					
Total Net Revenue	$69,210,011,647	$66,307,508,428	$63,210,572,496	$59,524,322,308	$58,163,406,060
Total Expenses	62,108,285,554	58,200,766,871	55,164,740,849	53,205,672,674	51,073,523,904
COMMUNITY HEALTH INDICATORS PER 1000 POPULATION					
Total Population (in thousands)	27,863	27,469	26,957	26,448	26,059
Inpatient					
Beds	2.2	2.3	2.3	2.3	2.4
Admissions	92.0	92.8	93.3	95.4	97.8
Inpatient Days	499.9	496.5	492.6	498.1	505.4
Inpatient Surgeries	25.6	26.4	26.5	27.2	28.0
Births	13.8	14.3	14.5	14.2	14.2
Outpatient					
Emergency Outpatient Visits	382.8	387.7	389.1	393.4	400.6
Other Outpatient Visits	1,150.8	1,133.5	1,124.6	1,124.2	1,161.6
Total Outpatient Visits	1,533.6	1,521.3	1,513.7	1,517.6	1,562.2
Outpatient Surgeries	40.7	40.9	40.7	40.0	39.3
Expense per Capita (per person)	$2,232.8	$2,123.7	$2,048.4	$2,014.2	$1,963.0

TABLE **6**

UTAH

U.S. Registered Community Hospitals
(Nonfederal, short-term general and other special hospitals)

Overview 2012–2016

	2016	2015	2014	2013	2012
Total Community Hospitals in Utah...................	**47**	**47**	**47**	**47**	**47**
Bed Size Category					
6-24	9	9	10	10	9
25-49	15	15	15	15	16
50-99	3	3	3	3	3
100-199	11	11	10	10	10
200-299	5	5	5	5	4
300-399	2	2	2	2	3
400-499	0	1	1	1	1
500 + ...	2	1	1	1	1
Location					
Hospitals Urban	29	29	29	28	28
Hospitals Rural	18	18	18	19	19
Control					
State and Local Government	6	6	6	6	6
Not for Profit...	26	26	26	26	26
Investor owned...	15	15	15	15	15
Physician Models					
Independent Practice Association......................	3	4	3	3	4
Group Practice without Walls	3	2	2	2	2
Open Physician-Hospital Organization	3	2	2	2	1
Closed Physician-Hospital Organization............	3	2	2	2	2
Management Service Organization....................	2	1	2	2	2
Integrated Salary Model...................................	18	20	17	16	19
Equity Model	2	1	1	1	1
Foundation	3	2	1	1	1
Insurance Products					
Health Maintenance Organization......................	12	11	14	16	16
Preferred Provider Organization	14	14	11	14	9
Indemnity Fee for Service	5	3	1	4	4
Managed Care Contracts					
Health Maintenance Organization......................	13	14	13	15	13
Preferred Provider Organization	17	19	18	20	18
Affiliations					
Hospitals in a System	38	38	38	38	38
Hospitals in a Network	10	9	14	15	8
Hospitals in a Group Purchasing Organization...	26	27	27	29	21

TABLE 6

UTAH

U.S. Registered Community Hospitals
(Nonfederal, short-term general and other special hospitals)

Utilization, Personnel, Revenue and Expenses, Community Health Indicators 2012–2016

	2016	2015	2014	2013	2012
TOTAL FACILITY (Includes Hospital and Nursing Home Units)					
Utilization - Inpatient					
Beds	5,423	5,323	5,207	5,216	5,212
Admissions	239,305	236,191	228,979	229,492	241,436
Inpatient Days	1,045,406	1,025,302	990,116	979,856	992,015
Average Length of Stay	4.4	4.3	4.3	4.3	4.1
Inpatient Surgeries	72,013	72,351	71,768	68,077	71,909
Births	48,919	47,212	48,337	47,854	51,575
Utilization - Outpatient					
Emergency Outpatient Visits	998,334	1,029,418	1,045,790	888,611	894,661
Other Outpatient Visits	7,480,913	6,791,570	6,364,654	5,292,520	5,459,212
Total Outpatient Visits	8,479,247	7,820,988	7,410,444	6,181,131	6,353,873
Outpatient Surgeries	190,669	183,321	186,640	174,163	166,063
Personnel					
Full Time RNs	9,466	9,128	8,573	8,280	7,273
Full Time LPNs	272	309	278	304	299
Part Time RNs	4,506	3,888	4,242	4,486	4,801
Part Time LPNs	99	108	121	148	171
Total Full Time	33,775	31,249	29,229	29,048	26,395
Total Part Time	13,333	11,949	13,061	13,993	14,612
Revenue - Inpatient					
Gross Inpatient Revenue	$11,829,655,136	$10,936,944,488	$10,068,204,660	$8,689,472,055	$8,253,048,052
Revenue - Outpatient					
Gross Outpatient Revenue	$11,490,905,378	$10,437,940,321	$9,365,225,858	$7,762,738,220	$6,983,551,734
Revenue and Expenses - Totals					
(Includes Inpatient and Outpatient)					
Total Gross Revenue	$23,320,560,514	$21,374,884,809	$19,433,430,518	$16,452,210,275	$15,236,599,786
Deductions from Revenue	15,428,873,208	14,280,426,410	12,693,106,100	10,308,471,435	9,233,540,993
Net Patient Revenue	7,891,687,306	7,094,458,399	6,740,324,418	6,143,738,840	6,003,058,793
Other Operating Revenue	207,460,953	221,960,238	204,338,018	229,460,960	221,419,572
Other Nonoperating Revenue	13,683,996	15,611,773	29,673,497	24,760,128	9,983,495
Total Net Revenue	8,112,832,255	7,332,030,410	6,974,335,933	6,397,959,928	6,234,461,860
Total Expenses	6,579,978,635	6,077,071,195	5,616,931,808	5,364,834,918	5,117,473,502
HOSPITAL UNIT (Excludes Separate Nursing Home Units)					
Utilization - Inpatient					
Beds	5,217	5,111	5,079	5,089	5,080
Admissions	238,314	235,255	228,206	228,932	240,784
Inpatient Days	983,371	959,130	956,057	946,093	951,874
Average Length of Stay	4.1	4.1	4.2	4.1	4.0
Personnel					
Total Full Time	33,689	31,185	29,176	28,977	26,322
Total Part Time	13,296	11,903	13,024	13,944	14,549
Revenue and Expenses - Totals					
(Includes Inpatient and Outpatient)					
Total Net Revenue	$8,097,892,599	$7,318,743,028	$6,966,500,892	$6,390,793,512	$6,225,430,738
Total Expenses	6,566,766,963	6,066,754,661	5,611,918,537	5,360,928,383	5,110,023,379
COMMUNITY HEALTH INDICATORS PER 1000 POPULATION					
Total Population (in thousands)	3,051	2,996	2,943	2,901	2,855
Inpatient					
Beds	1.8	1.8	1.8	1.8	1.8
Admissions	78.4	78.8	77.8	79.1	84.6
Inpatient Days	342.6	342.2	336.4	337.8	347.4
Inpatient Surgeries	23.6	24.1	24.4	23.5	25.2
Births	16.0	15.8	16.4	16.5	18.1
Outpatient					
Emergency Outpatient Visits	327.2	343.6	355.4	306.3	313.3
Other Outpatient Visits	2,451.8	2,266.9	2,162.7	1,824.5	1,912.0
Total Outpatient Visits	2,779.0	2,610.5	2,518.1	2,130.8	2,225.3
Outpatient Surgeries	62.5	61.2	63.4	60.0	58.2
Expense per Capita (per person)	$2,156.5	$2,028.4	$1,908.6	$1,849.4	$1,792.3

States

TABLE 6

VERMONT

U.S. Registered Community Hospitals
(Nonfederal, short-term general and other special hospitals)

Overview 2012–2016

	2016	2015	2014	2013	2012
Total Community Hospitals in Vermont...............	14	14	14	14	14
Bed Size Category					
6-24	1	1	1	1	2
25-49	7	7	7	7	6
50-99	3	3	3	3	3
100-199	1	1	1	1	1
200-299	1	1	1	1	1
300-399	0	0	0	0	0
400-499	1	1	1	1	1
500 + ...	0	0	0	0	0
Location					
Hospitals Urban	2	2	2	2	2
Hospitals Rural	12	12	12	12	12
Control					
State and Local Government	0	0	0	0	0
Not for Profit	14	14	14	14	14
Investor owned	0	0	0	0	0
Physician Models					
Independent Practice Association......................	0	0	0	0	0
Group Practice without Walls	1	1	1	1	0
Open Physician-Hospital Organization	1	1	2	1	3
Closed Physician-Hospital Organization............	0	0	0	0	0
Management Service Organization.....................	0	0	0	0	0
Integrated Salary Model.....................................	4	4	5	5	6
Equity Model	0	0	0	0	0
Foundation	0	0	0	0	0
Insurance Products					
Health Maintenance Organization......................	0	0	0	1	2
Preferred Provider Organization	0	0	0	1	1
Indemnity Fee for Service	0	0	0	1	2
Managed Care Contracts					
Health Maintenance Organization......................	7	4	4	3	2
Preferred Provider Organization	6	3	5	3	3
Affiliations					
Hospitals in a System	1	1	1	1	1
Hospitals in a Network	3	3	3	4	5
Hospitals in a Group Purchasing Organization...	8	9	10	11	10

TABLE 6

VERMONT

U.S. Registered Community Hospitals
(Nonfederal, short-term general and other special hospitals)

Utilization, Personnel, Revenue and Expenses, Community Health Indicators 2012–2016

	2016	2015	2014	2013	2012
TOTAL FACILITY (Includes Hospital and Nursing Home Units)					
Utilization - Inpatient					
Beds	1,241	1,206	1,200	1,201	1,231
Admissions	49,847	47,695	45,964	48,464	48,887
Inpatient Days	296,562	292,755	288,502	303,555	307,154
Average Length of Stay	5.9	6.1	6.3	6.3	6.3
Inpatient Surgeries	12,792	11,936	12,180	12,785	13,036
Births	5,284	5,475	5,557	5,246	5,250
Utilization - Outpatient					
Emergency Outpatient Visits	317,955	328,066	327,066	302,264	302,030
Other Outpatient Visits	2,585,321	2,832,878	2,817,446	2,779,607	2,740,382
Total Outpatient Visits	2,903,276	3,160,944	3,144,512	3,081,871	3,042,412
Outpatient Surgeries	38,439	37,638	45,616	46,251	46,671
Personnel					
Full Time RNs	2,231	2,196	2,219	2,006	1,852
Full Time LPNs	184	187	173	150	148
Part Time RNs	1,744	1,781	1,607	1,646	1,553
Part Time LPNs	110	124	97	91	104
Total Full Time	11,932	11,353	11,026	10,374	9,967
Total Part Time	5,090	5,349	4,685	4,657	4,590
Revenue - Inpatient					
Gross Inpatient Revenue	$1,571,303,645	$1,508,972,052	$1,374,615,928	$1,435,938,955	$1,089,276,425
Revenue - Outpatient					
Gross Outpatient Revenue	$3,778,225,703	$3,629,335,543	$3,444,718,900	$3,197,627,776	$3,001,872,051
Revenue and Expenses - Totals					
(Includes Inpatient and Outpatient)					
Total Gross Revenue	$5,349,529,348	$5,138,307,595	$4,819,334,828	$4,633,566,731	$4,091,148,476
Deductions from Revenue	3,050,523,420	2,921,665,803	2,710,952,529	2,565,323,969	2,173,153,296
Net Patient Revenue	2,299,005,928	2,216,641,792	2,108,382,299	2,068,242,762	1,917,995,180
Other Operating Revenue	161,148,808	161,470,550	139,867,987	102,107,130	71,915,614
Other Nonoperating Revenue	33,298,454	-16,926,169	27,570,031	68,713,604	39,281,120
Total Net Revenue	2,493,453,190	2,361,186,173	2,275,820,317	2,239,063,496	2,029,191,914
Total Expenses	2,314,763,842	2,202,744,108	2,101,149,726	2,042,602,482	1,931,290,820
HOSPITAL UNIT (Excludes Separate Nursing Home Units)					
Utilization - Inpatient					
Beds	1,088	1,053	1,047	1,048	1,053
Admissions	49,528	47,393	45,584	48,129	48,477
Inpatient Days	253,600	249,294	241,545	249,025	248,986
Average Length of Stay	5.1	5.3	5.3	5.2	5.1
Personnel					
Total Full Time	11,793	11,236	10,975	10,247	9,791
Total Part Time	4,998	5,246	4,668	4,601	4,502
Revenue and Expenses - Totals					
(Includes Inpatient and Outpatient)					
Total Net Revenue	$2,478,775,941	$2,347,550,643	$2,260,094,501	$2,222,318,627	$2,012,967,016
Total Expenses	2,297,463,113	2,187,053,331	2,085,458,949	2,026,117,019	1,915,144,417
COMMUNITY HEALTH INDICATORS PER 1000 POPULATION					
Total Population (in thousands)	625	626	627	627	626
Inpatient					
Beds	2.0	1.9	1.9	1.9	2.0
Admissions	79.8	76.2	73.4	77.3	78.1
Inpatient Days	474.8	467.6	460.5	484.4	490.7
Inpatient Surgeries	20.5	19.1	19.4	20.4	20.8
Births	8.5	8.7	8.9	8.4	8.4
Outpatient					
Emergency Outpatient Visits	509.1	524.0	522.0	482.4	482.5
Other Outpatient Visits	4,139.2	4,525.1	4,496.7	4,435.8	4,377.5
Total Outpatient Visits	4,648.3	5,049.1	5,018.7	4,918.2	4,860.0
Outpatient Surgeries	61.5	60.1	72.8	73.8	74.6
Expense per Capita (per person)	$3,706.0	$3,518.5	$3,353.5	$3,259.7	$3,085.1

TABLE 6

VIRGINIA

U.S. Registered Community Hospitals
(Nonfederal, short-term general and other special hospitals)

Overview 2012–2016

	2016	2015	2014	2013	2012
Total Community Hospitals in Virginia	92	92	93	93	94
Bed Size Category					
6-24	8	7	6	6	5
25-49	15	16	17	16	16
50-99	18	17	17	18	17
100-199	20	22	22	23	26
200-299	12	11	13	12	12
300-399	6	6	5	5	5
400-499	5	5	5	5	5
500 + ...	8	8	8	8	8
Location					
Hospitals Urban	65	65	66	64	64
Hospitals Rural	27	27	27	29	30
Control					
State and Local Government	4	4	5	5	5
Not for Profit	65	65	65	65	65
Investor owned	23	23	23	23	24
Physician Models					
Independent Practice Association	15	13	14	11	13
Group Practice without Walls	10	9	10	9	9
Open Physician-Hospital Organization	12	12	14	14	14
Closed Physician-Hospital Organization	3	4	4	3	2
Management Service Organization	17	19	15	15	16
Integrated Salary Model	48	51	41	44	45
Equity Model	9	9	10	9	9
Foundation	1	1	2	1	2
Insurance Products					
Health Maintenance Organization	28	28	24	28	18
Preferred Provider Organization	33	33	25	30	15
Indemnity Fee for Service	17	7	18	15	9
Managed Care Contracts					
Health Maintenance Organization	61	56	49	60	55
Preferred Provider Organization	62	57	50	61	57
Affiliations					
Hospitals in a System	83	83	83	81	78
Hospitals in a Network	42	43	42	44	41
Hospitals in a Group Purchasing Organization...	65	64	58	65	64

TABLE 6

VIRGINIA

U.S. Registered Community Hospitals
(Nonfederal, short-term general and other special hospitals)

Utilization, Personnel, Revenue and Expenses, Community Health Indicators 2012–2016

	2016	2015	2014	2013	2012
TOTAL FACILITY (Includes Hospital and Nursing Home Units)					
Utilization - Inpatient					
Beds..	17,884	17,816	18,234	17,975	18,150
Admissions..................................	790,179	787,013	775,015	780,153	796,004
Inpatient Days.............................	4,475,635	4,405,482	4,432,096	4,436,963	4,516,303
Average Length of Stay................	5.7	5.6	5.7	5.7	5.7
Inpatient Surgeries......................	203,414	199,757	206,310	213,323	209,255
Births..	94,302	93,526	92,449	93,002	93,114
Utilization - Outpatient					
Emergency Outpatient Visits........	3,733,349	3,677,070	3,644,169	3,626,500	3,600,733
Other Outpatient Visits................	13,993,045	13,289,788	12,877,851	12,187,544	11,952,608
Total Outpatient Visits.................	17,726,394	16,966,858	16,522,020	15,814,044	15,553,341
Outpatient Surgeries....................	528,552	522,352	500,657	501,555	451,407
Personnel					
Full Time RNs..............................	27,719	27,848	26,746	26,044	24,712
Full Time LPNs............................	2,230	2,036	1,761	1,935	2,104
Part Time RNs.............................	12,132	11,714	10,477	10,775	10,964
Part Time LPNs...........................	512	548	459	521	611
Total Full Time.............................	91,920	92,351	85,289	85,502	83,946
Total Part Time............................	33,538	33,323	27,755	29,524	29,934
Revenue - Inpatient					
Gross Inpatient Revenue..............	$35,329,685,368	$32,732,448,118	$31,343,762,241	$29,611,485,772	$28,228,430,166
Revenue - Outpatient					
Gross Outpatient Revenue...........	$37,708,280,287	$34,467,705,283	$31,397,192,819	$28,296,364,383	$25,551,564,541
Revenue and Expenses - Totals					
(Includes Inpatient and Outpatient)					
Total Gross Revenue....................	$73,037,965,655	$67,200,153,401	$62,740,955,060	$57,907,850,155	$53,779,994,707
Deductions from Revenue............	52,295,066,506	47,294,321,307	43,932,115,916	39,950,040,314	36,089,745,615
Net Patient Revenue....................	20,742,899,149	19,905,832,094	18,808,839,144	17,957,809,841	17,690,249,092
Other Operating Revenue............	791,936,890	763,032,564	726,060,044	685,703,799	614,154,152
Other Nonoperating Revenue.......	206,321,755	70,938,497	395,330,743	484,708,430	354,593,302
Total Net Revenue.......................	21,741,157,794	20,739,803,155	19,930,229,931	19,128,222,070	18,658,996,546
Total Expenses............................	19,592,660,253	18,693,010,711	17,726,816,378	17,002,869,179	16,505,378,259
HOSPITAL UNIT (Excludes Separate Nursing Home Units)					
Utilization - Inpatient					
Beds..	16,200	16,175	16,586	16,327	16,467
Admissions..................................	784,007	780,817	768,904	773,930	789,746
Inpatient Days.............................	3,929,097	3,868,090	3,902,908	3,879,122	3,951,225
Average Length of Stay................	5.0	5.0	5.1	5.0	5.0
Personnel					
Total Full Time.............................	90,719	91,368	84,380	84,464	82,960
Total Part Time............................	33,015	32,853	27,369	29,137	29,503
Revenue and Expenses - Totals					
(Includes Inpatient and Outpatient)					
Total Net Revenue.......................	$21,598,753,451	$20,597,558,161	$19,797,897,759	$18,989,222,239	$18,515,704,755
Total Expenses............................	19,459,342,651	18,564,072,240	17,600,918,382	16,873,364,471	16,368,213,160
COMMUNITY HEALTH INDICATORS PER 1000 POPULATION					
Total Population (in thousands)..........	8,412	8,383	8,326	8,260	8,186
Inpatient					
Beds..	2.1	2.1	2.2	2.2	2.2
Admissions..................................	93.9	93.9	93.1	94.4	97.2
Inpatient Days.............................	532.1	525.5	532.3	537.1	551.7
Inpatient Surgeries......................	24.2	23.8	24.8	25.8	25.6
Births..	11.2	11.2	11.1	11.3	11.4
Outpatient					
Emergency Outpatient Visits........	443.8	438.6	437.7	439.0	439.9
Other Outpatient Visits................	1,663.5	1,585.3	1,546.6	1,475.4	1,460.2
Total Outpatient Visits.................	2,107.3	2,024.0	1,984.3	1,914.4	1,900.0
Outpatient Surgeries....................	62.8	62.3	60.1	60.7	55.1
Expense per Capita (per person).........	$2,329.2	$2,229.9	$2,129.0	$2,058.4	$2,016.3

States

TABLE **6**

WASHINGTON

U.S. Registered Community Hospitals
(Nonfederal, short-term general and other special hospitals)

Overview 2012–2016

	2016	2015	2014	2013	2012
Total Community Hospitals in Washington.........	90	90	90	90	87
Bed Size Category					
6-24	10	10	10	9	8
25-49	28	28	28	27	27
50-99	15	15	15	16	14
100-199	14	15	15	16	15
200-299	11	10	11	11	12
300-399	6	7	5	5	4
400-499	3	2	3	4	5
500 + ...	3	3	3	2	2
Location					
Hospitals Urban	60	61	61	56	55
Hospitals Rural...	30	29	29	34	32
Control					
State and Local Government	41	40	40	40	38
Not for Profit..	42	43	43	44	42
Investor owned...	7	7	7	6	7
Physician Models					
Independent Practice Association.....................	1	2	1	1	1
Group Practice without Walls.........................	2	3	3	2	3
Open Physician-Hospital Organization	2	2	2	2	3
Closed Physician-Hospital Organization............	2	1	1	0	1
Management Service Organization.....................	2	2	1	2	3
Integrated Salary Model.................................	44	45	41	36	39
Equity Model	0	0	1	3	3
Foundation	0	0	0	6	4
Insurance Products					
Health Maintenance Organization.....................	8	8	6	4	4
Preferred Provider Organization	13	12	10	9	9
Indemnity Fee for Service..............................	2	2	2	1	2
Managed Care Contracts					
Health Maintenance Organization.....................	36	34	41	31	38
Preferred Provider Organization	38	35	41	34	40
Affiliations					
Hospitals in a System	48	49	45	42	40
Hospitals in a Network	36	35	29	24	17
Hospitals in a Group Purchasing Organization...	51	46	54	51	44

TABLE 6

WASHINGTON

U.S. Registered Community Hospitals
(Nonfederal, short-term general and other special hospitals)

Utilization, Personnel, Revenue and Expenses, Community Health Indicators 2012–2016

	2016	2015	2014	2013	2012
TOTAL FACILITY (Includes Hospital and Nursing Home Units)					
Utilization - Inpatient					
Beds	12,126	11,997	11,988	12,180	12,132
Admissions	590,958	593,082	576,655	600,519	597,338
Inpatient Days	2,895,079	2,815,242	2,711,414	2,763,826	2,731,437
Average Length of Stay	4.9	4.7	4.7	4.6	4.6
Inpatient Surgeries	174,718	171,762	175,364	170,566	165,978
Births	83,992	83,171	80,429	77,904	76,089
Utilization - Outpatient					
Emergency Outpatient Visits	2,684,130	2,672,401	2,440,819	2,338,002	2,390,525
Other Outpatient Visits	11,501,066	10,854,161	9,801,052	10,120,396	10,576,020
Total Outpatient Visits	14,185,196	13,526,562	12,241,871	12,458,398	12,966,545
Outpatient Surgeries	363,377	302,217	321,763	299,228	265,920
Personnel					
Full Time RNs	23,120	21,966	18,517	18,241	18,981
Full Time LPNs	1,140	1,019	705	826	946
Part Time RNs	9,845	11,368	11,903	14,128	12,219
Part Time LPNs	418	476	419	545	509
Total Full Time	86,752	81,982	74,255	74,227	75,760
Total Part Time	30,283	31,044	34,778	41,067	37,294
Revenue - Inpatient					
Gross Inpatient Revenue	$32,622,652,046	$31,208,099,731	$27,873,947,083	$27,370,345,005	$25,728,322,501
Revenue - Outpatient					
Gross Outpatient Revenue	$31,802,008,805	$29,858,509,374	$27,000,712,977	$25,026,435,484	$22,312,583,270
Revenue and Expenses - Totals					
(Includes Inpatient and Outpatient)					
Total Gross Revenue	$64,424,660,851	$61,066,609,105	$54,874,660,060	$52,396,780,489	$48,040,905,771
Deductions from Revenue	43,819,498,161	41,089,572,567	36,929,155,971	34,820,455,823	31,116,500,841
Net Patient Revenue	20,605,162,690	19,977,036,538	17,945,504,089	17,576,324,666	16,924,404,930
Other Operating Revenue	1,142,106,303	1,134,099,489	1,009,138,938	1,020,203,756	972,579,978
Other Nonoperating Revenue	222,970,546	62,167,743	242,467,401	249,956,325	210,144,087
Total Net Revenue	21,970,239,539	21,173,303,770	19,197,110,428	18,846,484,747	18,107,128,995
Total Expenses	20,918,226,540	19,772,591,226	17,790,525,968	17,864,679,102	16,739,742,990
HOSPITAL UNIT (Excludes Separate Nursing Home Units)					
Utilization - Inpatient					
Beds	11,897	11,716	11,824	11,997	11,914
Admissions	589,803	592,075	575,883	600,198	597,051
Inpatient Days	2,819,353	2,714,529	2,663,886	2,686,606	2,655,788
Average Length of Stay	4.8	4.6	4.6	4.5	4.4
Personnel					
Total Full Time	86,483	81,740	74,081	74,098	75,610
Total Part Time	30,082	30,835	34,617	40,938	37,137
Revenue and Expenses - Totals					
(Includes Inpatient and Outpatient)					
Total Net Revenue	$21,922,142,832	$21,143,610,996	$19,175,208,730	$18,825,783,157	$18,084,028,525
Total Expenses	20,879,286,541	19,745,112,020	17,769,219,934	17,844,227,960	16,718,398,352
COMMUNITY HEALTH INDICATORS PER 1000 POPULATION					
Total Population (in thousands)	7,288	7,170	7,062	6,971	6,897
Inpatient					
Beds	1.7	1.7	1.7	1.7	1.8
Admissions	81.1	82.7	81.7	86.1	86.6
Inpatient Days	397.2	392.6	384.0	396.5	396.0
Inpatient Surgeries	24.0	24.0	24.8	24.5	24.1
Births	11.5	11.6	11.4	11.2	11.0
Outpatient					
Emergency Outpatient Visits	368.3	372.7	345.7	335.4	346.6
Other Outpatient Visits	1,578.1	1,513.8	1,388.0	1,451.7	1,533.4
Total Outpatient Visits	1,946.4	1,886.5	1,733.6	1,787.1	1,880.0
Outpatient Surgeries	49.9	42.1	45.6	42.9	38.6
Expense per Capita (per person)	$2,870.2	$2,757.5	$2,519.4	$2,562.6	$2,427.1

States

TABLE 6

WEST VIRGINIA

U.S. Registered Community Hospitals
(Nonfederal, short-term general and other special hospitals)

Overview 2012–2016

	2016	2015	2014	2013	2012
Total Community Hospitals in West Virginia.......	54	54	54	55	55
Bed Size Category					
6-24	4	4	4	3	3
25-49	16	16	16	17	16
50-99	12	11	10	11	12
100-199	11	12	13	12	12
200-299	7	7	7	8	7
300-399	2	2	2	2	2
400-499	0	0	0	0	1
500 + ...	2	2	2	2	2
Location					
Hospitals Urban	28	28	28	26	26
Hospitals Rural	26	26	26	29	29
Control					
State and Local Government	7	7	7	7	8
Not for Profit	34	33	33	34	33
Investor owned...	13	14	14	14	14
Physician Models					
Independent Practice Association......................	2	2	2	2	2
Group Practice without Walls.........................	0	0	0	1	0
Open Physician-Hospital Organization	7	10	11	11	12
Closed Physician-Hospital Organization............	4	1	1	1	1
Management Service Organization.....................	1	2	2	1	2
Integrated Salary Model................................	25	26	27	27	27
Equity Model	0	0	0	0	0
Foundation	2	0	0	0	0
Insurance Products					
Health Maintenance Organization.....................	4	4	4	4	5
Preferred Provider Organization	7	8	8	8	6
Indemnity Fee for Service	2	3	3	4	4
Managed Care Contracts					
Health Maintenance Organization.....................	32	32	31	29	31
Preferred Provider Organization	39	40	40	41	40
Affiliations					
Hospitals in a System	33	30	30	30	30
Hospitals in a Network	17	18	20	20	20
Hospitals in a Group Purchasing Organization...	46	51	52	53	53

TABLE 6

WEST VIRGINIA

U.S. Registered Community Hospitals
(Nonfederal, short-term general and other special hospitals)

Utilization, Personnel, Revenue and Expenses, Community Health Indicators 2012–2016

	2016	2015	2014	2013	2012
TOTAL FACILITY (Includes Hospital and Nursing Home Units)					
Utilization - Inpatient					
Beds	6,803	6,861	6,841	7,054	7,212
Admissions	251,876	255,189	256,571	265,292	276,114
Inpatient Days	1,474,031	1,504,987	1,529,702	1,549,653	1,587,250
Average Length of Stay	5.9	5.9	6.0	5.8	5.7
Inpatient Surgeries	73,429	74,746	77,672	80,580	82,602
Births	19,621	20,145	20,447	20,974	20,758
Utilization - Outpatient					
Emergency Outpatient Visits	1,171,598	1,185,169	1,182,114	1,164,759	1,224,551
Other Outpatient Visits	6,738,424	6,280,016	5,928,683	5,732,531	5,585,774
Total Outpatient Visits	7,910,022	7,465,185	7,110,797	6,897,290	6,810,325
Outpatient Surgeries	242,580	238,108	227,500	231,365	228,957
Personnel					
Full Time RNs	9,585	9,357	9,292	9,300	8,852
Full Time LPNs	1,115	1,153	1,093	1,098	1,130
Part Time RNs	3,043	3,037	2,933	3,325	3,251
Part Time LPNs	208	232	226	325	332
Total Full Time	36,445	35,839	35,039	35,411	34,272
Total Part Time	9,410	9,484	9,278	10,751	10,125
Revenue - Inpatient					
Gross Inpatient Revenue	$7,744,126,898	$7,186,264,827	$6,849,859,734	$6,598,503,203	$6,272,466,443
Revenue - Outpatient					
Gross Outpatient Revenue	$9,270,871,302	$8,466,141,409	$7,556,674,350	$6,837,148,779	$6,361,117,278
Revenue and Expenses - Totals					
(Includes Inpatient and Outpatient)					
Total Gross Revenue	$17,014,998,200	$15,652,406,236	$14,406,534,084	$13,435,651,982	$12,633,583,721
Deductions from Revenue	10,827,698,291	9,844,999,544	8,850,299,429	8,165,212,258	7,391,004,309
Net Patient Revenue	6,187,299,909	5,807,406,692	5,556,234,655	5,270,439,724	5,242,579,412
Other Operating Revenue	281,808,354	242,822,013	214,353,652	222,761,392	182,070,517
Other Nonoperating Revenue	53,280,799	-19,450,686	87,577,976	191,330,033	86,836,379
Total Net Revenue	6,522,389,062	6,030,778,019	5,858,166,283	5,684,531,149	5,511,486,308
Total Expenses	6,178,731,358	5,812,987,606	5,514,045,147	5,371,862,686	5,151,427,691
HOSPITAL UNIT (Excludes Separate Nursing Home Units)					
Utilization - Inpatient					
Beds	6,136	6,122	6,102	6,270	6,423
Admissions	249,322	251,931	253,305	261,148	271,352
Inpatient Days	1,262,858	1,274,442	1,294,455	1,303,200	1,329,793
Average Length of Stay	5.1	5.1	5.1	5.0	4.9
Personnel					
Total Full Time	35,972	35,323	34,502	34,840	33,683
Total Part Time	9,270	9,304	9,056	10,370	9,785
Revenue and Expenses - Totals					
(Includes Inpatient and Outpatient)					
Total Net Revenue	$6,467,940,876	$5,969,693,294	$5,798,408,691	$5,617,231,970	$5,439,544,951
Total Expenses	6,148,570,405	5,778,075,665	5,469,138,973	5,329,382,003	5,097,076,501
COMMUNITY HEALTH INDICATORS PER 1000 POPULATION					
Total Population (in thousands)	1,831	1,844	1,850	1,854	1,855
Inpatient					
Beds	3.7	3.7	3.7	3.8	3.9
Admissions	137.6	138.4	138.7	143.1	148.8
Inpatient Days	805.0	816.1	826.7	835.7	855.5
Inpatient Surgeries	40.1	40.5	42.0	43.5	44.5
Births	10.7	10.9	11.1	11.3	11.2
Outpatient					
Emergency Outpatient Visits	639.8	642.7	638.9	628.1	660.0
Other Outpatient Visits	3,680.0	3,405.4	3,204.1	3,091.5	3,010.5
Total Outpatient Visits	4,319.8	4,048.1	3,843.0	3,719.6	3,670.5
Outpatient Surgeries	132.5	129.1	123.0	124.8	123.4
Expense per Capita (per person)	$3,374.3	$3,152.2	$2,980.0	$2,897.0	$2,776.4

States

TABLE 6

WISCONSIN

U.S. Registered Community Hospitals
(Nonfederal, short-term general and other special hospitals)

Overview 2012–2016

	2016	2015	2014	2013	2012
Total Community Hospitals in Wisconsin	127	127	129	129	128
Bed Size Category					
6-24	27	23	22	23	21
25-49	29	32	34	32	33
50-99	30	31	31	32	33
100-199	23	23	24	22	20
200-299	11	12	10	12	11
300-399	4	3	4	4	7
400-499	0	0	1	1	0
500 + ...	3	3	3	3	3
Location					
Hospitals Urban	70	70	72	73	72
Hospitals Rural	57	57	57	56	56
Control					
State and Local Government	2	2	2	2	2
Not for Profit	119	119	121	121	121
Investor owned	6	6	6	6	5
Physician Models					
Independent Practice Association	7	7	7	8	11
Group Practice without Walls	0	0	1	1	0
Open Physician-Hospital Organization	6	6	6	8	6
Closed Physician-Hospital Organization............	4	2	5	4	3
Management Service Organization....................	4	2	2	1	2
Integrated Salary Model..................................	47	52	51	54	62
Equity Model	14	12	9	11	7
Foundation	2	2	2	2	2
Insurance Products					
Health Maintenance Organization.....................	31	33	34	43	41
Preferred Provider Organization	42	41	44	45	41
Indemnity Fee for Service	18	16	18	18	19
Managed Care Contracts					
Health Maintenance Organization.....................	115	117	118	120	118
Preferred Provider Organization	115	117	119	122	121
Affiliations					
Hospitals in a System	84	80	80	76	75
Hospitals in a Network....................................	55	53	42	45	44
Hospitals in a Group Purchasing Organization...	122	124	125	124	126

TABLE 6

WISCONSIN

U.S. Registered Community Hospitals
(Nonfederal, short-term general and other special hospitals)

Utilization, Personnel, Revenue and Expenses, Community Health Indicators 2012–2016

	2016	2015	2014	2013	2012
TOTAL FACILITY (Includes Hospital and Nursing Home Units)					
Utilization - Inpatient					
Beds	12,242	12,477	12,659	12,760	13,020
Admissions	530,045	537,632	551,398	566,368	578,239
Inpatient Days	2,648,740	2,738,100	2,754,377	2,808,943	2,855,397
Average Length of Stay	5.0	5.1	5.0	5.0	4.9
Inpatient Surgeries	172,086	169,217	169,251	172,640	214,146
Births	64,222	64,513	64,433	64,598	65,632
Utilization - Outpatient					
Emergency Outpatient Visits	2,372,857	2,434,154	2,199,839	2,098,324	2,171,739
Other Outpatient Visits	16,223,738	15,261,873	15,081,475	14,400,592	13,957,038
Total Outpatient Visits	18,596,595	17,696,027	17,281,314	16,498,916	16,128,777
Outpatient Surgeries	483,024	467,853	458,157	454,518	526,585
Personnel					
Full Time RNs	18,823	16,875	15,953	15,560	15,095
Full Time LPNs	636	657	541	617	537
Part Time RNs	15,871	15,110	15,880	15,965	15,972
Part Time LPNs	583	637	587	689	645
Total Full Time	71,413	67,517	63,551	64,634	63,722
Total Part Time	49,115	46,127	47,846	49,311	48,388
Revenue - Inpatient					
Gross Inpatient Revenue	$20,659,910,592	$20,077,812,400	$18,851,445,421	$17,961,771,456	$17,011,582,655
Revenue - Outpatient					
Gross Outpatient Revenue	$30,498,557,816	$27,927,107,562	$24,798,270,276	$22,326,935,702	$20,638,540,030
Revenue and Expenses - Totals					
(Includes Inpatient and Outpatient)					
Total Gross Revenue	$51,158,468,408	$48,004,919,962	$43,649,715,697	$40,288,707,158	$37,650,122,685
Deductions from Revenue	31,978,107,400	29,320,014,829	26,515,019,643	24,091,152,555	21,459,464,213
Net Patient Revenue	19,180,361,008	18,684,905,133	17,134,696,054	16,197,554,603	16,190,658,472
Other Operating Revenue	1,042,676,426	832,025,492	962,594,262	715,806,300	751,235,572
Other Nonoperating Revenue	163,087,830	130,861,051	445,139,600	456,057,518	322,542,557
Total Net Revenue	20,386,125,264	19,647,791,676	18,542,429,916	17,369,418,421	17,264,436,601
Total Expenses	18,503,734,653	17,668,765,241	16,299,405,040	15,412,000,677	15,601,708,952
HOSPITAL UNIT (Excludes Separate Nursing Home Units)					
Utilization - Inpatient					
Beds	11,310	11,455	11,559	11,611	11,775
Admissions	527,941	535,499	548,980	563,976	575,966
Inpatient Days	2,354,599	2,422,739	2,405,017	2,450,661	2,439,508
Average Length of Stay	4.5	4.5	4.4	4.3	4.2
Personnel					
Total Full Time	70,995	67,242	63,101	64,288	63,255
Total Part Time	48,739	45,766	47,407	48,766	47,770
Revenue and Expenses - Totals					
(Includes Inpatient and Outpatient)					
Total Net Revenue	$20,305,638,391	$19,588,767,499	$18,474,744,255	$17,289,048,577	$17,182,065,794
Total Expenses	18,445,091,750	17,624,079,849	16,237,305,685	15,332,364,550	15,523,090,630
COMMUNITY HEALTH INDICATORS PER 1000 POPULATION					
Total Population (in thousands)	5,779	5,771	5,758	5,743	5,726
Inpatient					
Beds	2.1	2.2	2.2	2.2	2.3
Admissions	91.7	93.2	95.8	98.6	101.0
Inpatient Days	458.4	474.4	478.4	489.1	498.6
Inpatient Surgeries	29.8	29.3	29.4	30.1	37.4
Births	11.1	11.2	11.2	11.2	11.5
Outpatient					
Emergency Outpatient Visits	410.6	421.8	382.1	365.4	379.3
Other Outpatient Visits	2,807.5	2,644.4	2,619.4	2,507.6	2,437.3
Total Outpatient Visits	3,218.1	3,066.2	3,001.5	2,873.0	2,816.6
Outpatient Surgeries	83.6	81.1	79.6	79.1	92.0
Expense per Capita (per person)	$3,202.1	$3,061.5	$2,831.0	$2,683.7	$2,724.5

States

TABLE **6**

WYOMING

U.S. Registered Community Hospitals
(Nonfederal, short-term general and other special hospitals)

Overview 2012–2016

	2016	2015	2014	2013	2012
Total Community Hospitals in Wyoming	23	23	23	24	24
Bed Size Category					
6-24	3	3	1	0	0
25-49	7	7	9	11	11
50-99	6	6	6	6	6
100-199	6	5	6	6	5
200-299	1	2	1	1	2
300-399	0	0	0	0	0
400-499	0	0	0	0	0
500 + ...	0	0	0	0	0
Location					
Hospitals Urban	2	2	2	2	2
Hospitals Rural	21	21	21	22	22
Control					
State and Local Government	17	16	16	16	16
Not for Profit	4	5	5	5	5
Investor owned	2	2	2	3	3
Physician Models					
Independent Practice Association	2	3	1	3	2
Group Practice without Walls	0	0	1	0	0
Open Physician-Hospital Organization	1	1	2	2	1
Closed Physician-Hospital Organization ...	1	3	1	1	1
Management Service Organization	1	1	2	2	2
Integrated Salary Model	8	10	11	11	10
Equity Model	0	0	0	0	0
Foundation	1	1	1	0	0
Insurance Products					
Health Maintenance Organization	1	2	3	2	2
Preferred Provider Organization	1	2	2	1	1
Indemnity Fee for Service	1	1	1	0	0
Managed Care Contracts					
Health Maintenance Organization	4	7	5	5	5
Preferred Provider Organization	7	13	12	17	17
Affiliations					
Hospitals in a System	11	11	11	12	12
Hospitals in a Network	4	4	4	4	5
Hospitals in a Group Purchasing Organization...	17	19	21	22	22

TABLE 6

WYOMING

U.S. Registered Community Hospitals
(Nonfederal, short-term general and other special hospitals)

Utilization, Personnel, Revenue and Expenses, Community Health Indicators 2012–2016

	2016	2015	2014	2013	2012
TOTAL FACILITY (Includes Hospital and Nursing Home Units)					
Utilization - Inpatient					
Beds	1,715	1,834	1,835	1,920	1,923
Admissions	41,221	42,858	41,415	44,574	44,180
Inpatient Days	363,509	356,282	360,622	372,237	375,036
Average Length of Stay	8.8	8.3	8.7	8.4	8.5
Inpatient Surgeries	10,654	10,965	11,284	11,419	11,959
Births	6,445	6,725	6,506	6,404	6,364
Utilization - Outpatient					
Emergency Outpatient Visits	238,255	243,471	232,288	233,648	229,649
Other Outpatient Visits	996,419	1,054,593	1,012,979	1,029,872	976,926
Total Outpatient Visits	1,234,674	1,298,064	1,245,267	1,263,520	1,206,575
Outpatient Surgeries	27,080	24,556	25,394	26,232	28,021
Personnel					
Full Time RNs	1,949	1,911	1,934	1,864	1,798
Full Time LPNs	142	104	114	101	113
Part Time RNs	497	531	587	604	578
Part Time LPNs	34	34	41	43	50
Total Full Time	8,606	8,066	7,895	7,803	7,546
Total Part Time	1,705	1,818	1,979	2,211	2,166
Revenue - Inpatient					
Gross Inpatient Revenue	$1,344,740,856	$1,269,207,836	$1,135,893,538	$1,146,334,560	$1,129,646,064
Revenue - Outpatient					
Gross Outpatient Revenue	$1,999,543,407	$1,740,121,295	$1,549,440,634	$1,448,039,841	$1,327,536,898
Revenue and Expenses - Totals					
(Includes Inpatient and Outpatient)					
Total Gross Revenue	$3,344,284,263	$3,009,329,131	$2,685,334,172	$2,594,374,401	$2,457,182,962
Deductions from Revenue	1,867,143,973	1,587,326,963	1,386,941,712	1,320,845,075	1,211,190,965
Net Patient Revenue	1,477,140,290	1,422,002,168	1,298,392,460	1,273,529,326	1,245,991,997
Other Operating Revenue	92,628,020	92,174,288	89,479,580	82,996,786	74,346,388
Other Nonoperating Revenue	20,648,011	11,476,807	60,042,001	38,510,265	4,294,457
Total Net Revenue	1,590,416,321	1,525,653,263	1,447,914,041	1,395,036,377	1,324,632,842
Total Expenses	1,486,091,532	1,401,079,632	1,309,767,027	1,233,698,322	1,182,216,845
HOSPITAL UNIT (Excludes Separate Nursing Home Units)					
Utilization - Inpatient					
Beds	1,230	1,251	1,187	1,292	1,245
Admissions	40,735	42,214	40,698	43,817	43,484
Inpatient Days	198,439	173,290	161,800	177,813	167,355
Average Length of Stay	4.9	4.1	4.0	4.1	3.8
Personnel					
Total Full Time	8,246	7,706	7,510	7,420	7,150
Total Part Time	1,597	1,674	1,808	2,020	1,957
Revenue and Expenses - Totals					
(Includes Inpatient and Outpatient)					
Total Net Revenue	$1,555,405,267	$1,490,903,470	$1,405,149,699	$1,353,272,060	$1,282,240,814
Total Expenses	1,461,084,377	1,368,672,110	1,271,562,455	1,198,106,925	1,141,742,073
COMMUNITY HEALTH INDICATORS PER 1000 POPULATION					
Total Population (in thousands)	586	586	584	583	576
Inpatient					
Beds	2.9	3.1	3.1	3.3	3.3
Admissions	70.4	73.1	70.9	76.5	76.6
Inpatient Days	620.9	607.9	617.3	638.9	650.6
Inpatient Surgeries	18.2	18.7	19.3	19.6	20.7
Births	11.0	11.5	11.1	11.0	11.0
Outpatient					
Emergency Outpatient Visits	406.9	415.4	397.6	401.0	398.4
Other Outpatient Visits	1,701.8	1,799.3	1,734.1	1,767.5	1,694.8
Total Outpatient Visits	2,108.7	2,214.7	2,131.7	2,168.5	2,093.3
Outpatient Surgeries	46.3	41.9	43.5	45.0	48.6
Expense per Capita (per person)	$2,538.2	$2,390.5	$2,242.2	$2,117.4	$2,051.0

States

Table 7

The facilities and services presented in Table 7 are listed below in alphabetical order by major heading (where applicable).

Table 7

2016 Facilities and Services in the U.S. Census Divisions and States

These data include only hospital-based facilities and services as reported by responding hospitals in Section C of the 2016 AHA Annual Survey, beginning on page 215. All hospitals are represented with Community Hospitals listed separately under United States. No estimates have been made for nonresponding hospitals. Definitions of facilities and services are listed in the Glossary, page 203.

Classification	Hospitals Reporting	Adult Day Care Program No.	%	Airborne Infection Isolation Room No.	%	Alcohol/Drug Abuse or Dependency Inpatient Care Units No.	%	Alcohol/Drug Abuse or Dependency Outpatient Services No.	%	Alzheimer Center No.	%	Ambulance Service No.	%	Ambulatory Surgery Center No.	%	Arthritis Treatment Center No.	%	Assisted Living No.	%
UNITED STATES	4,590	158	3.4	3,689	80.4	442	9.6	663	14.9	214	4.7	705	15.4	1,179	25.7	275	6.0	160	3.5
COMMUNITY HOSPITALS	3,865	139	3.6	3,328	86.1	305	7.9	521	13.5	200	5.2	680	17.6	1,125	29.1	262	6.8	147	3.8
CENSUS DIVISION 1, NEW ENGLAND	172	7	4.1	140	81.4	15	8.7	56	32.6	17	9.9	25	14.5	75	43.6	16	9.3	6	3.5
Connecticut	30	1	3.3	25	83.3	3	10.0	16	53.3	3	13.3	5	16.7	20	66.7	0	0.0	2	6.7
Maine	32	1	3.1	27	84.4	3	9.4	11	34.4	3	9.4	8	25.0	15	46.9	0	0.0	2	6.3
Massachusetts	64	3	4.7	47	73.4	6	9.4	20	31.3	7	10.9	7	10.9	25	39.1	8	12.5	0	0.0
New Hampshire	25	2	8.0	23	92.0	0	0.0	3	12.0	1	4.0	3	12.0	8	32.0	3	12.0	1	4.0
Rhode Island	10	0	0.0	9	90.0	0	0.0	2	20.0	1	10.0	1	10.0	5	50.0	0	0.0	0	0.0
Vermont	11	0	0.0	9	81.8	3	27.3	4	36.4	1	9.1	1	9.1	2	18.2	1	9.1	1	9.1
CENSUS DIVISION 2, MIDDLE ATLANTIC	404	30	7.4	331	81.9	66	16.3	93	23.0	32	7.9	85	21.0	173	42.8	55	13.6	8	2.0
New Jersey	62	5	8.1	53	85.5	8	12.9	17	27.4	5	8.1	23	37.1	25	40.3	11	17.7	1	1.6
New York	142	16	11.3	123	86.6	40	28.2	50	35.2	14	9.9	27	19.0	91	64.1	28	19.7	1	0.7
Pennsylvania	200	9	4.5	155	77.5	18	9.0	26	13.0	13	6.5	35	17.5	57	28.5	16	8.0	6	3.0
CENSUS DIVISION 3, SOUTH ATLANTIC	671	13	1.9	553	82.4	78	11.6	109	16.2	34	5.1	81	12.1	164	24.4	42	6.3	13	1.9
Delaware	10	2	20.0	6	60.0	0	0.0	2	20.0	1	10.0	2	20.0	5	50.0	0	0.0	0	0.0
District of Columbia	11	0	0.0	7	63.6	3	27.3	4	36.4	1	9.1	1	9.1	4	36.4	0	0.0	1	9.1
Florida	180	2	1.1	152	84.4	21	11.7	18	10.0	11	6.1	15	8.3	49	27.2	8	4.4	3	1.7
Georgia	100	2	2.0	73	73.0	8	8.0	14	14.0	3	3.0	15	15.0	16	16.0	2	2.0	2	2.0
Maryland	44	2	4.5	38	86.4	5	11.4	15	34.1	6	13.6	2	4.5	13	29.5	8	18.2	2	4.5
North Carolina	108	1	0.9	100	92.6	12	11.1	19	17.6	5	4.6	18	16.7	30	27.8	8	7.4	1	0.9
South Carolina	79	1	1.3	60	75.9	15	19.0	10	12.7	2	2.5	13	16.5	15	19.0	3	3.8	3	3.6
Virginia	84	3	3.6	74	88.1	10	11.9	20	23.8	4	4.8	10	11.9	26	31.0	7	8.3	3	3.6
West Virginia	55	0	0.0	43	78.2	4	7.3	7	12.7	1	1.8	5	9.1	6	10.9	4	7.3	1	1.8
CENSUS DIVISION 4, EAST NORTH CENTRAL	706	23	3.3	594	84.1	81	11.5	159	22.5	59	8.4	97	13.7	206	29.2	64	9.1	23	3.3
Illinois	165	12	7.3	143	86.7	16	9.7	41	24.8	8	4.8	18	10.9	43	26.1	14	8.5	5	3.0
Indiana	122	1	0.8	101	82.8	11	9.0	25	20.5	5	4.1	27	22.1	31	25.4	4	3.3	3	2.5
Michigan	130	3	2.3	112	86.2	15	11.5	25	19.2	10	7.7	15	11.5	38	29.2	13	10.0	2	1.5
Ohio	144	1	0.7	130	90.3	10	6.9	33	22.9	7	4.9	27	18.8	53	36.8	13	9.0	3	2.1
Wisconsin	145	6	4.1	108	74.5	29	20.0	35	24.1	29	20.0	10	6.9	41	28.3	20	13.8	10	6.9
CENSUS DIVISION 5, EAST SOUTH CENTRAL	367	4	1.1	263	71.7	41	11.2	39	10.6	10	2.7	52	14.2	57	15.5	11	3.0	8	2.2
Alabama	102	1	1.0	67	65.7	9	8.8	8	7.8	2	2.0	11	10.8	18	17.6	4	3.9	2	2.3
Kentucky	88	2	2.3	76	86.4	7	8.0	13	14.8	1	1.1	9	10.2	17	19.3	1	1.1	2	2.3
Mississippi	104	1	1.0	63	60.6	15	14.4	7	6.7	3	2.9	17	16.3	6	5.8	2	1.9	3	2.9
Tennessee	73	0	0.0	57	78.1	10	13.7	11	15.1	4	5.5	15	20.5	16	21.9	4	5.5	1	1.4
CENSUS DIVISION 6, WEST NORTH CENTRAL	637	33	5.2	495	77.7	57	8.9	66	10.4	27	4.2	158	24.8	128	20.1	30	4.7	56	8.8
Iowa	124	3	2.4	93	75.0	9	7.3	17	13.7	4	3.2	52	41.9	30	24.2	3	2.4	7	5.6
Kansas	143	8	5.6	108	75.5	6	4.2	4	2.8	3	2.1	21	14.7	15	10.5	5	3.5	10	7.0
Minnesota	105	12	11.4	86	81.9	9	8.6	17	16.2	8	7.6	35	33.3	29	27.6	5	4.8	16	15.2
Missouri	143	3	2.1	117	81.8	26	18.2	19	13.3	8	5.6	23	16.1	23	16.1	11	7.7	2	1.4
Nebraska	54	2	3.7	42	77.8	4	7.4	4	7.4	5	9.3	10	18.5	14	25.9	1	1.9	10	18.5
North Dakota	26	1	3.8	16	61.5	2	7.7	2	7.7	3	11.5	8	30.8	7	26.9	4	15.4	1	3.8
South Dakota	42	4	9.5	33	78.6	1	2.4	3	7.1	0	0.0	9	21.4	10	23.8	1	2.4	10	23.8
CENSUS DIVISION 7, WEST SOUTH CENTRAL	891	3	0.3	706	79.2	49	5.5	57	6.4	5	0.6	106	11.9	131	14.7	12	1.3	17	1.9
Arkansas	88	0	0.0	73	83.0	4	4.5	6	6.8	0	0.0	12	13.6	11	12.5	1	1.1	1	1.1
Louisiana	95	1	1.1	65	68.4	5	5.3	6	6.3	2	2.1	9	9.5	21	22.1	2	2.1	3	3.2
Oklahoma	116	0	0.0	92	79.3	7	6.0	8	6.9	2	1.7	17	14.7	21	18.1	3	2.6	3	2.6
Texas	592	2	0.3	476	80.4	33	5.6	37	6.3	1	0.2	68	11.5	78	13.2	8	1.4	10	1.7
CENSUS DIVISION 8, MOUNTAIN	319	26	8.2	240	75.2	22	6.9	43	13.5	14	4.4	70	21.9	84	26.3	18	5.6	20	6.3
Arizona	48	1	2.1	37	77.1	3	6.3	8	16.7	2	4.2	0	0.0	9	18.8	3	6.3	1	2.1
Colorado	72	4	5.6	63	87.5	5	6.9	10	13.9	4	5.6	20	27.8	22	30.6	5	6.9	6	8.3
Idaho	32	4	12.5	24	75.0	2	6.3	5	15.6	0	0.0	10	31.3	11	34.4	4	12.5	2	6.3
Montana	57	15	26.3	38	66.7	3	5.3	4	7.0	3	5.3	16	28.1	8	14.0	2	3.5	8	14.0
Nevada	26	1	3.4	15	57.7	2	7.7	5	19.2	0	0.0	3	11.5	8	30.8	0	0.0	1	3.8
New Mexico	29	1	3.4	20	69.0	1	3.4	5	17.2	2	6.9	6	20.7	11	37.9	2	6.9	0	0.0
Utah	35	1	2.9	27	77.1	5	14.3	6	17.1	2	5.7	6	17.1	12	34.3	2	5.7	0	0.0
Wyoming	20	0	0.0	16	80.0	1	5.0	4	20.0	3	15.0	9	45.0	4	20.0	0	0.0	2	10.0
CENSUS DIVISION 9, PACIFIC	423	19	4.5	367	86.8	33	7.8	61	14.4	16	3.8	31	7.3	161	38.1	27	6.4	9	2.1
Alaska	15	0	0.0	11	73.3	2	13.3	4	26.7	0	0.0	0	0.0	2	13.3	0	0.0	0	0.0
California	248	12	4.8	216	87.1	25	10.1	44	17.7	14	5.6	16	6.5	110	44.4	18	7.3	3	1.2
Hawaii	17	1	5.9	16	94.1	0	0.0	1	5.9	0	0.0	1	5.9	4	23.5	1	5.9	0	0.0
Oregon	62	2	3.2	59	95.2	2	3.2	6	9.7	1	1.6	8	12.9	13	21.0	3	4.8	4	6.5
Washington	81	4	4.9	65	80.2	4	4.9	6	7.4	1	1.2	6	7.4	32	39.5	5	6.2	2	2.5

Table 7 (Continued)

These data include only hospital-based facilities and services as reported by responding hospitals in Section C of the 2016 AHA Annual Survey, beginning on page 215. All hospitals are represented with Community Hospitals listed separately under United States. No estimates have been made for nonresponding hospitals. Definitions of facilities and services are listed in the Glossary, page 203.

CLASSIFICATION	HOSPITALS REPORTING	AUXILIARY Number	AUXILIARY Percent	BARIATRIC/WEIGHT CONTROL SERVICES Number	BARIATRIC/WEIGHT CONTROL SERVICES Percent	BIRTHING/LDR/LDRP ROOM Number	BIRTHING/LDR/LDRP ROOM Percent	BLOOD DONOR CENTER Number	BLOOD DONOR CENTER Percent	BREAST CANCER SCREENING Number	BREAST CANCER SCREENING Percent	BURN CARE UNITS Number	BURN CARE UNITS Percent	CASE MANAGEMENT Number	CASE MANAGEMENT Percent	CHAPLAINCY/PASTORAL CARE SERVICES Number	CHAPLAINCY/PASTORAL CARE SERVICES Percent	CHEMOTHERAPY Number	CHEMOTHERAPY Percent
UNITED STATES	4,590	2,516	54.8	1,206	26.3	2,417	52.7	266	5.8	3,164	68.9	179	3.9	4,048	88.2	2,988	65.1	2,345	51.1
COMMUNITY HOSPITALS	3,865	2,446	63.3	1,133	29.3	2,378	61.5	256	6.6	3,078	79.6	175	4.5	3,550	91.8	2,723	70.5	2,260	58.5
CENSUS DIVISION 1, NEW ENGLAND	172	93	54.1	67	39.0	110	64.0	28	16.3	131	76.2	9	5.2	166	96.5	136	79.1	120	69.8
Connecticut	30	19	63.3	18	60.0	21	70.0	5	16.7	22	73.3	2	6.7	27	90.0	26	86.7	22	73.3
Maine	32	19	59.4	7	21.9	25	78.1	0	0.0	29	90.6	2	6.3	32	100.0	24	75.0	25	78.1
Massachusetts	64	29	45.3	30	46.9	36	56.3	18	28.1	44	68.8	4	6.3	62	96.9	52	81.3	39	60.9
New Hampshire	25	13	52.0	7	28.0	17	68.0	4	16.0	21	84.0	0	0.0	25	100.0	17	68.0	18	72.0
Rhode Island	10	6	60.0	3	30.0	4	40.0	1	10.0	7	70.0	1	10.0	9	90.0	8	80.0	8	80.0
Vermont	11	7	63.6	2	18.2	7	63.6	0	0.0	8	72.7	0	0.0	11	100.0	9	81.8	8	72.7
CENSUS DIVISION 2, MIDDLE ATLANTIC	404	248	61.4	180	44.6	226	55.9	55	13.6	316	78.2	20	5.0	370	91.6	317	78.5	266	65.8
New Jersey	62	45	72.6	39	62.9	40	64.5	10	16.1	49	79.0	5	8.1	57	91.9	57	91.9	47	75.8
New York	142	96	67.6	71	50.0	98	69.0	28	19.7	128	90.1	9	6.3	137	96.5	116	81.7	105	73.9
Pennsylvania	200	107	53.5	70	35.0	88	44.0	17	8.5	139	69.5	6	3.0	176	88.0	144	72.0	114	57.0
CENSUS DIVISION 3, SOUTH ATLANTIC	671	393	58.6	193	28.8	557	53.2	43	6.4	494	73.6	27	4.0	617	92.0	520	77.5	376	56.0
Delaware	10	5	50.0	6	60.0	5	50.0	1	10.0	5	50.0	1	10.0	7	70.0	7	70.0	6	60.0
District of Columbia	11	3	27.3	7	63.6	6	54.5	1	9.1	6	54.5	2	18.2	10	90.9	8	72.7	8	72.7
Florida	180	100	55.6	62	34.4	78	43.3	10	5.6	121	67.2	11	6.1	170	94.4	133	73.9	106	58.9
Georgia	100	63	63.0	26	26.0	53	53.0	2	2.0	76	76.0	2	2.0	90	90.0	73	73.0	48	48.0
Maryland	44	36	81.8	16	36.4	30	68.2	8	18.2	33	75.0	2	4.5	40	90.9	41	93.2	35	79.5
North Carolina	108	62	57.4	30	27.8	77	71.3	6	5.6	89	82.4	2	1.9	103	95.4	93	86.1	69	63.9
South Carolina	70	39	49.4	14	17.7	42	53.2	6	7.6	55	69.6	2	2.5	68	86.1	51	64.6	32	40.5
Virginia	84	53	63.1	25	29.8	42	50.0	9	10.7	67	79.8	4	4.8	79	94.0	74	88.1	50	59.5
West Virginia	55	32	58.2	7	12.7	24	43.6	0	0.0	42	76.4	1	1.8	50	90.9	40	72.7	22	40.0
CENSUS DIVISION 4, EAST NORTH CENTRAL	706	428	60.6	208	29.5	427	60.5	35	5.0	569	80.6	32	4.5	653	92.5	529	74.9	445	63.0
Illinois	165	110	66.7	55	33.3	101	61.2	11	6.7	144	87.3	7	4.2	160	97.0	137	83.0	118	71.5
Indiana	122	56	45.9	26	21.3	72	59.0	4	3.3	88	72.1	4	3.3	109	89.3	94	77.0	63	51.6
Michigan	130	93	71.5	53	40.8	71	54.6	6	4.6	107	82.3	8	6.2	116	89.2	95	73.1	87	66.9
Ohio	144	86	59.7	43	29.9	91	63.2	10	6.9	119	82.6	7	4.9	139	96.5	120	83.3	105	72.9
Wisconsin	145	83	57.2	31	21.4	92	63.4	4	2.8	111	76.6	6	4.1	129	89.0	83	57.2	72	49.7
CENSUS DIVISION 5, EAST SOUTH CENTRAL	367	172	46.9	73	19.9	158	43.1	9	2.5	240	65.4	12	3.3	318	86.6	199	54.2	127	34.6
Alabama	102	53	52.0	24	23.5	48	47.1	4	3.9	68	66.7	4	3.9	94	92.2	60	58.8	35	34.3
Kentucky	88	50	56.8	22	25.0	39	44.3	4	4.5	68	77.3	4	4.5	83	94.3	69	78.4	43	48.9
Mississippi	104	33	31.7	12	11.5	38	36.5	0	0.0	54	51.9	2	1.9	76	73.1	17	16.3	19	18.3
Tennessee	73	36	49.3	15	20.5	33	45.2	1	1.4	50	68.5	2	2.7	65	89.0	53	72.6	30	41.1
CENSUS DIVISION 6, WEST NORTH CENTRAL	637	408	64.1	129	20.3	341	53.5	19	3.0	478	75.0	29	4.6	502	78.8	335	52.6	347	54.5
Iowa	124	105	84.7	23	18.5	74	59.7	2	1.6	113	91.1	4	3.2	106	85.5	56	45.2	79	63.7
Kansas	143	77	53.8	21	14.7	66	46.2	0	0.0	82	57.3	7	4.9	95	66.4	62	43.4	48	33.6
Minnesota	105	71	67.6	28	26.7	75	71.4	4	3.8	93	88.6	4	3.8	87	82.9	60	57.1	69	65.7
Missouri	143	95	66.4	30	21.0	63	44.1	9	6.3	98	68.5	8	5.6	125	87.4	92	64.3	74	51.7
Nebraska	54	29	53.7	14	25.9	36	66.7	1	1.9	45	83.3	8	7.4	42	77.8	33	61.1	38	70.4
North Dakota	26	18	69.2	6	23.1	9	34.6	1	3.8	18	69.2	1	3.8	21	80.8	18	69.2	15	57.7
South Dakota	42	13	31.0	7	16.7	18	42.9	2	4.8	29	69.0	1	2.4	26	61.9	14	33.3	24	57.1
CENSUS DIVISION 7, WEST SOUTH CENTRAL	891	373	41.9	181	20.3	328	36.8	25	2.8	414	46.5	16	1.8	758	85.1	443	49.7	236	26.5
Arkansas	88	52	59.1	18	20.5	34	38.6	3	3.4	47	53.4	1	1.1	77	87.5	44	50.0	27	30.7
Louisiana	95	35	36.8	22	23.2	36	37.9	4	4.2	60	63.2	4	4.2	79	83.2	47	49.5	38	40.0
Oklahoma	116	57	49.1	14	12.1	43	37.1	5	4.3	59	50.9	3	2.6	99	85.3	68	58.6	26	22.4
Texas	592	229	38.7	127	21.5	215	36.3	13	2.2	248	41.9	8	1.4	503	85.0	284	48.0	145	24.5
CENSUS DIVISION 8, MOUNTAIN	319	169	53.0	61	19.1	198	62.1	18	5.6	216	67.7	10	3.1	270	84.6	186	58.3	167	52.4
Arizona	48	23	47.9	10	20.8	28	58.3	2	4.2	26	54.2	2	4.2	47	97.9	35	72.9	32	66.7
Colorado	72	45	62.5	19	26.4	50	69.4	10	13.9	59	81.9	3	4.2	65	90.3	51	70.8	48	66.7
Idaho	32	23	71.9	8	25.0	22	68.8	3	9.4	22	68.8	0	0.0	26	81.3	17	53.1	16	50.0
Montana	57	28	49.1	4	7.0	27	47.4	0	0.0	35	61.4	0	0.0	35	61.4	23	40.4	22	38.6
Nevada	26	8	30.8	4	15.4	9	34.6	0	0.0	12	46.2	0	0.0	25	96.2	13	50.0	11	42.3
New Mexico	29	17	58.6	4	13.8	20	69.0	1	3.4	21	72.4	3	10.3	25	86.2	22	75.9	10	34.5
Utah	35	14	40.0	10	28.6	27	77.1	1	2.9	27	77.1	2	5.7	29	82.9	14	40.0	19	54.3
Wyoming	20	11	55.0	2	10.0	15	75.0	1	5.0	14	70.0	0	0.0	18	90.0	11	55.0	9	45.0
CENSUS DIVISION 9, PACIFIC	423	232	54.8	114	27.0	272	64.3	34	8.0	306	72.3	24	5.7	394	93.1	323	76.4	261	61.7
Alaska	15	5	33.3	1	6.7	10	66.7	0	0.0	10	66.7	0	0.0	12	80.0	8	53.3	8	53.3
California	248	137	55.2	76	30.6	154	62.1	32	12.9	175	70.6	18	7.3	238	96.0	197	79.4	155	62.5
Hawaii	17	3	17.6	6	35.3	8	47.1	1	5.9	11	64.7	1	5.9	15	88.2	6	35.3	11	64.7
Oregon	62	44	71.0	14	22.6	49	79.0	0	0.0	54	87.1	3	4.8	60	96.8	51	82.3	42	67.7
Washington	81	43	53.1	17	21.0	51	63.0	1	1.2	56	69.1	1	1.2	69	85.2	61	75.3	45	55.6

Table 7 (Continued)

These data include only hospital-based facilities and services as reported by responding hospitals in Section C of the 2016 AHA Annual Survey, beginning on page 215. All hospitals are represented with Community Hospitals listed separately under United States. No estimates have been made for nonresponding hospitals. Definitions of facilities and services are listed in the Glossary, page 203.

CLASSIFICATION	HOSPITALS REPORTING	CHILDREN'S WELLNESS PROGRAM		CHIROPRACTIC SERVICES		COMMUNITY OUTREACH		COMPLEMENTARY AND ALTERNATIVE MEDICINE SERVICES		COMPUTER ASSISTED ORTHOPEDIC SURGERY (CAOS)		CRISIS PREVENTION		DENTAL SERVICES		ENABLING SERVICES		ENROLLMENT ASSISTANCE SERVICES		EXTRACORPOREAL SHOCK WAVE LITHOTRIPTER (ESWL)	
		Number	Percent	Number	Percent	Number	Percent	Number	Percent	Number	Percent	Number	Percent	Number	Percent	Number	Percent	Number	Percent	Number	Percent
UNITED STATES	4,590	894	19.5	131	2.9	3,221	70.2	950	20.7	770	16.8	1,075	23.4	896	19.5	1,332	29.0	2,759	60.1	1,317	28.7
COMMUNITY HOSPITALS	3,865	864	22.4	100	2.6	2,970	76.8	887	22.9	739	19.1	926	24.0	777	20.1	1,237	32.0	2,572	66.5	1,255	32.5
CENSUS DIVISION 1, NEW ENGLAND	172	62	36.0	9	5.2	145	84.3	82	47.7	42	24.4	67	39.0	46	26.7	75	43.6	138	80.2	85	49.4
Connecticut	30	9	30.0	0	0.0	26	86.7	19	63.3	9	30.0	19	63.3	13	43.3	13	43.3	25	83.3	17	56.7
Maine	32	12	37.5	2	6.3	27	84.4	13	40.6	3	9.4	7	21.9	5	15.6	14	43.8	21	65.6	14	43.8
Massachusetts	64	25	39.1	3	4.7	52	81.3	27	42.2	17	26.6	25	39.1	13	20.3	24	37.5	55	85.9	32	50.0
New Hampshire	25	12	48.0	2	8.0	21	84.0	14	56.0	8	32.0	8	32.0	9	36.0	12	48.0	21	84.0	12	48.0
Rhode Island	10	1	10.0	1	10.0	9	90.0	3	30.0	2	20.0	4	40.0	2	20.0	7	70.0	7	70.0	6	60.0
Vermont	11	3	27.3	1	9.1	10	90.9	6	54.5	3	27.3	4	36.4	4	36.4	5	45.5	9	81.8	4	36.4
CENSUS DIVISION 2, MIDDLE ATLANTIC	404	131	32.4	20	5.0	322	79.7	140	34.7	100	24.8	177	43.8	162	40.1	185	45.8	298	73.8	163	40.3
New Jersey	62	33	53.2	2	3.2	53	85.5	31	50.0	20	32.3	42	67.7	30	48.4	40	64.5	50	80.6	25	40.3
New York	142	58	40.8	11	7.7	125	88.0	56	39.4	44	31.0	76	53.5	70	49.3	65	45.8	122	85.9	67	47.2
Pennsylvania	200	40	20.0	7	3.5	144	72.0	53	26.5	36	18.0	59	29.5	62	31.0	80	40.0	126	63.0	71	35.5
CENSUS DIVISION 3, SOUTH ATLANTIC	671	115	17.1	10	1.5	499	74.4	131	19.5	147	21.9	157	23.4	155	23.1	228	34.0	427	63.6	231	34.4
Delaware	10	6	60.0	0	0.0	6	60.0	3	30.0	4	40.0	4	40.0	3	30.0	4	40.0	5	50.0	4	40.0
District of Columbia	11	5	45.5	0	0.0	9	81.8	6	54.5	3	27.3	4	36.4	5	45.5	7	63.6	8	72.7	4	36.4
Florida	180	21	11.7	4	2.2	125	69.4	31	17.2	48	26.7	31	17.2	27	15.0	48	26.7	108	60.0	71	39.4
Georgia	100	9	9.0	2	2.0	70	70.0	17	17.0	19	19.0	22	22.0	14	14.0	29	29.0	56	56.0	31	31.0
Maryland	44	15	34.1	0	0.0	38	86.4	22	50.0	12	27.3	21	47.7	20	45.5	28	63.6	37	84.1	26	59.1
North Carolina	108	18	16.7	0	0.0	90	83.3	17	15.7	20	18.5	23	21.3	34	32.4	35	32.4	67	62.0	24	22.2
South Carolina	79	14	17.7	0	0.0	57	72.2	5	6.3	10	12.7	8	10.1	16	20.3	13	16.5	39	49.4	25	31.6
Virginia	84	13	15.5	2	2.4	66	78.6	26	31.0	26	31.0	32	38.1	26	31.0	50	59.5	71	84.5	28	33.3
West Virginia	55	14	25.5	1	1.8	38	69.1	4	7.3	5	9.1	12	21.8	10	18.2	14	25.5	36	65.5	18	32.7
CENSUS DIVISION 4, EAST NORTH CENTRAL	706	184	26.1	31	4.4	560	79.3	226	32.0	130	18.4	223	31.6	133	18.8	287	40.7	495	70.1	227	32.2
Illinois	165	55	33.3	8	4.8	137	83.0	46	27.9	43	26.1	69	41.8	45	27.3	69	41.8	120	72.7	46	27.9
Indiana	122	25	20.5	5	4.1	100	82.0	29	23.8	14	11.5	28	23.0	19	15.6	31	25.4	84	68.9	29	23.8
Michigan	130	45	34.6	5	3.8	113	86.9	46	35.4	20	15.4	43	33.1	33	25.4	62	47.7	106	81.5	46	35.4
Ohio	144	29	20.1	10	6.9	123	85.4	52	36.1	30	20.8	47	32.6	36	25.0	64	44.4	105	72.9	65	45.1
Wisconsin	145	30	20.7	3	2.1	87	60.0	53	36.6	23	15.9	36	24.8	0	0.0	61	42.1	80	55.2	41	28.3
CENSUS DIVISION 5, EAST SOUTH CENTRAL	367	49	13.4	4	1.1	230	62.7	23	6.3	39	10.6	53	14.4	59	16.1	59	16.1	166	45.2	89	24.3
Alabama	102	9	8.8	2	2.0	55	53.9	0	0.0	8	7.8	13	12.7	5	4.9	7	6.9	52	51.0	28	27.5
Kentucky	88	14	15.9	1	1.1	64	72.7	12	13.6	12	13.6	11	12.5	19	21.6	21	23.9	53	60.2	27	30.7
Mississippi	104	17	16.3	1	1.0	64	61.5	4	3.8	5	4.8	11	10.6	23	22.1	7	6.7	25	24.0	11	10.6
Tennessee	73	9	12.3	0	0.0	47	64.4	7	9.6	14	19.2	18	24.7	12	16.4	24	32.9	36	49.3	23	31.5
CENSUS DIVISION 6, WEST NORTH CENTRAL	637	111	17.4	26	4.1	421	66.1	109	17.1	51	8.0	119	18.7	89	14.0	138	21.7	359	56.4	105	16.5
Iowa	124	25	20.2	4	3.2	96	77.4	29	23.4	12	9.7	32	25.8	18	14.5	33	26.6	95	76.6	15	12.1
Kansas	143	10	7.0	1	0.7	64	44.8	8	5.6	7	4.9	9	6.3	12	8.4	16	11.2	62	43.4	18	12.6
Minnesota	105	24	22.9	8	7.6	81	77.1	31	29.5	9	8.6	23	21.9	14	13.3	18	17.1	61	58.1	19	18.1
Missouri	143	28	19.6	6	4.2	95	66.4	24	16.8	12	8.4	33	23.1	35	24.5	51	35.7	79	55.2	34	23.8
Nebraska	54	11	20.4	0	0.0	44	81.5	7	13.0	7	13.0	9	16.7	3	5.6	10	18.5	30	55.6	11	20.4
North Dakota	26	6	23.1	6	23.1	16	61.5	6	23.1	3	11.5	7	26.9	2	7.7	6	23.1	17	65.4	4	15.4
South Dakota	42	7	16.7	1	2.4	25	59.5	4	9.5	1	2.4	6	14.3	5	11.9	4	9.5	15	35.7	4	9.5
CENSUS DIVISION 7, WEST SOUTH CENTRAL	891	94	10.5	6	0.7	471	52.9	48	5.4	105	11.8	97	10.9	113	12.7	131	14.7	376	42.2	176	19.8
Arkansas	88	8	9.1	0	0.0	50	56.8	5	5.7	4	4.5	12	13.6	9	10.2	8	9.1	42	47.7	12	13.6
Louisiana	95	20	21.1	1	1.1	52	54.7	8	8.4	15	15.8	22	23.2	16	16.8	17	17.9	55	57.9	20	21.1
Oklahoma	116	9	7.8	0	0.0	60	51.7	5	4.3	14	12.1	9	7.8	17	14.7	21	18.1	48	41.4	25	21.6
Texas	592	57	9.6	5	0.8	309	52.2	30	5.1	72	12.2	54	9.1	71	12.0	85	14.4	231	39.0	119	20.1
CENSUS DIVISION 8, MOUNTAIN	319	71	22.3	13	4.1	235	73.7	83	26.0	54	16.9	77	24.1	57	17.9	80	25.1	197	61.8	83	26.0
Arizona	48	13	27.1	3	6.3	35	72.9	19	39.6	13	27.1	13	27.1	9	18.8	19	39.6	35	72.9	20	41.7
Colorado	72	16	22.2	4	5.6	58	80.6	33	45.8	19	26.4	17	23.6	11	15.3	24	33.3	50	69.4	15	20.8
Idaho	32	9	28.1	2	6.3	26	81.3	6	18.8	8	25.0	8	25.0	7	21.9	8	25.0	17	53.1	4	12.5
Montana	57	11	19.3	2	3.5	37	64.9	10	17.5	4	7.0	9	15.8	4	7.0	5	8.8	29	50.9	9	15.8
Nevada	26	4	15.4	2	7.7	16	61.5	3	11.5	1	3.8	7	26.9	3	11.5	5	19.2	15	57.7	6	23.1
New Mexico	29	9	31.0	0	0.0	22	75.9	3	10.3			6	20.7	8	27.6	8	27.6	20	69.0	12	41.4
Utah	35	7	20.0	0	0.0	24	68.6	6	17.1	7	20.0	18	51.4	14	40.0	13	37.1	22	62.9	13	37.1
Wyoming	20	2	10.0	0	0.0	17	85.0	3	15.0	2	10.0	3	15.0	1	5.0	3	15.0	9	45.0	4	20.0
CENSUS DIVISION 9, PACIFIC	423	77	18.2	12	2.8	338	79.9	108	25.5	102	24.1	105	24.8	82	19.4	149	35.2	303	71.6	158	37.4
Alaska	15	4	26.7	1	6.7	8	53.3	2	13.3			4	26.7	5	33.3	3	20.0	10	66.7	4	26.7
California	248	38	15.3	6	2.4	197	79.4	65	26.2	64	25.8	53	21.4	58	23.4	85	34.3	179	72.2	105	42.3
Hawaii	17	6	35.3	1	5.9	14	82.4	5	29.4	3	17.6	4	23.5	3	17.6	10	58.8	11	64.7	4	23.5
Oregon	62	12	19.4	2	3.2	56	90.3	18	29.0	18	29.0	15	24.2	8	12.9	23	37.1	46	74.2	20	32.3
Washington	81	17	21.0	2	2.5	63	77.8	18	22.2	17	21.0	29	35.8	8	9.9	28	34.6	57	70.4	25	30.9

Table 7 (Continued)

These data include only hospital-based facilities and services as reported by responding hospitals in Section C of the 2016 AHA Annual Survey, beginning on page 215. All hospitals are represented with Community Hospitals listed separately under United States. No estimates have been made for nonresponding hospitals. Definitions of facilities and services are listed in the Glossary, page 203.

CLASSIFICATION	HOSPITALS REPORTING	FERTILITY CLINIC Number	FERTILITY CLINIC Percent	FITNESS CENTER Number	FITNESS CENTER Percent	FREESTANDING OUTPATIENT CARE CENTER Number	FREESTANDING OUTPATIENT CARE CENTER Percent	GENETIC TESTING/COUNSELING Number	GENETIC TESTING/COUNSELING Percent	GERIATRIC SERVICES Number	GERIATRIC SERVICES Percent	HEALTH FAIR Number	HEALTH FAIR Percent	COMMUNITY HEALTH EDUCATION Number	COMMUNITY HEALTH EDUCATION Percent	HEALTH RESEARCH Number	HEALTH RESEARCH Percent	HEALTH SCREENINGS Number	HEALTH SCREENINGS Percent	HEMODIALYSIS Number	HEMODIALYSIS Percent	HIV/AIDS SERVICES Number	HIV/AIDS SERVICES Percent
UNITED STATES	4,590	237	5.2	1,353	29.5	1,519	33.1	813	17.7	1,772	38.6	3,305	72.0	3,553	77.4	1,186	25.8	3,461	75.4	1,411	30.7	1,052	22.9
COMMUNITY HOSPITALS	3,865	228	5.9	1,268	32.8	1,412	36.5	778	20.1	1,612	41.7	3,109	80.4	3,293	85.2	1,093	28.3	3,243	83.9	1,320	34.2	970	25.1
CENSUS DIVISION 1, NEW ENGLAND	172	24	14.0	52	30.2	96	55.8	60	34.9	84	48.8	135	78.5	151	87.8	81	47.1	147	85.5	56	32.6	74	43.0
Connecticut	30	6	20.0	13	43.3	24	80.0	13	43.3	17	56.7	21	70.0	26	86.7	19	63.3	26	86.7	12	40.0	17	56.7
Maine	32	2	6.3	11	34.4	16	50.0	8	25.0	15	46.9	29	90.6	30	93.8	7	21.9	29	90.6	4	12.5	13	40.6
Massachusetts	64	10	15.6	10	15.6	35	54.7	25	39.1	31	48.4	49	76.6	53	82.8	35	54.7	52	81.3	29	45.3	25	39.1
New Hampshire	25	4	16.0	9	36.0	12	48.0	8	32.0	12	48.0	20	80.0	23	92.0	10	40.0	23	92.0	2	8.0	11	44.0
Rhode Island	10	1	10.0	5	50.0	6	60.0	3	30.0	6	60.0	9	90.0	9	90.0	6	60.0	8	80.0	7	70.0	5	50.0
Vermont	11	1	9.1	4	36.4	3	27.3	3	27.3	3	27.3	7	63.6	10	90.9	4	36.4	9	81.8	2	18.2	3	27.3
CENSUS DIVISION 2, MIDDLE ATLANTIC	404	55	13.6	116	28.7	225	55.7	141	34.9	222	55.0	318	78.7	339	83.9	170	42.1	334	82.7	189	46.8	174	43.1
New Jersey	62	11	17.7	21	33.9	33	53.2	33	53.2	42	67.7	48	77.4	50	80.6	38	61.3	50	80.6	43	69.4	38	61.3
New York	142	29	20.4	41	28.9	98	69.0	61	43.0	88	62.0	122	85.9	133	93.7	69	48.6	129	90.8	89	62.7	73	51.4
Pennsylvania	200	15	7.5	54	27.0	94	47.0	47	23.5	92	46.0	148	74.0	156	78.0	63	31.5	155	77.5	57	28.5	63	31.5
CENSUS DIVISION 3, SOUTH ATLANTIC	671	24	3.6	218	32.5	257	38.3	145	21.6	254	37.9	506	75.4	529	78.8	211	31.4	539	80.3	290	43.2	204	30.4
Delaware	10	0	0.0	4	40.0	6	60.0	5	50.0	4	40.0	6	60.0	7	70.0	5	50.0	7	70.0	6	60.0	5	50.0
District of Columbia	11	0	0.0	3	27.3	10	90.9	6	54.5	7	63.6	7	63.6	8	72.7	8	72.7	9	81.8	5	45.5	5	45.5
Florida	180	5	2.8	55	30.6	66	36.7	39	21.7	60	33.3	128	71.1	142	78.9	63	35.0	131	72.8	89	49.4	50	27.8
Georgia	100	2	2.0	31	31.0	34	34.0	17	17.0	28	28.0	71	71.0	73	73.0	25	25.0	84	84.0	40	40.0	26	26.0
Maryland	44	3	6.8	15	34.1	18	40.9	20	45.5	28	63.6	37	84.1	34	77.3	24	54.5	39	88.6	29	65.9	23	52.3
North Carolina	108	5	4.6	39	36.1	44	40.7	19	17.6	44	40.7	85	78.7	93	86.1	30	27.8	90	83.3	38	35.2	26	24.1
South Carolina	79	2	2.5	23	29.1	22	27.8	6	7.6	31	39.2	55	69.6	57	72.2	16	20.3	57	72.2	30	38.0	26	32.9
Virginia	84	4	4.8	30	35.7	40	47.6	26	31.0	35	41.7	71	84.5	70	83.3	31	36.9	73	86.9	39	46.4	32	38.1
West Virginia	55	3	5.5	18	32.7	17	30.9	7	12.7	38	69.1	46	83.6	45	81.8	9	16.4	49	89.1	14	25.5	11	20.0
CENSUS DIVISION 4, EAST NORTH CENTRAL	706	38	5.4	267	37.8	307	43.5	146	20.7	338	47.9	562	79.6	616	87.3	216	30.6	575	81.4	218	30.9	169	23.9
Illinois	165	12	7.3	58	35.2	73	44.2	37	22.4	84	50.9	147	89.1	150	90.9	60	36.4	147	89.1	54	32.7	48	29.1
Indiana	122	5	4.1	36	29.5	45	36.9	22	18.0	42	34.4	95	77.9	95	77.9	32	26.2	92	75.4	23	18.9	19	15.6
Michigan	130	7	5.4	51	39.2	61	46.9	27	20.8	66	50.8	104	80.0	114	87.7	52	40.0	114	87.7	44	33.8	49	37.7
Ohio	144	8	5.6	60	41.7	79	54.9	35	24.3	53	36.8	126	87.5	132	91.7	52	36.1	127	88.2	62	43.1	45	31.3
Wisconsin	145	6	4.1	62	42.8	49	33.8	25	17.2	93	64.1	90	62.1	125	86.2	20	13.8	95	65.5	35	24.1	8	5.5
CENSUS DIVISION 5, EAST SOUTH CENTRAL	367	13	3.5	94	25.6	83	22.6	41	11.2	112	30.5	249	67.8	252	68.7	62	16.9	243	66.2	94	25.6	52	14.2
Alabama	102	4	3.9	31	30.4	19	18.6	7	6.9	33	32.4	69	67.6	62	60.8	15	14.7	67	65.7	35	34.3	11	10.8
Kentucky	88	2	2.3	18	20.5	26	29.5	12	13.6	27	30.7	68	77.3	75	85.2	20	22.7	70	79.5	25	28.4	14	15.9
Mississippi	104	2	1.9	28	26.9	16	15.4	8	7.7	22	21.2	56	53.8	59	56.7	7	6.7	55	52.9	11	10.6	13	12.5
Tennessee	73	5	6.8	17	23.3	22	30.1	14	19.2	30	41.1	56	76.7	56	76.7	20	27.4	51	69.9	23	31.5	14	19.2
CENSUS DIVISION 6, WEST NORTH CENTRAL	637	28	4.4	224	35.2	120	18.8	68	10.7	248	38.9	470	73.8	516	81.0	103	16.2	520	81.6	133	20.9	102	16.0
Iowa	124	3	2.4	47	37.9	21	16.9	11	8.9	55	44.4	108	87.1	114	91.9	16	12.9	118	95.2	18	15.3	24	19.4
Kansas	143	4	2.8	40	28.0	18	12.6	10	7.0	47	32.9	82	57.3	84	58.7	11	7.7	94	65.7	18	12.6	13	9.1
Minnesota	105	6	5.7	36	34.3	19	18.1	15	14.3	49	46.7	82	78.1	97	92.4	17	16.2	89	84.8	17	16.2	18	17.1
Missouri	143	10	7.0	50	35.0	43	30.1	17	11.9	53	37.1	103	72.0	112	78.3	36	25.2	113	79.0	49	34.3	31	21.7
Nebraska	54	1	1.9	25	46.3	7	13.0	8	14.8	17	31.5	43	79.6	48	88.9	11	20.4	46	85.2	14	25.9	6	11.1
North Dakota	26	3	11.5	10	38.5	6	23.1	4	15.4	14	53.8	18	69.2	22	84.6	7	26.9	21	80.8	7	26.9	5	19.2
South Dakota	42	1	2.4	16	38.1	6	14.3	3	7.1	13	31.0	34	81.0	39	92.9	5	11.9	39	92.9	9	21.4	5	11.9
CENSUS DIVISION 7, WEST SOUTH CENTRAL	891	17	1.9	195	21.9	186	20.9	64	7.2	240	26.9	531	59.6	553	62.1	114	12.8	529	59.4	188	21.1	98	11.0
Arkansas	88	3	3.4	19	21.6	12	13.6	2	2.3	27	30.7	63	71.6	59	67.0	9	10.2	62	70.5	15	17.0	9	10.2
Louisiana	95	4	4.2	24	25.3	32	33.7	15	15.8	38	40.0	62	65.3	66	69.5	20	21.1	60	63.2	24	25.3	21	22.1
Oklahoma	116	2	1.7	19	16.4	18	15.5	6	5.2	25	21.6	71	61.2	79	68.1	18	15.5	76	65.5	17	14.7	9	7.8
Texas	592	10	1.7	133	22.5	124	20.9	41	6.9	154	26.0	335	56.6	349	59.0	67	11.3	331	55.9	132	22.3	59	10.0
CENSUS DIVISION 8, MOUNTAIN	319	13	4.1	85	26.6	101	31.7	49	15.4	116	36.4	236	74.0	258	80.9	74	23.2	249	78.1	83	26.0	65	20.4
Arizona	48	1	2.1	13	27.1	15	31.3	6	12.5	16	33.3	36	75.0	42	87.5	21	43.8	35	72.9	24	50.0	18	37.5
Colorado	72	4	5.6	29	40.3	37	51.4	22	30.6	24	33.3	51	70.8	63	87.5	23	31.9	58	80.6	21	29.2	18	25.0
Idaho	32	2	6.3	7	21.9	11	34.4	3	9.4	13	40.6	28	87.5	27	84.4	6	18.8	27	84.4	7	21.9	4	12.5
Montana	57	2	3.5	11	19.3	10	17.5	8	14.0	23	40.6	44	77.2	43	75.4	8	14.0	49	86.0	5	8.8	6	10.5
Nevada	26	0	0.0	1	3.8	7	26.9	0	0.0	10	38.5	14	53.8	16	61.5	3	11.5	15	57.7	4	15.4	6	23.1
New Mexico	29	0	0.0	9	31.0	9	31.0	1	3.4	8	27.6	22	75.9	22	75.9	4	13.8	23	79.3	4	13.8	4	13.8
Utah	35	4	11.4	13	37.1	11	31.4	8	22.9	11	31.4	28	80.0	31	88.6	9	25.7	28	80.0	12	34.3	12	34.3
Wyoming	20	0	0.0	2	10.0	1	5.0	1	5.0	5	25.0	13	65.0	14	70.0	0	0.0	14	70.0	6	30.0	4	20.0
CENSUS DIVISION 9, PACIFIC	423	25	5.9	102	24.1	144	34.0	99	23.4	158	37.4	298	70.4	339	80.1	155	36.6	325	76.8	160	37.8	114	27.0
Alaska	15	0	0.0	3	20.0	2	13.3	2	13.3	5	33.3	9	60.0	10	66.7	4	26.7	10	66.7	3	20.0	2	13.3
California	248	16	6.5	61	24.6	92	37.1	68	27.4	104	41.9	177	71.4	193	77.8	104	41.9	185	74.6	112	45.2	77	31.0
Hawaii	17	2	11.8	3	17.6	8	47.1	5	29.4	6	35.3	11	64.7	14	82.4	6	35.3	12	70.6	4	23.5	4	23.5
Oregon	62	1	1.6	20	32.3	24	38.7	6	9.7	20	32.3	46	74.2	55	88.7	15	24.2	55	88.7	17	27.4	15	24.2
Washington	81	6	7.4	15	18.5	18	22.2	18	22.2	23	28.4	55	67.9	67	82.7	26	32.1	63	77.8	24	29.6	18	22.2

Table 7 (Continued)

These data include only hospital-based facilities and services as reported by responding hospitals in Section C of the 2016 AHA Annual Survey, beginning on page 215. All hospitals are represented with Community Hospitals listed separately under United States. No estimates have been made for nonresponding hospitals. Definitions of facilities and services are listed in the Glossary, page 203.

CLASSIFICATION	HOSPITALS REPORTING	HOME HEALTH SERVICES Number	Percent	HOSPICE Number	Percent	HOSPITAL-BASED OUTPATIENT CARE CENTER SERVICES Number	Percent	IMMUNIZATION PROGRAM Number	Percent	INDIGENT CARE CLINIC Number	Percent	LINGUISTIC/TRANSLATION SERVICES Number	Percent	MEALS ON WHEELS Number	Percent	MOBILE HEALTH SERVICES Number	Percent	NEONATAL INTERMEDIATE CARE UNITS Number	Percent	NEUROLOGICAL SERVICES Number	Percent	NUTRITION PROGRAMS CENTER Number	Percent
UNITED STATES	4,590	1,062	23.1	932	20.3	3,381	73.7	1,953	42.5	794	17.3	2,582	56.3	351	7.6	539	11.7	698	15.2	2,253	49.1	3,390	73.9
COMMUNITY HOSPITALS	3,865	1,002	25.9	876	22.7	3,129	81.0	1,800	46.6	747	19.3	2,353	60.9	338	8.7	500	12.9	690	17.9	2,093	54.2	3,052	79.0
CENSUS DIVISION 1, NEW ENGLAND	172	26	15.1	43	25.0	150	87.2	105	61.0	48	27.9	123	71.5	8	4.7	24	14.0	25	14.5	115	66.9	153	89.0
Connecticut	30	2	6.7	12	40.0	26	86.7	17	56.7	13	43.3	22	73.3	0	0.0	4	13.3	4	13.3	24	80.0	26	86.7
Maine	32	4	12.5	2	6.3	28	87.5	23	71.9	7	21.9	19	59.4	2	6.3	4	12.5	4	12.5	15	46.9	31	96.9
Massachusetts	64	13	20.3	14	21.9	57	89.1	35	54.7	15	23.4	49	76.6	3	4.7	10	15.6	13	20.3	45	70.3	57	89.1
New Hampshire	25	5	20.0	7	28.0	21	84.0	16	64.0	7	28.0	18	72.0	1	4.0	4	16.0	2	8.0	16	64.0	24	96.0
Rhode Island	10	2	20.0	3	30.0	9	90.0	6	60.0	3	30.0	9	90.0	0	0.0	1	10.0	1	10.0	8	80.0	7	70.0
Vermont	11	0	0.0	5	45.5	9	81.8	8	72.7	3	27.3	6	54.5	2	18.2	1	9.1	1	9.1	7	63.6	8	72.7
CENSUS DIVISION 2, MIDDLE ATLANTIC	404	106	26.2	121	30.0	333	82.4	222	55.0	149	36.9	265	65.6	32	7.9	76	18.8	118	29.2	282	69.8	338	83.7
New Jersey	62	14	22.6	24	38.7	55	88.7	37	59.7	38	61.3	48	77.4	10	16.1	21	33.9	38	61.3	51	82.3	55	88.7
New York	142	36	25.4	45	31.7	128	90.1	94	66.2	70	49.3	119	83.8	13	9.2	36	25.4	54	38.0	109	76.8	124	87.3
Pennsylvania	200	56	28.0	52	26.0	150	75.0	91	45.5	41	20.5	98	49.0	9	4.5	19	9.5	26	13.0	122	61.0	159	79.5
CENSUS DIVISION 3, SOUTH ATLANTIC	671	138	20.6	127	18.9	497	74.1	240	35.8	125	18.6	393	58.6	24	3.6	111	16.5	145	21.6	411	61.3	519	77.3
Delaware	10	4	40.0	0	0.0	6	60.0	6	60.0	2	20.0	7	70.0	0	0.0	1	10.0	3	30.0	7	70.0	7	70.0
District of Columbia	11	1	9.1	2	18.2	9	81.8	7	63.6	4	36.4	8	72.7	0	0.0	4	36.4	4	36.4	9	81.8	9	81.8
Florida	180	39	21.7	28	15.6	127	70.6	50	27.8	30	16.7	99	55.0	2	1.1	22	12.2	30	16.7	131	72.8	132	73.3
Georgia	100	14	14.0	17	17.0	65	65.0	24	24.0	15	15.0	61	61.0	1	1.0	12	12.0	26	26.0	48	48.0	74	74.0
Maryland	44	3	6.8	10	22.7	39	88.6	27	61.4	23	52.3	36	81.8	4	9.1	11	25.0	6	13.6	36	81.8	40	90.9
North Carolina	108	25	23.1	17	15.7	88	81.5	37	34.3	19	17.6	65	60.2	3	2.8	22	20.4	34	31.5	63	58.3	84	77.8
South Carolina	79	14	17.7	13	16.5	52	65.8	22	27.8	8	10.1	40	50.6	5	6.3	12	15.2	25	31.6	35	44.3	55	69.6
Virginia	84	26	31.0	36	42.9	68	81.0	40	47.6	18	21.4	53	63.1	6	7.1	22	26.2	15	17.9	56	66.7	74	88.1
West Virginia	55	12	21.8	4	7.3	43	78.2	27	49.1	6	10.9	24	43.6	3	5.5	5	9.1	2	3.6	26	47.3	44	80.0
CENSUS DIVISION 4, EAST NORTH CENTRAL	706	191	27.1	176	24.9	567	80.3	342	48.4	153	21.7	423	59.9	95	13.5	79	11.2	89	12.6	379	53.7	597	84.6
Illinois	165	46	27.9	49	29.7	141	85.5	77	46.7	36	21.8	100	60.6	21	12.7	17	10.3	35	21.2	98	59.4	135	81.8
Indiana	122	35	28.7	30	24.6	88	72.1	50	41.0	17	13.9	62	50.8	24	19.7	10	8.2	17	13.9	57	46.7	100	82.0
Michigan	130	41	31.5	42	32.3	112	86.2	85	65.4	41	31.5	80	61.5	9	6.9	20	15.4	14	10.8	76	58.5	114	87.7
Ohio	144	46	31.9	40	27.8	119	82.6	66	45.8	42	29.2	107	74.3	12	8.3	20	13.9	23	16.0	95	66.0	121	84.0
Wisconsin	145	23	15.9	15	10.3	107	73.8	64	44.1	17	11.7	74	51.0	29	20.0	12	8.3	0	0.0	53	36.6	127	87.6
CENSUS DIVISION 5, EAST SOUTH CENTRAL	367	73	19.9	47	12.8	218	59.4	93	25.3	32	8.7	165	45.0	8	2.2	29	7.9	56	15.3	142	38.7	202	55.0
Alabama	102	27	26.5	12	11.8	61	59.8	20	19.6	7	6.9	45	44.1	4	3.9	4	3.9	8	7.8	42	41.2	51	50.0
Kentucky	88	23	26.1	10	11.4	64	72.7	21	23.9	11	12.5	46	52.3	4	4.5	9	10.2	14	15.9	47	53.4	62	70.5
Mississippi	104	9	8.7	11	10.6	51	49.0	37	35.6	8	7.7	29	27.9	0	0.0	9	8.7	25	24.0	23	22.1	37	35.6
Tennessee	73	14	19.2	14	19.2	42	57.5	15	20.5	6	8.2	45	61.6	0	0.0	7	9.6	9	12.3	30	41.1	52	71.2
CENSUS DIVISION 6, WEST NORTH CENTRAL	637	221	34.7	163	25.6	509	79.9	306	48.0	63	9.9	316	49.6	106	16.6	61	9.6	77	12.1	214	33.6	464	72.8
Iowa	124	52	41.9	48	38.7	110	88.7	70	56.5	14	11.3	69	55.6	28	22.6	13	10.5	11	8.9	36	29.0	113	91.1
Kansas	143	37	25.9	16	11.2	111	77.6	46	32.2	7	4.9	59	41.3	30	21.0	6	4.2	13	9.1	30	21.0	75	52.4
Minnesota	105	40	38.1	36	34.3	89	84.8	61	58.1	10	9.5	49	46.7	15	14.3	9	9.5	9	8.6	38	36.2	84	80.0
Missouri	143	43	30.1	24	16.8	105	73.4	64	44.8	20	14.0	77	53.8	15	10.5	16	11.2	32	22.4	78	54.5	110	76.9
Nebraska	54	23	42.6	18	33.3	44	81.5	24	44.4	6	11.1	33	61.1	8	14.8	5	9.3	4	7.4	17	31.5	39	72.2
North Dakota	26	7	26.9	9	34.6	18	69.2	16	61.5	3	11.5	13	50.0	3	11.5	3	11.5	5	19.2	8	30.8	17	65.4
South Dakota	42	19	45.2	12	28.6	32	76.2	25	59.5	6	14.3	16	38.1	7	16.7	8	19.0	3	7.1	7	16.7	26	61.9
CENSUS DIVISION 7, WEST SOUTH CENTRAL	891	129	14.5	78	8.8	555	62.3	279	31.3	91	10.2	392	44.0	35	3.9	72	8.1	87	9.8	325	36.5	555	62.3
Arkansas	88	30	34.1	8	9.1	57	64.8	21	23.9	1	1.1	43	48.9	4	4.5	10	11.4	7	8.0	25	28.4	49	55.7
Louisiana	95	14	14.7	8	8.4	59	62.1	38	40.0	20	21.1	41	43.2	3	3.2	11	11.6	11	11.6	42	44.2	64	67.4
Oklahoma	116	18	15.5	13	11.2	78	67.2	36	31.0	11	9.5	57	49.1	11	9.5	7	6.0	7	6.0	33	28.4	55	47.4
Texas	592	67	11.3	49	8.3	361	61.0	184	31.1	59	10.0	251	42.4	17	2.9	44	7.4	62	10.5	225	38.0	387	65.4
CENSUS DIVISION 8, MOUNTAIN	319	69	21.6	69	21.6	232	72.7	150	47.0	55	17.2	203	63.6	25	7.8	40	12.5	34	10.7	127	39.8	228	71.5
Arizona	48	4	8.3	8	16.7	36	75.0	18	37.5	9	18.8	34	70.8	6	12.5	10	20.8	6	12.5	26	54.2	39	81.3
Colorado	72	14	19.4	9	12.5	59	81.9	31	43.1	14	19.4	51	70.8	9	12.5	6	8.3	9	12.5	41	56.9	55	76.8
Idaho	32	8	25.0	9	28.1	24	75.0	15	46.9	5	15.6	24	75.0	8	25.0	8	25.0	0	0.0	9	28.1	22	68.8
Montana	57	17	29.8	18	31.6	41	71.9	34	59.6	11	19.3	23	40.4	0	0.0	8	14.0	1	1.8	13	22.8	36	63.2
Nevada	26	6	23.1	5	19.2	14	53.8	11	42.3	4	15.4	16	61.5	0	0.0	1	3.8	1	3.8	9	34.6	16	61.5
New Mexico	29	8	27.6	7	24.1	21	72.4	18	62.1	5	17.2	18	62.1	1	3.4	1	3.4	4	13.8	10	34.5	20	69.0
Utah	35	7	20.0	9	25.7	25	71.4	15	42.9	5	14.3	24	68.6	1	2.9	5	14.3	10	28.6	12	34.3	27	77.1
Wyoming	20	5	25.0	4	20.0	12	60.0	8	40.0	2	10.0	13	65.0	0	0.0	2	10.0	3	15.0	7	35.0	13	65.0
CENSUS DIVISION 9, PACIFIC	423	109	25.8	108	25.5	320	75.7	216	51.1	78	18.4	302	71.4	18	4.3	47	11.1	67	15.8	258	61.0	334	79.0
Alaska	15	7	46.7	4	26.7	9	60.0	8	53.3	3	20.0	8	53.3	0	0.0	1	6.7	1	6.7	6	40.0	11	73.3
California	248	62	25.0	66	26.6	185	74.6	134	54.0	53	21.4	187	75.4	14	5.6	32	12.9	37	14.9	169	68.1	193	77.8
Hawaii	17	3	17.6	5	29.4	12	70.6	7	41.2	2	11.8	13	76.5	3	17.6	1	5.9	1	5.9	10	58.8	13	76.5
Oregon	62	24	38.7	20	32.3	54	87.1	27	43.5	11	17.7	43	69.4	0	0.0	6	9.7	7	11.3	25	40.3	56	90.3
Washington	81	13	16.0	13	16.0	60	74.1	39	48.1	9	11.1	51	63.0	1	1.2	7	8.6	21	25.9	48	59.3	61	75.3

Table 7 (Continued)

These data include only hospital-based facilities and services as reported by responding hospitals in Section C of the 2016 AHA Annual Survey, beginning on page 215. All hospitals are represented with Community Hospitals listed separately under United States. No estimates have been made for nonresponding hospitals. Definitions of facilities and services are listed in the Glossary, page 203.

CLASSIFICATION	HOSPITALS REPORTING	OBSTETRICS INPATIENT CARE UNITS Number	Percent	OCCUPATIONAL HEALTH SERVICES Number	Percent	ONCOLOGY SERVICES Number	Percent	ORTHOPEDIC SERVICES Number	Percent	OTHER SPECIAL CARE UNITS Number	Percent	OUTPATIENT SURGERY Number	Percent	PAIN MANAGEMENT PROGRAM Number	Percent	PALLIATIVE CARE PROGRAM Number	Percent	PALLIATIVE CARE INPATIENT UNIT Number	Percent	PATIENT CONTROLLED ANALGESIA (PCA) Number	Percent	PATIENT EDUCATION CENTER Number	Percent
UNITED STATES	4,590	2,454	53.5	2,940	64.1	2,342	51.0	3,146	68.5	778	16.9	3,640	79.3	2,403	52.4	1,738	37.9	449	9.8	3,184	69.4	2,471	53.8
COMMUNITY HOSPITALS	3,865	2,411	62.4	2,719	70.3	2,259	58.4	2,935	75.9	738	19.1	3,424	88.6	2,209	57.2	1,637	42.4	394	10.2	2,950	76.3	2,247	58.1
CENSUS DIVISION 1, NEW ENGLAND	172	111	64.5	136	79.1	121	70.3	143	83.1	35	20.3	143	83.1	122	70.9	94	54.7	26	15.1	136	79.1	114	66.3
Connecticut	30	22	73.3	18	60.0	23	76.7	23	76.7	10	33.3	23	76.7	25	83.3	21	70.0	4	13.3	23	76.7	19	63.3
Maine	32	25	78.1	25	78.1	24	75.0	31	96.9	11	34.4	30	93.8	19	59.4	18	56.3	5	15.6	25	78.1	17	53.1
Massachusetts	64	36	56.3	56	87.5	39	60.9	51	79.7	9	14.1	50	79.7	49	76.6	27	42.2	9	14.1	48	75.0	48	75.0
New Hampshire	25	17	68.0	20	80.0	18	72.0	23	92.0	5	20.0	23	92.0	15	60.0	17	68.0	6	24.0	23	92.0	16	64.0
Rhode Island	10	4	40.0	9	90.0	8	80.0	7	70.0	0	0.0	8	80.0	6	60.0	5	50.0	0	0.0	8	80.0	8	80.0
Vermont	11	7	63.6	8	72.7	9	81.8	8	72.7	0	0.0	9	81.8	6	54.5	6	54.5	2	18.2	9	81.8	6	54.5
CENSUS DIVISION 2, MIDDLE ATLANTIC	404	232	57.4	312	77.2	279	69.1	335	82.9	83	20.5	336	83.2	282	69.8	232	57.4	62	15.3	316	78.2	260	64.4
New Jersey	62	41	66.1	47	75.8	51	82.3	54	87.1	16	25.8	51	82.3	49	79.0	38	61.3	11	17.7	48	77.4	47	75.8
New York	142	100	70.4	121	85.2	107	75.4	125	88.0	26	18.3	130	91.5	102	71.8	103	72.5	33	23.2	123	86.6	91	64.1
Pennsylvania	200	91	45.5	144	72.0	121	60.5	156	78.0	41	20.5	155	77.5	131	65.5	91	45.5	18	9.0	145	72.5	122	61.0
CENSUS DIVISION 3, SOUTH ATLANTIC	671	367	54.7	468	69.7	386	57.5	504	75.1	136	20.3	543	80.9	350	52.2	295	44.0	64	9.5	508	75.7	403	60.1
Delaware	10	5	50.0	6	60.0	6	60.0	7	70.0	3	30.0	6	60.0	4	40.0	6	60.0	0	0.0	5	50.0	6	60.0
District of Columbia	11	6	54.5	6	54.5	8	72.7	8	72.7	5	45.5	7	63.6	7	63.6	6	54.5	2	18.2	7	63.6	10	90.9
Florida	180	85	47.2	117	65.0	109	60.6	140	77.8	47	26.1	146	81.1	92	51.1	78	43.3	16	8.9	140	77.8	94	52.2
Georgia	100	52	52.0	65	65.0	45	45.0	65	65.0	16	16.0	78	78.0	47	47.0	36	36.0	8	8.0	70	70.0	57	57.0
Maryland	44	30	68.2	40	90.9	38	86.4	39	88.6	9	20.5	38	86.4	29	65.7	35	79.5	7	15.9	38	86.4	34	77.3
North Carolina	108	78	72.2	87	80.6	74	68.5	91	84.3	24	22.2	101	93.5	71	65.7	44	40.7	13	12.0	90	83.3	68	63.0
South Carolina	79	43	54.4	51	64.6	32	40.5	57	72.2	18	22.8	55	69.6	27	34.2	22	27.8	6	7.6	55	69.6	44	55.7
Virginia	84	43	51.2	66	78.6	53	63.1	61	72.6	13	15.5	70	83.3	48	57.1	49	58.3	9	10.7	70	83.3	55	65.5
West Virginia	55	25	45.5	30	54.5	21	38.2	36	65.5	1	1.8	33	74.5	18	32.7	19	34.5	3	5.5	33	60.0	35	63.6
CENSUS DIVISION 4, EAST NORTH CENTRAL	706	435	61.6	493	69.8	449	63.6	539	76.3	197	27.9	617	87.4	460	65.2	287	40.7	89	12.6	546	77.3	478	67.7
Illinois	165	101	61.2	104	63.0	111	67.3	128	77.6	16	9.7	151	91.5	117	70.9	76	46.1	14	8.5	130	78.8	99	60.0
Indiana	122	73	59.8	86	70.5	65	53.3	92	75.4	22	18.0	99	81.1	59	48.4	36	29.5	15	12.3	96	78.7	70	57.4
Michigan	130	75	57.7	103	79.2	90	69.2	109	83.8	28	21.5	114	87.7	82	63.1	55	42.3	18	13.8	101	77.7	80	61.5
Ohio	144	92	63.9	116	80.6	103	71.5	126	87.5	23	16.0	129	89.6	110	76.4	62	43.1	23	16.0	120	83.3	101	70.1
Wisconsin	145	94	64.8	84	57.9	80	55.2	84	57.9	108	74.5	124	85.5	92	63.4	58	40.0	19	13.1	99	68.3	128	88.3
CENSUS DIVISION 5, EAST SOUTH CENTRAL	367	159	43.3	172	46.9	127	34.6	189	51.5	55	15.0	261	71.1	142	38.7	81	22.1	22	6.0	191	52.0	161	43.9
Alabama	102	48	47.1	50	49.0	36	35.3	61	59.8	16	15.7	76	74.5	40	39.2	20	19.6	6	5.9	54	52.9	43	42.2
Kentucky	88	39	44.3	46	52.3	45	51.1	60	68.2	9	10.2	69	78.4	48	54.5	27	30.7	7	8.0	60	68.2	45	51.1
Mississippi	104	38	36.5	33	31.7	13	12.5	28	26.9	14	13.5	64	61.5	30	28.8	14	13.5	3	2.9	32	30.8	42	40.4
Tennessee	73	34	46.6	43	58.9	33	45.2	40	54.8	16	21.9	52	71.2	24	32.9	20	27.4	6	8.2	45	61.6	31	42.5
CENSUS DIVISION 6, WEST NORTH CENTRAL	637	337	52.9	423	66.4	299	46.9	400	62.8	72	11.3	557	87.4	312	49.0	206	32.3	53	8.3	421	66.1	308	48.4
Iowa	124	74	59.7	88	71.0	70	56.5	86	69.4	8	6.5	117	94.4	69	55.6	41	33.1	5	4.0	96	77.4	65	52.4
Kansas	143	64	44.8	81	56.6	39	27.3	68	47.6	11	7.7	116	81.1	59	41.3	29	20.3	10	7.0	81	56.6	55	38.5
Minnesota	105	74	70.5	81	77.1	54	51.4	77	73.3	14	13.3	101	96.2	53	50.5	40	38.1	8	7.6	76	72.4	54	51.4
Missouri	143	63	44.1	96	67.1	78	54.5	101	70.6	27	18.9	109	76.2	72	50.3	53	37.1	15	10.5	104	72.7	83	58.0
Nebraska	54	33	61.1	34	63.0	33	61.1	39	72.2	6	11.1	53	98.1	31	57.4	23	42.6	4	7.4	33	61.1	30	46.3
North Dakota	26	11	42.3	15	57.7	12	46.2	12	46.2	3	11.5	25	96.2	12	46.2	8	30.8	7	26.9	14	53.8	9	34.6
South Dakota	42	18	42.9	28	66.7	13	31.0	17	40.5	3	7.1	36	85.7	16	38.1	12	28.6	4	9.5	17	40.5	17	40.5
CENSUS DIVISION 7, WEST SOUTH CENTRAL	891	337	37.8	432	48.5	264	29.6	472	53.0	89	10.0	560	62.9	327	36.7	177	19.9	35	3.9	517	58.0	351	39.4
Arkansas	88	35	39.8	41	46.6	28	31.8	45	51.1	7	8.0	62	70.5	25	28.4	16	18.2	3	3.4	50	56.8	27	30.7
Louisiana	95	40	42.1	50	52.6	39	41.1	50	52.6	10	10.5	64	67.4	31	32.6	26	27.4	3	3.2	57	60.0	45	47.4
Oklahoma	116	44	37.9	53	45.7	26	22.4	61	52.6	12	10.3	81	69.8	48	41.4	21	18.1	9	7.8	70	60.3	42	36.2
Texas	592	218	36.8	288	48.6	171	28.9	316	53.4	60	10.1	353	59.6	223	37.7	114	19.3	20	3.4	340	57.4	237	40.0
CENSUS DIVISION 8, MOUNTAIN	319	192	60.2	209	65.5	146	45.8	216	67.7	36	11.3	251	78.7	164	51.4	116	36.4	41	12.9	214	67.1	159	49.8
Arizona	48	27	56.3	38	79.2	28	58.3	36	75.0	9	18.8	38	79.2	26	54.2	26	54.2	9	18.8	37	77.1	28	58.3
Colorado	72	50	69.4	57	79.2	45	62.5	55	76.4	10	13.9	62	86.1	42	58.3	35	48.6	8	11.1	56	77.8	37	51.4
Idaho	32	21	65.6	22	68.8	12	37.5	27	84.4	3	9.4	31	96.9	17	53.1	8	25.0	6	18.8	21	65.6	18	56.3
Montana	57	25	43.9	30	52.6	18	31.6	25	43.9	2	3.5	35	61.4	22	38.6	20	35.1	8	14.0	28	49.1	20	35.1
Nevada	26	9	34.6	12	46.2	10	38.5	14	53.8	4	15.4	24	53.8	11	42.3	6	23.1	2	7.7	15	57.7	12	46.2
New Mexico	29	20	69.0	16	55.2	12	41.4	19	65.5	4	13.8	24	82.8	12	41.4	7	24.1	5	17.2	21	72.4	12	41.4
Utah	35	25	71.4	21	60.0	16	45.7	25	71.4	4	11.4	30	85.7	24	68.6	10	28.6	2	5.7	22	62.9	23	65.7
Wyoming	20	15	75.0	13	65.0	5	25.0	15	75.0	0	0.0	17	85.0	10	50.0	4	20.0	1	5.0	14	70.0	9	45.0
CENSUS DIVISION 9, PACIFIC	423	284	67.1	295	69.7	271	64.1	348	82.3	75	17.7	372	87.9	244	57.7	250	59.1	57	13.5	335	79.2	237	56.0
Alaska	15	10	66.7	11	73.3	6	40.0	8	53.3	0	0.0	11	73.3	10	66.7	7	46.7	1	6.7	10	66.7	6	40.0
California	248	166	66.9	179	72.2	164	66.1	213	85.9	39	15.7	221	89.1	144	58.1	160	64.5	39	15.7	200	80.6	142	57.3
Hawaii	17	9	52.9	14	82.4	12	70.6	12	70.6	5	29.4	11	64.7	7	41.2	9	52.9	1	5.9	10	58.8	11	64.7
Oregon	62	49	79.0	41	66.1	41	66.1	53	85.5	5	8.1	59	95.2	37	59.7	33	53.2	7	11.3	54	87.1	38	61.3
Washington	81	50	61.7	50	61.7	48	59.3	62	76.5	26	32.1	70	86.4	46	56.8	41	50.6	9	11.1	61	75.3	40	49.4

Table 7 (Continued)

These data include only hospital-based facilities and services as reported by responding hospitals in Section C of the 2016 AHA Annual Survey, beginning on page 215. All hospitals are represented with Community Hospitals listed separately under United States. No estimates have been made for nonresponding hospitals. Definitions of facilities and services are listed in the Glossary, page 203.

CLASSIFICATION	HOSPITALS REPORTING	PATIENT REPRESENTATIVE SERVICES		PHYSICAL REHABILITATION INPATIENT CARE UNITS		PRIMARY CARE DEPARTMENT		PSYCHIATRIC INPATIENT CARE UNITS		RETIREMENT HOUSING		ROBOTIC SURGERY		RURAL HEALTH CLINIC		SLEEP CENTER		SOCIAL WORK SERVICES		SPORTS MEDICINE		SUPPORT GROUPS	
		Number	Percent	Number	Percent	Number	Percent	Number	Percent	Number	Percent	Number	Percent	Number	Percent	Number	Percent	Number	Percent	Number	Percent	Number	Percent
UNITED STATES	4,590	3,160	68.8	1,372	29.9	1,922	41.9	1,561	34.0	121	2.6	1,383	30.1	1,053	22.9	2,153	46.9	3,866	84.2	1,956	42.6	2,899	63.2
COMMUNITY HOSPITALS	3,865	2,850	73.7	1,254	32.4	1,810	46.8	1,189	30.8	120	3.1	1,321	34.2	991	25.6	2,069	53.5	3,371	87.2	1,888	48.8	2,649	68.5
CENSUS DIVISION 1, NEW ENGLAND	172	137	79.7	45	26.2	102	59.3	87	50.6	3	1.7	61	35.5	26	15.1	96	55.8	161	93.6	109	63.4	145	84.3
Connecticut	30	25	83.3	10	33.3	17	56.7	23	76.7	1	3.3	18	60.0	1	3.3	20	66.7	27	90.0	27	63.3	27	90.0
Maine	32	27	84.4	10	31.3	29	90.6	9	28.1	1	3.1	4	12.5	14	43.8	19	59.4	31	96.9	18	56.3	30	93.8
Massachusetts	64	49	76.6	12	18.8	26	40.6	33	51.6	0	0.0	23	35.9	2	3.1	32	50.0	60	93.8	42	65.6	55	85.9
New Hampshire	25	19	76.0	8	32.0	18	72.0	10	40.0	0	0.0	9	36.0	6	24.0	16	64.0	24	96.0	21	84.0	18	72.0
Rhode Island	10	9	90.0	3	30.0	6	60.0	6	60.0	0	0.0	6	60.0	0	0.0	4	40.0	9	90.0	3	30.0	8	80.0
Vermont	11	8	72.7	2	18.2	6	54.5	6	54.5	1	9.1	1	9.1	3	27.3	5	45.5	10	90.9	6	54.5	7	63.6
CENSUS DIVISION 2, MIDDLE ATLANTIC	404	318	78.7	150	37.1	228	56.4	216	53.5	3	0.7	174	43.1	40	9.9	229	56.7	381	94.3	210	52.0	326	80.7
New Jersey	62	53	85.5	16	25.8	42	67.7	34	54.8	0	0.0	34	54.8	0	0.0	41	66.1	61	98.4	37	59.7	54	87.1
New York	142	128	90.1	57	40.1	110	77.5	82	57.7	2	1.4	69	48.6	23	16.2	77	54.2	139	97.9	85	59.9	124	87.3
Pennsylvania	200	137	68.5	77	38.5	76	38.0	100	50.0	1	0.5	71	35.5	17	8.5	111	55.5	181	90.5	88	44.0	148	74.0
CENSUS DIVISION 3, SOUTH ATLANTIC	671	489	72.9	210	31.3	252	37.6	255	38.0	5	0.7	255	38.0	96	14.3	337	50.2	563	83.9	291	43.4	454	67.7
Delaware	10	7	70.0	4	40.0	4	40.0	5	50.0	0	0.0	4	40.0	2	20.0	5	50.0	8	80.0	5	50.0	7	70.0
District of Columbia	11	8	72.7	6	54.5	6	54.5	9	81.8	0	0.0	5	45.5	0	0.0	6	54.5	10	90.9	6	54.5	9	81.8
Florida	180	122	67.8	51	28.3	56	31.1	61	33.9	1	0.6	93	51.7	19	10.6	73	40.6	136	75.6	79	43.9	116	64.4
Georgia	100	68	68.0	23	23.0	30	30.0	27	27.0	3	3.0	32	32.0	14	14.0	53	53.0	77	77.0	31	31.0	59	59.0
Maryland	44	41	93.2	10	22.7	21	47.7	30	68.2	1	2.3	22	50.0	1	2.3	28	63.6	42	95.5	23	52.3	38	86.4
North Carolina	108	84	77.8	27	25.0	47	43.5	46	42.6	1	0.9	42	38.9	17	15.7	63	58.3	102	94.4	57	52.8	78	72.2
South Carolina	79	48	60.8	51	64.6	22	27.8	26	32.9	0	0.0	16	20.3	14	17.7	33	41.8	64	81.0	27	34.2	49	62.0
Virginia	84	72	85.7	26	31.0	38	45.2	35	41.7	1	1.2	28	33.3	14	14.3	47	56.0	76	90.5	45	53.6	62	73.8
West Virginia	55	39	70.9	12	21.8	28	50.9	16	29.1	0	0.0	13	23.6	17	30.9	29	52.7	48	87.3	18	32.7	36	65.5
CENSUS DIVISION 4, EAST NORTH CENTRAL	706	560	79.3	259	36.7	357	50.6	262	37.1	21	3.0	237	33.6	155	22.0	448	63.5	648	91.8	403	57.1	550	77.9
Illinois	165	137	83.0	54	32.7	87	52.7	70	42.4	12	7.3	70	42.4	48	29.1	120	72.7	151	91.5	95	57.6	137	83.0
Indiana	122	87	71.3	38	31.1	48	39.3	41	33.6	3	2.5	32	26.2	16	13.1	74	60.7	99	81.1	52	42.6	97	79.5
Michigan	130	107	82.3	47	36.2	92	70.8	51	39.2	2	1.5	47	36.2	48	36.9	88	67.7	124	95.4	85	65.4	110	84.6
Ohio	144	117	81.3	44	30.6	67	46.5	59	41.0	0	0.0	55	38.2	14	9.7	100	69.4	136	94.4	92	63.9	117	81.3
Wisconsin	145	112	77.2	76	52.4	63	43.4	41	28.3	4	2.8	33	22.8	29	20.0	66	45.5	138	95.2	79	54.5	89	61.4
CENSUS DIVISION 5, EAST SOUTH CENTRAL	367	221	60.2	99	27.0	102	27.8	143	39.0	6	1.6	92	25.1	79	21.5	148	40.3	289	78.7	113	30.8	179	48.8
Alabama	102	51	50.0	24	23.5	21	20.6	44	43.1	3	2.9	26	25.5	19	18.6	41	40.2	72	70.6	37	36.3	44	43.1
Kentucky	88	64	72.7	17	19.3	37	42.0	29	33.0	1	1.1	20	27.3	27	30.7	50	56.8	71	80.7	30	34.1	54	61.4
Mississippi	104	60	57.7	40	38.5	25	24.0	42	40.4	1	1.0	20	19.2	29	27.9	22	21.2	87	83.7	21	20.2	39	37.5
Tennessee	73	46	63.0	18	24.7	19	26.0	28	38.4	1	1.4	22	30.1	4	5.5	35	47.9	59	80.8	25	34.2	42	57.5
CENSUS DIVISION 6, WEST NORTH CENTRAL	637	380	59.7	190	29.8	319	50.1	167	26.2	64	10.0	111	17.4	288	45.2	319	50.1	524	82.3	302	47.4	394	61.9
Iowa	124	76	61.3	27	21.8	76	61.3	34	27.4	15	12.1	25	20.2	58	46.8	69	55.6	104	83.9	66	53.2	97	78.2
Kansas	143	73	51.0	30	21.0	57	39.9	26	18.1	12	8.4	20	14.0	78	54.5	44	30.8	101	70.6	51	35.7	53	37.1
Minnesota	105	69	65.7	19	18.1	62	59.0	26	24.8	17	16.2	19	18.1	31	29.5	56	53.3	98	93.3	54	51.4	84	80.0
Missouri	143	102	71.3	87	60.8	56	39.2	42	42.7	2	1.4	19	19.6	59	41.3	85	59.4	124	86.7	68	47.6	86	60.1
Nebraska	54	24	44.4	15	27.8	24	44.4	11	20.4	4	7.4	10	18.5	28	51.9	32	59.3	46	85.2	32	59.3	34	63.0
North Dakota	26	16	61.5	6	23.1	18	69.2	7	26.9	5	19.2	5	19.2	13	50.0	15	57.7	23	88.5	14	53.8	14	53.8
South Dakota	42	20	47.6	6	14.3	26	61.9	5	11.9	9	21.4	3	9.5	21	50.0	18	42.9	28	66.7	17	40.5	26	61.9
CENSUS DIVISION 7, WEST SOUTH CENTRAL	891	515	57.8	222	24.9	205	23.0	227	25.5	10	1.1	207	23.2	180	20.2	284	31.9	665	74.6	231	25.9	382	42.9
Arkansas	88	49	55.7	21	23.9	18	20.5	32	36.4	1	1.1	15	17.0	22	25.0	44	50.0	65	73.9	25	28.4	44	50.0
Louisiana	95	53	55.8	36	37.9	37	38.9	38	40.0	4	4.2	28	29.5	22	23.2	38	40.0	76	80.0	30	31.6	43	45.3
Oklahoma	116	72	62.1	28	24.1	29	25.0	37	31.9	3	2.6	24	20.7	24	20.7	48	41.4	84	72.4	39	33.6	46	39.7
Texas	592	341	57.6	137	23.1	121	20.4	120	20.3	2	0.3	142	24.0	112	18.9	154	26.0	440	74.3	137	23.1	249	42.1
CENSUS DIVISION 8, MOUNTAIN	319	225	70.5	84	26.3	167	52.4	77	24.1	7	2.2	90	28.2	105	32.9	149	46.7	254	79.6	137	42.9	173	54.2
Arizona	48	35	72.9	15	31.3	15	31.3	14	29.2	0	0.0	22	45.8	7	14.6	17	35.4	41	85.4	34	45.8	34	70.8
Colorado	72	56	77.8	22	30.6	48	66.7	13	18.1	2	2.8	32	44.4	22	30.6	48	66.7	56	77.8	38	52.8	46	63.9
Idaho	32	23	71.9	11	34.4	20	62.5	7	21.9	0	0.0	6	18.8	20	62.5	17	53.1	25	78.1	18	56.3	17	53.1
Montana	57	35	61.4	8	14.0	35	61.4	7	12.3	3	5.3	10	17.5	33	57.9	19	33.3	40	70.2	20	35.1	22	38.6
Nevada	26	16	61.5	4	15.4	8	30.8	10	38.5	1	3.8	4	15.4	6	23.1	5	19.2	22	84.6	5	19.2	13	50.0
New Mexico	29	19	65.5	10	34.5	16	55.2	10	34.5	0	0.0	4	13.8	6	20.7	14	48.3	26	89.7	6	20.7	14	48.3
Utah	35	27	77.1	11	31.4	15	42.9	12	34.3	1	2.9	9	25.7	5	14.3	20	57.1	28	80.0	16	45.7	18	51.4
Wyoming	20	14	70.0	3	15.0	10	50.0	4	20.0	0	0.0	3	15.0	6	30.0	9	45.0	16	80.0	12	60.0	9	45.0
CENSUS DIVISION 9, PACIFIC	423	315	74.5	113	26.7	190	44.9	127	30.0	2	0.5	156	36.9	84	19.9	143	33.8	381	90.1	160	37.8	296	70.0
Alaska	15	10	66.7	4	26.7	8	53.3	5	33.3	0	0.0	2	13.3	3	20.0	6	40.0	12	80.0	5	33.3	6	40.0
California	248	182	73.4	76	30.6	89	35.9	73	29.4	0	0.0	102	41.1	33	13.3	60	24.2	231	93.1	83	33.5	169	68.1
Hawaii	17	10	58.8	1	5.9	8	47.1	5	29.4	0	0.0	5	29.4	4	23.5	5	29.4	17	100.0	11	47.1	11	64.7
Oregon	62	51	82.3	13	21.0	47	75.8	20	32.3	2	3.2	18	29.0	23	37.1	32	51.6	52	83.9	29	46.8	54	87.1
Washington	81	62	76.5	19	23.5	38	46.9	24	29.6	0	0.0	29	35.8	21	25.9	40	49.4	69	85.2	35	43.2	56	69.1

Table 7 (Continued)

These data include only hospital-based facilities and services as reported by responding hospitals in Section C of the 2016 AHA Annual Survey, beginning on page 215. All hospitals are represented with Community Hospitals listed separately under United States. No estimates have been made for nonresponding hospitals. Definitions of facilities and services are listed in the Glossary, page 203.

CLASSIFICATION	HOSPITALS REPORTING	SWING BED SERVICES Number	Percent	TEEN OUTREACH SERVICES Number	Percent	TOBACCO TREATMENT/ CESSATION PROGRAM Number	Percent	TRANSPORTATION TO HEALTH FACILITIES Number	Percent	URGENT CARE CENTER Number	Percent	VIOLENCE PREVENTION PROGRAM - COMMUNITY Number	Percent	VIOLENCE PREVENTION PROGRAM - WORKPLACE Number	Percent	VIRTUAL COLONOSCOPY Number	Percent	VOLUNTEER SERVICES DEPARTMENT Number	Percent	WOMEN'S HEALTH SERVICES Number	Percent	WOUND MANAGEMENT SERVICES Number	Percent
UNITED STATES	4,590	1,373	29.9	573	12.5	2,377	51.8	1,028	22.4	1,087	23.7	453	9.9	2,160	47.1	815	17.8	3,391	73.9	2,326	50.7	3,099	67.5
COMMUNITY HOSPITALS	3,865	1,329	34.4	536	13.9	2,151	55.7	877	22.7	1,003	26.7	409	10.6	1,884	48.7	787	20.4	3,156	81.7	2,223	57.5	2,836	73.4
CENSUS DIVISION 1, NEW ENGLAND	172	43	25.0	52	30.2	119	69.2	56	32.6	68	39.5	31	18.0	111	64.5	43	25.0	158	91.9	123	71.5	137	79.7
Connecticut	30	0	0.0	12	40.0	22	73.3	5	16.7	15	50.0	6	20.0	24	80.0	12	40.0	27	90.0	19	63.3	23	76.7
Maine	32	15	46.9	6	18.8	24	75.0	11	34.4	13	40.6	2	6.3	18	56.3	5	15.6	30	93.8	24	75.0	27	84.4
Massachusetts	64	5	7.8	21	32.8	38	59.4	22	34.4	26	40.6	17	26.6	42	65.6	16	25.0	59	92.2	43	67.2	51	79.7
New Hampshire	25	15	60.0	8	32.0	17	68.0	7	28.0	11	44.0	3	12.0	16	64.0	6	24.0	24	96.0	23	92.0	21	84.0
Rhode Island	10	2	20.0	3	30.0	7	70.0	6	60.0	1	10.0	2	20.0	5	50.0	3	30.0	8	80.0	6	60.0	6	60.0
Vermont	11	6	54.5	2	18.2	11	100.0	5	45.5	2	18.2	1	9.1	6	54.5	1	9.1	10	90.9	8	72.7	9	81.8
CENSUS DIVISION 2, MIDDLE ATLANTIC	404	63	15.6	103	25.5	259	64.1	131	32.4	118	29.2	74	18.3	237	58.7	105	26.0	354	87.6	266	65.8	289	71.5
New Jersey	62	6	9.7	31	50.0	37	62.9	37	59.7	22	35.5	18	29.0	52	83.9	22	35.5	53	85.5	48	77.4	52	83.9
New York	142	24	16.9	38	26.8	104	73.2	46	32.4	54	38.0	31	21.8	89	62.7	47	33.1	136	95.8	106	74.6	102	71.8
Pennsylvania	200	33	16.5	34	17.0	116	58.0	48	24.0	42	21.0	25	12.5	96	48.0	36	18.0	165	82.5	112	56.0	135	67.5
CENSUS DIVISION 3, SOUTH ATLANTIC	671	115	17.1	79	11.8	386	57.5	151	22.5	150	22.4	59	8.8	317	47.2	142	21.2	546	81.4	382	56.9	480	71.5
Delaware	10	0	0.0	4	40.0	6	60.0	5	50.0	5	50.0	1	10.0	6	60.0	1	10.0	6	60.0	5	50.0	7	70.0
District of Columbia	11	0	0.0	3	27.3	5	45.5	2	18.2	2	18.2	1	9.1	5	45.5	1	9.1	10	90.9	5	45.5	8	72.7
Florida	180	19	10.6	16	8.9	87	48.3	36	20.0	35	19.4	16	8.9	97	53.9	38	21.1	141	78.3	98	54.4	131	72.8
Georgia	100	27	27.0	10	10.0	56	56.0	20	20.0	22	22.0	5	5.0	41	41.0	12	12.0	72	72.0	55	55.0	69	69.0
Maryland	44	2	4.5	15	34.1	36	81.8	16	36.4	13	29.5	8	18.2	28	63.6	11	25.0	44	100.0	24	54.5	32	72.7
North Carolina	108	20	18.5	9	8.3	69	63.9	26	24.1	33	30.6	11	10.2	52	48.1	30	27.8	100	92.6	68	63.0	81	75.0
South Carolina	79	10	12.7	9	11.4	43	54.4	12	15.2	8	10.1	3	3.8	15	19.0	13	16.5	59	74.7	44	55.7	49	62.0
Virginia	84	16	19.0	9	10.7	55	65.5	21	25.0	20	23.8	7	8.3	50	59.5	28	33.3	75	89.3	53	63.1	69	82.1
West Virginia	55	21	38.2	4	7.3	29	52.7	13	23.6	12	21.8	7	12.7	23	41.8	8	14.5	39	70.9	30	54.5	34	61.8
CENSUS DIVISION 4, EAST NORTH CENTRAL	706	196	27.8	114	16.1	462	65.4	183	25.9	294	41.6	100	14.2	384	54.4	160	22.7	592	83.9	419	59.3	503	71.2
Illinois	165	54	32.7	27	16.4	93	56.4	56	33.9	61	37.0	28	17.0	91	55.2	46	27.9	148	89.7	100	60.6	111	67.3
Indiana	122	35	28.7	16	13.1	90	73.8	19	15.6	38	31.1	13	10.7	51	41.8	19	15.6	94	77.0	64	52.5	86	70.5
Michigan	130	23	17.7	27	20.8	93	71.5	34	26.2	59	45.4	19	14.6	82	63.1	25	19.2	117	90.0	86	66.2	98	75.4
Ohio	144	34	23.6	27	18.8	111	77.1	46	31.9	59	41.0	19	13.2	87	60.4	38	26.4	132	91.7	93	64.6	113	78.5
Wisconsin	145	50	34.5	17	11.7	75	51.7	28	19.3	77	53.1	21	14.5	73	50.3	32	22.1	101	69.7	76	52.4	95	65.5
CENSUS DIVISION 5, EAST SOUTH CENTRAL	367	122	33.2	29	7.9	141	38.4	54	14.7	47	12.8	25	6.8	96	26.2	39	10.6	248	67.6	140	38.1	156	42.5
Alabama	102	23	22.5	7	6.9	41	40.2	13	12.7	12	11.8	1	1.0	23	22.5	9	8.8	67	65.7	37	36.3	50	49.0
Kentucky	88	30	34.1	6	6.8	48	54.5	9	10.2	14	15.9	15	17.0	31	35.2	14	15.9	68	77.3	45	51.1	50	56.8
Mississippi	104	53	51.0	9	8.7	13	12.5	21	20.2	12	11.5	0	0.0	14	13.5	7	6.7	62	59.6	28	26.9	12	11.5
Tennessee	73	16	21.9	7	9.6	39	53.4	11	15.1	9	12.3	9	12.3	28	38.4	9	12.3	51	69.9	30	41.1	44	60.3
CENSUS DIVISION 6, WEST NORTH CENTRAL	637	384	60.3	53	8.3	305	47.9	153	24.0	148	23.2	56	8.8	300	47.1	96	15.1	424	66.6	261	41.0	439	68.9
Iowa	124	89	71.8	15	12.1	79	63.7	23	18.5	23	18.5	12	9.7	53	42.7	17	13.7	98	79.0	59	47.6	89	71.8
Kansas	143	100	69.9	4	2.8	43	30.1	30	21.0	26	18.2	7	4.9	49	34.3	21	14.7	72	50.3	44	30.8	88	61.5
Minnesota	105	58	55.2	11	10.5	56	53.3	19	18.1	43	41.0	11	10.5	86	81.9	20	19.0	82	78.1	44	41.9	83	79.0
Missouri	143	48	33.6	15	10.5	73	51.0	49	34.3	33	23.1	14	9.8	73	51.0	20	14.0	98	68.5	68	47.6	103	72.0
Nebraska	54	34	63.0	6	11.1	29	53.7	14	25.9	7	13.0	2	3.7	14	25.9	13	24.1	34	63.0	21	38.9	32	59.3
North Dakota	26	21	80.8	0	0.0	12	46.2	10	38.5	8	30.8	7	26.9	12	46.2	3	11.5	20	76.9	11	42.3	14	53.8
South Dakota	42	34	81.0	2	4.8	13	31.0	8	19.0	8	19.0	3	7.1	13	31.0	2	4.8	20	47.6	14	33.3	30	71.4
CENSUS DIVISION 7, WEST SOUTH CENTRAL	891	232	26.0	50	5.6	314	35.2	117	13.1	95	10.7	41	4.6	334	37.5	96	10.8	472	53.0	310	34.8	542	60.8
Arkansas	88	37	42.0	7	8.0	33	37.5	14	15.9	9	10.2	5	5.7	26	29.5	10	11.4	53	60.2	29	33.0	55	62.5
Louisiana	95	24	25.3	11	11.6	47	49.5	20	21.1	18	18.9	2	2.1	43	45.3	6	6.3	55	57.9	44	46.3	54	56.8
Oklahoma	116	47	40.5	5	4.3	51	44.0	18	15.5	13	11.2	2	1.7	49	42.2	13	11.2	75	64.7	44	37.9	66	56.9
Texas	592	124	20.9	27	4.6	183	30.9	65	11.0	55	9.3	32	5.4	216	36.5	67	11.3	289	48.8	193	32.6	367	62.0
CENSUS DIVISION 8, MOUNTAIN	319	135	42.3	34	10.7	168	52.7	73	22.9	69	21.6	22	6.9	130	40.8	49	15.4	241	75.5	182	57.1	221	69.3
Arizona	48	8	16.7	5	10.4	28	58.3	10	14.6	7	14.6	4	8.3	20	41.7	18	37.5	41	85.4	29	60.4	35	72.9
Colorado	72	31	43.1	11	15.3	42	58.3	15	20.8	15	20.8	11	15.3	28	38.9	9	12.5	60	83.3	55	76.4	60	83.3
Idaho	32	19	59.4	6	18.8	18	56.3	10	31.3	8	25.0	1	3.1	13	40.6	3	9.4	26	81.3	16	50.0	20	62.5
Montana	57	43	75.4	3	5.3	28	49.1	20	35.1	18	31.6	0	0.0	17	29.8	10	17.5	37	64.9	25	43.9	32	56.1
Nevada	26	5	19.2	0	0.0	11	42.3	6	23.1	4	15.4	0	0.0	11	42.3	0	0.0	16	61.5	9	34.6	17	65.4
New Mexico	29	7	24.1	2	6.9	17	58.6	5	17.2	8	27.6	4	13.8	10	34.5	2	6.9	19	65.5	16	55.2	17	58.6
Utah	35	9	25.7	5	14.3	14	40.0	4	11.4	4	11.4	1	2.9	20	57.1	3	8.6	28	80.0	20	57.1	25	71.4
Wyoming	20	13	65.0	2	10.0	10	50.0	6	30.0	5	25.0	1	5.0	11	55.0	4	20.0	14	70.0	12	60.0	13	65.0
CENSUS DIVISION 9, PACIFIC	423	83	19.6	59	13.9	223	52.7	110	26.0	98	23.2	45	10.6	251	59.3	85	20.1	356	84.2	243	57.4	332	78.5
Alaska	15	6	40.0	3	20.0	9	60.0	2	13.3	3	20.0	1	6.7	7	46.7	1	6.7	6	40.0	6	40.0	11	73.3
California	248	19	7.7	36	14.5	109	44.0	72	29.0	44	17.7	39	15.7	166	66.9	54	21.8	216	87.1	142	57.3	196	79.0
Hawaii	17	5	29.4	4	23.5	12	70.6	5	29.4	2	11.8	0	0.0	10	58.8	3	17.6	14	82.4	11	64.7	14	82.4
Oregon	62	31	50.0	8	12.9	49	79.0	19	30.6	22	35.5	1	1.6	33	53.2	13	21.0	56	90.3	45	72.6	45	90.3
Washington	81	22	27.2	8	9.9	44	54.3	12	14.8	27	33.3	4	4.9	35	43.2	14	17.3	64	79.0	39	48.1	55	67.9

Table 7 (Continued)

These data include only hospital-based facilities and services as reported by responding hospitals in Section C of the 2016 AHA Annual Survey, beginning on page 215. All hospitals are represented with Community Hospitals listed separately under United States. No estimates have been made for nonresponding hospitals. Definitions of facilities and services are listed in the Glossary, page 203.

CLASSIFICATION	HOSPITALS REPORTING	GENERAL MEDICAL SURGICAL CARE — ADULT UNITS No.	Pct.	PEDIATRIC UNITS No.	Pct.	INTENSIVE CARE UNITS — CARDIAC UNITS No.	Pct.	MEDICAL SURGICAL UNITS No.	Pct.	NEONATAL UNITS No.	Pct.	OTHER UNITS No.	Pct.	PEDIATRIC UNITS No.	Pct.	ACUTE LONG-TERM CARE UNITS No.	Pct.	LONG-TERM CARE UNITS — SKILLED NURSING No.	Pct.	INTERMEDIATE NURSING No.	Pct.	OTHER LONG-TERM No.	Pct.
UNITED STATES	4,590	3,837	83.6	1,799	39.2	1,159	25.3	2,779	60.5	960	20.9	472	10.3	410	8.9	325	7.1	948	20.7	362	7.9	214	4.7
COMMUNITY HOSPITALS	3,865	3,583	92.7	1,745	45.1	1,131	29.3	2,653	68.6	941	24.3	449	11.6	397	10.3	212	5.5	877	22.7	333	8.6	178	4.6
CENSUS DIVISION 1, NEW ENGLAND	172	140	81.4	87	50.6	44	25.6	122	70.9	31	18.0	12	7.0	16	9.3	10	5.8	29	16.9	19	11.0	9	5.2
Connecticut	30	22	73.3	15	50.0	9	30.0	21	70.0	11	36.7	3	10.0	3	10.0	3	10.0	2	6.7	1	3.3	1	3.3
Maine	32	30	93.8	16	50.0	5	15.6	22	68.8	4	12.5	4	12.5	3	9.4	1	3.1	12	37.5	8	25.0	5	15.6
Massachusetts	64	47	73.4	36	56.3	22	34.4	44	68.8	11	17.2	4	6.3	6	9.4	4	6.3	5	7.8	2	3.1	2	3.1
New Hampshire	25	23	92.0	12	48.0	5	20.0	19	76.0	3	12.0	1	4.0	2	8.0	0	0.0	7	28.0	5	20.0	2	8.0
Rhode Island	10	8	80.0	2	20.0	2	20.0	7	70.0	1	10.0	1	10.0	1	10.0	1	10.0	0	0.0	2	20.0	0	0.0
Vermont	11	10	90.9	6	54.5	1	9.1	9	81.8	1	9.1	0	0.0	1	9.1	1	9.1	3	27.3	1	9.1	1	9.1
CENSUS DIVISION 2, MIDDLE ATLANTIC	404	342	84.7	192	47.5	167	41.3	305	75.5	125	30.9	55	13.6	49	12.1	23	5.7	86	21.3	19	4.7	16	4.0
New Jersey	62	53	85.5	36	58.1	28	45.2	52	83.9	22	35.5	11	17.7	14	22.6	1	1.6	8	12.9	3	4.8	2	3.2
New York	142	134	94.4	89	62.7	76	53.5	122	85.9	56	39.4	19	13.4	27	19.0	10	7.0	41	28.9	8	5.6	7	4.9
Pennsylvania	200	155	77.5	67	33.5	63	31.5	131	65.5	47	23.5	25	12.5	8	4.0	12	6.0	37	18.5	8	4.0	7	3.5
CENSUS DIVISION 3, SOUTH ATLANTIC	671	557	83.0	270	40.2	204	30.4	484	72.1	158	23.5	103	15.4	73	10.9	60	8.9	138	20.6	60	8.9	42	6.3
Delaware	10	5	50.0	5	50.0	5	50.0	5	50.0	3	30.0	1	10.0	2	20.0	1	10.0	0	0.0	1	10.0	0	0.0
District of Columbia	11	6	54.5	4	36.4	6	54.5	7	63.6	6	54.5	2	18.2	2	18.2	2	18.2	4	36.4	3	27.3	3	27.3
Florida	180	149	82.8	60	33.3	72	40.0	136	75.6	50	27.8	31	17.2	32	17.8	20	11.1	26	14.4	15	8.3	10	5.6
Georgia	100	82	82.0	30	30.0	21	21.0	63	63.0	22	22.0	6	6.0	3	3.0	5	5.0	23	23.0	6	6.0	5	5.0
Maryland	44	39	88.6	31	70.5	15	34.1	38	86.4	15	34.1	6	13.6	4	9.1	4	9.1	7	15.9	0	0.0	1	2.3
North Carolina	108	100	92.6	48	44.4	29	26.9	87	80.6	24	22.2	17	15.7	12	11.1	4	3.7	21	19.4	10	9.3	2	1.9
South Carolina	79	61	77.2	43	54.4	22	27.8	53	67.1	12	15.2	28	35.4	8	10.1	19	24.1	24	30.4	11	13.9	13	16.5
Virginia	84	70	83.3	28	33.3	20	23.8	63	75.0	21	25.0	8	9.5	7	8.3	2	2.4	17	20.2	7	8.3	6	6.0
West Virginia	55	45	81.8	21	38.2	14	25.5	32	58.2	5	9.1	4	7.3	3	5.5	3	5.5	16	29.1	7	12.7	3	5.5
CENSUS DIVISION 4, EAST NORTH CENTRAL	706	611	86.5	336	47.6	190	26.9	465	65.9	128	18.1	118	16.7	71	10.1	36	5.1	124	17.6	39	5.5	30	4.2
Illinois	165	151	91.5	89	53.9	37	22.4	119	72.1	30	18.2	15	9.1	21	12.7	6	3.6	40	24.2	9	5.5	9	5.5
Indiana	122	97	79.5	56	45.9	25	20.5	73	59.8	22	18.0	7	5.7	9	7.4	7	5.7	20	16.4	11	9.0	4	3.3
Michigan	130	114	87.7	50	38.5	32	24.6	90	69.2	24	16.9	19	14.6	12	9.2	6	4.6	28	21.5	8	6.2	8	6.2
Ohio	144	127	88.2	47	32.6	45	31.3	113	78.5	22	16.7	13	9.0	10	6.9	5	3.5	20	13.9	9	6.3	4	2.8
Wisconsin	145	122	84.1	94	64.8	51	35.2	70	48.3	30	20.7	64	44.1	19	13.1	12	8.3	16	11.0	2	1.4	5	3.4
CENSUS DIVISION 5, EAST SOUTH CENTRAL	367	305	83.1	138	37.6	93	25.3	199	54.2	56	15.3	32	8.7	28	7.6	29	7.9	63	17.2	17	4.6	11	3.0
Alabama	102	84	82.4	34	33.3	26	25.5	62	60.8	15	14.7	13	12.7	7	6.9	9	8.8	13	12.7	7	6.9	3	2.9
Kentucky	88	72	81.8	29	33.0	20	22.7	54	61.4	14	17.0	5	5.7	4	4.5	9	10.2	21	23.9	4	4.5	1	1.1
Mississippi	104	93	89.4	56	53.8	29	27.9	40	38.5	14	13.5	4	3.8	9	8.7	9	8.7	19	18.3	0	0.0	8	7.7
Tennessee	73	56	76.7	19	26.0	18	24.7	43	58.9	13	16.4	10	13.7	8	11.0	2	2.7	10	13.7	6	8.2	0	0.0
CENSUS DIVISION 6, WEST NORTH CENTRAL	637	587	92.2	272	42.7	128	20.1	302	47.4	85	13.3	48	7.5	46	7.2	33	5.2	258	40.5	119	18.7	56	8.8
Iowa	124	118	95.2	58	46.8	22	17.7	62	50.0	16	12.9	8	6.5	9	7.3	6	4.8	57	46.0	34	27.4	11	8.9
Kansas	143	133	93.0	44	30.8	17	11.9	49	34.3	13	9.1	8	5.6	9	6.3	6	4.2	57	39.9	41	28.7	13	9.1
Minnesota	105	103	98.1	48	45.7	23	21.9	58	55.2	12	11.4	7	6.7	6	5.7	3	2.9	41	39.0	6	5.7	6	5.7
Missouri	143	115	80.4	80	55.9	40	28.0	80	55.9	22	15.4	15	10.5	8	5.6	12	8.4	34	23.8	16	11.2	9	6.3
Nebraska	54	50	92.6	17	31.5	11	20.4	21	38.9	11	20.4	6	11.1	4	7.4	4	7.4	28	51.9	10	18.5	8	14.8
North Dakota	26	26	100.0	9	34.6	8	30.8	12	46.2	7	26.9	2	7.7	1	3.8	1	3.8	15	57.7	4	15.4	3	11.5
South Dakota	42	42	100.0	16	38.1	7	16.7	20	47.6	4	9.5	2	4.8	3	7.1	1	2.4	26	61.9	8	19.0	5	11.9
CENSUS DIVISION 7, WEST SOUTH CENTRAL	891	631	70.8	223	25.0	140	15.7	397	44.6	164	18.4	51	5.7	49	5.5	95	10.7	84	9.4	34	3.8	11	1.2
Arkansas	88	68	77.3	24	27.3	24	27.3	38	43.2	22	13.6	3	3.4	1	1.1	8	9.1	12	13.6	6	6.8	0	0.0
Louisiana	95	72	75.8	36	37.9	20	21.1	56	58.9	27	28.4	6	6.3	11	11.6	8	8.4	15	15.8	6	6.3	4	4.2
Oklahoma	116	96	82.8	31	26.7	17	14.7	48	41.4	11	9.5	6	5.2	5	4.3	6	5.2	22	19.0	8	6.9	4	3.4
Texas	592	395	66.7	132	22.3	79	13.3	255	43.1	114	19.3	36	6.1	32	5.4	74	12.5	35	5.9	14	2.4	4	0.7
CENSUS DIVISION 8, MOUNTAIN	319	289	90.6	117	36.7	52	16.3	181	56.7	67	21.0	18	5.6	21	6.6	13	4.1	70	21.9	23	7.2	20	6.3
Arizona	48	42	87.5	11	22.9	11	22.9	33	68.8	13	27.1	6	12.5	4	8.3	2	4.2	3	6.3	2	4.2	4	8.3
Colorado	72	68	94.4	29	40.3	14	19.4	47	65.3	27	37.5	5	6.9	6	8.3	3	4.2	13	18.1	6	8.3	6	8.3
Idaho	32	31	96.9	15	46.9	8	25.0	15	46.9	7	21.9	0	0.0	2	6.3	3	9.4	8	25.0	2	6.3	2	6.3
Montana	57	55	96.5	21	36.8	4	7.0	21	36.8	4	7.0	2	3.5	1	1.8	1	1.8	26	45.6	4	7.0	8	14.0
Nevada	26	16	61.5	4	15.4	3	11.5	17	65.4	7	26.9	2	7.7	4	15.4	2	7.7	4	15.4	1	3.8	0	0.0
New Mexico	29	27	93.1	12	41.4	4	13.8	14	48.3	7	24.1	0	0.0	2	6.9	1	3.4	3	10.3	2	6.9	0	0.0
Utah	35	31	88.6	16	45.7	7	20.0	19	54.3	2	5.7	3	8.6	1	2.9	1	2.9	7	20.0	4	11.4	2	5.7
Wyoming	20	19	95.0	9	45.0	1	5.0	15	75.0	0	0.0	0	0.0	1	5.0	0	0.0	6	30.0	2	10.0	3	15.0
CENSUS DIVISION 9, PACIFIC	423	375	88.7	164	38.8	141	33.3	324	76.6	146	34.5	35	8.3	57	13.5	26	6.1	96	22.7	32	7.6	19	4.5
Alaska	15	12	80.0	6	40.0	1	6.7	8	53.3	3	20.0	1	6.7	2	13.3	2	13.3	5	33.3	5	33.3	3	20.0
California	248	218	87.9	97	39.1	104	41.9	199	80.2	110	44.4	23	9.3	41	16.5	19	7.7	65	26.2	16	6.5	11	4.4
Hawaii	17	12	70.6	4	23.5	3	17.6	11	64.7	3	17.6	0	0.0	3	17.6	0	0.0	5	29.4	2	11.8	1	5.9
Oregon	62	61	98.4	24	38.7	16	25.8	52	83.9	11	17.7	6	9.7	5	8.1	2	3.2	9	14.5	7	11.3	1	1.6
Washington	81	72	88.9	33	40.7	17	21.0	54	66.7	19	23.5	5	6.2	6	7.4	3	3.7	12	14.8	2	2.5	3	3.7

Table 7 (Continued)

These data include only hospital-based facilities and services as reported by responding hospitals in Section C of the 2016 AHA Annual Survey, beginning on page 215. All hospitals are represented with Community Hospitals listed separately under United States. No estimates have been made for nonresponding hospitals. Definitions of facilities and services are listed in the Glossary, page 203.

CARDIOLOGY AND CARDIAC SERVICES

CLASSIFICATION	HOSPITALS REPORTING	ADULT CARDIOLOGY SERVICES		PEDIATRIC CARDIOLOGY SERVICES		ADULT DIAGNOSTIC CATHETERIZATION		PEDIATRIC DIAGNOSTIC CATHETERIZATION		ADULT INTERVENTIONAL CARDIAC CATHETERIZATION		PEDIATRIC INTERVENTIONAL CARDIAC CATHETERIZATION		ADULT CARDIAC SURGERY		PEDIATRIC CARDIAC SURGERY		ADULT CARDIAC ELECTRO-PHYSIOLOGY		PEDIATRIC CARDIAC ELECTRO-PHYSIOLOGY		CARDIAC REHABILITATION	
		Number	Percent	Number	Percent	Number	Percent	Number	Percent	Number	Percent	Number	Percent	Number	Percent	Number	Percent	Number	Percent	Number	Percent	Number	Percent
UNITED STATES	4,590	2,360	51.4	422	9.2	1,784	38.9	183	4.0	1,576	34.3	162	3.5	1,121	24.4	164	3.6	1,403	30.6	196	4.3	2,483	54.1
COMMUNITY HOSPITALS	3,865	2,249	58.2	412	10.7	1,710	44.2	180	4.7	1,513	39.1	159	4.1	1,072	27.7	159	4.1	1,347	34.9	190	4.9	2,406	62.3
CENSUS DIVISION 1, NEW ENGLAND	172	113	65.7	16	9.3	68	39.5	9	5.2	52	30.2	9	5.2	36	20.9	7	4.1	60	34.9	8	4.7	119	69.2
Connecticut	30	21	70.0	3	10.0	15	50.0	2	6.7	14	46.7	2	6.7	10	33.3	1	3.3	13	43.3	2	6.7	21	70.0
Maine	32	19	59.4	3	9.4	11	34.4	1	3.1	5	15.6	1	3.1	3	9.4	1	3.1	7	21.9	2	6.3	25	78.1
Massachusetts	64	44	68.8	6	9.4	27	42.2	3	4.7	21	32.8	3	4.7	18	28.1	3	4.7	27	42.2	3	4.7	43	67.2
New Hampshire	25	15	60.0	2	8.0	9	36.0	1	4.0	8	32.0	1	4.0	3	12.0	1	4.0	8	32.0	1	4.0	18	72.0
Rhode Island	10	7	70.0	1	10.0	5	50.0	1	10.0	3	30.0	1	10.0	1	10.0	0	0.0	4	40.0	0	0.0	4	40.0
Vermont	11	7	63.6	1	9.1	1	9.1	1	9.1	1	9.1	1	9.1	1	9.1	1	9.1	1	9.1	0	0.0	8	72.7
CENSUS DIVISION 2, MIDDLE ATLANTIC	404	284	70.3	73	18.1	205	50.7	23	5.7	175	43.3	20	5.0	121	30.0	18	4.5	159	39.4	28	6.9	239	59.2
New Jersey	62	50	80.6	19	30.6	46	74.2	2	3.2	38	61.3	2	3.2	15	24.2	2	3.2	20	32.3	3	4.8	41	66.1
New York	142	111	78.2	38	26.8	64	45.1	15	10.6	53	37.3	13	9.2	38	26.8	10	7.0	61	43.0	14	9.9	83	58.5
Pennsylvania	200	123	61.5	16	8.0	95	47.5	6	3.0	84	42.0	5	2.5	68	34.0	6	3.0	78	39.0	11	5.5	115	57.5
CENSUS DIVISION 3, SOUTH ATLANTIC	671	417	62.1	65	9.7	335	49.9	31	4.6	278	41.4	27	4.0	173	25.8	27	4.0	269	40.1	31	4.6	374	55.7
Delaware	10	7	70.0	1	10.0	6	60.0	1	10.0	6	60.0	1	10.0	5	50.0	1	10.0	5	50.0	1	10.0	5	50.0
District of Columbia	11	5	45.5	1	9.1	5	45.5	1	9.1	1	9.1	1	9.1	3	27.3	1	9.1	5	45.5	1	9.1	3	27.3
Florida	180	125	69.4	25	13.9	107	59.4	15	8.3	93	51.7	11	6.1	66	36.7	12	6.7	83	46.1	11	6.1	86	47.8
Georgia	100	53	53.0	2	2.0	44	44.0	0	0.0	37	37.0	0	0.0	16	16.0	0	0.0	36	36.0	1	1.0	45	45.0
Maryland	44	34	77.3	6	13.6	32	72.7	2	4.5	23	52.3	2	4.5	9	20.5	2	4.5	32	72.7	3	6.8	28	63.6
North Carolina	108	75	69.4	13	12.0	52	48.1	5	4.6	42	38.9	5	4.6	25	23.1	5	4.6	41	38.0	7	6.5	79	73.1
South Carolina	79	38	48.1	5	6.3	31	39.2	2	2.5	19	24.1	1	1.3	19	24.1	1	1.3	20	25.3	2	2.5	42	53.2
Virginia	84	54	64.3	9	10.7	40	47.6	4	4.8	40	47.6	5	6.0	22	26.2	4	4.8	38	45.2	4	4.8	60	71.4
West Virginia	55	26	47.3	3	5.5	18	32.7	1	1.8	15	27.3	1	1.8	8	14.5	1	1.8	9	16.4	1	1.8	26	47.3
CENSUS DIVISION 4, EAST NORTH CENTRAL	706	421	59.6	81	11.5	316	44.8	25	3.5	280	39.7	23	3.3	208	29.5	26	3.7	261	37.0	31	4.4	506	71.7
Illinois	165	117	70.9	33	20.0	87	52.7	7	4.2	84	50.9	8	4.8	64	38.8	10	6.1	74	44.8	12	7.3	129	78.2
Indiana	122	64	52.5	12	9.8	47	38.5	4	3.3	43	35.2	4	3.3	29	23.8	4	3.3	35	28.7	5	4.1	77	63.1
Michigan	130	73	56.2	14	10.8	57	43.8	4	3.1	45	34.6	3	2.3	33	25.4	4	3.1	50	38.5	5	3.8	93	71.5
Ohio	144	108	75.0	13	9.0	79	54.9	8	5.6	62	43.1	6	4.2	52	36.1	6	4.2	60	41.7	6	4.2	103	71.5
Wisconsin	145	59	40.7	9	6.2	46	31.7	2	1.4	46	31.7	2	1.4	30	20.7	2	1.4	42	29.0	4	2.8	104	71.7
CENSUS DIVISION 5, EAST SOUTH CENTRAL	367	156	42.5	22	6.0	128	34.9	15	4.1	103	28.1	10	2.7	79	21.5	13	3.5	74	20.2	12	3.3	150	40.9
Alabama	102	39	38.2	4	3.9	36	35.3	5	4.9	29	28.4	2	2.0	24	23.5	2	2.0	27	26.5	3	2.9	35	34.3
Kentucky	88	50	56.8	5	5.7	42	47.7	2	2.3	31	35.2	2	2.3	20	22.7	2	2.3	21	23.9	3	3.4	52	59.1
Mississippi	104	29	27.9	6	5.8	20	19.2	2	1.9	18	17.3	1	1.0	19	18.3	5	4.8	4	3.8	1	1.0	23	22.1
Tennessee	73	38	52.1	7	9.6	30	41.1	6	8.2	25	34.2	5	6.8	16	21.9	4	5.5	22	30.1	5	6.8	40	54.8
CENSUS DIVISION 6, WEST NORTH CENTRAL	637	240	37.7	39	6.1	150	23.5	16	2.5	147	23.1	14	2.2	95	14.9	16	2.5	125	19.6	20	3.1	471	73.9
Iowa	124	43	34.7	4	3.2	28	21.0	2	1.6	26	21.0	2	1.6	13	10.5	2	1.6	22	17.7	2	1.6	111	89.5
Kansas	143	35	24.5	9	6.3	23	16.1	2	1.4	24	16.8	1	0.7	15	10.5	1	0.7	14	13.3	3	2.1	73	51.0
Minnesota	105	45	42.9	10	9.5	20	19.0	4	3.8	19	18.1	3	2.9	15	14.3	3	2.9	21	20.0	5	4.8	94	89.5
Missouri	143	74	51.7	8	5.6	54	37.8	3	2.1	52	36.4	3	2.1	35	24.5	5	3.5	42	29.4	5	3.5	88	61.5
Nebraska	54	20	37.0	3	5.6	14	25.9	1	1.9	14	25.9	1	1.9	7	13.0	1	1.9	13	24.1	2	3.7	46	85.2
North Dakota	26	11	42.3	2	7.7	6	23.1	2	7.7	6	23.1	2	7.7	6	23.1	3	11.5	6	23.1	1	3.8	22	84.6
South Dakota	42	12	28.6	3	7.1	7	16.7	2	4.8	6	14.3	2	4.8	4	9.5	1	2.4	2	4.8	2	4.8	37	88.1
CENSUS DIVISION 7, WEST SOUTH CENTRAL	891	338	37.9	44	4.9	273	30.6	23	2.6	257	28.8	22	2.5	197	22.1	22	2.5	198	22.2	23	2.6	289	32.4
Arkansas	88	28	31.8	2	2.3	24	27.3	2	2.3	24	27.3	1	1.1	18	20.5	1	1.1	14	15.9	2	2.3	34	38.6
Louisiana	95	52	54.7	8	8.4	41	43.2	5	5.3	37	38.9	4	4.2	29	30.5	4	4.2	33	34.7	4	4.2	35	36.8
Oklahoma	116	46	39.7	3	2.6	30	25.9	2	1.7	29	25.0	2	1.7	15	12.9	2	1.7	17	14.7	2	1.7	34	29.3
Texas	592	212	35.8	31	5.2	178	30.1	14	2.4	167	28.2	15	2.5	135	22.8	15	2.5	134	22.6	15	2.5	186	31.4
CENSUS DIVISION 8, MOUNTAIN	319	138	43.3	26	8.2	107	33.5	12	3.8	104	32.6	12	3.8	65	20.4	10	3.1	86	27.0	15	4.7	154	48.3
Arizona	48	29	60.4	6	12.5	27	56.3	3	4.2	27	56.3	3	4.2	19	39.6	2	4.2	20	41.7	3	6.3	23	47.9
Colorado	72	44	61.1	6	8.3	35	48.6	3	4.2	33	45.8	3	4.2	18	25.0	2	2.8	27	37.5	5	6.9	47	65.3
Idaho	32	12	37.5	3	9.4	9	28.1	1	3.1	9	28.1	1	3.1	4	12.5	1	3.1	8	25.0	1	3.1	13	40.6
Montana	57	10	17.5	3	5.3	8	14.0	0	0.0	8	14.0	0	0.0	6	10.5	0	0.0	5	14.0	2	3.5	28	49.1
Nevada	26	12	46.2	3	11.5	9	34.6	1	3.8	8	30.8	1	3.8	5	19.2	1	3.8	5	19.2	1	3.8	8	30.8
New Mexico	29	12	41.4	3	10.3	8	27.6	3	10.3	8	27.6	2	6.9	4	13.8	2	6.9	7	24.1	2	6.9	10	34.5
Utah	35	13	37.1	2	5.7	8	22.9	2	5.7	8	22.9	2	5.7	6	17.1	2	5.7	7	20.0	1	2.9	12	34.3
Wyoming	20	6	30.0	0	0.0	3	15.0	0	0.0	3	15.0	0	0.0	3	15.0	0	0.0	4	20.0	0	0.0	13	65.0
CENSUS DIVISION 9, PACIFIC	423	253	59.8	56	13.2	202	47.8	29	6.9	180	42.6	25	5.9	147	34.8	25	5.9	171	40.4	28	6.6	181	42.8
Alaska	15	6	40.0	2	13.3	3	20.0	1	6.7	3	20.0	0	0.0	1	6.7	1	6.7	1	6.7	0	0.0	6	40.0
California	248	162	65.3	38	15.3	129	52.0	15	6.0	117	47.2	15	6.0	104	41.9	15	6.0	114	46.0	18	7.3	108	43.5
Hawaii	17	9	52.9	3	17.6	7	41.2	3	17.6	7	41.2	2	11.8	6	35.3	2	11.8	8	47.1	2	11.8	5	29.4
Oregon	62	31	50.0	6	9.7	25	40.3	5	8.1	20	32.3	3	4.8	17	27.4	3	4.8	22	35.5	4	6.5	28	45.2
Washington	81	45	55.6	7	8.6	38	46.9	5	6.2	33	40.7	5	6.2	19	23.5	4	4.9	26	32.1	4	4.9	34	42.0

Table 7 (Continued)

These data include only hospital-based facilities and services as reported by responding hospitals in Section C of the 2016 AHA Annual Survey, beginning on page 215. All hospitals are represented with Community Hospitals listed separately under United States. No estimates have been made for nonresponding hospitals. Definitions of facilities and services are listed in the Glossary, page 203.

Facilities and Services

CLASSIFICATION	HOSPITALS REPORTING	EMERGENCY DEPARTMENT — Number	EMERGENCY DEPARTMENT — Percent	PEDIATRIC EMERGENCY DEPARTMENT — Number	PEDIATRIC EMERGENCY DEPARTMENT — Percent	FREESTANDING/SATELLITE EMERGENCY DEPARTMENT — Number	FREESTANDING/SATELLITE EMERGENCY DEPARTMENT — Percent	TRAUMA CENTER (CERTIFIED) — Number	TRAUMA CENTER (CERTIFIED) — Percent	ENDOSCOPIC ULTRASOUND — Number	ENDOSCOPIC ULTRASOUND — Percent	ABLATION OF BARRETT'S ESOPHAGUS — Number	ABLATION OF BARRETT'S ESOPHAGUS — Percent	ESOPHAGEAL IMPEDANCE STUDY — Number	ESOPHAGEAL IMPEDANCE STUDY — Percent	ENDOSCOPIC RETROGRADE CHOLANGIO-PANCREATOGRAPHY — Number	ENDOSCOPIC RETROGRADE CHOLANGIO-PANCREATOGRAPHY — Percent	OPTICAL COLONOSCOPY — Number	OPTICAL COLONOSCOPY — Percent
UNITED STATES	4,590	3,769	82.1	897	19.5	340	7.4	1,713	37.3	1,636	35.6	1,212	26.4	1,133	24.7	1,940	42.3	3,037	66.2
COMMUNITY HOSPITALS	3,865	3,551	91.9	869	22.5	325	8.4	1,688	43.7	1,563	40.4	1,155	29.9	1,082	28.0	1,862	48.2	2,879	74.5
CENSUS DIVISION 1, NEW ENGLAND	172	140	81.4	45	26.2	19	11.0	53	30.8	73	42.4	58	33.7	58	33.7	89	51.7	124	72.1
Connecticut	30	23	76.7	8	26.7	5	16.7	11	36.7	16	53.3	13	43.3	14	46.7	20	66.7	20	66.7
Maine	32	30	93.8	6	18.8	5	15.6	12	37.5	12	37.5	6	18.8	7	21.9	8	25.0	27	84.4
Massachusetts	64	46	71.9	19	29.7	5	7.8	15	23.4	27	42.2	21	32.8	21	32.8	36	56.3	40	62.5
New Hampshire	25	23	92.0	10	40.0	4	16.0	11	44.0	11	44.0	11	44.0	8	32.0	13	52.0	21	84.0
Rhode Island	10	8	80.0	1	10.0	0	0.0	1	10.0	5	50.0	4	40.0	4	40.0	7	70.0	7	70.0
Vermont	11	10	90.9	1	9.1	0	0.0	3	27.3	2	18.2	3	27.3	4	36.4	5	45.5	9	81.8
CENSUS DIVISION 2, MIDDLE ATLANTIC	404	323	80.0	118	29.2	30	7.4	117	29.0	216	53.5	153	37.9	135	33.4	263	65.1	294	72.8
New Jersey	62	51	82.3	36	58.1	10	16.1	21	33.9	42	67.7	34	54.8	30	48.4	48	77.4	43	69.4
New York	142	128	90.1	60	42.3	13	9.2	54	38.0	83	58.5	67	47.2	50	35.2	100	70.4	120	84.5
Pennsylvania	200	144	72.0	22	11.0	7	3.5	42	21.0	91	45.5	52	26.0	55	27.5	115	57.5	131	65.5
CENSUS DIVISION 3, SOUTH ATLANTIC	671	541	80.6	141	21.0	62	9.2	149	22.2	270	40.2	215	32.0	218	32.5	370	55.1	473	70.5
Delaware	10	6	60.0	4	40.0	2	20.0	6	60.0	3	30.0	4	40.0	4	40.0	6	60.0	6	60.0
District of Columbia	11	6	54.5	3	27.3	1	9.1	4	36.4	7	63.6	5	45.5	6	54.5	6	54.5	7	63.6
Florida	180	147	81.7	51	28.3	20	11.1	30	16.7	80	44.4	68	37.8	63	35.0	119	66.1	131	72.8
Georgia	100	80	80.0	11	11.0	0	0.0	17	17.0	36	36.0	28	28.0	28	28.0	51	51.0	69	69.0
Maryland	44	37	84.1	19	43.2	4	9.1	13	29.5	26	59.1	15	34.1	18	40.9	30	68.2	32	72.7
North Carolina	108	97	89.8	16	14.8	15	13.9	19	17.6	42	38.9	36	33.3	38	35.2	61	56.5	87	80.6
South Carolina	79	56	70.9	6	7.6	3	3.8	18	22.8	22	27.8	15	19.0	16	20.3	30	38.0	39	49.4
Virginia	84	70	83.3	26	31.0	16	19.0	15	17.9	39	46.4	30	35.7	30	35.7	45	53.6	65	77.4
West Virginia	55	42	76.4	5	9.1	1	1.8	27	49.1	15	27.3	14	25.5	15	27.3	22	40.0	37	67.3
CENSUS DIVISION 4, EAST NORTH CENTRAL	706	603	85.4	147	20.8	60	8.5	281	39.8	272	38.5	226	32.0	206	29.2	330	46.7	504	71.4
Illinois	165	153	92.7	44	26.7	9	5.5	62	37.6	77	46.7	63	38.2	50	30.3	101	61.2	134	81.2
Indiana	122	95	77.9	17	13.9	5	4.1	23	18.9	42	34.4	37	30.3	26	21.3	52	42.6	84	68.9
Michigan	130	110	84.6	28	21.5	14	10.8	52	40.0	56	43.1	36	27.7	35	26.9	60	46.2	100	76.9
Ohio	144	124	86.1	31	21.5	27	18.8	45	31.3	62	43.1	50	34.7	57	39.6	70	48.6	102	70.8
Wisconsin	145	121	83.4	27	18.6	5	3.4	99	68.3	35	24.1	40	27.6	38	26.2	47	32.4	84	57.9
CENSUS DIVISION 5, EAST SOUTH CENTRAL	367	292	79.6	45	12.3	18	4.9	137	37.3	87	23.7	74	20.2	75	20.4	119	32.4	184	50.1
Alabama	102	83	81.4	8	7.8	3	2.9	36	35.3	25	24.5	18	17.6	20	19.6	32	31.4	49	48.0
Kentucky	88	74	84.1	8	9.1	9	10.2	19	21.6	25	28.4	23	26.1	19	21.6	40	45.5	54	61.4
Mississippi	104	81	77.9	13	12.5	3	2.9	70	67.3	15	14.4	12	11.5	14	13.5	19	18.3	36	34.6
Tennessee	73	54	74.0	16	21.9	3	4.1	12	16.4	22	30.1	21	28.8	22	30.1	28	38.4	45	61.6
CENSUS DIVISION 6, WEST NORTH CENTRAL	637	573	90.0	102	16.0	27	4.2	309	48.5	150	23.5	109	17.1	105	16.5	143	22.4	450	70.6
Iowa	124	117	94.4	17	13.7	2	1.6	94	75.8	32	25.8	19	15.3	15	12.1	21	16.9	99	79.8
Kansas	143	125	87.4	17	11.9	3	2.1	34	23.8	18	12.6	20	14.0	19	13.3	22	15.4	94	65.7
Minnesota	105	101	96.2	19	18.1	6	5.7	74	70.5	31	29.5	20	19.0	17	16.2	25	23.8	79	75.2
Missouri	143	111	77.6	21	14.7	7	4.9	33	23.1	38	26.6	31	21.7	31	21.7	50	35.0	88	61.5
Nebraska	54	51	94.4	17	31.5	4	7.4	29	53.7	16	29.6	10	18.5	12	22.2	13	24.1	40	74.1
North Dakota	26	26	100.0	3	11.5	2	7.7	17	65.4	7	26.9	3	11.5	5	19.2	6	23.1	22	84.6
South Dakota	42	42	100.0	8	19.0	3	7.1	28	66.7	8	19.0	6	14.3	6	14.3	6	14.3	28	66.7
CENSUS DIVISION 7, WEST SOUTH CENTRAL	891	654	73.4	108	12.1	69	7.7	347	38.9	222	24.9	151	16.9	132	14.8	271	30.4	474	53.2
Arkansas	88	68	77.3	9	10.2	3	3.4	46	52.3	23	26.1	9	10.2	15	17.0	20	22.7	58	65.9
Louisiana	95	67	70.5	16	16.8	6	6.3	11	11.6	35	36.8	20	21.1	21	22.1	31	32.6	53	55.8
Oklahoma	116	102	87.9	11	9.5	3	2.6	52	44.8	19	16.4	22	19.0	15	12.9	30	25.9	72	62.1
Texas	592	417	70.4	72	12.2	57	9.6	238	40.2	145	24.5	100	16.9	81	13.7	190	32.1	291	49.2
CENSUS DIVISION 8, MOUNTAIN	319	277	86.8	71	22.3	36	11.3	150	47.0	117	36.7	74	23.2	78	24.5	112	35.1	211	66.1
Arizona	48	39	81.3	14	29.2	4	8.3	17	35.4	30	62.5	22	45.8	15	31.3	28	58.3	33	68.8
Colorado	72	68	94.4	16	22.2	18	25.0	58	80.6	30	41.7	17	23.6	24	33.3	36	50.0	56	77.8
Idaho	32	28	87.5	10	31.3	3	9.4	8	25.0	10	31.3	9	28.1	8	25.0	8	25.0	23	71.9
Montana	57	53	93.0	11	19.3	4	7.0	29	50.9	9	15.8	5	8.8	6	10.5	9	15.8	27	47.4
Nevada	26	16	61.5	4	15.4	1	3.8	2	7.7	9	34.6	6	23.1	3	11.5	5	19.2	12	46.2
New Mexico	29	25	86.2	4	13.8	3	10.3	7	24.1	10	34.5	6	20.7	7	24.1	9	31.0	21	72.4
Utah	35	29	82.9	8	22.9	3	8.6	16	45.7	14	40.0	8	22.9	11	31.4	15	42.9	25	71.4
Wyoming	20	19	95.0	4	20.0	0	0.0	13	65.0	5	25.0	1	5.0	4	20.0	2	10.0	14	70.0
CENSUS DIVISION 9, PACIFIC	423	366	86.5	120	28.4	19	4.5	170	40.2	229	54.1	152	35.9	126	29.8	243	57.4	323	76.4
Alaska	15	12	80.0	3	20.0	1	6.7	7	46.7	6	40.0	4	26.7	5	33.3	4	26.7	12	80.0
California	248	207	83.5	78	31.5	10	4.0	65	26.2	145	58.5	98	39.5	82	33.1	171	69.0	186	75.0
Hawaii	17	14	82.4	4	23.5	1	5.9	7	41.2	7	41.2	5	29.4	4	23.5	8	47.1	10	58.8
Oregon	62	60	96.8	9	14.5	1	1.6	40	64.5	35	56.5	21	33.9	12	19.4	21	33.9	50	80.6
Washington	81	73	90.1	26	32.1	6	7.4	51	63.0	36	44.4	24	29.6	23	28.4	39	48.1	65	80.2

Table 7 (Continued)

These data include only hospital-based facilities and services as reported by responding hospitals in Section C of the 2016 AHA Annual Survey, beginning on page 215. All hospitals are represented with Community Hospitals listed separately under United States. No estimates have been made for nonresponding hospitals. Definitions of facilities and services are listed in the Glossary, page 203.

Header groups: PHYSICAL REHABILITATION SERVICES (Assistive Technology Center, Electro-Diagnostic Services, Physical Rehabilitation Outpatient Services, Prosthetic Orthotic Services, Robot Assisted Walking Therapy, Simulated Rehabilitation Environment); PSYCHIATRIC SERVICES (Child/Adolescent Services, Consultation/Liaison Services, Education Services, Emergency Services, Geriatric Services)

CLASSIFICATION	HOSPITALS REPORTING	Assistive Technology Center No.	%	Electro-Diagnostic Services No.	%	Physical Rehab Outpatient Services No.	%	Prosthetic Orthotic Services No.	%	Robot Assisted Walking Therapy No.	%	Simulated Rehab Environment No.	%	Child/Adolescent Services No.	%	Consultation/Liaison Services No.	%	Education Services No.	%	Emergency Services No.	%	Geriatric Services No.	%
UNITED STATES	4,590	1,177	25.6	1,263	27.5	3,292	71.7	883	19.2	206	4.5	1,355	29.5	856	18.6	1,574	34.3	1,180	25.7	1,567	34.1	1,439	31.4
COMMUNITY HOSPITALS	3,865	1,038	26.9	1,201	31.1	3,113	80.5	796	20.6	195	5.0	1,238	32.0	645	16.7	1,337	34.6	910	23.5	1,367	35.4	1,159	30.0
CENSUS DIVISION 1, NEW ENGLAND	172	48	27.9	63	36.6	151	87.8	44	25.6	9	5.2	65	37.8	65	37.8	103	59.9	74	43.0	89	51.7	76	44.2
Connecticut	30	11	36.7	13	43.3	24	80.0	10	33.3	4	13.3	14	46.7	16	53.3	22	73.3	17	56.7	23	76.7	19	63.3
Maine	32	8	25.0	9	28.1	28	87.5	5	15.6	1	3.1	15	46.9	9	28.1	11	34.4	8	25.0	11	34.4	8	25.0
Massachusetts	64	16	25.0	23	35.9	58	90.6	14	21.9	3	4.7	19	29.7	23	35.9	43	67.2	32	50.0	31	48.4	28	43.8
New Hampshire	25	9	36.0	9	36.0	24	96.0	8	32.0	0	0.0	10	40.0	9	36.0	14	56.0	9	36.0	14	56.0	9	36.0
Rhode Island	10	2	20.0	4	40.0	7	70.0	4	40.0	0	0.0	2	20.0	4	40.0	7	70.0	4	40.0	5	50.0	6	60.0
Vermont	11	2	18.2	5	45.5	10	90.9	3	27.3	1	9.1	5	45.5	4	36.4	6	54.5	4	36.4	5	45.5	6	54.5
CENSUS DIVISION 2, MIDDLE ATLANTIC	404	137	33.9	200	49.5	316	78.2	122	30.2	30	7.4	173	42.8	131	32.4	242	59.9	161	39.9	216	53.5	199	49.3
New Jersey	62	27	43.5	35	56.5	50	80.6	25	40.3	4	6.5	33	53.2	26	41.9	44	71.0	35	56.5	42	67.7	33	53.2
New York	142	49	34.5	77	54.2	131	92.3	55	38.7	10	7.0	60	42.3	62	43.7	98	69.0	63	44.4	87	61.3	79	55.6
Pennsylvania	200	61	30.5	88	44.0	135	67.5	42	21.0	16	8.0	80	40.0	43	21.5	100	50.0	63	31.5	87	43.5	87	43.5
CENSUS DIVISION 3, SOUTH ATLANTIC	671	187	27.9	201	30.0	481	71.7	182	27.1	36	5.4	203	30.3	120	17.9	259	38.6	185	27.6	272	40.5	215	32.0
Delaware	10	1	10.0	2	20.0	6	60.0	3	30.0	0	0.0	3	30.0	5	50.0	6	60.0	5	50.0	6	60.0	5	50.0
District of Columbia	11	6	54.5	5	45.5	8	72.7	6	54.5	1	9.1	5	45.5	4	36.4	5	45.5	3	27.3	4	36.4	4	36.4
Florida	180	62	34.4	55	30.6	140	77.8	40	22.2	15	8.3	55	30.6	28	15.6	65	36.1	40	22.2	65	36.1	48	26.7
Georgia	100	12	12.0	14	14.0	68	68.0	13	13.0	1	1.0	20	20.0	9	9.0	32	32.0	20	20.0	26	26.0	23	23.0
Maryland	44	12	27.3	23	52.3	36	81.8	16	36.4	3	6.8	18	40.9	17	38.6	31	70.5	26	59.1	33	75.0	27	61.4
North Carolina	108	36	33.3	41	38.0	91	84.3	19	17.6	4	3.7	39	36.1	18	16.7	41	38.0	35	32.4	51	47.2	40	37.0
South Carolina	79	8	10.1	9	11.4	31	39.2	50	63.3	5	6.3	16	20.3	13	16.5	23	29.1	15	19.0	32	40.5	21	26.6
Virginia	84	43	51.2	35	41.7	65	77.4	25	29.8	6	7.1	37	44.0	16	19.0	41	48.8	25	29.8	40	47.6	31	36.9
West Virginia	55	7	12.7	17	30.9	36	65.5	10	18.2	1	1.8	10	18.2	10	18.2	15	27.3	16	29.1	15	27.3	16	29.1
CENSUS DIVISION 4, EAST NORTH CENTRAL	706	189	26.8	269	38.1	565	80.0	166	23.5	27	3.8	284	40.2	154	21.8	299	42.4	233	33.0	274	38.8	259	36.7
Illinois	165	44	26.7	70	42.4	137	83.0	41	24.8	6	3.6	66	40.0	50	30.3	79	47.9	74	44.8	79	47.9	80	48.5
Indiana	122	34	27.9	36	29.5	89	73.0	29	23.8	4	3.3	40	32.8	23	18.9	32	26.2	28	23.0	34	27.9	38	31.1
Michigan	130	42	32.3	58	44.6	109	83.8	26	20.0	8	6.2	57	43.8	21	16.2	67	51.5	49	37.7	60	46.2	45	34.6
Ohio	144	51	35.4	67	46.5	117	81.3	34	23.6	7	4.9	65	45.1	25	17.4	65	45.1	44	30.6	57	39.6	49	34.0
Wisconsin	145	18	12.4	38	26.2	113	77.9	36	24.8	2	1.4	56	38.6	35	24.1	56	38.6	38	26.2	44	30.3	47	32.4
CENSUS DIVISION 5, EAST SOUTH CENTRAL	367	76	20.7	69	18.8	236	64.3	44	12.0	18	4.9	71	19.3	44	12.0	89	24.3	80	21.8	93	25.3	133	36.2
Alabama	102	17	16.7	20	19.6	65	63.7	13	12.7	7	6.9	13	12.7	13	12.7	26	25.5	24	23.5	26	25.5	37	36.3
Kentucky	88	28	31.8	21	23.9	63	71.6	9	10.2	6	6.8	19	21.6	10	11.4	27	30.7	21	23.9	27	30.7	24	27.3
Mississippi	104	9	8.7	14	13.5	58	55.8	11	10.6	3	2.9	20	19.2	9	8.7	20	19.2	18	17.3	17	16.3	43	41.3
Tennessee	73	22	30.1	14	19.2	50	68.5	11	15.1	2	2.7	19	26.0	12	16.4	16	21.9	17	23.3	23	31.5	29	39.7
CENSUS DIVISION 6, WEST NORTH CENTRAL	637	117	18.4	131	20.6	513	80.5	106	16.6	19	3.0	164	25.7	119	18.7	159	25.0	132	20.7	179	28.1	171	26.8
Iowa	124	30	24.2	22	17.7	103	83.1	15	12.1	4	3.2	35	28.2	31	25.0	34	27.4	34	27.4	47	37.9	38	30.6
Kansas	143	15	10.5	18	12.6	115	80.4	13	9.1	5	3.5	25	17.5	9	6.3	14	9.8	11	7.7	24	16.8	22	15.4
Minnesota	105	22	21.0	24	22.9	93	88.6	19	18.1	3	2.9	35	33.3	29	27.6	41	39.0	27	25.7	32	30.5	31	29.5
Missouri	143	18	12.6	35	24.5	100	69.9	33	23.1	6	4.2	46	32.2	26	18.2	46	32.2	39	27.3	52	36.4	54	37.8
Nebraska	54	12	22.2	14	25.9	41	75.9	13	24.1	1	1.9	12	22.2	11	20.4	10	18.5	8	14.8	8	14.8	11	20.4
North Dakota	26	8	30.8	7	26.9	23	88.5	6	23.1	0	0.0	6	23.1	7	26.9	6	23.1	6	23.1	7	26.9	7	26.9
South Dakota	42	12	28.6	11	26.2	38	90.5	7	16.7	0	0.0	5	11.9	6	14.3	8	19.0	7	16.7	9	21.4	8	19.0
CENSUS DIVISION 7, WEST SOUTH CENTRAL	891	213	23.9	110	12.3	498	55.9	86	9.7	32	3.6	192	21.5	97	10.9	161	18.1	145	16.3	188	21.1	215	24.1
Arkansas	88	16	18.2	11	12.5	55	62.5	8	9.1	5	5.7	20	22.7	11	12.5	17	19.3	12	13.6	24	27.3	28	31.8
Louisiana	95	31	32.6	13	13.7	56	58.9	13	13.7	2	2.1	26	27.4	9	9.5	20	21.1	22	23.2	34	35.8	32	33.7
Oklahoma	116	29	25.0	18	15.5	74	63.8	15	12.9	1	0.9	18	15.5	11	9.5	28	24.1	17	14.7	27	23.3	30	25.9
Texas	592	137	23.1	68	11.5	313	52.9	50	8.4	24	4.1	128	21.6	66	11.1	96	16.2	94	15.9	103	17.4	125	21.1
CENSUS DIVISION 8, MOUNTAIN	319	89	27.9	80	25.1	234	73.4	53	16.6	14	4.4	86	27.0	56	17.6	100	31.3	71	22.3	107	33.5	78	24.5
Arizona	48	13	27.1	19	39.6	29	60.4	11	22.9	2	4.4	19	39.6	4	8.3	26	54.2	11	22.9	18	37.5	16	33.3
Colorado	72	23	31.9	23	31.9	63	87.5	15	20.8	4	5.6	26	36.1	12	16.7	24	33.3	18	25.0	25	34.7	13	18.1
Idaho	32	10	31.3	4	12.5	23	71.9	2	6.3	1	3.1	10	31.3	3	9.4	5	15.6	7	21.9	8	25.0	5	15.6
Montana	57	17	29.8	12	21.1	47	82.5	8	14.0	0	0.0	7	12.3	11	19.3	11	19.3	10	17.5	16	28.1	10	17.5
Nevada	26	5	19.2	4	15.4	14	53.8	3	11.5	4	15.4	6	23.1	6	23.1	4	15.4	6	23.1	8	30.8	8	30.8
New Mexico	29	9	31.0	6	20.7	20	69.0	2	6.9	0	0.0	5	17.2	6	20.7	11	37.9	5	17.2	10	34.5	10	34.5
Utah	35	9	25.7	10	28.6	23	65.7	8	22.9	2	5.7	9	25.7	9	25.7	15	42.9	11	31.4	17	48.6	10	28.6
Wyoming	20	3	15.0	2	10.0	15	75.0	4	20.0	1	5.0	4	20.0	5	25.0	4	20.0	3	15.0	5	25.0	5	25.0
CENSUS DIVISION 9, PACIFIC	423	121	28.6	140	33.1	298	70.4	80	18.9	21	5.0	117	27.7	70	16.5	162	38.3	99	23.4	149	35.2	93	22.0
Alaska	15	3	20.0	3	20.0	12	80.0	5	33.3	0	0.0	2	13.3	6	40.0	8	53.3	6	40.0	8	53.3	3	20.0
California	248	68	27.4	81	32.7	165	66.5	47	19.0	14	5.6	73	29.4	39	15.7	102	41.1	63	25.4	82	33.1	64	25.8
Hawaii	17	6	35.3	6	35.3	11	64.7	4	23.5	1	5.9	3	17.6	5	29.4	6	35.3	4	23.5	4	23.5	4	23.5
Oregon	62	22	35.5	21	33.9	52	83.9	8	12.9	2	3.2	10	16.1	9	14.5	21	33.9	9	14.5	27	43.5	10	16.1
Washington	81	22	27.2	29	35.8	58	71.6	16	19.8	4	4.9	29	35.8	11	13.6	25	30.9	17	21.0	28	34.6	12	14.8

Table 7 (Continued)

These data include only hospital-based facilities and services as reported by responding hospitals in Section C of the 2016 AHA Annual Survey, beginning on page 215. All hospitals are represented with Community Hospitals listed separately under United States. No estimates have been made for nonresponding hospitals. Definitions of facilities and services are listed in the Glossary, page 203.

CLASSIFICATION	HOSPITALS REPORTING	OUTPATIENT SERVICES (Number)	(Percent)	PARTIAL HOSPITALIZATION PROGRAM (Number)	(Percent)	RESIDENTIAL TREATMENT (Number)	(Percent)	CT SCANNER (Number)	(Percent)	DIAGNOSTIC RADIOISOTOPE FACILITY (Number)	(Percent)	ELECTRON BEAM COMPUTED TOMOGRAPHY (EBCT) (Number)	(Percent)	FULL-FIELD DIGITAL MAMMOGRAPHY (FFDM) (Number)	(Percent)	MAGNETIC RESONANCE IMAGING (MRI) (Number)	(Percent)	INTRAOPERATIVE MAGNETIC IMAGING (Number)	(Percent)	MAGNETO-ENCEPHALOGRAPHY (Number)	(Percent)	MULTI-SLICE SPIRAL COMPUTED TOMOGRAPHY (<64 SLICE CT) (Number)	(Percent)
UNITED STATES	4,590	1,343	29.3	701	15.3	283	6.2	3,821	83.2	2,566	55.9	358	7.8	2,697	58.8	3,051	66.5	225	4.9	129	2.8	2,525	55.0
COMMUNITY HOSPITALS	3,865	1,097	28.4	514	13.3	142	3.7	3,580	92.6	2,463	63.7	337	8.7	2,525	67.9	2,870	74.3	213	5.5	120	3.1	2,392	61.9
CENSUS DIVISION 1, NEW ENGLAND	172	97	56.4	52	30.2	13	7.6	143	83.1	122	70.9	11	6.4	124	72.1	114	66.3	8	4.7	6	3.5	96	55.8
Connecticut	30	23	76.7	16	53.3	5	16.7	24	80.0	21	70.0	3	10.0	21	70.0	22	73.3	2	6.7	0	0.0	17	56.7
Maine	32	13	40.6	6	18.8	0	0.0	30	93.8	27	84.4	1	3.1	25	78.1	22	68.8	0	0.0	0	0.0	17	53.1
Massachusetts	64	36	56.3	21	32.8	5	7.8	48	75.0	44	68.8	5	7.8	43	67.2	38	59.4	5	7.8	4	6.3	32	50.0
New Hampshire	25	13	52.0	3	12.0	0	0.0	23	92.0	15	60.0	1	4.0	20	80.0	15	60.0	1	4.0	2	8.0	16	64.0
Rhode Island	10	5	50.0	4	40.0	1	10.0	8	80.0	8	80.0	0	0.0	7	70.0	8	80.0	0	0.0	0	0.0	7	70.0
Vermont	11	7	63.6	2	18.2	2	18.2	10	90.9	8	72.7	1	9.1	8	72.7	9	81.8	0	0.0	0	0.0	7	63.6
CENSUS DIVISION 2, MIDDLE ATLANTIC	404	172	42.6	83	20.5	31	7.7	341	84.4	299	74.0	57	14.1	286	70.8	305	75.5	26	6.4	14	3.5	241	59.7
New Jersey	62	32	51.6	21	33.9	6	9.7	52	83.9	50	80.6	14	22.6	44	71.0	49	79.0	5	8.1	5	8.1	46	74.2
New York	142	80	56.3	30	21.1	10	7.0	135	95.1	111	78.2	19	13.4	117	82.4	112	78.9	11	7.7	3	2.1	94	66.2
Pennsylvania	200	60	30.0	32	16.0	15	7.5	154	77.0	138	69.0	24	12.0	125	62.5	144	72.0	10	5.0	6	3.0	101	50.5
CENSUS DIVISION 3, SOUTH ATLANTIC	671	181	27.0	114	17.0	49	7.3	562	83.8	439	65.3	64	9.5	434	64.7	492	73.3	29	4.3	18	2.7	435	64.8
Delaware	10	6	60.0	2	20.0	1	10.0	6	60.0	5	50.0	1	10.0	4	40.0	6	60.0	1	10.0	1	10.0	5	50.0
District of Columbia	11	6	54.5	3	27.3	1	9.1	7	63.6	5	45.5	3	27.3	6	54.5	7	63.6	2	18.2	1	9.1	6	54.5
Florida	180	39	21.7	27	15.0	12	6.7	155	86.1	123	68.3	34	18.9	118	65.6	138	76.7	13	7.2	7	3.9	129	71.7
Georgia	100	23	23.0	13	13.0	5	5.0	81	81.0	56	56.0	2	2.0	68	68.0	73	73.0	1	1.0	1	1.0	57	57.0
Maryland	44	26	59.1	22	50.0	4	9.1	39	88.6	36	81.8	3	6.8	25	56.8	33	75.0	3	6.8	1	2.3	30	68.2
North Carolina	108	28	25.9	15	13.9	5	4.6	101	93.5	75	69.4	9	8.3	75	69.4	89	82.4	4	3.7	4	3.7	82	75.9
South Carolina	79	15	19.0	11	13.9	6	7.6	58	73.4	44	55.7	2	2.5	48	60.8	54	68.4	1	1.3	2	2.5	47	59.5
Virginia	84	27	32.1	16	19.0	10	11.9	71	84.5	59	70.2	7	8.3	56	66.7	63	75.0	3	3.6	1	1.2	48	57.1
West Virginia	55	11	20.0	5	9.1	5	9.1	44	80.0	35	63.6	3	5.5	34	61.8	29	52.7	1	1.8	0	0.0	31	56.4
CENSUS DIVISION 4, EAST NORTH CENTRAL	706	251	35.6	137	19.4	49	6.9	618	87.5	467	66.1	59	8.4	490	69.4	525	74.4	41	5.8	20	2.8	379	53.7
Illinois	165	78	47.3	40	24.2	8	4.8	155	93.9	114	69.1	6	3.6	129	78.2	124	75.2	8	4.8	2	1.2	103	62.4
Indiana	122	33	27.0	18	14.8	12	9.8	98	80.3	68	55.7	12	9.8	80	65.6	91	74.6	7	5.7	5	4.1	68	55.7
Michigan	130	41	31.5	21	16.2	8	6.2	114	87.7	95	73.1	8	6.2	92	70.8	93	71.5	5	3.8	4	3.1	69	53.1
Ohio	144	51	35.4	35	24.3	8	5.6	131	91.0	108	75.0	18	12.5	101	70.1	119	82.6	10	6.9	6	4.2	96	66.7
Wisconsin	145	48	33.1	23	15.9	13	9.0	120	82.8	82	56.6	15	10.3	88	60.7	98	67.6	11	7.6	3	2.1	43	29.7
CENSUS DIVISION 5, EAST SOUTH CENTRAL	367	88	24.0	50	13.6	30	8.2	290	79.0	197	53.7	30	8.2	183	49.9	230	62.7	20	5.4	12	3.3	186	50.7
Alabama	102	20	19.6	11	10.8	3	2.9	84	82.4	55	53.9	5	4.9	46	45.1	67	65.7	2	2.0	4	3.9	58	56.9
Kentucky	88	20	22.7	15	17.0	5	5.7	72	81.8	54	61.4	5	5.7	53	60.2	66	75.0	4	4.5	3	3.4	47	53.4
Mississippi	104	29	27.9	12	11.5	18	17.3	82	78.8	48	46.2	12	11.5	38	36.5	48	46.2	8	7.7	3	2.9	41	39.4
Tennessee	73	19	26.0	12	16.4	4	5.5	52	71.2	40	54.8	8	11.0	46	63.0	49	67.1	6	8.2	2	2.7	40	54.8
CENSUS DIVISION 6, WEST NORTH CENTRAL	637	182	28.6	59	9.3	31	4.9	571	89.6	252	39.6	21	3.3	381	59.8	389	61.1	29	4.6	14	2.2	350	54.9
Iowa	124	40	32.3	12	9.7	5	4.0	115	92.7	44	35.5	5	4.0	95	76.6	75	60.5	1	0.8	2	1.6	80	64.5
Kansas	143	17	11.9	5	3.5	5	3.5	122	85.3	48	33.6	5	3.5	57	39.9	63	44.1	6	4.2	2	1.4	75	52.4
Minnesota	105	42	40.0	16	15.2	7	6.7	102	97.1	43	41.0	3	2.9	75	71.4	77	73.3	9	8.6	3	2.9	66	62.9
Missouri	143	51	35.7	13	9.1	11	7.7	113	79.0	73	51.0	6	4.2	79	55.2	105	73.4	7	4.9	4	2.8	55	38.5
Nebraska	54	14	25.9	6	11.1	2	3.7	53	98.1	20	37.0	1	1.9	42	77.8	36	66.7	4	7.4	2	3.7	33	61.1
North Dakota	26	7	26.9	5	19.2	1	3.8	25	96.2	11	42.3	1	3.8	14	53.8	15	57.7	2	7.7	1	3.8	12	46.2
South Dakota	42	11	26.2	2	4.8	0	0.0	41	97.6	13	31.0	0	0.0	19	45.2	18	42.9	0	0.0	0	0.0	28	66.7
CENSUS DIVISION 7, WEST SOUTH CENTRAL	891	167	18.7	95	10.7	38	4.3	648	72.7	355	39.8	42	4.7	353	39.6	472	53.0	32	3.6	16	1.8	420	47.1
Arkansas	88	19	21.6	8	9.1	6	6.8	69	78.4	36	40.9	5	5.7	41	46.6	56	63.6	4	4.5	2	2.3	39	44.3
Louisiana	95	29	30.5	19	20.0	4	4.2	69	72.6	49	51.6	8	8.4	56	58.9	57	60.0	6	6.3	1	1.1	49	51.6
Oklahoma	116	18	15.5	6	5.2	13	11.2	97	83.6	45	38.8	4	3.4	52	44.8	70	60.3	1	0.9	0	0.0	63	54.3
Texas	592	101	17.1	62	10.5	15	2.5	413	69.8	225	38.0	25	4.2	204	34.5	289	48.8	21	3.5	13	2.2	269	45.4
CENSUS DIVISION 8, MOUNTAIN	319	83	26.0	47	14.7	21	6.6	273	85.6	161	50.5	33	10.3	215	67.4	215	67.4	18	5.6	9	2.8	168	52.7
Arizona	48	15	31.6	5	10.4	1	2.1	40	83.3	31	64.6	6	12.5	37	77.1	37	77.1	3	6.3	2	4.2	31	64.6
Colorado	72	17	23.6	10	13.9	5	6.9	68	94.4	45	62.5	9	12.5	58	80.6	58	80.6	8	11.1	3	4.2	44	61.1
Idaho	32	8	25.0	3	9.4	2	6.3	30	93.8	15	46.9	1	3.1	19	59.4	26	81.3	1	3.1	1	3.1	18	56.3
Montana	57	13	22.8	8	14.0	2	3.5	45	78.9	18	31.6	2	3.5	30	52.6	26	45.6	0	0.0	0	0.0	31	54.4
Nevada	26	9	34.6	6	23.1	3	11.5	16	61.5	13	50.0	3	11.5	10	38.5	16	61.5	0	0.0	0	0.0	7	26.9
New Mexico	29	8	27.6	2	6.9	2	6.9	25	86.2	13	44.8	3	10.3	18	62.1	16	55.2	4	13.8	1	3.4	13	44.8
Utah	35	9	25.7	9	25.7	4	11.4	30	85.7	18	51.4	3	8.6	24	68.6	26	74.3	2	5.7	2	5.7	18	51.4
Wyoming	20	4	20.0	4	20.0	2	10.0	19	95.0	8	40.0	2	10.0	12	60.0	12	60.0	0	0.0	0	0.0	6	30.0
CENSUS DIVISION 9, PACIFIC	423	122	28.8	64	15.1	21	5.0	375	88.7	274	64.8	41	9.7	261	61.7	309	73.0	22	5.2	20	4.7	250	59.1
Alaska	15	4	26.7	3	20.0	3	20.0	13	86.7	5	33.3	1	6.7	8	53.3	8	53.3	0	0.0	0	0.0	6	40.0
California	248	77	31.0	41	16.5	13	3.2	214	86.3	167	67.3	26	10.5	145	58.5	186	75.0	16	6.5	16	6.5	149	60.1
Hawaii	17	5	29.4	3	17.6	2	11.8	13	76.5	12	70.6	1	5.9	11	64.7	11	64.7	0	0.0	0	0.0	6	35.3
Oregon	62	14	22.6	6	9.7	2	3.2	60	96.8	40	64.5	4	6.5	47	75.8	47	75.8	5	8.1	1	1.6	38	61.3
Washington	81	22	27.2	11	13.6	6	7.4	75	92.6	50	61.7	9	11.1	47	58.0	57	70.4	1	1.2	3	3.7	51	63.0

Table 7 (Continued)

These data include only hospital-based facilities and services as reported by responding hospitals in Section C of the 2016 AHA Annual Survey, beginning on page 215. All hospitals are represented with Community Hospitals listed separately under United States. No estimates have been made for nonresponding hospitals. Definitions of facilities and services are listed in the Glossary, page 203.

CLASSIFICATION	HOSPITALS REPORTING	MULTI-SLICE SPIRAL CT (64+ SLICE CT) Number	Percent	POSITRON EMISSION TOMOGRAPHY (PET) Number	Percent	POSITRON EMISSION TOMOGRAPHY/CT (PET/CT) Number	Percent	SINGLE PHOTON EMISSION COMPUTERIZED TOMOGRAPHY (SPECT) Number	Percent	ULTRASOUND Number	Percent	IMAGE-GUIDED RADIATION THERAPY (IGRT) Number	Percent	INTENSITY-MODULATED RADIATION THERAPY (IMRT) Number	Percent	PROTON BEAM THERAPY Number	Percent	SHAPED BEAM RADIATION SYSTEM Number	Percent	STEREOTACTIC RADIOSURGERY Number	Percent
UNITED STATES	4,590	2,460	53.6	788	17.2	1,022	22.3	1,707	37.2	3,709	80.8	1,095	23.9	1,154	25.1	121	2.6	932	20.3	922	20.1
COMMUNITY HOSPITALS	3,865	2,348	60.8	750	19.4	978	25.3	1,639	42.4	3,476	89.9	1,058	27.4	1,119	29.0	112	2.9	902	23.3	897	23.2
CENSUS DIVISION 1, NEW ENGLAND	172	111	64.5	37	21.5	52	30.2	92	53.5	150	87.2	57	33.1	57	33.1	3	1.7	52	30.2	48	27.9
Connecticut	30	22	73.3	11	36.7	17	56.7	19	63.3	26	86.7	18	60.0	17	56.7	1	3.3	16	53.3	14	46.7
Maine	32	19	59.4	3	9.4	6	18.8	14	43.8	30	93.8	5	15.6	6	18.8	0	0.0	5	15.6	4	12.5
Massachusetts	64	46	71.9	15	23.4	20	31.3	32	50.0	53	82.8	24	37.5	24	37.5	2	3.1	21	32.8	21	32.8
New Hampshire	25	15	60.0	4	16.0	5	20.0	14	56.0	23	92.0	6	24.0	6	24.0	0	0.0	6	24.0	6	24.0
Rhode Island	10	5	50.0	2	20.0	1	10.0	6	60.0	8	80.0	1	10.0	1	10.0	0	0.0	1	10.0	1	10.0
Vermont	11	4	36.4	2	18.2	3	27.3	7	63.6	10	90.9	3	27.3	3	27.3	0	0.0	3	27.3	2	18.2
CENSUS DIVISION 2, MIDDLE ATLANTIC	404	267	66.1	104	25.7	139	34.4	224	55.4	342	84.7	157	38.9	169	41.8	18	4.5	137	33.9	126	31.2
New Jersey	62	42	67.7	22	35.5	31	50.0	39	62.9	53	85.5	33	53.2	35	56.5	2	3.2	34	54.8	27	43.5
New York	142	105	73.9	38	26.8	45	31.7	81	57.0	135	95.1	57	40.1	62	43.7	11	7.7	51	35.9	43	30.3
Pennsylvania	200	120	60.0	44	22.0	63	31.5	104	52.0	154	77.0	67	33.5	72	36.0	5	2.5	52	26.0	56	28.0
CENSUS DIVISION 3, SOUTH ATLANTIC	671	407	60.7	129	19.2	170	25.3	310	46.2	561	83.6	203	30.3	213	31.7	12	1.8	170	25.3	159	23.7
Delaware	10	6	60.0	4	40.0	5	50.0	5	50.0	8	60.0	4	40.0	4	40.0	0	0.0	4	40.0	3	30.0
District of Columbia	11	7	63.6	6	54.5	5	45.5	6	54.5	8	72.7	4	36.4	4	36.4	0	0.0	4	36.4	4	36.4
Florida	180	118	65.6	46	25.6	55	30.6	72	40.0	152	84.4	48	26.7	46	25.6	1	0.6	40	22.2	53	29.4
Georgia	100	54	54.0	17	17.0	27	27.0	35	35.0	84	84.0	29	29.0	28	28.0	1	1.0	25	25.0	25	25.0
Maryland	44	34	77.3	8	18.2	11	25.0	29	65.9	38	86.4	23	52.3	24	54.5	3	6.8	15	34.1	15	34.1
North Carolina	108	67	62.0	16	14.8	26	24.1	62	57.4	99	91.7	41	38.0	44	40.7	5	4.6	37	34.3	22	20.4
South Carolina	79	40	50.6	5	6.3	11	13.9	24	30.4	60	75.9	11	13.9	15	19.0	0	0.0	10	12.7	9	11.4
Virginia	84	56	66.7	18	21.4	21	25.0	55	65.5	71	84.5	34	40.5	37	44.0	2	2.4	25	29.8	18	21.4
West Virginia	55	25	45.5	9	16.4	9	16.4	22	40.0	43	78.2	9	16.4	11	20.0	0	0.0	10	18.2	10	18.2
CENSUS DIVISION 4, EAST NORTH CENTRAL	706	461	65.3	157	22.2	203	28.8	331	46.9	603	85.4	209	29.6	224	31.7	22	3.1	183	25.9	172	24.4
Illinois	165	120	72.7	34	20.6	52	31.5	77	46.7	149	90.3	52	31.5	58	35.2	4	2.4	45	27.3	50	30.3
Indiana	122	71	58.2	20	16.4	23	18.9	44	36.1	96	78.7	39	32.0	40	32.8	5	4.1	29	23.8	24	19.7
Michigan	130	91	70.0	26	20.0	37	28.5	61	46.9	118	90.8	37	28.5	41	31.5	3	2.3	38	29.2	35	26.9
Ohio	144	96	66.7	44	30.6	57	39.6	83	57.6	129	89.6	47	32.6	46	31.9	6	4.2	40	27.8	39	27.1
Wisconsin	145	83	57.2	33	22.8	34	23.4	66	45.5	111	76.6	34	23.4	39	26.9	4	2.8	31	21.4	24	16.6
CENSUS DIVISION 5, EAST SOUTH CENTRAL	367	161	43.9	56	15.3	68	18.5	129	35.1	292	79.6	62	16.9	70	19.1	5	1.4	52	14.2	67	18.3
Alabama	102	39	38.2	15	14.7	20	19.6	27	26.5	83	81.4	13	12.7	14	13.7	0	0.0	9	8.8	14	13.7
Kentucky	88	50	56.8	13	14.8	18	20.5	38	43.2	73	83.0	17	19.3	18	20.5	3	3.4	13	14.8	19	21.6
Mississippi	104	33	31.7	16	15.4	12	11.5	31	29.8	82	78.8	11	10.6	11	10.6	1	1.0	9	8.7	11	10.6
Tennessee	73	39	53.4	12	16.4	18	24.7	33	45.2	54	74.0	21	28.8	27	37.0	1	1.4	21	28.8	23	31.5
CENSUS DIVISION 6, WEST NORTH CENTRAL	637	282	44.3	65	10.2	113	17.7	175	27.5	519	81.5	112	17.6	117	18.4	16	2.5	88	13.8	82	12.9
Iowa	124	59	47.6	11	8.9	20	16.1	35	28.2	115	92.7	17	13.7	16	12.9	1	0.8	16	12.9	14	11.3
Kansas	143	36	25.2	7	4.9	12	8.4	21	14.7	103	72.0	15	10.5	16	11.2	3	2.1	14	9.8	11	7.7
Minnesota	105	62	59.0	12	11.4	19	18.1	38	36.2	90	85.7	19	18.1	23	21.9	3	2.9	15	10.5	15	14.3
Missouri	143	78	54.5	19	13.3	42	29.4	54	37.8	108	75.5	36	25.2	38	26.6	5	3.5	28	19.6	22	15.4
Nebraska	54	23	42.6	7	13.0	10	18.5	11	20.4	48	88.9	14	25.9	12	22.2	3	5.6	11	20.4	11	20.4
North Dakota	26	12	46.2	4	15.4	6	23.1	7	26.9	21	80.8	5	19.2	5	19.2	1	3.8	4	15.4	5	19.2
South Dakota	42	12	28.6	5	11.9	4	9.5	9	21.4	34	81.0	6	14.3	7	16.7	0	0.0	4	9.5	4	9.5
CENSUS DIVISION 7, WEST SOUTH CENTRAL	891	329	36.9	83	9.3	102	11.4	190	21.3	599	67.2	93	10.4	103	11.6	11	1.2	79	8.9	105	11.8
Arkansas	88	36	40.9	9	10.2	11	12.5	19	21.6	64	72.7	9	10.2	8	9.1	1	1.1	6	6.8	11	12.5
Louisiana	95	41	43.2	16	16.8	23	24.2	25	26.3	67	70.5	20	21.1	20	21.1	3	3.2	15	15.8	21	22.1
Oklahoma	116	46	39.7	13	11.2	19	16.4	25	21.6	87	75.0	16	13.8	18	15.5	0	0.0	15	12.9	12	10.3
Texas	592	206	34.8	45	7.6	49	8.3	121	20.4	381	64.4	48	8.1	57	9.6	7	1.2	43	7.3	61	10.3
CENSUS DIVISION 8, MOUNTAIN	319	187	58.6	57	17.9	56	17.6	85	26.6	270	84.6	69	21.6	73	22.6	17	5.3	61	19.1	52	16.3
Arizona	48	29	60.4	10	20.8	12	25.0	22	45.8	40	83.3	12	25.0	13	27.1	3	6.3	11	22.9	12	25.0
Colorado	72	54	75.0	19	26.4	18	25.0	21	29.2	68	94.4	22	30.6	22	30.6	5	6.9	20	27.8	13	18.1
Idaho	32	16	50.0	4	12.5	4	12.5	7	21.9	30	93.8	5	15.6	6	18.8	2	6.3	4	12.5	7	21.9
Montana	57	19	33.3	7	12.3	7	12.3	10	17.5	44	77.2	11	19.3	10	17.5	2	3.5	8	14.0	9	15.8
Nevada	26	12	46.2	3	11.5	3	11.5	4	15.4	16	61.5	2	7.7	2	7.7	0	0.0	2	7.7	2	7.7
New Mexico	29	20	69.0	3	10.3	2	6.9	7	24.1	23	79.3	5	17.2	7	24.1	3	10.3	5	17.2	2	6.9
Utah	35	23	65.7	8	22.9	8	22.9	9	25.7	30	85.7	8	22.9	8	22.9			8	22.9	4	11.4
Wyoming	20	14	70.0	3	15.0	2	10.0	5	25.0	19	95.0	5	25.0	4	20.0	2	10.0	3	15.0	3	15.0
CENSUS DIVISION 9, PACIFIC	423	255	60.3	100	23.6	119	28.1	171	40.4	373	88.2	133	31.4	129	30.5	17	4.0	110	26.0	111	26.2
Alaska	15	8	53.3	0	0.0	0	0.0	1	6.7	12	80.0	4	26.7	2	13.3	0	0.0	1	6.7	1	6.7
California	248	154	62.1	68	27.4	83	33.5	110	44.4	220	88.7	88	35.5	85	34.3	11	4.4	74	29.8	76	30.6
Hawaii	17	11	64.7	1	5.9	3	17.6	4	23.5	13	76.5	4	23.5	4	23.5	0	0.0	2	11.8	2	11.8
Oregon	62	38	61.3	12	19.4	12	19.4	31	50.0	59	95.2	15	24.2	15	24.2	3	4.8	13	21.0	10	16.1
Washington	81	44	54.3	19	23.5	21	25.9	25	30.9	69	85.2	22	27.2	23	28.4	3	3.7	20	24.7	22	27.2

Table 7 (Continued)

These data include only hospital-based facilities and services as reported by responding hospitals in Section C of the 2016 AHA Annual Survey, beginning on page 215. All hospitals are represented with Community Hospitals listed separately under United States. No estimates have been made for nonresponding hospitals. Definitions of facilities and services are listed in the Glossary, page 203.

| | | TRANSPLANT | | | | | | | | | | | | | |
| | | BONE MARROW | | HEART | | KIDNEY | | LIVER | | LUNG | | TISSUE | | OTHER | |
CLASSIFICATION	HOSPITALS REPORTING	Number	Percent	Number	Percent	Number	Percent	Number	Percent	Number	Percent	Number	Percent	Number	Percent
UNITED STATES	4,590	201	4.4	137	3.0	222	4.8	135	2.9	75	1.6	430	9.4	240	5.2
COMMUNITY HOSPITALS	3,865	192	5.0	131	3.4	215	5.6	130	3.4	72	1.9	407	10.5	229	5.9
CENSUS DIVISION 1, NEW ENGLAND	172	12	7.0	6	3.5	15	8.7	7	4.1	3	1.7	18	10.5	11	6.4
Connecticut	30	1	3.3	2	6.7	2	6.7	2	6.7	0	0.0	3	10.0	1	3.3
Maine	32	0	0.0	0	0.0	1	3.1	0	0.0	0	0.0	1	3.1	0	0.0
Massachusetts	64	9	14.1	4	6.3	9	14.1	5	7.8	0	0.0	9	14.1	7	10.9
New Hampshire	25	1	4.0	0	0.0	1	4.0	0	0.0	0	0.0	1	4.0	1	4.0
Rhode Island	10	0	0.0	0	0.0	1	10.0	0	0.0	0	0.0	1	10.0	1	10.0
Vermont	11	1	9.1	0	0.0	1	9.1	0	0.0	0	0.0	3	27.3	1	9.1
CENSUS DIVISION 2, MIDDLE ATLANTIC	404	32	7.9	16	4.0	34	8.4	20	5.0	7	1.7	81	20.0	42	10.4
New Jersey	62	2	3.2	2	3.2	4	6.5	2	3.2	1	1.6	22	35.5	5	8.1
New York	142	15	10.6	5	3.5	12	8.5	6	4.2	1	0.7	27	19.0	17	12.0
Pennsylvania	200	15	7.5	9	4.5	18	9.0	12	6.0	5	2.5	32	16.0	20	10.0
CENSUS DIVISION 3, SOUTH ATLANTIC	671	38	5.7	26	3.9	30	4.5	21	3.1	14	2.1	80	11.9	43	6.4
Delaware	10	2	20.0	1	10.0	2	20.0	1	10.0	0	0.0	0	0.0	0	0.0
District of Columbia	11	3	27.3	2	18.2	3	27.3	1	9.1	0	0.0	3	27.3	2	18.2
Florida	180	11	6.1	8	4.4	8	4.4	7	3.9	5	2.8	19	10.6	7	3.9
Georgia	100	3	3.0	2	2.0	2	2.0	2	2.0	1	1.0	8	8.0	3	3.0
Maryland	44	4	9.1	2	4.5	2	4.5	2	4.5	2	4.5	6	13.6	7	15.9
North Carolina	108	5	4.6	5	4.6	6	5.6	5	4.6	3	2.8	16	14.8	12	11.1
South Carolina	79	4	5.1	1	1.3	1	1.3	1	1.3	2	2.4	5	6.3	3	3.8
Virginia	84	5	6.0	5	6.0	5	6.0	2	2.4	2	2.4	18	21.4	7	8.3
West Virginia	55	1	1.8	0	0.0	1	1.8	0	0.0	0	0.0	5	9.1	2	3.6
CENSUS DIVISION 4, EAST NORTH CENTRAL	706	32	4.5	25	3.5	35	5.0	21	3.0	19	2.7	77	10.9	29	4.1
Illinois	165	10	6.1	6	3.6	9	5.5	6	3.6	4	2.4	19	11.5	8	4.8
Indiana	122	3	2.5	3	2.5	3	2.5	1	0.8	1	0.8	8	6.6	5	4.1
Michigan	130	7	5.4	6	4.6	10	7.7	6	4.6	5	3.8	23	17.7	7	5.4
Ohio	144	7	4.9	6	4.2	9	6.3	5	3.5	5	3.5	21	14.6	6	4.2
Wisconsin	145	5	3.4	4	2.8	4	2.8	3	2.1	4	2.8	6	4.1	3	2.1
CENSUS DIVISION 5, EAST SOUTH CENTRAL	367	14	3.8	10	2.7	10	2.7	7	1.9	4	1.1	23	6.3	18	4.9
Alabama	102	2	2.0	2	2.0	2	2.0	2	2.0	1	1.0	4	3.9	4	3.9
Kentucky	88	4	4.5	3	3.4	3	3.4	2	2.3	2	2.3	9	10.2	3	3.4
Mississippi	104	1	1.0	1	1.0	1	1.0	1	1.0	0	0.0	0	0.0	1	1.0
Tennessee	73	7	9.6	4	5.5	4	5.5	2	2.7	1	1.4	10	13.7	10	13.7
CENSUS DIVISION 6, WEST NORTH CENTRAL	637	17	2.7	12	1.9	23	3.6	12	1.9	7	1.1	32	5.0	25	3.9
Iowa	124	1	0.8	1	0.8	4	3.2	1	0.8	1	0.8	2	1.6	4	3.2
Kansas	143	2	1.4	0	0.0	1	0.7	1	0.7	0	0.0	3	2.1	2	1.4
Minnesota	105	4	3.8	3	2.9	4	3.8	2	1.9	2	1.9	8	7.6	3	2.9
Missouri	143	5	3.5	5	3.5	8	5.6	6	4.2	2	1.4	10	7.0	10	7.0
Nebraska	54	3	5.6	2	3.7	1	1.9	1	1.9	1	1.9	5	9.3	2	3.7
North Dakota	26	1	3.8	1	3.8	3	11.5	1	3.8	1	3.8	2	7.7	2	7.7
South Dakota	42	1	2.4	0	0.0	2	4.8	0	0.0	0	0.0	2	4.8	2	4.8
CENSUS DIVISION 7, WEST SOUTH CENTRAL	891	19	2.1	16	1.8	34	3.8	18	2.0	9	1.0	38	4.3	29	3.3
Arkansas	88	2	2.3	2	2.3	3	3.4	1	1.1	1	1.1	3	3.4	1	1.1
Louisiana	95	2	2.1	1	1.1	3	3.2	3	3.2	1	1.1	6	6.3	5	5.3
Oklahoma	116	3	2.6	1	0.9	4	3.4	1	0.9	1	0.9	5	4.3	4	3.4
Texas	592	12	2.0	12	2.0	24	4.1	13	2.2	7	1.2	24	4.1	19	3.2
CENSUS DIVISION 8, MOUNTAIN	319	11	3.4	8	2.5	13	4.1	11	3.4	4	1.3	23	7.2	8	2.5
Arizona	48	3	6.3	2	4.2	4	8.3	4	8.3	2	4.2	7	14.6	2	4.2
Colorado	72	3	4.2	2	2.8	4	5.6	4	5.6	1	1.4	9	12.5	3	4.2
Idaho	32	1	3.1	0	0.0	0	0.0	0	0.0	0	0.0	1	3.1	0	0.0
Montana	57	0	0.0	0	0.0	0	0.0	0	0.0	0	0.0	0	0.0	0	0.0
Nevada	26	0	0.0	0	0.0	0	0.0	0	0.0	0	0.0	0	0.0	0	0.0
New Mexico	29	1	3.4	0	0.0	2	6.9	0	0.0	0	0.0	2	6.9	0	0.0
Utah	35	3	8.6	4	11.4	3	8.6	3	8.6	1	2.9	3	8.6	3	8.6
Wyoming	20	0	0.0	0	0.0	0	0.0	0	0.0	0	0.0	0	0.0	0	0.0
CENSUS DIVISION 9, PACIFIC	423	26	6.1	18	4.3	28	6.6	18	4.3	8	1.9	58	13.7	35	8.3
Alaska	15	0	0.0	0	0.0	0	0.0	0	0.0	0	0.0	1	6.7	1	6.7
California	248	18	7.3	14	5.6	19	7.7	12	4.8	7	2.8	43	17.3	24	9.7
Hawaii	17	1	5.9	1	5.9	1	5.9	1	5.9	0	0.0	0	0.0	0	0.0
Oregon	62	2	3.2	1	1.6	3	4.8	2	3.2	0	0.0	6	9.7	4	6.5
Washington	81	5	6.2	3	3.7	5	6.2	3	3.7	1	1.2	8	9.9	6	7.4

Table 8

MSAs

Metropolitan Statistical Areas

Metropolitan Statistical Areas (MSAs) definitions announced by the U.S. Office of Management and Budget (OMB) effective June 6, 2003 were added with the 2006 edition.

According to the OMB, an MSA is a geographical designation that represents an integrated social and economic unit with a large population nucleus. Under these standards, an area qualifies for recognition as an MSA if there is a city within the area of at least 50,000 with a total metropolitan population of at least 100,000. MSAs are defined as entire counties. In addition to the county containing the main city, an MSA also includes additional counties having strong economic and social ties to the central county. Such counties must have a specified level of commuting to the central counties and must meet certain standards regarding metropolitan character, such as population density.

When an MSA encompasses two or more central cities, up to three cities may be specified in the MSA title. They will be listed in order of population size. When a single central city exists, the MSA is named for that particular city. A MSA may extend beyond a single state.

An MSA containing a single core with a population of 2.5 million or more may be subdivided to form smaller groupings of counties referred to as Metropolitan Divisions. Where they exist the Metropolitan Divisions are shown in this table rather than the entire MSA.

TABLE 8

U.S. CENSUS DIVISION 1, NEW ENGLAND

U.S. Community Hospitals
(Nonfederal, short-term general and other special hospitals)

2016 Utilization, Personnel and Finances

MSAs

CLASSIFICATION	Hospitals	Beds	Admissions	Inpatient Days	Adjusted Inpatient Days	Average Daily Census	Adjusted Average Daily Census	Average Stay (days)	Surgical Operations	NEWBORNS Bassinets	NEWBORNS Births	OUTPATIENT VISITS Emergency	OUTPATIENT VISITS Total
UNITED STATES	4,840	780,272	33,424,253	182,291,689	386,210,917	499,407	1,056,009	5.5	27,227,227	55,149	3,727,427	142,557,879	747,089,013
Nonmetropolitan	1,825	111,987	3,103,592	20,547,750	68,564,794	56,294	187,486	6.6	3,578,377	9,181	371,659	22,118,524	126,900,302
Metropolitan	3,015	668,285	30,320,661	161,743,939	317,646,123	443,113	868,523	5.3	23,648,850	45,968	3,355,768	120,439,355	620,188,711
CENSUS DIVISION 1, NEW ENGLAND	194	32,623	1,567,105	8,350,338	20,352,635	22,877	55,630	5.3	1,372,626	2,300	145,980	7,187,817	48,625,131
Nonmetropolitan	55	3,397	138,071	826,261	2,831,296	2,262	7,739	6.0	153,844	358	12,484	913,832	7,998,875
Metropolitan	139	29,226	1,429,034	7,524,077	17,521,339	20,615	47,891	5.3	1,218,782	1,942	133,496	6,273,985	40,626,256
Connecticut	32	7,278	375,154	1,951,522	4,210,086	5,345	11,506	5.2	331,636	444	36,478	1,671,516	9,315,825
Nonmetropolitan	2	150	8,768	39,191	103,946	107	284	4.5	7,197	7	816	56,481	359,364
Metropolitan	30	7,128	366,386	1,912,331	4,106,140	5,238	11,222	5.2	324,439	437	35,662	1,615,035	8,956,461
Bridgeport-Stamford-Norwalk	6	1,774	88,675	450,243	1,011,757	1,233	2,765	5.1	72,198	126	11,754	377,930	2,004,557
Hartford-West Hartford-East Hartford	11	2,604	129,238	691,596	1,384,995	1,895	3,785	5.4	118,440	133	11,732	626,786	2,984,705
New Haven-Milford	9	2,194	119,706	649,918	1,325,107	1,780	3,623	5.4	99,833	110	9,102	391,537	2,312,643
Norwich-New London	2	435	23,093	97,281	291,136	266	795	4.2	28,513	42	2,429	162,213	861,169
Worcester	2	121	5,674	23,293	93,145	64	254	4.1	5,455	26	645	56,569	793,387
Maine	34	3,397	135,281	851,357	2,335,107	2,332	6,383	6.3	149,498	272	12,524	678,948	5,950,144
Nonmetropolitan	21	1,153	39,034	277,875	972,745	761	2,660	7.1	46,265	150	4,081	316,785	2,698,004
Metropolitan	13	2,244	96,247	573,482	1,362,362	1,571	3,723	6.0	103,233	122	8,443	362,163	3,252,140
Bangor	4	501	24,746	132,194	309,064	362	844	5.3	29,853	20	1,841	78,644	702,397
Lewiston-Auburn	2	543	17,022	146,221	379,349	401	1,036	8.6	12,531	35	1,269	70,985	1,056,110
Portland-South Portland	7	1,200	54,479	295,067	673,949	808	1,843	5.4	60,849	67	5,333	212,534	1,493,633
Massachusetts	75	15,678	766,005	4,043,067	9,551,134	11,079	26,107	5.3	623,966	1,077	67,394	3,318,069	22,852,221
Nonmetropolitan	3	133	6,707	26,617	98,363	72	269	4.0	6,304	28	772	51,908	283,703
Metropolitan	72	15,545	759,298	4,016,450	9,452,771	11,007	25,838	5.3	617,662	1,049	66,622	3,266,161	22,568,518
Barnstable Town	3	414	22,050	105,935	298,286	290	815	4.8	14,458	18	1,218	119,805	876,635
Boston	26	6,440	316,109	1,809,037	3,867,398	4,957	10,572	5.7	275,385	343	25,470	1,024,377	8,948,061
Cambridge-Newton-Framingham	20	4,122	196,249	994,523	2,640,978	2,726	7,218	5.1	144,064	348	20,411	891,972	6,055,230
Pittsfield	2	300	15,075	67,216	215,272	184	588	4.5	13,973	24	915	84,099	209,656
Providence-Warwick	4	1,125	54,701	249,179	564,025	683	1,542	4.6	36,188	68	4,265	370,771	1,511,765
Springfield	8	1,552	72,024	372,004	863,851	1,019	2,361	5.2	59,658	94	6,095	343,498	2,328,667
Worcester	9	1,592	83,090	418,556	1,002,961	1,148	2,742	5.0	73,936	154	8,248	431,639	2,638,504
New Hampshire	28	2,792	124,840	654,451	1,980,443	1,795	5,412	5.2	120,960	265	13,017	653,672	5,242,847
Nonmetropolitan	17	1,235	56,205	309,510	1,054,579	849	2,881	5.5	62,781	98	4,246	259,127	2,936,789
Metropolitan	11	1,557	68,635	344,941	925,864	946	2,531	5.0	58,179	167	8,771	394,545	2,306,058
Manchester-Nashua	5	838	38,954	184,811	523,175	508	1,429	4.7	28,115	103	5,161	173,689	1,193,485
Rockingham County-Strafford County	6	719	29,681	160,130	402,689	438	1,102	5.4	30,064	64	3,610	220,856	1,112,573
Rhode Island	11	2,237	115,978	553,379	1,244,555	1,515	3,403	4.8	95,335	124	11,283	547,657	2,360,818
Metropolitan	11	2,237	115,978	553,379	1,244,555	1,515	3,403	4.8	95,335	124	11,283	547,657	2,360,818
Providence-Warwick	11	2,237	115,978	553,379	1,244,555	1,515	3,403	4.8	95,335	124	11,283	547,657	2,360,818
Vermont	14	1,241	49,847	296,562	1,031,310	811	2,819	5.9	51,231	118	5,284	317,955	2,903,276
Nonmetropolitan	12	726	27,357	173,068	601,663	473	1,645	6.3	31,297	75	2,569	229,531	1,721,015
Metropolitan	2	515	22,490	123,494	429,647	338	1,174	5.5	19,934	43	2,715	88,424	1,182,261
Burlington-South Burlington	2	515	22,490	123,494	429,647	338	1,174	5.5	19,934	43	2,715	88,424	1,182,261

TABLE 8   **U.S. CENSUS DIVISION 1, NEW ENGLAND**

U.S. Community Hospitals
(Nonfederal, short-term general and other special hospitals)

2016 Utilization, Personnel and Finances

FULL-TIME EQUIVALENT PERSONNEL					FULL-TIME EQUIV. TRAINEES			EXPENSES						
								LABOR				TOTAL		
Physicians and Dentists	Registered Nurses	Licensed Practical Nurses	Other Salaried Personnel	Total Personnel	Medical and Dental Residents	Other Trainees	Total Trainees	Payroll (in thousands)	Employee Benefits (in thousands)	Total (in thousands)	Percent of Total	Amount (in thousands)	Adjusted per Admission	Adjusted per Inpatient Day
135,693	1,478,657	74,344	2,612,576	4,991,775	113,111	9,619	122,730	$340,132,974	$90,463,641	$430,596,618	47.7	$902,891,035	$12,777.25	$2,337.82
15,408	149,651	20,977	339,776	612,547	1,714	261	1,975	35,531,908	9,378,885	44,910,794	50.2	89,420,776	8,694.35	1,304.18
120,285	1,329,006	53,367	2,272,800	4,379,228	111,397	9,358	120,755	304,601,066	81,084,755	385,685,824	47.4	813,470,258	13,472.72	2,560.93
14,670	72,554	2,386	173,570	293,757	10,080	1,291	11,371	21,449,567	5,665,058	27,114,623	48.8	55,525,755	14,207.31	2,728.19
1,768	7,908	573	21,420	35,553	401	20	421	2,620,399	655,479	3,275,880	54.9	5,963,934	12,375.03	2,106.43
12,902	64,646	1,813	152,150	258,204	9,679	1,271	10,950	18,829,167	5,009,578	23,838,743	48.1	49,561,822	14,465.03	2,828.65
1,517	15,631	296	31,167	55,469	2,135	86	2,221	4,176,689	1,120,425	5,297,114	46.5	11,386,587	13,656.62	2,704.60
12	279	13	575	961	1	0	1	94,010	22,240	116,250	52.5	221,461	9,465.78	2,130.54
1,505	15,352	283	30,592	54,508	2,134	86	2,220	4,082,679	1,098,185	5,180,864	46.4	11,165,126	13,777.61	2,719.13
431	3,692	36	6,746	12,832	519	41	560	1,030,595	269,927	1,300,522	46.3	2,807,489	13,995.81	2,774.87
751	5,025	105	12,442	20,297	208	43	251	1,434,228	359,176	1,793,405	47.2	3,798,308	14,260.7	2,742.47
224	5,819	114	8,292	16,985	1,407	2	1,409	1,291,953	361,047	1,653,000	44.0	3,755,236		2,833.91
43	616	1	1,845	2,751	0	0	0	250,299	83,500	333,799	54.4	614,120	8,927.85	2,109.39
56	200	27	1,267	1,643	0	0	0	75,604	24,534	100,138	52.7	189,972	8,349.70	2,039.53
1,801	7,236	326	19,756	32,294	319	24	343	2,219,740	571,371	2,791,109	52.8	5,281,350	14,165.27	2,261.72
559	2,417	158	7,482	11,867	9	5	14	738,903	182,204	921,107	53.0	1,736,674	12,059.48	1,785.33
1,242	4,819	168	12,274	20,427	310	19	329	1,480,837	389,167	1,870,002	52.8	3,544,676	15,490.50	2,601.86
358	1,270	39	2,487	4,580	28	18	46	380,690	101,764	482,454	51.4	937,848	15,990.58	3,034.48
243	725	51	1,791	3,141	21	0	21	233,058	43,662	276,720	48.1	575,292	13,841.77	1,516.52
641	2,824	78	7,996	12,706	261	1	262	867,088	243,741	1,110,828	54.7	2,031,537	15,795.24	3,014.38
8,468	35,523	1,087	88,447	147,339	6,165	1,087	7,252	10,480,894	2,765,657	13,246,552	46.9	28,226,013	15,041.99	2,955.25
17	241	10	643	1,014	1	2	3	90,867	19,686	110,554	50.2	220,344	8,535.50	2,240.11
8,451	35,282	1,077	87,804	146,325	6,164	1,085	7,249	10,390,027	2,745,971	13,135,998	46.9	28,005,669	15,132.75	2,962.69
77	553	13	1,667	2,472	0	0	0	271,348	68,282	339,629	51.3	662,333	10,272.55	2,220.46
5,279	18,207	424	47,486	77,999	4,600	958	5,558	5,392,693	1,461,608	6,854,301	43.8	15,655,141	22,745.44	4,047.98
1,548	7,868	308	19,691	32,609	470	67	537	2,285,041	584,244	2,869,286	52.8	5,438,066	9,834.27	2,059.11
83	633	81	1,543	2,729	76	7	83	223,512	59,940	283,453	58.2	487,032	10,023.93	2,262.41
41	1,897	39	4,183	6,786	9	1	10	524,293	142,908	667,200	53.8	1,239,234	9,958.33	2,197.13
463	2,784	63	5,374	10,384	365	33	398	724,714	160,531	885,244	47.4	1,867,213	11,168.28	2,161.50
960	3,340	149	7,860	13,346	644	19	663	968,425	268,459	1,236,885	46.6	2,656,649	12,976.67	2,648.81
1,269	6,620	347	16,767	28,140	403	8	411	2,075,929	547,105	2,623,036	54.5	4,814,609	12,512.86	2,431.08
856	3,535	233	8,398	14,675	384	8	392	1,210,294	308,977	1,519,272	56.7	2,679,116	14,034.06	2,540.46
413	3,085	114	8,369	13,465	19	0	19	865,636	238,128	1,103,764	51.7	2,135,494	11,014.97	2,306.49
332	1,808	55	4,600	7,614	9	0	9	477,214	135,084	612,299	52.3	1,170,799	10,392.14	2,237.87
81	1,277	59	3,769	5,851	10	0	10	388,421	103,044	491,465	50.9	964,695	11,879.02	2,395.63
655	4,441	90	9,467	16,413	724	44	768	1,423,994	388,670	1,812,663	51.8	3,502,432	13,299.99	2,814.20
655	4,441	90	9,467	16,413	724	44	768	1,423,994	388,670	1,812,663	51.8	3,502,432	13,299.99	2,814.20
655	4,441	90	9,467	16,413	724	44	768	1,423,994	388,670	1,812,663	51.8	3,502,432	13,299.99	2,814.20
960	3,103	240	7,966	14,102	334	42	376	1,072,322	271,829	1,344,149	58.1	2,314,764	13,074.66	2,244.49
324	1,436	159	4,322	7,036	6	5	11	486,326	122,372	608,697	55.0	1,106,339	11,310.87	1,838.88
636	1,667	81	3,644	7,066	328	37	365	585,996	149,457	735,452	60.9	1,208,425	15,252.11	2,812.66
636	1,667	81	3,644	7,066	328	37	365	585,996	149,457	735,452	60.9	1,208,425	15,252.11	2,812.66

MSAs

TABLE 8   U.S. CENSUS DIVISION 2, MIDDLE ATLANTIC

U.S. Community Hospitals
(Nonfederal, short-term general and other special hospitals)

2016 Utilization, Personnel and Finances

CLASSIFICATION	Hospitals	Beds	Admissions	Inpatient Days	Adjusted Inpatient Days	Average Daily Census	Adjusted Average Daily Census	Average Stay (days)	Surgical Operations	NEWBORNS Bassinets	Births	OUTPATIENT VISITS Emergency	Total
UNITED STATES	4,840	780,272	33,424,253	182,291,689	386,210,917	499,407	1,056,009	5.5	27,227,227	55,149	3,727,427	142,557,879	747,089,013
Nonmetropolitan	1,825	111,987	3,103,592	20,547,750	68,564,794	56,294	187,486	6.6	3,578,377	9,181	371,659	22,118,524	126,900,302
Metropolitan	3,015	668,285	30,320,661	161,743,939	317,646,123	443,113	868,523	5.3	23,648,850	45,968	3,355,768	120,439,355	620,188,711
CENSUS DIVISION 2, MIDDLE ATLANTIC	428	110,393	4,831,249	28,667,552	55,871,101	78,534	152,845	5.9	4,018,176	6,219	455,921	19,067,851	112,520,819
Nonmetropolitan	73	7,899	209,660	1,705,440	5,608,880	4,673	15,331	8.1	291,278	484	19,412	1,484,229	10,721,501
Metropolitan	355	102,494	4,621,589	26,962,112	50,262,221	73,861	137,514	5.8	3,726,898	5,735	436,509	17,583,622	101,799,318
New Jersey	75	20,711	989,292	4,859,232	8,365,629	13,313	23,016	4.9	578,700	1,326	96,894	3,696,748	14,498,631
Metropolitan	75	20,711	989,292	4,859,232	8,365,629	13,313	23,016	4.9	578,700	1,326	96,894	3,696,748	14,498,631
Allentown-Bethlehem-Easton	2	183	8,085	36,787	82,975	101	227	4.6	6,462	0	142	48,775	166,870
Atlantic City-Hammonton	4	838	33,214	155,037	299,060	426	966	4.7	15,186	56	2,369	118,739	357,531
Camden	10	2,953	139,305	676,916	1,093,182	1,853	2,988	4.9	89,645	125	11,904	592,498	1,634,225
New York-Jersey City-White Plains	31	9,661	496,596	2,246,436	3,851,745	6,153	10,529	4.5	270,943	702	51,666	1,692,242	7,824,629
Newark	18	5,473	241,733	1,380,863	2,352,208	3,785	6,431	5.7	147,971	351	24,833	933,549	3,406,627
Ocean City	1	180	6,779	28,443	74,374	78	203	4.2	3,615	16	390	44,697	193,731
Trenton	5	833	37,846	213,512	415,073	585	1,134	5.6	23,770	36	3,442	147,309	531,419
Vineland-Bridgeton	2	376	18,795	96,661	150,512	265	411	5.1	14,357	32	1,833	77,455	263,438
Wilmington	2	214	6,939	24,577	46,500	67	127	3.5	6,751	8	315	41,484	120,161
New York	169	52,550	2,275,571	15,242,826	29,355,852	41,757	80,237	6.7	2,052,112	3,152	226,884	9,053,118	57,669,548
Nonmetropolitan	35	4,047	96,925	965,564	3,230,259	2,645	8,833	10.0	143,832	262	10,440	786,788	5,701,846
Metropolitan	134	48,503	2,178,646	14,277,262	26,125,593	39,112	71,404	6.6	1,908,280	2,890	216,444	8,266,330	51,967,702
Albany-Schenectady-Troy	9	2,431	110,526	689,939	1,311,743	1,891	3,586	6.2	97,526	110	8,082	484,441	2,804,598
Binghamton	2	618	26,860	140,396	451,780	385	1,234	5.2	36,322	38	2,393	101,626	2,640,994
Buffalo-Cheektowaga-Niagara Falls	11	4,337	153,409	1,215,428	2,147,679	3,329	5,870	7.9	170,956	240	12,976	532,355	3,149,559
Dutchess County-Putnam County	3	597	32,211	153,411	290,663	420	794	4.8	35,630	39	3,444	118,669	552,833
Elmira	2	307	15,174	91,374	206,114	250	565	6.0	11,194	20	1,250	85,871	427,410
Glens Falls	1	275	13,163	69,913	173,046	192	473	5.3	12,094	10	1,225	43,471	731,420
Ithaca	1	193	6,551	28,436	107,014	78	292	4.3	6,697	21	898	28,907	263,996
Kingston	3	295	11,510	63,524	151,921	174	416	5.5	6,490	11	395	34,713	176,828
Nassau County-Suffolk County	21	7,424	409,624	2,472,639	4,391,887	6,775	12,006	6.0	333,384	458	39,096	1,223,257	5,451,639
New York-Jersey City-White Plains	58	26,037	1,157,535	7,716,784	13,074,899	21,138	35,736	6.7	979,761	1,532	123,264	4,619,588	26,007,982
Rochester	10	3,124	121,175	911,946	2,273,005	2,499	6,210	7.5	114,602	176	11,467	479,750	5,748,339
Syracuse	6	1,901	83,671	501,846	970,686	1,375	2,652	6.0	70,617	149	7,708	313,864	2,409,099
Utica-Rome	4	687	27,923	165,875	410,591	454	1,121	5.9	22,269	48	2,391	118,276	1,148,865
Watertown-Fort Drum	3	277	9,314	55,751	164,565	152	449	6.0	10,738	38	1,855	81,542	454,140
Pennsylvania	184	37,132	1,566,386	8,565,494	18,149,620	23,464	49,592	5.5	1,387,364	1,741	132,143	6,317,985	40,352,640
Nonmetropolitan	38	3,852	112,735	739,876	2,378,621	2,028	6,498	6.6	147,446	222	8,972	697,441	5,019,655
Metropolitan	146	33,280	1,453,651	7,825,618	15,770,999	21,436	43,094	5.4	1,239,918	1,519	123,171	5,620,544	35,332,985
Allentown-Bethlehem-Easton	7	2,252	98,571	585,365	1,178,498	1,603	3,219	5.9	77,119	88	8,908	344,162	2,004,486
Altoona	4	492	22,204	116,534	275,693	320	754	5.2	21,932	16	1,256	90,154	481,577
Bloomsburg-Berwick	5	792	36,277	206,483	493,972	566	1,350	5.7	30,423	34	2,121	122,905	1,233,376
Chambersburg-Waynesboro	2	313	15,485	60,491	157,655	166	431	3.9	11,919	31	1,769	79,001	489,798
East Stroudsburg	1	239	12,056	49,375	124,728	135	341	4.1	6,715	20	1,049	78,026	182,390
Erie	6	1,045	41,418	248,757	480,764	682	1,313	6.0	36,463	76	3,410	164,528	505,109
Gettysburg	1	76	3,888	15,382	55,514	42	152	4.0	4,086	16	531	27,921	195,875
Harrisburg-Carlisle	8	1,825	77,708	449,864	881,500	1,232	2,409	5.8	70,533	74	7,617	275,334	2,312,150
Johnstown	3	608	21,172	118,325	256,202	324	701	5.6	17,315	14	1,567	71,453	495,870
Lancaster	4	1,058	44,908	201,835	421,209	554	1,151	4.5	46,003	83	6,047	187,020	2,064,849
Lebanon	1	157	7,450	36,971	105,589	101	288	5.0	8,035	19	722	54,222	262,255
Montgomery County-Bucks County-Chester County	19	3,700	172,316	764,879	1,477,990	2,095	4,038	4.4	130,110	237	21,265	599,373	3,454,451
Philadelphia	27	8,127	363,952	2,049,294	3,713,430	5,615	10,146	5.6	301,215	280	24,163	1,326,655	7,587,863
Pittsburgh	33	7,971	335,881	1,881,819	3,829,171	5,153	10,463	5.6	305,132	302	24,536	1,232,229	7,758,710
Reading	3	954	41,153	219,489	455,022	602	1,244	5.3	23,930	56	4,413	179,974	1,326,025
Scranton-Wilkes-Barre-Hazleton	9	1,674	69,553	348,981	811,568	956	2,217	5.0	56,878	55	5,906	274,714	2,209,822
State College	2	333	15,404	68,907	155,817	188	426	4.5	8,461	5	1,362	57,536	341,417
Williamsport	3	401	13,162	100,781	252,712	276	690	7.7	17,208	15	1,130	72,798	202,377
York-Hanover	5	869	43,790	215,717	423,551	590	1,158	4.9	46,733	71	4,237	157,564	1,497,997
Youngstown-Warren-Boardman	3	394	17,303	86,369	220,414	236	603	5.0	19,708	27	1,162	224,975	726,588

MSAs

TABLE 8

U.S. CENSUS DIVISION 2, MIDDLE ATLANTIC

U.S. Community Hospitals
(Nonfederal, short-term general and other special hospitals)

2016 Utilization, Personnel and Finances

FULL-TIME EQUIVALENT PERSONNEL					FULL-TIME EQUIV. TRAINEES			EXPENSES						
								LABOR				TOTAL		
Physicians and Dentists	Registered Nurses	Licensed Practical Nurses	Other Salaried Personnel	Total Personnel	Medical and Dental Residents	Other Trainees	Total Trainees	Payroll (in thousands)	Employee Benefits (in thousands)	Total (in thousands)	Percent of Total	Amount (in thousands)	Adjusted per Admission	Adjusted per Inpatient Day
135,693	1,478,657	74,344	2,612,576	4,991,775	113,111	9,619	122,730	$340,132,974	$90,463,641	$430,596,618	47.7	$902,891,035	$12,777.25	$2,337.82
15,408	149,651	20,977	339,776	612,547	1,714	261	1,975	35,531,908	9,378,885	44,910,794	50.2	89,420,776	8,694.35	1,304.18
120,285	1,329,006	53,367	2,272,800	4,379,228	111,397	9,358	120,755	304,601,066	81,084,755	385,685,824	47.4	813,470,258	13,472.72	2,560.93
27,817	210,656	8,586	404,817	750,799	30,480	1,226	31,706	55,776,066	15,883,811	71,659,887	51.2	139,997,028	14,944.47	2,505.71
907	9,593	1,362	23,249	41,094	164	9	173	2,325,609	626,937	2,952,546	51.8	5,704,240	8,506.98	1,017.00
26,910	201,063	7,224	381,568	709,705	30,316	1,217	31,533	53,450,457	15,256,874	68,707,341	51.2	134,292,788	15,440.78	2,671.84
3,104	37,615	807	69,195	125,941	2,747	59	2,806	9,159,608	2,140,449	11,300,057	50.1	22,539,690	13,106.71	2,694.32
3,104	37,615	807	69,195	125,941	2,747	59	2,806	9,159,608	2,140,449	11,300,057	50.1	22,539,690	13,106.71	2,694.32
13	322	2	790	1,300	24	2	26	77,268	17,274	94,542	48.0	196,850	10,852.91	2,372.40
58	1,466	44	2,553	4,836	62	1	63	329,446	82,226	411,671	51.8	794,832	12,497.16	2,657.77
812	5,006	164	10,793	18,452	353	4	357	1,131,049	273,525	1,404,574	44.8	3,132,712	13,900.80	2,865.68
1,262	17,974	282	31,631	58,240	1,217	27	1,244	4,375,720	982,387	5,358,108	50.7	10,565,474	12,293.25	2,743.04
810	10,249	192	19,368	34,892	898	20	918	2,631,919	599,905	3,231,823	51.3	6,295,840	15,174.87	2,676.57
0	206	0	448	795	0	4	4	51,927	21,239	73,165	59.2	123,577	6,971.51	1,661.56
141	1,657	62	2,549	5,201	45	1	46	359,188	97,881	457,068	48.6	939,677	12,181.13	2,263.88
3	521	43	739	1,567	145	0	145	152,735	51,374	204,109	56.4	362,149	11,969.89	2,406.11
5	214	18	324	658	3	0	3	50,358	14,640	64,997	50.5	128,580	9,783.15	2,765.16
16,597	102,734	5,119	214,667	389,406	19,552	536	20,088	31,640,970	9,850,620	41,491,590	55.2	75,132,634	17,477.86	2,559.38
556	4,861	770	12,612	21,945	49	4	53	1,309,674	348,286	1,657,959	54.3	3,050,613	9,865.96	944.39
16,041	97,873	4,349	202,055	367,461	19,503	532	20,035	30,331,296	9,502,334	39,833,631	55.3	72,082,021	18,067.82	2,759.06
291	4,949	139	8,711	16,762	550	6	556	832,992	178,821	1,011,814	45.7	2,212,582	10,691.38	1,686.75
291	1,201	165	3,643	5,799	99	0	99	346,735	100,968	447,703	49.1	911,716	10,212.45	2,018.05
433	6,727	449	12,066	22,446	59	71	130	1,636,808	627,867	2,264,677	55.8	4,058,978	14,875.19	1,889.94
0	1,292	0	1,465	3,225	0	1	1	240,335	82,637	322,972	41.6	775,753	12,666.60	2,668.91
66	776	47	1,437	2,726	16	2	18	145,656	38,099	183,754	47.7	385,614	11,266.05	1,870.88
66	521	54	1,429	2,240	0	0	0	156,360	29,246	185,606	55.3	335,633	10,301.51	1,939.56
13	381	9	859	1,424	1	4	5	70,540	27,662	98,203	52.0	189,014	7,666.68	1,766.26
39	432	28	830	1,534	8	1	9	81,927	21,478	103,405	47.8	216,546	8,058.72	1,425.38
5,095	16,959	349	35,304	64,918	4,621	23	4,644	6,068,094	1,632,559	7,700,653	60.2	12,787,811	17,604.78	2,911.69
8,237	52,487	1,966	111,780	201,213	12,626	356	12,982	17,779,516	5,928,972	23,708,484	54.7	43,339,116	21,944.74	3,314.68
1,127	7,049	734	14,035	26,450	834	55	889	1,661,955	437,963	2,099,920	57.3	3,665,388	12,583.25	1,612.57
185	3,449	220	6,519	11,868	641	11	652	883,822	302,296	1,186,118	51.9	2,285,276	14,753.14	2,354.29
123	1,172	105	2,973	4,933	37	2	39	301,305	60,793	362,099	56.6	640,065	9,636.77	1,558.89
75	478	84	1,004	1,923	11	0	11	125,250	32,973	158,223	56.8	278,528	10,338.84	1,692.51
8,116	70,307	2,660	120,955	235,452	8,181	631	8,812	14,975,488	3,892,742	18,868,240	44.6	42,324,704	12,636.59	2,331.99
351	4,732	592	10,637	19,149	115	5	120	1,015,936	278,651	1,294,587	48.8	2,653,627	7,344.05	1,115.62
7,765	65,575	2,068	110,318	216,303	8,066	626	8,692	13,959,552	3,614,091	17,573,653	44.3	39,671,077	13,276.59	2,515.44
716	4,695	86	8,204	15,956	500	26	526	951,426	192,214	1,143,640	44.0	2,599,911	13,356.85	2,206.12
61	853	53	1,508	2,756	11	1	12	171,187	43,334	214,521	45.7	469,195	8,605.92	1,701.87
186	1,638	80	2,811	5,564	223	11	234	345,047	102,477	447,525	36.9	1,212,547	13,524.14	2,454.69
5	467	9	1,225	1,956	0	16	16	146,358	49,675	196,033	58.7	333,978	8,119.67	2,118.41
65	286	36	1,039	1,530	0	1	1	91,093	26,651	117,744	48.8	241,220	7,920.53	1,933.97
144	1,693	49	2,137	4,816	65	1	66	232,497	54,812	287,309	38.6	744,394	9,493.85	1,548.36
0	175	2	336	662	0	0	0	39,427	15,297	54,725	37.0	148,103	10,554.68	2,667.85
1,165	3,917	379	10,156	17,152	736	32	768	906,842	246,203	1,153,046	44.8	2,576,422	16,493.53	2,922.77
15	805	54	1,948	3,201	83	0	83	169,286	44,222	213,508	51.2	416,998	8,799.84	1,627.61
154	1,701	78	4,195	6,890	57	0	57	464,915	144,048	608,962	50.2	1,211,976	12,894.32	2,877.37
42	220	27	777	1,258	14	0	14	65,013	19,684	84,696	44.5	190,268	8,942.43	1,801.97
621	6,890	113	10,799	21,266	299	6	305	1,461,318	349,144	1,810,463	49.1	3,686,509	10,773.66	2,494.27
3,019	20,253	340	31,570	63,952	4,348	257	4,605	4,809,254	1,269,185	6,078,439	48.0	12,663,939	19,328.42	3,410.31
1,052	14,350	330	19,782	42,821	1,317	263	1,580	2,427,993	593,342	3,021,340	36.4	8,306,874	11,478.23	2,169.37
34	1,636	63	3,432	6,219	121	0	121	358,979	105,703	464,682	45.7	1,016,439	11,894.30	2,233.82
266	2,393	148	4,265	8,273	66	0	66	450,505	127,526	578,032	38.6	1,496,171	9,277.83	1,843.56
14	409	8	1,014	1,686	1	0	1	170,447	45,713	216,160	54.2	398,593	11,378.31	2,558.09
12	638	113	773	1,888	26	0	26	124,483	36,229	160,713	44.1	364,061	12,228.31	1,440.62
177	1,743	67	3,275	6,138	182	11	193	452,726	119,184	571,911	47.2	1,210,960	13,816.64	2,859.06
17	813	33	1,072	2,319	17	1	18	120,754	29,450	150,204	39.3	382,517	8,301.70	1,735.45

TABLE 8

U.S. CENSUS DIVISION 3, SOUTH ATLANTIC

U.S. Community Hospitals
(Nonfederal, short-term general and other special hospitals)

2016 Utilization, Personnel and Finances

CLASSIFICATION	Hospitals	Beds	Admissions	Inpatient Days	Adjusted Inpatient Days	Average Daily Census	Adjusted Average Daily Census	Average Stay (days)	Surgical Operations	NEWBORNS Bassinets	NEWBORNS Births	OUTPATIENT VISITS Emergency	OUTPATIENT VISITS Total
UNITED STATES	4,840	780,272	33,424,253	182,291,689	386,210,917	499,407	1,056,009	5.5	27,227,227	55,149	3,727,427	142,557,879	747,089,013
Nonmetropolitan	1,825	111,987	3,103,592	20,547,750	68,564,794	56,294	187,486	6.6	3,578,377	9,181	371,659	22,118,524	126,900,302
Metropolitan	3,015	668,285	30,320,661	161,743,939	317,646,123	443,113	868,523	5.3	23,648,850	45,968	3,355,768	120,439,355	620,188,711
CENSUS DIVISION 3, SOUTH ATLANTIC	745	154,298	6,907,154	37,649,870	76,988,836	103,147	210,555	5.5	5,387,557	10,001	716,992	29,837,837	118,563,456
Nonmetropolitan	197	17,383	523,763	3,582,764	10,929,315	9,814	29,880	6.8	514,218	1,293	51,148	3,952,388	15,007,628
Metropolitan	548	136,915	6,383,391	34,067,106	66,059,521	93,333	180,675	5.3	4,873,339	8,708	665,844	25,885,449	103,555,828
Delaware	7	2,059	100,716	519,070	1,032,187	1,423	2,819	5.2	90,127	119	11,430	469,403	2,180,249
Metropolitan	7	2,059	100,716	519,070	1,032,187	1,423	2,819	5.2	90,127	119	11,430	469,403	2,180,249
Dover	1	351	17,555	91,192	214,487	250	586	5.2	15,240	13	2,342	91,890	626,205
Salisbury	2	254	15,572	62,906	146,753	172	401	4.0	18,847	25	1,826	86,151	540,390
Wilmington	4	1,454	67,589	364,972	670,947	1,001	1,832	5.4	56,040	81	7,262	291,362	1,013,654
District of Columbia	11	3,449	126,578	948,524	1,608,674	2,599	4,398	7.5	102,744	182	14,725	476,259	2,605,599
Metropolitan	11	3,449	126,578	948,524	1,608,674	2,599	4,398	7.5	102,744	182	14,725	476,259	2,605,599
Washington-Arlington-Alexandria	11	3,449	126,578	948,524	1,608,674	2,599	4,398	7.5	102,744	182	14,725	476,259	2,605,599
Florida	210	53,708	2,543,053	12,753,577	22,502,261	34,940	61,547	5.0	1,502,877	2,711	217,309	9,417,424	26,375,397
Nonmetropolitan	22	970	37,155	156,632	494,034	428	1,351	4.2	35,205	52	1,884	296,578	827,720
Metropolitan	188	52,738	2,505,898	12,596,945	22,008,227	34,512	60,196	5.0	1,467,672	2,659	215,425	9,120,846	25,547,677
Cape Coral-Fort Myers	4	1,514	79,891	359,097	710,459	984	1,943	4.5	43,345	72	6,187	281,211	537,646
Crestview-Fort Walton Beach-Destin	5	540	26,367	104,251	217,533	285	596	4.0	20,956	48	2,926	126,133	395,930
Deltona-Daytona Beach-Ormond Beach	6	1,461	68,370	351,833	684,577	964	1,902	5.1	37,831	66	4,024	330,009	1,024,965
Fort Lauderdale-Pompano Beach-Deerfield Beach	16	4,946	220,079	1,131,715	1,972,264	3,100	5,391	5.1	130,566	256	22,421	914,893	2,011,798
Gainesville	3	1,442	74,181	410,876	646,051	1,126	1,766	5.5	56,762	40	6,043	171,623	1,171,179
Homosassa Springs	2	332	17,508	70,180	127,909	192	350	4.0	12,308	20	1,083	86,911	215,726
Jacksonville	13	4,083	200,444	1,010,546	1,836,256	2,769	5,018	5.0	142,704	255	18,320	787,444	2,215,720
Lakeland-Winter Haven	5	1,567	75,392	339,090	625,093	930	1,707	4.5	41,621	62	5,485	347,238	531,098
Miami-Miami Beach-Kendall	25	7,852	318,620	1,892,686	3,134,507	5,184	8,572	5.9	169,223	340	29,081	1,115,892	3,810,439
Naples-Immokalee-Marco Island	2	914	33,013	166,141	290,724	456	795	5.0	16,925	36	3,644	135,434	385,172
North Port-Sarasota-Bradenton	8	2,028	86,617	430,403	737,997	1,179	2,019	5.0	50,995	55	5,016	279,927	975,679
Ocala	3	601	36,777	162,837	264,473	446	723	4.4	18,324	34	2,488	150,595	223,219
Orlando-Kissimmee-Sanford	13	6,306	335,587	1,668,759	2,790,438	4,572	7,627	5.0	184,645	363	32,706	1,260,438	2,933,873
Palm Bay-Melbourne-Titusville	7	1,416	58,247	290,316	524,945	796	1,435	5.0	34,072	75	4,956	255,210	702,193
Panama City	5	586	28,538	155,790	252,372	426	689	5.5	21,576	37	2,912	96,956	270,443
Pensacola-Ferry Pass-Brent	7	1,341	66,867	325,789	640,014	892	1,750	4.9	48,430	65	6,678	321,540	993,370
Port St. Lucie	3	860	55,161	240,842	445,015	660	1,217	4.4	33,341	64	4,985	181,049	295,554
Punta Gorda	3	681	27,183	145,738	234,115	400	639	5.4	16,996	22	983	76,183	182,777
Sebastian-Vero Beach	3	454	20,541	106,180	218,129	291	596	5.2	15,233	22	988	73,022	160,115
Sebring	2	277	14,278	64,376	137,220	176	375	4.5	12,061	29	1,248	70,005	214,151
Tallahassee	4	798	43,913	209,346	413,248	574	1,130	4.8	23,650	62	4,719	142,877	901,624
Tampa-St. Petersburg-Clearwater	34	8,878	423,968	2,095,079	3,618,979	5,740	9,894	4.9	229,949	444	31,116	1,392,009	3,869,849
West Palm Beach-Boca Raton-Delray Beach	15	3,861	194,356	865,075	1,485,909	2,370	4,062	4.5	106,159	192	17,416	524,247	1,525,157
Georgia	141	24,758	980,496	6,197,094	13,228,803	16,976	36,172	6.3	739,071	1,907	123,918	4,611,446	18,842,398
Nonmetropolitan	56	5,485	126,865	1,234,571	3,337,633	3,383	9,129	9.7	131,333	352	15,866	950,683	3,468,382
Metropolitan	85	19,273	853,631	4,962,523	9,891,170	13,593	27,043	5.8	607,738	1,555	108,052	3,660,763	15,374,016
Albany	2	542	20,192	113,786	285,674	312	781	5.6	13,686	42	2,341	99,353	1,157,925
Athens-Clarke County	2	526	29,217	133,811	253,354	366	692	4.6	24,050	54	3,966	133,586	509,355
Atlanta-Sandy Springs-Roswell	42	9,975	474,895	2,673,073	5,240,163	7,322	14,325	5.6	326,708	856	68,953	2,080,361	8,509,188
Augusta-Richmond County	8	1,558	65,888	372,644	688,119	1,021	1,883	5.7	53,283	123	5,741	303,876	1,397,082
Brunswick	1	532	11,714	140,280	326,817	384	893	12.0	9,953	8	1,302	54,258	237,496
Chattanooga	1	179	6,300	56,085	144,926	154	397	8.9	4,896	15	694	26,152	121,587
Columbus	5	1,132	40,030	260,869	527,958	714	1,445	6.5	25,711	43	3,161	118,715	481,425
Dalton	2	256	10,140	42,737	91,595	117	250	4.2	4,442	40	1,824	68,396	266,880
Gainesville	1	906	36,099	251,124	443,493	688	1,212	7.0	22,303	77	4,024	141,062	520,382
Hinesville	1	25	1,642	5,475	22,910	15	63	3.3	1,616	6	352	5,913	36,795
Macon-Bibb County	5	1,072	46,579	273,525	470,969	749	1,288	5.9	34,137	106	3,303	131,146	576,280
Rome	3	602	27,560	140,256	265,859	384	727	5.1	17,524	30	2,354	124,106	296,140
Savannah	5	1,196	51,277	326,385	723,014	894	1,975	6.4	42,334	71	5,839	220,903	639,909
Valdosta	3	414	14,627	94,367	208,928	258	572	6.5	8,326	40	1,823	54,425	256,370
Warner Robins	4	358	17,471	78,106	197,391	215	540	4.5	18,769	44	2,375	98,511	367,202

MSAs

TABLE 8   U.S. CENSUS DIVISION 3, SOUTH ATLANTIC

U.S. Community Hospitals
(Nonfederal, short-term general and other special hospitals)

2016 Utilization, Personnel and Finances

	FULL-TIME EQUIVALENT PERSONNEL					FULL-TIME EQUIV. TRAINEES			EXPENSES						
									LABOR				TOTAL		
Physicians and Dentists	Registered Nurses	Licensed Practical Nurses	Other Salaried Personnel	Total Personnel	Medical and Dental Residents	Other Trainees	Total Trainees	Payroll (in thousands)	Employee Benefits (in thousands)	Total (in thousands)	Percent of Total	Amount (in thousands)	Adjusted per Admission	Adjusted per Inpatient Day
135,693	1,478,657	74,344	2,612,576	4,991,775	113,111	9,619	122,730	$340,132,974	$90,463,641	$430,596,618	47.7	$902,891,035	$12,777.25	$2,337.82
15,408	149,651	20,977	339,776	612,547	1,714	261	1,975	35,531,908	9,378,885	44,910,794	50.2	89,420,776	8,694.35	1,304.18
120,285	1,329,006	53,367	2,272,800	4,379,228	111,397	9,358	120,755	304,601,066	81,084,755	385,685,824	47.4	813,470,258	13,472.72	2,560.93
18,396	286,651	12,914	456,997	918,213	17,120	1,005	18,125	57,593,853	14,248,140	71,841,989	46.0	156,153,964	11,095.13	2,028.27
1,615	21,995	2,719	43,269	83,523	299	14	313	4,427,890	1,143,981	5,571,867	48.4	11,512,050	7,321.65	1,053.32
16,781	264,656	10,195	413,728	834,690	16,821	991	17,812	53,165,963	13,104,159	66,270,122	45.8	144,641,915	11,569.72	2,189.57
584	5,502	137	11,278	19,276	361	14	375	1,401,544	427,002	1,828,547	56.3	3,246,811	15,929.25	3,145.56
584	5,502	137	11,278	19,276	361	14	375	1,401,544	427,002	1,828,547	56.3	3,246,811	15,929.25	3,145.56
64	879	33	1,892	3,235	0	0	0	244,663	72,280	316,943	57.7	548,909	13,294.00	2,559.17
106	867	44	1,724	2,978	0	0	0	159,996	58,075	218,070	45.7	477,556	13,039.42	3,254.15
414	3,756	60	7,662	13,063	361	14	375	996,886	296,647	1,293,534	58.3	2,220,346	17,633.97	3,309.27
1,594	7,114	188	12,282	24,250	1,337	59	1,396	1,967,740	371,401	2,339,142	51.9	4,503,225	20,670.93	2,799.34
1,594	7,114	188	12,282	24,250	1,337	59	1,396	1,967,740	371,401	2,339,142	51.9	4,503,225	20,670.93	2,799.34
1,594	7,114	188	12,282	24,250	1,337	59	1,396	1,967,740	371,401	2,339,142	51.9	4,503,225	20,670.93	2,799.34
4,531	91,625	3,271	133,812	275,241	5,022	210	5,232	17,302,377	4,159,265	21,461,639	45.6	47,056,719	10,381.90	2,091.20
89	1,363	182	2,706	5,138	12	1	13	261,793	59,510	321,301	47.1	682,072	6,184.18	1,380.62
4,442	90,262	3,089	131,106	270,103	5,010	209	5,219	17,040,584	4,099,754	21,140,338	45.6	46,374,648	10,486.59	2,107.15
165	1,877	101	3,519	6,742	324	18	342	673,491	217,001	890,491	50.3	1,771,961	11,181.68	2,494.11
31	666	61	1,007	2,072	13	0	13	95,443	19,718	115,161	32.3	356,146	6,223.17	1,637.20
214	2,042	116	4,347	7,691	40	0	40	527,239	106,297	633,536	49.2	1,287,707	9,577.02	1,881.03
663	7,964	280	10,354	23,024	304	24	328	1,456,969	309,523	1,766,491	46.1	3,834,918	9,883.86	1,944.42
18	3,204	74	4,755	9,252	626	14	640	551,126	163,346	714,472	45.0	1,587,952	13,529.57	2,457.94
13	594	28	737	1,627	18	1	19	69,138	17,757	86,895	40.2	216,147	6,756.91	1,689.85
575	7,677	140	9,074	21,150	627	25	652	1,227,326	338,057	1,565,383	41.4	3,776,720	10,428.26	2,056.75
13	2,680	46	3,701	7,900	11	0	11	434,008	106,866	540,874	48.6	1,111,933	7,978.97	1,778.83
728	12,829	479	20,651	40,380	1,622	49	1,671	2,780,073	657,883	3,437,955	46.2	7,438,738	13,820.41	2,373.18
3	1,265	31	1,345	3,225	5	1	6	199,891	31,837	231,727	46.1	502,480	8,653.30	1,728.37
125	2,969	203	4,458	9,005	39	3	42	511,898	110,028	621,926	44.6	1,394,733	9,374.78	1,889.89
32	1,646	73	1,902	4,393	60	3	63	188,819	41,777	230,597	43.6	528,430	8,797.93	1,998.05
595	13,737	305	20,808	40,554	494	4	498	2,429,109	702,922	3,132,031	48.6	6,449,337	11,522.70	2,311.23
55	2,062	64	2,481	5,684	35	3	38	371,808	77,847	449,656	45.0	999,442	9,384.08	1,903.90
34	845	113	1,137	2,587	5	0	5	139,141	26,782	165,923	38.3	433,272	8,660.07	1,716.80
77	2,137	85	3,057	6,332	68	6	74	347,151	55,132	402,283	37.0	1,087,019	8,097.16	1,698.43
126	1,576	80	3,090	5,728	21	1	22	320,847	73,347	394,195	48.3	816,213	7,968.65	1,834.13
11	835	28	955	2,212	14	0	14	125,297	25,959	151,257	43.0	351,567	8,133.99	1,501.69
80	674	22	1,237	2,274	5	0	5	151,742	24,980	176,722	50.9	347,151	8,315.78	1,591.49
30	584	26	992	1,877	2	0	2	100,774	26,130	126,903	49.0	259,099	8,495.88	1,888.20
148	1,520	101	2,392	4,807	72	3	75	322,250	63,578	385,829	48.0	803,694	9,312.04	1,944.82
607	15,368	455	22,161	46,339	511	49	560	2,931,013	678,457	3,609,471	44.9	8,041,283	10,922.04	2,221.98
99	5,511	178	6,946	15,248	94	5	99	1,086,032	224,529	1,310,560	44.0	2,978,706	8,834.51	2,004.64
2,416	40,761	2,825	71,273	139,341	1,410	288	1,698	8,431,187	2,080,877	10,512,068	45.7	23,013,231	11,185.28	1,739.63
459	5,319	1,038	11,695	22,257	37	4	41	1,168,421	308,596	1,477,017	49.1	3,010,762	8,259.73	902.06
1,957	35,442	1,787	59,578	117,084	1,373	284	1,657	7,262,766	1,772,282	9,035,051	45.2	20,002,469	11,815.19	2,022.26
4	783	60	1,688	2,821	19	0	19	154,506	48,220	202,726	47.3	543,276	11,016.22	1,901.73
27	1,087	28	2,258	3,943	15	0	15	225,777	53,784	279,562	47.7	586,136	10,615.91	2,313.51
941	20,350	816	30,683	63,662	755	110	865	4,192,940	1,015,792	5,208,735	44.5	11,706,166	12,431.20	2,233.93
126	2,816	130	4,212	8,545	119	6	125	586,013	138,918	724,931	45.5	1,591,548	12,982.79	2,312.90
96	296	11	659	1,313	0	0	0	144,063	34,274	178,337	55.4	321,773	11,790.43	984.56
28	262	27	576	1,049	8	0	8	57,973	18,563	76,536	51.9	147,478	9,059.41	1,017.61
146	1,527	89	2,852	5,540	68	4	72	316,302	78,374	394,676	45.4	869,033	10,286.23	1,646.03
6	420	22	752	1,323	0	0	0	102,139	27,572	129,711	47.1	275,276	12,336.48	3,005.36
263	1,435	185	4,851	7,206	0	154	154	296,826	78,181	375,006	47.3	792,474	12,430.58	1,786.89
6	59	14	154	272	0	0	0	19,340	5,001	24,341	53.0	45,962	6,689.29	2,006.20
61	1,735	69	2,693	5,614	131	3	134	325,538	82,184	407,722	46.2	883,048	11,245.44	1,874.96
70	981	98	2,097	3,729	39	0	39	199,816	55,793	255,609	49.6	514,824	9,666.05	1,936.45
104	2,186	90	3,348	6,668	171	3	174	384,236	71,754	455,991	42.9	1,063,243	10,778.48	1,470.57
63	822	33	1,349	2,664	30	3	33	136,845	35,352	172,197	46.7	368,903	13,048.80	1,765.69
16	683	115	1,406	2,735	18	1	19	120,452	28,518	148,971	50.8	293,330	6,598.06	1,486.03

Table continues

MSAs

TABLE 8

U.S. CENSUS DIVISION 3, SOUTH ATLANTIC CONTINUED

U.S. Community Hospitals
(Nonfederal, short-term general and other special hospitals)

2016 Utilization, Personnel and Finances

CLASSIFICATION	Hospitals	Beds	Admissions	Inpatient Days	Adjusted Inpatient Days	Average Daily Census	Adjusted Average Daily Census	Average Stay (days)	Surgical Operations	NEWBORNS Bassinets	Births	OUTPATIENT VISITS Emergency	Total
Maryland	50	11,547	584,519	3,009,310	5,783,899	8,243	15,810	5.1	529,977	896	66,271	2,492,585	12,785,893
Nonmetropolitan	4	362	15,187	86,840	221,585	239	607	5.7	17,386	30	1,306	125,048	610,569
Metropolitan	46	11,185	569,332	2,922,470	5,562,314	8,004	15,203	5.1	512,591	866	64,965	2,367,537	12,175,324
Baltimore-Columbia-Towson	24	7,308	356,008	1,937,491	3,603,466	5,308	9,847	5.4	352,739	459	35,040	1,325,476	8,519,107
California-Lexington Park	1	91	7,689	27,890	63,990	76	175	3.6	7,933	16	1,283	52,429	191,026
Cumberland	1	316	12,038	86,017	190,001	236	519	7.1	7,761	20	944	49,854	557,772
Hagerstown-Martinsburg	1	278	16,060	64,013	132,278	175	361	4.0	8,798	41	1,873	73,576	199,709
Salisbury	4	490	24,305	117,855	294,316	323	805	4.8	24,750	28	1,943	128,167	794,921
Silver Spring-Frederick-Rockville	7	1,673	96,762	428,187	766,561	1,173	2,096	4.4	58,035	238	18,212	362,828	1,106,460
Washington-Arlington-Alexandria	7	920	50,693	239,375	456,940	654	1,250	4.7	47,071	52	5,028	335,765	663,769
Wilmington	1	109	5,777	21,642	54,762	59	150	3.7	5,504	12	642	39,442	142,560
North Carolina	112	21,791	1,006,097	5,472,055	13,282,882	14,994	36,383	5.4	868,224	1,608	115,681	4,922,026	20,706,718
Nonmetropolitan	48	4,300	172,896	899,183	3,247,653	2,464	8,877	5.2	147,902	433	17,684	1,255,096	4,571,487
Metropolitan	64	17,491	833,201	4,572,872	10,035,229	12,530	27,506	5.5	720,322	1,175	97,997	3,666,930	16,135,231
Asheville	6	1,260	57,157	302,409	697,273	828	1,906	5.3	58,624	58	5,346	183,322	1,507,230
Burlington	1	218	10,786	42,104	135,250	115	370	3.9	10,371	21	1,290	68,148	203,038
Charlotte-Concord-Gastonia	17	4,243	214,744	1,104,896	2,380,584	3,027	6,505	5.1	179,505	344	29,001	1,057,306	3,617,155
Durham-Chapel Hill	6	2,209	99,445	653,584	1,396,238	1,791	3,815	6.6	90,243	62	9,215	252,687	2,333,517
Fayetteville	1	612	30,663	156,609	284,651	429	778	5.1	13,239	48	4,678	129,447	260,242
Goldsboro	1	274	8,047	36,682	89,576	100	327	4.6	9,347	36	998	51,903	111,234
Greensboro-High Point	6	1,690	76,793	402,893	946,774	1,105	2,586	5.2	44,239	111	8,711	375,574	1,357,149
Greenville	1	909	37,733	240,239	356,863	658	975	6.4	21,449	42	3,790	121,547	407,301
Hickory-Lenoir-Morganton	4	744	33,155	164,649	392,402	452	1,072	5.0	32,215	62	3,602	182,641	579,749
Jacksonville	1	149	7,074	29,124	89,756	80	245	4.1	6,150	23	1,566	61,235	139,157
Myrtle Beach-Conway-North Myrtle Beach	2	143	5,464	27,555	114,742	76	314	5.0	6,351	5	475	45,026	180,291
New Bern	1	205	12,763	64,465	141,922	177	388	5.1	14,571	22	1,190	70,031	179,412
Raleigh	5	1,809	88,616	494,984	1,165,227	1,356	3,184	5.6	96,448	166	15,012	468,610	2,871,401
Rocky Mount	3	438	16,696	91,636	203,484	250	557	5.5	11,284	34	1,432	99,987	254,887
Wilmington	2	753	40,636	215,049	450,198	590	1,230	5.3	37,937	43	4,018	159,612	430,202
Winston-Salem	7	1,835	93,429	545,994	1,190,289	1,496	3,254	5.8	88,349	98	7,673	339,854	1,703,266
South Carolina	68	12,299	523,640	2,800,574	5,916,896	7,673	16,169	5.3	506,562	843	53,735	2,543,747	9,430,786
Nonmetropolitan	14	1,786	51,800	302,894	852,241	830	2,328	5.8	49,237	160	4,937	389,908	1,366,254
Metropolitan	54	10,513	471,840	2,497,680	5,064,655	6,843	13,841	5.3	457,325	683	48,798	2,153,839	8,064,532
Augusta-Richmond County	2	296	12,228	61,722	112,297	170	307	5.0	8,752	18	1,058	61,599	155,455
Charleston-North Charleston	7	1,912	90,593	475,801	889,016	1,304	2,429	5.3	95,826	116	10,353	409,198	1,917,081
Charlotte-Concord-Gastonia	4	542	23,184	118,491	236,921	325	647	5.1	15,702	41	2,216	127,114	274,776
Columbia	8	2,075	99,003	527,236	1,098,948	1,444	3,003	5.3	73,525	126	9,914	380,739	1,419,180
Florence	7	1,273	46,763	265,751	462,964	728	1,265	5.7	54,428	54	3,404	162,779	473,778
Greenville-Anderson-Mauldin	14	2,119	89,645	490,492	1,073,920	1,342	2,936	5.5	109,014	135	10,921	469,334	2,288,067
Hilton Head Island-Bluffton-Beaufort	3	325	19,491	75,731	179,347	208	490	3.9	13,832	52	2,456	96,481	314,844
Myrtle Beach-Conway-North Myrtle Beach	4	889	41,432	205,962	425,326	564	1,162	5.0	38,937	66	3,403	244,141	580,059
Spartanburg	4	844	42,299	208,171	403,317	571	1,103	4.9	37,469	51	3,813	161,540	509,899
Sumter	1	238	7,202	68,323	182,599	187	499	9.5	9,840	24	1,260	60,914	131,393
Virginia	92	17,884	790,179	4,475,635	10,003,528	12,264	27,339	5.7	731,966	1,340	94,302	3,733,349	17,726,394
Nonmetropolitan	27	2,369	65,635	510,014	1,439,257	1,396	3,936	7.8	65,307	132	4,881	494,845	1,731,298
Metropolitan	65	15,515	724,544	3,965,621	8,564,271	10,868	23,403	5.5	666,659	1,208	89,421	3,238,504	15,995,096
Blacksburg-Christiansburg-Radford	4	242	15,852	64,511	163,291	178	447	4.1	18,935	26	1,875	93,530	274,154
Charlottesville	3	787	38,224	218,590	498,211	600	1,361	5.7	89,996	42	3,247	114,389	2,304,582
Harrisonburg	1	244	13,585	50,936	162,793	140	445	3.7	21,036	16	1,761	75,067	409,045
Kingsport-Bristol-Bristol	2	141	8,945	34,481	89,373	95	244	3.9	7,279	16	701	41,030	157,336
Lynchburg	2	1,199	31,326	321,827	729,230	881	1,993	10.3	17,236	39	2,641	127,741	673,919
Richmond	14	3,588	156,252	878,235	1,736,605	2,408	4,746	5.6	111,628	253	15,340	618,131	1,893,593
Roanoke	3	1,167	63,547	371,190	639,612	1,017	1,750	5.8	47,772	67	4,525	299,809	772,923
Staunton-Waynesboro	2	241	11,389	45,932	145,535	126	398	4.0	16,102	21	1,175	60,589	761,203
Virginia Beach-Norfolk-Newport News	15	3,437	164,367	881,670	2,090,306	2,414	5,710	5.4	177,727	299	18,859	881,172	5,706,202
Washington-Arlington-Alexandria	18	3,984	198,629	984,421	2,070,230	2,697	5,656	5.0	141,911	417	37,090	850,667	2,673,567
Winchester	1	485	22,428	113,828	239,085	312	653	5.1	17,037	12	2,207	76,379	368,572

MSAs

TABLE 8

U.S. CENSUS DIVISION 3, SOUTH ATLANTIC CONTINUED

U.S. Community Hospitals
(Nonfederal, short-term general and other special hospitals)

2016 Utilization, Personnel and Finances

FULL-TIME EQUIVALENT PERSONNEL					FULL-TIME EQUIV. TRAINEES			EXPENSES						
								LABOR				TOTAL		
Physicians and Dentists	Registered Nurses	Licensed Practical Nurses	Other Salaried Personnel	Total Personnel	Medical and Dental Residents	Other Trainees	Total Trainees	Payroll (in thousands)	Employee Benefits (in thousands)	Total (in thousands)	Percent of Total	Amount (in thousands)	Adjusted per Admission	Adjusted per Inpatient Day
1,986	25,654	469	47,538	87,815	1,775	125	1,900	5,895,231	1,407,533	7,302,762	46.9	15,583,580	13,540.91	2,694.30
47	653	37	1,204	2,248	10	1	11	128,109	35,669	163,778	49.1	333,643	8,347.54	1,505.71
1,939	25,001	432	46,334	85,567	1,765	124	1,889	5,767,122	1,371,865	7,138,984	46.8	15,249,937	13,727.76	2,741.65
1,563	17,644	212	31,802	59,829	1,683	117	1,800	4,046,294	976,593	5,022,886	46.3	10,840,926	15,745.81	3,008.47
10	318	3	509	1,052	0	0	0	63,019	11,083	74,102	49.2	150,572	8,535.34	2,353.05
32	487	25	908	1,599	0	0	0	105,283	35,862	141,145	44.9	314,070	11,811.58	1,652.99
7	613	16	895	1,695	0	0	0	97,273	26,860	124,134	41.5	299,131	9,013.49	2,261.38
75	985	51	2,065	3,704	3	2	5	236,580	52,621	289,201	48.5	595,857	9,763.03	2,024.55
126	3,011	86	5,815	10,214	28	2	30	704,134	160,280	864,413	48.0	1,802,556	10,576.58	2,351.48
96	1,714	37	3,799	6,508	51	1	52	446,829	96,142	542,970	49.6	1,093,974	11,062.53	2,394.13
30	229	2	541	966	0	2	2	67,710	12,423	80,133	52.4	152,851	10,456.35	2,791.19
1,977	47,721	1,515	75,581	153,427	2,755	89	2,844	9,162,325	2,310,421	11,472,747	45.0	25,492,417	10,692.67	1,919.19
401	7,605	511	13,749	26,642	73	6	79	1,374,699	343,416	1,718,115	48.3	3,554,899	6,551.59	1,094.61
1,576	40,116	1,004	61,832	126,785	2,682	83	2,765	7,787,626	1,967,006	9,754,632	44.5	21,937,518	11,912.84	2,186.05
162	2,664	34	4,034	8,707	0	0	0	482,725	112,254	594,979	38.0	1,565,481	11,464.19	2,245.15
13	481	1	735	1,493	10	3	13	73,970	27,305	101,275	41.1	246,151	7,104.33	1,819.97
85	9,361	197	12,215	26,559	48	12	60	1,654,561	413,124	2,067,685	40.5	5,101,225	10,752.23	2,142.85
65	6,667	78	9,633	20,302	1,189	10	1,199	1,335,413	319,054	1,654,467	42.3	3,906,933	18,597.98	2,798.19
153	1,121	139	2,614	4,560	0	0	0	316,193	51,162	367,355	57.1	642,856	11,534.56	2,258.4
0	500	12	744	1,618	0	0	0	63,789	27,063	90,852	54.8	165,658	8,430.43	1,849.36
495	3,280	178	7,004	12,780	71	6	77	659,933	215,054	874,988	48.7	1,795,078	9,937.54	1,895.99
0	1,949	10	2,408	5,732	443	13	456	347,404	113,367	460,771	47.1	977,315	17,436.49	2,738.63
147	1,141	31	2,644	4,842	35	0	35	321,621	74,569	396,190	48.3	819,764	10,117.79	2,089.09
0	280	17	467	922	0	0	0	51,165	14,461	65,625	47.6	137,777	6,319.74	1,535.01
12	189	10	346	677	0	0	0	41,397	9,363	50,760	39.4	128,815	6,954.31	1,122.65
0	591	2	782	1,784	0	0	0	94,652	25,915	120,567	46.5	259,038	9,219.10	1,825.21
439	5,238	69	7,495	15,837	6	4	10	1,093,074	230,989	1,324,063	52.1	2,542,643	11,959.52	2,182.10
3	738	18	1,070	2,228	0	0	0	124,024	34,343	158,367	49.8	318,271	8,070.57	1,564.11
0	1,490	24	2,446	5,011	9	0	9	319,934	94,110	414,044	48.3	857,745	10,815.50	1,905.26
2	4,426	184	7,195	13,733	871	35	906	807,771	204,872	1,012,644	41.0	2,472,770	12,816.73	2,077.45
1,868	23,381	808	33,038	72,269	1,424	6	1,430	3,981,385	1,180,541	5,161,921	44.9	11,486,590	10,088.41	1,941.32
148	2,091	112	3,686	7,578	31	1	32	442,785	120,529	563,313	47.7	1,180,055	8,135.00	1,384.65
1,720	21,290	696	29,352	64,691	1,393	5	1,398	3,538,600	1,060,012	4,598,608	44.6	10,306,535	10,373.61	2,034.99
12	381	11	332	967	0	0	0	61,274	14,729	76,003	43.5	174,526	8,015.34	1,554.15
21	4,538	93	5,031	12,272	675	0	675	800,508	235,994	1,036,502	42.8	2,420,295	13,827.73	2,722.44
2	855	44	973	2,562	0	0	0	122,329	30,627	152,957	41.6	367,465	7,957.41	1,551.00
142	4,710	145	7,450	14,535	270	0	270	816,945	250,294	1,067,237	49.9	2,139,931	9,708.12	1,947.25
71	1,869	84	2,529	5,614	49	2	51	310,461	72,868	383,327	42.8	896,095	10,358.52	1,935.56
1,335	4,677	108	6,305	15,036	305	2	307	773,856	273,009	1,046,864	42.6	2,454,577	11,815.56	2,285.62
35	584	36	978	2,045	11	0	11	110,305	36,201	146,506	46.1	317,818	6,916.75	1,772.08
14	1,255	55	1,315	3,329	17	1	18	202,883	54,364	257,246	40.9	628,456	7,326.97	1,477.59
88	2,020	116	3,789	7,042	66	0	66	290,982	80,097	371,078	48.4	766,694	9,030.23	1,900.97
0	401	4	650	1,289	0	0	0	49,058	11,829	60,888	43.3	140,678	7,308.69	770.42
2,578	33,783	2,482	51,166	106,120	2,383	187	2,570	7,198,668	1,660,463	8,859,132	45.2	19,592,660	11,064.97	1,958.58
170	2,648	361	4,667	9,368	74	0	74	534,376	135,353	669,729	46.6	1,437,244	7,628.48	998.60
2,408	31,135	2,121	46,499	96,752	2,309	187	2,496	6,664,292	1,525,110	8,189,403	45.1	18,155,417	11,474.15	2,119.90
11	624	42	960	1,974	4	0	4	128,379	29,754	158,133	46.0	343,951	8,599.63	2,106.37
119	2,678	153	3,626	8,497	801	0	801	634,334	162,480	796,814	46.1	1,726,583	18,613.85	3,465.57
120	652	96	1,269	2,404	0	0	0	159,606	36,443	196,049	50.3	389,681	8,975.10	2,393.72
2	283	30	387	771	0	0	0	41,811	11,655	53,466	38.4	139,245	5,987.76	1,558.03
162	915	222	3,895	5,668	19	8	27	362,239	86,124	448,363	54.0	829,809	11,919.63	1,137.93
291	7,698	509	9,592	20,711	1,025	138	1,163	1,443,667	337,018	1,780,684	45.5	3,913,061	12,410.91	2,253.28
555	2,837	146	3,552	8,665	299	3	302	674,480	149,882	824,362	50.5	1,631,680	14,655.99	2,551.05
74	472	84	1,199	2,056	0	0	0	132,838	30,452	163,290	51.1	319,545	9,001.76	2,195.65
585	6,941	636	10,817	22,746	0	15	15	1,478,789	346,260	1,825,050	44.0	4,147,937	10,614.86	1,984.37
471	7,242	182	9,917	20,838	161	23	184	1,437,223	296,919	1,734,142	41.5	4,181,914	10,119.65	2,020.02
18	793	21	1,285	2,422	0	0	0	170,926	38,123	209,050	39.3	532,010	11,293.42	2,225.19

Table continues

MSAs

TABLE 8

U.S. CENSUS DIVISION 3, SOUTH ATLANTIC CONTINUED

U.S. Community Hospitals
(Nonfederal, short-term general and other special hospitals)

2016 Utilization, Personnel and Finances

CLASSIFICATION	Hospitals	Beds	Admissions	Inpatient Days	Adjusted Inpatient Days	Average Daily Census	Adjusted Average Daily Census	Average Stay (days)	Surgical Operations	NEWBORNS		OUTPATIENT VISITS	
										Bassinets	Births	Emergency	Total
West Virginia	54	6,803	251,876	1,474,031	3,629,706	4,035	9,918	5.9	316,009	395	19,621	1,171,598	7,910,022
Nonmetropolitan	26	2,111	54,225	392,630	1,336,912	1,074	3,652	7.2	67,848	134	4,590	440,230	2,431,918
Metropolitan	28	4,692	197,651	1,081,401	2,292,794	2,961	6,266	5.5	248,161	261	15,031	731,368	5,478,104
Beckley	4	493	18,298	102,937	259,590	282	710	5.6	17,648	29	1,020	87,521	303,091
Charleston	6	1,185	45,406	247,992	497,195	679	1,358	5.5	91,617	68	3,549	149,173	1,200,537
Cumberland	1	25	991	2,977	17,473	8	48	3.0	359	0	0	13,130	43,486
Hagerstown-Martinsburg	1	195	8,787	38,010	92,835	104	254	4.3	11,201	21	1,044	59,745	259,882
Huntington-Ashland	3	758	44,560	209,706	394,036	575	1,077	4.7	40,107	55	3,057	113,632	847,981
Morgantown	4	861	40,145	228,072	388,780	624	1,063	5.7	41,892	10	2,686	88,306	1,155,650
Parkersburg-Vienna	2	285	12,583	61,269	111,271	168	304	4.9	10,158	22	1,372	51,854	293,807
Washington-Arlington-Alexandria	1	25	1,270	3,515	18,704	10	51	2.8	2,747	4	247	26,023	68,156
Weirton-Steubenville	1	167	6,254	33,299	111,512	91	305	5.3	6,716	21	384	38,229	409,211
Wheeling	4	654	18,897	140,240	325,485	383	889	7.4	25,086	31	1,672	94,016	848,823
Winchester	1	44	460	13,384	75,913	37	207	29.1	630	0	0	9,739	47,480

MSAs

TABLE 8

U.S. CENSUS DIVISION 3, SOUTH ATLANTIC CONTINUED

U.S. Community Hospitals
(Nonfederal, short-term general and other special hospitals)

2016 Utilization, Personnel and Finances

FULL-TIME EQUIVALENT PERSONNEL					FULL-TIME EQUIV. TRAINEES			EXPENSES						
								LABOR				TOTAL		
Physicians and Dentists	Registered Nurses	Licensed Practical Nurses	Other Salaried Personnel	Total Personnel	Medical and Dental Residents	Other Trainees	Total Trainees	Payroll (in thousands)	Employee Benefits (in thousands)	Total (in thousands)	Percent of Total	Amount (in thousands)	Adjusted per Admission	Adjusted per Inpatient Day
862	11,110	1,219	21,029	40,474	653	27	680	2,253,396	650,636	2,904,031	47.0	6,178,731	9,995.57	1,702.27
301	2,316	478	5,562	10,292	62	1	63	517,706	140,909	658,614	50.1	1,313,376	7,236.51	982.40
561	8,794	741	15,467	30,182	591	26	617	1,735,690	509,727	2,245,417	46.2	4,865,355	11,142.36	2,122.02
35	458	120	838	1,742	1	4	5	91,933	26,056	117,989	41.6	283,611	6,749.75	1,092.53
197	2,393	282	3,958	8,131	170	1	171	500,619	128,716	629,335	46.5	1,353,658	14,421.48	2,722.59
2	37	5	100	186	0	0	0	9,005	2,064	11,069	54.0	20,494	3,523.16	1,172.91
3	397	10	582	1,185	0	0	0	60,547	17,005	77,552	43.4	178,831	8,332.86	1,926.34
79	1,485	111	2,684	5,103	0	2	2	300,136	126,426	426,562	48.0	889,563	10,257.4	2,257.57
61	2,047	117	3,826	7,132	344	17	361	407,062	121,735	528,797	43.8	1,207,926	16,474.26	3,106.96
36	584	24	881	1,753	16	0	16	73,918	20,427	94,344	40.5	232,677	9,515.27	2,091.08
0	115	4	139	330	0	2	2	15,825	3,676	19,501	45.2	43,187	6,390.53	2,308.98
49	360	12	534	1,101	0	0	0	71,186	17,179	88,365	54.3	162,679	7,767.35	1,458.85
96	890	54	1,847	3,367	60	0	60	196,118	44,378	240,496	51.4	467,859	7,972.51	1,437.42
3	28	2	78	152	0	0	0	9,341	2,066	11,407	45.9	24,870	9,532.28	327.61

MSAs

TABLE 8

U.S. CENSUS DIVISION 4, EAST NORTH CENTRAL

U.S. Community Hospitals
(Nonfederal, short-term general and other special hospitals)

2016 Utilization, Personnel and Finances

CLASSIFICATION	Hospitals	Beds	Admissions	Inpatient Days	Adjusted Inpatient Days	Average Daily Census	Adjusted Average Daily Census	Average Stay (days)	Surgical Operations	NEWBORNS Bassinets	NEWBORNS Births	OUTPATIENT VISITS Emergency	OUTPATIENT VISITS Total
UNITED STATES	4,840	780,272	33,424,253	182,291,689	386,210,917	499,407	1,056,009	5.5	27,227,227	55,149	3,727,427	142,557,879	747,089,013
Nonmetropolitan	1,825	111,987	3,103,592	20,547,750	68,564,794	56,294	187,486	6.6	3,578,377	9,181	371,659	22,118,524	126,900,302
Metropolitan	3,015	668,285	30,320,661	161,743,939	317,646,123	443,113	868,523	5.3	23,648,850	45,968	3,355,768	120,439,355	620,188,711
CENSUS DIVISION 4, EAST NORTH CENTRAL	759	119,195	5,160,744	26,008,388	60,994,881	71,256	166,762	5.0	4,588,580	9,379	519,043	23,336,090	155,703,936
Nonmetropolitan	266	16,439	538,793	2,873,761	11,735,864	7,872	32,136	5.3	697,360	1,640	59,435	4,064,297	27,676,450
Metropolitan	493	102,756	4,621,951	23,134,627	49,259,017	63,384	134,626	5.0	3,891,220	7,739	459,608	19,271,793	128,027,486
Illinois	188	31,805	1,374,759	6,889,705	15,224,509	18,874	41,608	5.0	1,087,262	2,543	146,341	5,516,659	38,053,456
Nonmetropolitan	58	3,292	105,330	512,431	1,912,062	1,403	5,225	4.9	130,228	268	9,683	718,219	5,651,753
Metropolitan	130	28,513	1,269,429	6,377,274	13,312,447	17,471	36,383	5.0	957,034	2,275	136,658	4,798,440	32,401,703
Bloomington	3	372	15,649	60,616	125,421	166	343	3.9	12,717	52	2,422	64,321	308,804
Carbondale-Marion	4	398	23,685	84,171	264,760	232	724	3.6	16,591	43	2,469	128,863	515,243
Champaign-Urbana	4	676	31,890	160,258	401,918	439	1,098	5.0	23,350	55	3,648	127,788	1,612,476
Chicago-Naperville-Arlington Heights	69	18,798	848,997	4,359,786	8,693,718	11,941	23,764	5.1	599,939	1,405	92,541	2,969,759	20,729,011
Danville	2	130	5,445	17,927	52,520	49	143	3.3	4,432	26	645	41,246	200,199
Davenport-Moline-Rock Island	5	586	20,642	96,754	284,326	266	776	4.7	17,386	73	2,029	116,983	576,364
Decatur	2	446	16,086	71,849	157,214	197	429	4.5	14,512	40	1,448	79,718	439,970
Elgin	7	1,022	44,086	199,134	436,232	545	1,191	4.5	35,797	99	5,177	209,365	1,574,937
Kankakee	2	474	16,725	79,710	213,944	219	585	4.8	13,305	35	1,448	74,320	677,010
Lake County-Kenosha County	5	918	46,932	192,314	426,261	528	1,164	4.1	37,991	114	6,007	207,038	1,143,595
Peoria	7	1,259	53,916	309,709	621,219	848	1,698	5.7	59,537	67	4,941	182,039	1,555,681
Rockford	4	870	41,297	200,191	379,009	548	1,035	4.8	33,403	100	4,604	178,521	824,575
Springfield	3	934	44,763	233,362	442,653	640	1,209	5.2	38,408	44	3,491	123,532	772,203
St. Louis	13	1,630	59,316	311,493	813,252	853	2,224	5.3	49,666	122	5,788	294,947	1,471,635
Indiana	119	16,947	669,044	3,502,421	8,685,289	9,594	23,743	5.2	608,953	1,536	72,730	3,316,584	20,426,946
Nonmetropolitan	41	2,638	76,840	453,033	2,226,560	1,242	6,086	5.9	108,070	280	9,861	693,731	4,339,758
Metropolitan	78	14,309	592,204	3,049,388	6,458,729	8,352	17,657	5.1	500,883	1,256	62,869	2,622,853	16,087,188
Bloomington	3	330	13,777	60,514	146,378	166	400	4.4	10,247	74	2,071	74,351	841,926
Cincinnati	1	88	4,147	13,973	39,977	38	109	3.4	5,620	11	384	21,964	148,025
Columbus	1	198	8,961	33,559	85,717	92	234	3.7	12,221	20	1,269	45,263	244,844
Elkhart-Goshen	2	388	16,297	64,787	154,918	178	424	4.0	15,501	39	2,768	98,566	475,306
Evansville	6	1,224	52,005	277,652	539,934	762	1,477	5.3	41,588	62	4,371	182,762	1,097,318
Fort Wayne	8	1,563	72,635	356,498	689,320	975	1,884	4.9	86,584	143	7,700	244,375	1,343,885
Gary	11	2,560	94,706	536,195	1,109,093	1,468	3,034	5.7	64,834	224	6,087	468,576	2,149,241
Indianapolis-Carmel-Anderson	25	4,983	199,311	1,097,142	2,335,940	3,006	6,385	5.5	152,266	422	22,902	928,023	6,585,270
Kokomo	3	318	10,104	44,348	122,917	121	336	4.4	7,961	28	1,221	56,696	387,859
Lafayette-West Lafayette	1	191	8,615	38,039	122,731	104	335	4.4	10,248	11	1,606	46,154	103,328
Louisville-Jefferson County	6	559	25,487	116,102	276,639	318	756	4.6	23,025	53	3,081	110,584	1,065,033
Michigan City-La Porte	2	300	11,990	49,575	116,928	136	320	4.1	13,892	35	1,270	64,655	321,691
Muncie	1	339	15,770	83,179	157,743	228	431	5.3	5,767	20	1,454	59,294	302,321
South Bend-Mishawaka	3	771	35,009	176,479	298,310	483	815	5.0	23,391	71	4,184	114,225	404,476
Terre Haute	5	497	23,390	101,346	262,184	277	717	4.3	27,738	43	2,501	107,365	616,665
Michigan	146	24,924	1,159,341	5,802,970	13,655,260	15,901	37,319	5.0	990,469	1,635	106,510	5,157,734	37,432,768
Nonmetropolitan	54	3,646	118,913	698,124	3,019,728	1,911	8,253	5.9	166,217	299	12,120	839,054	6,569,116
Metropolitan	92	21,278	1,040,428	5,104,846	10,635,532	13,990	29,066	4.9	824,252	1,336	94,390	4,318,680	30,863,652
Ann Arbor	5	1,615	88,762	467,891	1,020,531	1,282	2,788	5.3	86,294	69	8,355	211,069	3,755,425
Battle Creek	3	301	12,848	56,965	146,987	156	402	4.4	10,991	26	1,115	89,932	704,571
Bay City	2	359	15,331	77,747	143,271	213	392	5.1	10,401	14	842	45,708	312,755
Detroit-Dearborn-Livonia	20	4,997	251,297	1,237,934	2,506,173	3,393	6,848	4.9	180,886	284	20,608	1,104,810	7,035,671
Flint	4	1,219	60,195	300,146	530,889	822	1,450	5.0	38,265	89	5,104	230,275	1,362,631
Grand Rapids-Wyoming	13	2,368	110,016	548,845	1,177,096	1,503	3,216	5.0	108,544	205	13,609	561,738	4,574,506
Jackson	2	371	17,856	87,565	198,069	240	541	4.9	10,073	19	1,617	86,647	492,187
Kalamazoo-Portage	4	921	43,523	201,284	431,662	552	1,180	4.6	38,709	63	5,044	189,064	1,644,735
Lansing-East Lansing	6	1,073	49,160	243,458	514,472	668	1,408	5.0	39,648	42	5,100	268,127	1,656,329
Midland	1	304	12,540	47,432	126,723	130	346	3.8	14,128	23	1,249	38,518	273,139
Monroe	1	152	7,619	30,686	80,393	84	220	4.0	5,618	13	800	43,757	156,595
Muskegon	2	432	18,859	79,307	193,352	217	529	4.2	21,106	26	1,963	112,450	1,029,714
Niles-Benton Harbor	2	341	17,008	79,713	158,064	219	433	4.7	6,093	35	346	97,613	531,360
Saginaw	3	796	38,095	202,490	403,086	555	1,102	5.3	20,096	31	3,103	142,353	648,124
South Bend-Mishawaka	1	25	359	1,174	11,888	3	32	3.3	408	0	0	10,968	105,067
Warren-Troy-Farmington Hills	23	6,004	296,960	1,442,209	2,992,876	3,953	8,179	4.9	232,992	397	25,535	1,085,651	6,580,843

TABLE 8

U.S. CENSUS DIVISION 4, EAST NORTH CENTRAL

U.S. Community Hospitals
(Nonfederal, short-term general and other special hospitals)

2016 Utilization, Personnel and Finances

FULL-TIME EQUIVALENT PERSONNEL					FULL-TIME EQUIV. TRAINEES			EXPENSES						
								LABOR				TOTAL		
Physicians and Dentists	Registered Nurses	Licensed Practical Nurses	Other Salaried Personnel	Total Personnel	Medical and Dental Residents	Other Trainees	Total Trainees	Payroll (in thousands)	Employee Benefits (in thousands)	Total (in thousands)	Percent of Total	Amount (in thousands)	Adjusted per Admission	Adjusted per Inpatient Day
135,693	1,478,657	74,344	2,612,576	4,991,775	113,111	9,619	122,730	$340,132,974	$90,463,641	$430,596,618	47.7	$902,891,035	$12,777.25	$2,337.82
15,408	149,651	20,977	339,776	612,547	1,714	261	1,975	35,531,908	9,378,885	44,910,794	50.2	89,420,776	8,694.35	1,304.18
120,285	1,329,006	53,367	2,272,800	4,379,228	111,397	9,358	120,755	304,601,066	81,084,755	385,685,824	47.4	813,470,258	13,472.72	2,560.93
24,943	245,764	9,162	449,582	839,974	23,611	1,851	25,462	55,879,203	14,454,353	70,333,547	47.2	148,881,103	12,348.25	2,440.88
3,057	27,574	2,930	66,193	114,063	215	62	277	6,937,015	2,015,556	8,952,569	50.7	17,642,701	8,599.01	1,503.32
21,886	218,190	6,232	383,389	725,911	23,396	1,789	25,185	48,942,189	12,438,798	61,380,978	46.8	131,238,402	13,117.09	2,664.25
7,104	61,250	1,693	104,331	203,929	7,068	430	7,498	13,444,665	3,467,112	16,911,775	45.7	37,012,401	11,946.76	2,431.11
530	5,448	686	12,806	22,645	28	1	29	1,285,941	399,359	1,685,300	51.7	3,262,601	8,280.27	1,706.33
6,574	55,802	1,007	91,525	181,284	7,040	429	7,469	12,158,723	3,067,753	15,226,475	45.1	33,749,800	12,481.01	2,535.21
4	630	14	1,061	2,034	26	0	26	109,286	30,361	139,646	43.0	324,928	10,094.69	2,590.70
7	917	44	1,530	2,826	21	0	21	161,563	49,184	210,746	37.2	565,827	8,471.85	2,137.13
26	1,613	59	1,806	4,435	33	0	33	248,560	65,472	314,031	38.4	817,267	10,911.58	2,033.42
5,471	38,411	575	60,570	123,312	6,345	392	6,737	8,619,313	2,139,191	10,758,504	45.8	23,472,421	13,568.20	2,699.93
4	211	11	337	703	0	0	0	40,101	9,838	49,939	41.4	120,569	7,590.11	2,295.68
51	873	14	1,569	2,778	5	0	5	158,741	40,599	199,340	40.4	493,229	8,179.46	1,734.73
51	689	37	1,464	2,635	19	2	21	162,936	39,112	202,047	47.6	424,471	12,147.88	2,699.96
108	1,937	17	3,072	6,097	0	0	0	381,398	92,896	474,295	40.6	1,168,317	11,481.33	2,678.20
69	805	29	1,577	2,733	20	0	20	164,982	34,165	199,147	48.2	413,362	9,282.35	1,932.10
245	2,031	13	3,400	6,700	16	2	18	420,680	92,214	512,894	45.0	1,139,957	11,035.19	2,674.32
219	2,364	34	4,473	7,983	253	6	259	558,749	138,848	697,596	46.5	1,500,569	13,856.31	2,415.52
218	1,680	15	2,824	5,553	5	27	32	355,354	107,970	463,324	46.3	1,001,740	12,380.31	2,643.05
2	1,539	46	3,613	5,937	289	0	289	355,657	114,185	469,841	39.9	1,177,030	13,669.23	2,659.04
99	2,102	99	4,229	7,558	8	0	8	421,405	113,719	535,125	47.4	1,130,113	6,881.74	1,389.62
2,088	30,599	1,383	60,091	107,970	1,129	167	1,296	7,162,472	1,814,222	8,976,694	43.8	20,473,532	12,453.24	2,357.27
626	4,104	534	10,775	18,192	3	40	43	1,141,852	301,936	1,443,788	50.3	2,871,244	8,498.45	1,289.54
1,462	26,495	849	49,316	89,778	1,126	127	1,253	6,020,621	1,512,286	7,532,906	42.8	17,602,288	13,476.18	2,725.35
16	757	10	1,119	2,302	2	1	3	126,283	35,489	161,772	42.4	381,539	11,169.49	2,606.53
0	143	11	400	660	0	0	0	34,833	10,311	45,144	57.6	78,396	6,607.34	1,961.03
3	308	17	995	1,534	0	0	0	76,194	25,072	101,267	42.5	238,022	10,399.43	2,776.84
63	847	19	1,556	2,847	1	0	1	148,726	48,642	197,368	41.8	472,219	12,018.51	3,048.19
192	2,108	73	3,735	7,230	82	17	99	494,187	134,342	628,529	47.8	1,315,263	12,551.77	2,435.97
4	2,838	72	4,269	7,997	0	44	44	455,424	123,393	578,818	38.2	1,514,504	10,387.05	2,197.10
181	3,907	131	6,365	11,947	78	7	85	799,997	207,264	1,007,261	45.3	2,224,973	11,517.56	2,006.12
571	10,131	281	21,280	37,049	799	42	841	2,707,510	615,570	3,323,080	41.4	8,021,805	17,756.35	3,434.08
12	445	10	764	1,440	0	7	7	84,202	20,743	104,944	39.9	262,945	9,042.45	2,139.21
169	434	38	882	1,742	0	2	2	161,536	32,145	193,681	50.8	381,628	13,729.61	3,109.47
125	1,086	120	2,364	4,251	0	0	0	273,139	73,321	346,459	52.5	659,492	10,381.46	2,383.95
69	476	17	1,162	2,055	4	1	5	137,049	35,625	172,673	45.7	377,826	13,337.07	3,231.27
1	569	5	908	1,737	65	2	67	103,930	37,357	141,287	41.5	340,833	11,396.42	2,160.68
22	1,494	20	2,111	4,164	65	4	69	234,530	60,553	295,083	40.8	723,132	12,065.87	2,424.09
34	952	25	1,406	2,823	30	0	30	183,081	52,459	235,540	38.6	609,711	9,547.62	2,325.51
5,232	52,946	1,880	98,737	184,239	6,689	328	7,017	12,016,044	2,723,105	14,739,143	48.1	30,657,065	11,620.96	2,245.07
730	5,518	630	14,100	24,110	70	10	80	1,480,048	411,691	1,891,735	49.2	3,848,361	8,403.09	1,274.41
4,502	47,428	1,250	84,637	160,129	6,619	318	6,937	10,535,996	2,311,414	12,847,408	47.9	26,808,704	12,296.93	2,520.67
99	6,670	112	11,784	20,908	1,529	0	1,529	1,423,081	413,128	1,836,209	48.1	3,817,255	19,120.79	3,740.46
66	708	34	1,283	2,507	2	3	5	172,221	38,060	210,280	56.8	370,409	10,749.90	2,520.01
47	546	26	1,288	2,114	16	0	16	126,012	25,690	151,702	53.0	286,204	9,858.91	1,997.64
1,450	11,557	140	17,865	36,931	2,471	106	2,577	2,643,162	503,901	3,147,063	48.2	6,530,023	12,917.05	2,605.58
111	2,632	41	3,759	7,341	378	16	394	541,924	150,229	692,153	55.1	1,255,829	11,723.03	2,365.52
541	4,862	299	11,321	19,684	105	90	195	1,064,656	280,975	1,345,630	40.4	3,331,941	14,196.72	2,830.65
88	739	37	2,363	3,641	96	0	96	235,644	48,034	283,678	54.9	517,050	11,975.67	2,610.45
330	1,889	36	3,605	6,987	3	6	9	551,649	117,333	688,982	54.7	1,224,030	13,012.19	2,835.62
367	2,339	30	4,202	8,276	266	5	271	601,814	159,444	761,258	55.9	1,360,970	12,318.37	2,645.37
9	565	10	1,065	1,864	30	2	32	107,556	31,647	139,203	37.9	367,483	10,968.66	2,899.89
2	318	3	682	1,101	55	0	55	52,289	13,646	65,935	45.1	146,243	7,326.44	1,819.10
126	761	12	2,247	3,430	58	7	65	229,491	48,177	277,669	53.2	522,002	11,110.22	2,699.75
68	934	36	1,540	3,001	32	4	36	147,908	37,617	185,525	47.3	392,342	11,758.38	2,482.17
204	1,264	53	3,682	5,774	0	0	0	357,529	86,550	444,080	52.5	845,728	11,032.20	2,098.13
10	37	0	92	172	0	0	0	11,987	2,598	14,585	58.7	24,867	6,840.99	2,091.77
984	11,607	381	17,859	36,398	1,578	79	1,657	2,269,074	354,384	2,623,456	45.1	5,816,326	9,569.58	1,943.39

Table continues

MSAs

TABLE 8

U.S. CENSUS DIVISION 4, EAST NORTH CENTRAL CONTINUED

U.S. Community Hospitals
(Nonfederal, short-term general and other special hospitals)

2016 Utilization, Personnel and Finances

CLASSIFICATION	Hospitals	Beds	Admissions	Inpatient Days	Adjusted Inpatient Days	Average Daily Census	Adjusted Average Daily Census	Average Stay (days)	Surgical Operations	NEWBORNS		OUTPATIENT VISITS	
										Bassinets	Births	Emergency	Total
Ohio	179	33,277	1,427,555	7,164,552	15,619,814	19,633	42,750	5.0	1,246,786	2,571	129,240	6,972,256	41,194,171
Nonmetropolitan	56	4,344	157,836	689,493	2,116,259	1,892	5,847	4.4	195,848	539	17,078	1,280,916	7,088,733
Metropolitan	123	28,933	1,269,719	6,475,059	13,503,555	17,741	36,903	5.1	1,050,938	2,032	112,162	5,691,340	34,105,438
Akron	7	1,841	79,059	400,996	913,845	1,098	2,497	5.1	63,668	108	7,338	436,596	2,506,044
Canton-Massillon	5	1,205	46,389	262,523	585,375	720	1,599	5.7	33,163	111	4,494	237,361	1,407,920
Cincinnati	19	4,602	202,072	1,042,336	1,963,471	2,856	5,369	5.2	159,682	337	18,727	761,466	4,668,105
Cleveland-Elyria	27	7,374	318,425	1,746,516	3,942,568	4,786	10,775	5.5	331,334	375	24,284	1,265,710	11,930,308
Columbus	22	5,697	256,541	1,287,473	2,441,980	3,527	6,672	5.0	211,731	426	28,674	1,144,788	5,984,048
Dayton	11	2,654	115,514	488,867	1,037,603	1,339	2,834	4.2	86,801	199	11,354	616,728	1,985,485
Lima	5	526	27,687	116,638	252,366	320	690	4.2	21,974	78	2,351	114,375	740,863
Mansfield	2	276	11,896	59,413	126,471	163	346	5.0	7,230	32	927	49,310	343,100
Springfield	1	259	13,677	63,918	127,375	175	349	4.7	3,658	25	820	59,643	302,626
Toledo	11	2,356	104,352	524,251	1,125,258	1,436	3,074	5.0	87,147	164	8,364	409,438	2,351,243
Weirton-Steubenville	2	372	10,418	76,827	187,962	211	514	7.4	4,618	18	537	43,902	285,719
Wheeling	3	211	4,513	34,673	112,602	95	307	7.7	7,260	0	0	36,956	230,013
Youngstown-Warren-Boardman	8	1,560	79,176	370,628	686,679	1,015	1,877	4.7	32,672	159	4,292	515,067	1,369,964
Wisconsin	127	12,242	530,045	2,648,740	7,810,009	7,254	21,342	5.0	655,110	1,094	64,222	2,372,857	18,596,595
Nonmetropolitan	57	2,519	79,874	520,680	2,461,255	1,424	6,725	6.5	96,997	254	10,693	532,377	4,027,090
Metropolitan	70	9,723	450,171	2,128,060	5,348,754	5,830	14,617	4.7	558,113	840	53,529	1,840,480	14,569,505
Appleton	3	352	16,912	68,942	164,409	189	450	4.1	35,656	41	2,412	62,955	395,906
Duluth	1	25	503	2,730	45,807	7	125	5.4	1,961	0	0	15,067	52,428
Eau Claire	5	538	23,568	110,397	240,032	304	655	4.7	12,084	33	2,395	63,746	471,139
Fond du Lac	2	178	7,387	29,357	122,868	80	336	4.0	15,085	23	839	38,569	793,517
Green Bay	5	680	32,446	131,896	390,355	362	1,067	4.1	46,460	95	4,497	137,110	1,601,924
Janesville-Beloit	4	306	15,088	64,516	212,887	177	582	4.3	15,220	15	1,817	90,107	1,472,896
La Crosse-Onalaska	2	350	20,744	89,049	333,141	244	910	4.3	26,457	20	2,354	75,492	744,918
Lake County-Kenosha County	3	502	21,883	90,493	237,987	248	651	4.1	21,952	51	2,844	194,859	1,003,470
Madison	9	1,630	76,007	409,660	1,047,587	1,123	2,863	5.4	169,293	99	8,295	202,928	1,832,745
Milwaukee-Waukesha-West Allis	22	3,823	174,085	874,486	1,879,083	2,393	5,134	5.0	140,096	316	20,068	712,758	4,627,796
Minneapolis-St. Paul-Bloomington	4	76	3,452	9,540	54,518	27	148	2.8	5,793	19	936	29,199	202,046
Oshkosh-Neenah	4	354	15,734	63,413	158,234	173	433	4.0	27,775	59	2,592	58,728	375,053
Racine	2	405	15,172	80,882	225,954	222	618	5.3	11,945	31	1,683	76,203	684,940
Sheboygan	2	182	8,001	27,160	84,248	74	230	3.4	12,243	15	1,105	34,869	172,163
Wausau	2	322	19,189	75,539	151,644	207	415	3.9	16,093	23	1,692	47,890	138,564

MSAs

TABLE 8

U.S. CENSUS DIVISION 4, EAST NORTH CENTRAL CONTINUED

U.S. Community Hospitals
(Nonfederal, short-term general and other special hospitals)

2016 Utilization, Personnel and Finances

FULL-TIME EQUIVALENT PERSONNEL					FULL-TIME EQUIV. TRAINEES			EXPENSES						
								LABOR				TOTAL		
Physicians and Dentists	Registered Nurses	Licensed Practical Nurses	Other Salaried Personnel	Total Personnel	Medical and Dental Residents	Other Trainees	Total Trainees	Payroll (in thousands)	Employee Benefits (in thousands)	Total (in thousands)	Percent of Total	Amount (in thousands)	Adjusted per Admission	Adjusted per Inpatient Day
9,057	74,204	3,277	129,890	249,147	7,854	518	8,372	16,657,643	4,522,936	21,180,580	50.2	42,234,370	13,192.38	2,703.90
750	8,549	827	17,725	32,070	110	8	118	1,703,869	527,842	2,231,715	48.9	4,562,918	8,788.82	2,156.12
8,307	65,655	2,450	112,165	217,077	7,744	510	8,254	14,953,774	3,995,095	18,948,865	50.3	37,671,452	14,044.73	2,789.74
624	4,423	281	9,298	15,774	534	76	610	959,287	239,765	1,199,051	50.0	2,395,899	13,024.09	2,621.78
186	2,091	197	4,901	8,122	80	12	92	391,669	105,769	497,438	51.1	972,738	9,806.52	1,661.74
1,560	9,997	261	19,783	35,790	1,421	156	1,577	2,640,071	656,559	3,296,630	50.5	6,529,681	16,378.33	3,325.58
3,292	18,363	886	33,022	64,255	2,976	228	3,204	5,037,282	1,336,016	6,373,297	56.1	11,368,114	15,824.57	2,883.43
2,174	14,226	208	21,417	44,445	1,572	13	1,585	2,649,138	729,650	3,378,787	45.8	7,382,887	14,397.54	3,023.32
118	6,119	65	8,041	17,079	418	14	432	1,247,679	386,098	1,633,778	51.5	3,173,098	12,737.53	3,058.10
101	1,033	103	2,019	3,727	20	2	22	180,861	61,170	242,031	43.8	552,828	8,926.52	2,190.58
2	438	34	1,182	1,816	0	0	0	103,244	30,865	134,110	51.4	260,669	9,646.21	2,061.10
37	416	17	752	1,406	14	1	15	83,233	22,028	105,261	47.2	222,800	8,174.63	1,749.16
64	4,674	164	6,698	13,635	514	0	514	1,010,104	259,015	1,269,120	43.9	2,893,062	13,726.22	2,571.02
38	572	23	876	1,781	20	3	23	95,000	30,891	125,890	46.2	272,432	9,508.31	1,449.40
31	253	36	496	942	1	1	2	44,291	10,355	54,647	46.1	118,502	7,885.93	1,052.40
80	3,050	175	3,680	8,305	174	4	178	511,914	126,912	638,825	41.8	1,528,740	10,227.40	2,226.28
1,462	26,765	929	56,533	94,689	871	408	1,279	6,598,380	1,926,977	8,525,355	46.1	18,503,735	12,543.10	2,369.23
421	3,955	253	10,787	17,046	4	3	7	1,325,304	374,728	1,700,031	54.9	3,097,577	9,038.93	1,258.54
1,041	22,810	676	45,746	77,643	867	405	1,272	5,273,076	1,552,250	6,825,324	44.3	15,406,158	13,603.44	2,880.33
27	684	27	1,185	2,154	5	1	6	156,920	43,523	200,443	48.6	412,671	10,225.75	2,510.02
0	34	7	139	190	0	0	0	18,533	4,768	23,301	65.0	35,835	4,245.82	782.30
26	1,036	11	1,861	3,174	0	0	0	225,870	98,564	324,434	55.2	588,200	11,718.06	2,450.51
61	391	107	1,461	2,073	0	0	0	137,733	38,122	175,855	47.7	368,407	11,914.47	2,998.40
167	1,488	131	3,701	5,841	0	15	15	425,381	111,530	536,911	43.5	1,233,828	12,559.71	3,160.78
327	818	34	1,849	3,258	19	0	19	262,998	80,780	343,777	48.2	713,144	14,491.25	3,349.87
167	1,236	97	2,734	4,523	16	16	32	471,743	144,577	616,320	52.9	1,165,525	15,017.14	3,498.59
44	1,238	37	2,478	4,290	16	6	22	268,686	75,394	344,079	49.6	694,404	11,869.54	2,917.82
98	4,048	52	9,511	15,376	638	159	797	984,585	336,479	1,321,064	48.1	2,746,614	16,403.37	2,621.85
115	9,185	92	14,270	26,636	157	207	364	1,732,532	456,889	2,189,419	38.0	5,757,119	14,960.98	3,063.79
9	183	11	597	864	0	0	0	67,390	16,375	83,766	47.5	176,187	9,034.29	3,231.72
0	663	13	1,060	1,976	0	1	1	140,893	39,926	180,819	46.1	392,263	9,504.80	2,479.01
0	737	41	2,061	3,081	0	0	0	144,192	39,633	183,825	45.0	408,595	9,434.42	1,808.31
0	343	3	509	947	0	0	0	60,394	18,156	78,550	37.7	208,288	8,388.23	2,472.32
0	726	13	2,330	3,260	16	0	16	175,225	47,536	222,761	44.1	505,080	13,334.38	3,330.69

MSAs

TABLE **8**

U.S. CENSUS DIVISION 5, EAST SOUTH CENTRAL

U.S. Community Hospitals
(Nonfederal, short-term general and other special hospitals)

2016 Utilization, Personnel and Finances

CLASSIFICATION	Hospitals	Beds	Admissions	Inpatient Days	Adjusted Inpatient Days	Average Daily Census	Adjusted Average Daily Census	Average Stay (days)	Surgical Operations	NEWBORNS Bassinets	Births	OUTPATIENT VISITS Emergency	Total
UNITED STATES	4,840	780,272	33,424,253	182,291,689	386,210,917	499,407	1,056,009	5.5	27,227,227	55,149	3,727,427	142,557,879	747,089,013
Nonmetropolitan	1,825	111,987	3,103,592	20,547,750	68,564,794	56,294	187,486	6.6	3,578,377	9,181	371,659	22,118,524	126,900,302
Metropolitan	3,015	668,285	30,320,661	161,743,939	317,646,123	443,113	868,523	5.3	23,648,850	45,968	3,355,768	120,439,355	620,188,711
CENSUS DIVISION 5, EAST SOUTH CENTRAL	411	60,487	2,393,807	13,556,446	29,599,581	37,135	80,899	5.7	2,078,845	3,958	216,461	10,162,137	41,841,580
Nonmetropolitan	214	18,531	524,242	3,345,895	9,612,471	9,164	26,268	6.4	535,135	1,277	52,779	3,207,781	12,496,632
Metropolitan	197	41,956	1,869,565	10,210,551	19,987,110	27,971	54,631	5.5	1,543,710	2,681	163,682	6,954,356	29,344,948
Alabama	95	15,115	630,982	3,556,712	7,314,471	9,740	19,985	5.6	579,190	1,097	58,959	2,204,653	8,770,252
Nonmetropolitan	40	2,574	74,857	398,247	1,196,561	1,091	3,269	5.3	89,430	186	7,162	464,635	1,729,833
Metropolitan	55	12,541	556,125	3,158,465	6,117,910	8,649	16,716	5.7	489,760	911	51,797	1,740,018	7,040,419
Anniston-Oxford-Jacksonville	3	429	17,034	82,742	194,910	226	534	4.9	12,003	15	1,373	49,089	169,008
Auburn-Opelika	1	475	15,214	114,025	205,614	312	562	7.5	17,910	38	1,842	19,143	131,948
Birmingham-Hoover	15	4,607	189,985	1,188,565	2,150,978	3,255	5,878	6.3	185,419	365	16,515	577,408	2,722,071
Columbus	1	48	1,284	16,491	41,434	45	113	12.8	0	0	0	0	3,858
Daphne-Fairhope-Foley	3	298	17,542	71,716	160,057	196	437	4.1	18,876	37	2,090	80,070	288,173
Decatur	2	153	6,945	36,291	98,589	99	269	5.2	8,552	20	547	33,641	163,867
Dothan	4	744	34,044	212,674	466,784	583	1,276	6.2	31,757	57	2,801	108,049	341,281
Florence-Muscle Shoals	3	560	25,263	107,795	268,153	295	732	4.3	15,378	50	2,039	68,992	185,492
Gadsden	3	598	23,155	117,888	211,127	323	577	5.1	18,781	26	1,078	54,603	147,199
Huntsville	4	1,232	63,787	312,059	661,975	854	1,808	4.9	71,677	79	6,571	240,785	1,056,917
Mobile	5	1,385	69,156	396,601	686,747	1,086	1,876	5.7	49,365	93	6,302	201,981	613,882
Montgomery	8	1,064	49,412	268,380	507,102	736	1,385	5.4	41,335	64	5,514	226,148	620,425
Tuscaloosa	3	948	43,304	233,238	464,440	639	1,269	5.4	18,707	67	5,125	80,109	596,298
Kentucky	103	13,978	560,235	3,055,410	6,833,131	8,369	18,677	5.5	539,362	884	55,003	2,596,349	13,848,503
Nonmetropolitan	62	5,656	190,936	990,314	2,764,307	2,712	7,556	5.2	208,728	436	18,444	1,139,299	5,219,441
Metropolitan	41	8,322	369,299	2,065,096	4,068,824	5,657	11,121	5.6	330,634	448	36,559	1,457,050	8,629,062
Bowling Green	3	545	22,369	116,120	233,818	317	639	5.2	19,871	19	2,518	89,588	201,283
Cincinnati	5	918	48,791	219,592	437,034	601	1,194	4.5	31,894	38	4,448	207,799	1,511,804
Clarksville	2	158	6,164	32,599	75,758	89	207	5.3	3,440	18	740	40,293	176,359
Elizabethtown-Fort Knox	2	308	13,493	65,482	198,901	180	544	4.9	14,342	26	1,625	67,144	420,221
Evansville	1	115	4,015	18,621	66,212	51	181	4.6	3,653	12	677	29,911	336,694
Huntington-Ashland	2	595	21,786	184,163	393,320	505	1,077	8.5	29,610	18	2,384	184,998	1,177,335
Lexington-Fayette	12	2,283	92,521	550,828	1,021,537	1,509	2,791	6.0	80,350	125	8,915	290,634	2,289,405
Louisville-Jefferson County	13	3,040	142,166	789,956	1,454,471	2,165	3,975	5.6	128,436	162	13,129	473,609	1,592,097
Owensboro	1	360	17,994	87,735	187,773	240	513	4.9	19,038	30	2,123	73,074	923,864
Mississippi	93	12,032	378,550	2,447,098	6,127,167	6,706	16,739	6.5	279,066	712	35,787	1,814,490	6,056,451
Nonmetropolitan	67	6,890	166,467	1,361,954	4,015,779	3,732	10,970	8.2	138,017	407	17,909	933,638	3,175,094
Metropolitan	26	5,142	212,083	1,085,144	2,111,388	2,974	5,769	5.1	141,049	305	17,878	880,852	2,881,357
Gulfport-Biloxi-Pascagoula	6	1,312	46,325	225,021	458,981	616	1,255	4.9	37,574	90	4,276	282,497	1,086,998
Hattiesburg	3	756	36,205	177,407	294,880	486	805	4.9	19,084	30	3,690	121,125	230,966
Jackson	14	2,798	112,453	604,261	1,195,182	1,657	3,265	5.4	79,180	149	8,270	402,313	1,423,236
Memphis	3	276	17,100	78,455	162,345	215	444	4.6	5,211	36	1,642	74,917	140,157
Tennessee	120	19,362	824,040	4,497,226	9,324,812	12,320	25,498	5.5	681,227	1,265	66,712	3,546,645	13,166,374
Nonmetropolitan	45	3,411	91,982	595,380	1,635,824	1,629	4,473	6.5	98,960	248	9,264	670,209	2,372,264
Metropolitan	75	15,951	732,058	3,901,846	7,688,988	10,691	21,025	5.3	582,267	1,017	57,448	2,876,436	10,794,110
Chattanooga	5	1,772	83,445	477,043	900,869	1,307	2,462	5.7	70,164	90	7,819	325,789	1,109,098
Clarksville	1	247	13,157	53,880	88,467	148	242	4.1	7,762	30	383	78,293	187,777
Cleveland	2	210	9,573	41,550	97,227	114	266	4.3	8,389	19	1,060	51,899	113,341
Jackson	2	769	35,153	197,252	397,681	541	1,087	5.6	28,706	46	3,450	114,236	247,633
Johnson City	4	833	39,870	207,773	435,720	569	1,191	5.2	18,664	42	2,652	118,460	415,073
Kingsport-Bristol-Bristol	6	906	37,520	178,210	391,543	488	1,072	4.7	25,003	73	2,603	141,386	474,267
Knoxville	13	2,512	116,546	637,617	1,268,108	1,747	3,467	5.5	108,151	146	10,071	507,808	1,840,985
Memphis	12	3,319	139,058	796,107	1,499,795	2,180	4,100	5.7	86,472	217	14,356	616,038	1,597,830
Morristown	3	320	11,850	51,332	117,595	141	322	4.3	15,001	25	1,188	74,929	213,618
Nashville-Davidson-Murfreesboro-Franklin	27	5,063	245,886	1,261,082	2,491,983	3,456	6,816	5.1	213,955	329	13,866	847,598	4,594,488

TABLE 8

U.S. CENSUS DIVISION 5, EAST SOUTH CENTRAL

U.S. Community Hospitals
(Nonfederal, short-term general and other special hospitals)

2016 Utilization, Personnel and Finances

| FULL-TIME EQUIVALENT PERSONNEL | | | | | FULL-TIME EQUIV. TRAINEES | | | EXPENSES | | | | | | |
| | | | | | | | | LABOR | | | | TOTAL | | |
Physicians and Dentists	Registered Nurses	Licensed Practical Nurses	Other Salaried Personnel	Total Personnel	Medical and Dental Residents	Other Trainees	Total Trainees	Payroll (in thousands)	Employee Benefits (in thousands)	Total (in thousands)	Percent of Total	Amount (in thousands)	Adjusted per Admission	Adjusted per Inpatient Day
135,693	1,478,657	74,344	2,612,576	4,991,775	113,111	9,619	122,730	$340,132,974	$90,463,641	$430,596,618	47.7	$902,891,035	$12,777.25	$2,337.82
15,408	149,651	20,977	339,776	612,547	1,714	261	1,975	35,531,908	9,378,885	44,910,794	50.2	89,420,776	8,694.35	1,304.18
120,285	1,329,006	53,367	2,272,800	4,379,228	111,397	9,358	120,755	304,601,066	81,084,755	385,685,824	47.4	813,470,258	13,472.72	2,560.93
4,774	98,549	5,977	152,042	308,799	5,127	403	5,530	17,263,773	4,251,354	21,515,120	45.2	47,567,158	9,133.85	1,607.02
1,550	21,260	2,570	42,526	80,381	287	71	358	3,892,350	996,335	4,888,681	47.3	10,325,077	7,002.66	1,074.13
3,224	77,289	3,407	109,516	228,418	4,840	332	5,172	13,371,423	3,255,019	16,626,439	44.6	37,242,082	9,975.55	1,863.30
1,429	26,331	1,258	37,940	78,303	1,834	53	1,887	4,007,293	969,973	4,977,260	46.0	10,823,759	8,172.25	1,479.77
200	2,973	358	5,995	11,144	34	1	35	462,888	118,275	581,160	47.9	1,212,362	5,215.94	1,013.21
1,229	23,358	900	31,945	67,159	1,800	52	1,852	3,544,404	851,698	4,396,100	45.7	9,611,397	8,801.49	1,571.03
37	450	36	1,023	1,776	21	2	23	94,577	25,354	119,931	52.0	230,660	5,843.78	1,183.42
84	760	44	1,480	2,784	137	4	141	105,299	35,887	141,186	53.1	265,718	9,685.71	1,292.31
266	8,986	204	10,699	24,271	930	3	933	1,447,239	319,467	1,766,707	42.9	4,120,349	11,782.93	1,915.57
1	48	6	92	172	0	0	0	6,386	1,363	7,748	38.6	20,091	6,227.73	484.88
37	579	39	972	1,925	13	0	13	88,298	22,081	110,378	46.5	237,236	6,101.45	1,482.20
33	294	37	667	1,211	8	1	9	50,559	15,673	66,231	52.1	127,215	6,708.21	1,290.35
100	1,087	134	2,280	4,140	12	0	12	221,680	42,250	263,930	47.4	556,913	7,850.15	1,193.08
48	649	39	1,370	2,403	22	2	24	108,655	29,877	138,531	52.0	266,312	4,226.98	993.14
14	764	34	919	2,059	26	1	27	91,691	20,053	111,743	41.5	269,455	6,709.86	1,276.27
230	4,046	157	3,768	9,077	24	4	28	443,886	132,236	576,121	50.6	1,138,431	8,320.34	1,719.75
220	2,626	51	3,946	7,880	404	8	412	409,886	101,151	511,036	47.7	1,072,406	8,875.10	1,561.57
73	1,842	55	2,521	5,304	1	1	2	284,644	48,232	332,877	41.5	801,217	8,305.26	1,579.99
86	1,227	64	2,208	4,157	202	26	228	191,605	58,076	249,681	49.4	505,396	5,868.44	1,088.18
963	24,039	1,180	37,203	75,360	934	39	973	4,374,530	1,146,040	5,520,570	43.6	12,661,869	9,731.28	1,853.01
638	7,463	798	15,006	28,251	126	21	147	1,462,127	414,939	1,877,066	46.6	4,029,099	7,406.02	1,457.54
325	16,576	382	22,197	47,109	808	18	826	2,912,403	731,101	3,643,504	42.2	8,632,770	11,402.10	2,121.69
37	908	7	1,370	2,596	5	0	5	141,095	35,391	176,486	36.7	481,223	10,541.81	2,058.11
29	1,542	31	3,011	5,026	24	0	24	388,718	105,108	493,827	51.7	955,066	9,798.97	2,185.34
22	282	19	542	1,037	6	0	6	53,336	12,840	66,176	46.9	141,022	9,586.14	1,861.48
68	527	26	1,496	2,310	0	0	0	127,434	32,090	159,524	56.1	284,467	6,534.22	1,430.20
28	278	9	602	1,054	8	9	17	40,572	13,874	54,446	49.0	111,133	7,784.02	1,678.43
102	1,154	36	2,069	3,949	78	5	83	236,821	65,573	302,394	46.2	654,253	13,307.29	1,663.41
30	4,726	88	5,696	13,200	662	4	666	781,046	205,272	986,317	39.4	2,500,197	13,722.49	2,447.49
9	6,400	154	5,932	15,329	25	0	25	986,228	215,906	1,202,134	39.4	3,047,809	11,221.27	2,095.48
0	759	12	1,479	2,608	0	0	0	157,153	45,047	202,200	44.2	457,601	11,882.35	2,436.99
901	15,178	1,358	25,628	52,468	718	53	771	2,848,099	654,733	3,502,832	48.6	7,206,410	8,393.64	1,176.14
496	7,113	965	14,042	27,027	61	35	96	1,333,049	314,469	1,647,517	48.2	3,416,551	7,852.06	850.78
405	8,065	393	11,586	25,441	657	18	675	1,515,050	340,264	1,855,315	49.0	3,789,859	8,950.15	1,794.96
244	2,324	114	2,701	6,669	5	0	5	414,958	83,884	498,843	49.4	1,009,863	10,373.21	2,200.23
43	1,207	49	1,998	4,093	41	5	46	208,704	51,815	260,520	45.6	571,376	9,301.40	1,937.66
118	4,044	203	6,225	13,272	611	1	612	796,334	182,819	979,152	50.4	1,943,185	8,469.14	1,625.85
0	490	27	662	1,407	0	12	12	95,054	21,747	116,800	44.0	265,435	7,537.35	1,635.01
1,481	33,001	2,181	51,271	102,668	1,641	258	1,899	6,033,851	1,480,608	7,514,458	44.5	16,875,121	9,790.47	1,809.70
216	3,711	449	7,483	13,959	66	14	80	634,286	148,652	782,938	47.0	1,667,065	6,341.76	1,019.10
1,265	29,290	1,732	43,788	88,709	1,575	244	1,819	5,399,565	1,331,956	6,731,520	44.3	15,208,056	10,411.08	1,977.90
307	3,218	151	5,023	9,938	208	57	265	573,440	153,535	726,976	46.1	1,576,138	10,158.34	1,749.57
8	420	17	486	1,108	15	1	16	59,004	13,148	72,152	43.3	166,611	7,712.38	1,883.31
5	408	21	576	1,246	0	1	1	48,996	9,974	58,970	40.5	145,647	6,497.16	1,498.01
10	1,361	171	2,512	4,751	4	0	4	254,172	70,882	325,055	48.5	670,033	9,469.63	1,684.85
0	1,101	52	1,379	2,759	0	0	0	177,186	46,910	224,095	42.2	530,761	7,088.34	1,218.12
46	1,408	65	2,153	4,211	21	3	24	238,146	66,318	304,465	40.9	744,860	8,636.86	1,902.37
242	4,376	320	6,602	13,648	18	63	81	859,461	193,997	1,053,458	45.4	2,318,662	9,949.29	1,828.44
91	6,366	153	7,907	17,093	109	16	125	1,045,266	255,939	1,301,205	40.9	3,177,825	11,542.63	2,118.84
5	389	26	503	1,111	3	1	4	61,048	12,047	73,095	44.7	163,706	5,975.10	1,392.12
551	10,243	756	16,647	32,844	1,197	102	1,299	2,082,844	509,206	2,592,049	45.4	5,713,813	11,567.69	2,292.88

MSAs

TABLE 8 U.S. CENSUS DIVISION 6, WEST NORTH CENTRAL

U.S. Community Hospitals
(Nonfederal, short-term general and other special hospitals)

2016 Utilization, Personnel and Finances

CLASSIFICATION	Hospitals	Beds	Admissions	Inpatient Days	Adjusted Inpatient Days	Average Daily Census	Adjusted Average Daily Census	Average Stay (days)	Surgical Operations	NEWBORNS Bassinets	NEWBORNS Births	OUTPATIENT VISITS Emergency	OUTPATIENT VISITS Total
UNITED STATES	4,840	780,272	33,424,253	182,291,689	386,210,917	499,407	1,056,009	5.5	27,227,227	55,149	3,727,427	142,557,879	747,089,013
Nonmetropolitan	1,825	111,987	3,103,592	20,547,750	68,564,794	56,294	187,486	6.6	3,578,377	9,181	371,659	22,118,524	126,900,302
Metropolitan	3,015	668,285	30,320,661	161,743,939	317,646,123	443,113	868,523	5.3	23,648,850	45,968	3,355,768	120,439,355	620,188,711
CENSUS DIVISION 6, WEST NORTH CENTRAL	677	65,919	2,317,720	14,233,792	36,278,702	38,995	99,144	6.1	2,056,717	4,733	268,072	9,263,852	67,661,860
Nonmetropolitan	443	21,877	442,007	4,146,686	14,364,708	11,364	39,257	9.4	547,494	1,647	60,086	2,806,266	23,784,252
Metropolitan	234	44,042	1,875,713	10,087,106	21,913,994	27,631	59,887	5.4	1,509,223	3,086	207,986	6,457,586	43,877,608
Iowa	117	9,536	314,865	1,926,274	5,926,585	5,276	16,190	6.1	336,630	737	39,034	1,369,607	11,436,367
Nonmetropolitan	83	3,901	81,800	709,551	2,996,804	1,941	8,183	8.7	130,449	323	10,246	538,944	5,326,575
Metropolitan	34	5,635	233,065	1,216,723	2,929,781	3,335	8,007	5.2	206,181	414	28,788	830,663	6,109,792
Ames	2	248	8,292	60,259	149,707	165	409	7.3	10,566	17	1,098	31,692	197,322
Cedar Rapids	4	736	26,634	157,684	513,558	432	1,403	5.9	25,202	54	3,233	119,554	1,002,901
Davenport-Moline-Rock Island	3	494	21,170	89,726	180,539	247	494	4.2	12,833	33	3,072	103,850	279,388
Des Moines-West Des Moines	7	1,506	70,678	340,083	698,840	931	1,910	4.8	47,606	113	10,213	219,201	981,349
Dubuque	3	364	13,674	72,658	150,950	200	413	5.3	13,983	34	1,520	53,155	147,926
Iowa City	3	1,026	41,043	261,589	565,743	717	1,546	6.4	36,156	67	3,609	91,057	1,808,426
Omaha-Council Bluffs	3	293	13,277	49,596	113,071	136	309	3.7	12,331	22	970	56,313	164,680
Sioux City	3	367	18,924	85,067	160,994	233	439	4.5	11,370	35	2,408	68,923	364,829
Waterloo-Cedar Falls	6	601	19,373	100,061	396,379	274	1,084	5.2	36,134	39	2,665	86,918	1,162,971
Kansas	131	9,656	300,573	1,919,932	4,808,044	5,259	13,138	6.4	232,577	665	37,712	1,207,379	7,683,836
Nonmetropolitan	95	4,101	74,811	775,555	2,478,056	2,125	6,770	10.4	82,659	281	9,846	376,142	3,341,500
Metropolitan	36	5,555	225,762	1,144,377	2,329,988	3,134	6,368	5.1	149,918	384	27,866	831,237	4,342,336
Kansas City	14	2,507	111,646	551,078	1,138,118	1,509	3,112	4.9	81,723	181	13,178	351,715	2,595,207
Lawrence	1	145	6,872	24,281	97,731	67	267	3.5	5,283	22	1,113	38,796	185,449
Manhattan	3	264	5,779	44,153	144,637	120	395	7.6	4,500	26	1,300	30,309	236,712
Topeka	5	791	30,832	160,945	351,006	440	960	5.2	17,318	39	2,788	103,117	430,852
Wichita	13	1,848	70,633	363,920	598,496	998	1,634	5.2	41,094	116	9,487	307,300	894,116
Minnesota	129	14,277	546,613	3,319,384	8,448,971	9,092	23,090	6.1	509,901	1,275	67,449	2,019,387	13,519,190
Nonmetropolitan	76	4,021	81,745	849,247	3,294,122	2,329	9,006	10.4	120,206	319	12,974	562,922	5,224,446
Metropolitan	53	10,256	464,868	2,470,137	5,154,849	6,763	14,084	5.3	389,695	956	54,475	1,456,465	8,294,744
Duluth	10	1,185	38,019	253,901	732,112	694	1,999	6.7	40,372	74	2,935	132,248	1,710,333
Grand Forks	2	123	1,408	26,518	105,866	73	289	18.8	3,330	11	222	10,594	101,562
Mankato-North Mankato	2	182	10,835	37,601	91,103	103	249	3.5	7,865	26	1,387	36,675	307,875
Minneapolis-St. Paul-Bloomington	31	6,453	326,711	1,563,816	2,989,344	4,282	8,169	4.8	254,365	701	43,481	1,096,134	4,860,942
Rochester	4	1,566	59,407	399,375	780,232	1,094	2,132	6.7	65,440	109	3,353	105,687	726,611
St. Cloud	4	747	28,488	188,926	456,192	517	1,246	6.6	18,323	35	3,097	75,127	587,421
Missouri	119	18,575	770,748	4,090,544	9,440,271	11,209	25,798	5.3	590,615	1,208	73,188	3,139,087	24,361,617
Nonmetropolitan	50	2,870	89,758	432,037	1,582,415	1,186	4,325	4.8	82,197	289	10,886	637,575	5,191,851
Metropolitan	69	15,705	680,990	3,658,507	7,857,856	10,023	21,473	5.4	508,418	919	62,302	2,501,512	19,169,766
Cape Girardeau	2	498	21,123	98,383	221,947	269	606	4.7	18,072	40	1,864	80,824	1,093,421
Columbia	3	940	42,166	215,980	370,068	591	1,011	5.1	35,266	41	3,849	106,328	1,113,618
Jefferson City	3	290	12,245	49,781	158,248	136	433	4.1	10,742	28	1,570	79,859	712,985
Joplin	4	669	28,256	146,449	366,995	401	1,003	5.2	17,029	59	3,196	148,996	1,212,796
Kansas City	23	3,814	166,757	921,239	1,995,869	2,525	5,452	5.5	105,411	198	14,626	690,395	3,854,433
Springfield	4	1,482	71,866	353,212	872,200	967	2,383	4.9	69,455	85	6,916	263,486	2,456,522
St. Joseph	1	352	15,371	65,690	172,296	180	471	4.3	11,725	28	1,600	62,147	1,179,326
St. Louis	29	7,660	323,206	1,807,773	3,700,233	4,954	10,114	5.6	240,718	440	28,681	1,069,477	7,546,665
Nebraska	88	6,540	192,539	1,281,265	3,145,638	3,512	8,602	6.7	197,381	498	25,223	824,722	5,159,650
Nonmetropolitan	66	2,908	59,460	510,755	1,538,554	1,401	4,208	8.6	71,517	251	6,679	392,372	2,459,447
Metropolitan	22	3,632	133,079	770,510	1,607,084	2,111	4,394	5.8	125,864	247	18,544	432,350	2,700,203
Grand Island	4	312	7,254	63,916	184,436	176	505	8.8	5,926	34	1,032	30,702	135,762
Lincoln	5	1,193	39,503	254,376	461,168	697	1,262	6.4	25,433	48	4,905	120,132	399,656
Omaha-Council Bluffs	13	2,127	86,322	452,218	961,480	1,238	2,627	5.2	94,505	165	12,607	281,516	2,164,785
North Dakota	40	3,260	90,877	701,386	1,884,236	1,920	5,152	7.7	103,660	160	13,137	371,089	2,644,212
Nonmetropolitan	32	1,742	24,150	341,327	891,125	935	2,437	14.1	24,986	57	4,465	141,506	735,684
Metropolitan	8	1,518	66,727	360,059	993,111	985	2,715	5.4	78,674	103	8,672	229,583	1,908,528
Bismarck	3	486	22,221	103,671	272,675	284	746	4.7	20,315	36	2,678	54,023	380,042
Fargo	3	654	31,978	172,641	447,072	472	1,221	5.4	45,910	42	4,189	95,454	576,931
Grand Forks	2	378	12,528	83,747	273,364	229	748	6.7	12,449	25	1,805	80,106	951,555
South Dakota	53	4,075	101,505	995,007	2,624,957	2,727	7,174	9.8	85,953	190	12,329	332,581	2,856,988
Nonmetropolitan	41	2,334	30,283	528,214	1,583,632	1,447	4,328	17.4	35,480	127	4,990	156,805	1,504,749
Metropolitan	12	1,741	71,222	466,793	1,041,325	1,280	2,846	6.6	50,473	63	7,339	175,776	1,352,239
Rapid City	4	616	20,555	162,720	329,997	447	902	7.9	9,409	24	1,904	70,844	392,074
Sioux Falls	8	1,125	50,667	304,073	711,328	833	1,944	6.0	41,064	39	5,435	104,932	960,165

TABLE 8

U.S. CENSUS DIVISION 6, WEST NORTH CENTRAL

U.S. Community Hospitals
(Nonfederal, short-term general and other special hospitals)

2016 Utilization, Personnel and Finances

MSAs

Physicians and Dentists	Registered Nurses	Licensed Practical Nurses	Other Salaried Personnel	Total Personnel	Medical and Dental Residents	Other Trainees	Total Trainees	Payroll (in thousands)	Employee Benefits (in thousands)	Total (in thousands)	Percent of Total	Amount (in thousands)	Adjusted per Admission	Adjusted per inpatient Day
135,693	1,478,657	74,344	2,612,576	4,991,775	113,111	9,619	122,730	$340,132,974	$90,463,641	$430,596,618	47.7	$902,891,035	$12,777.25	$2,337.82
15,408	149,651	20,977	339,776	612,547	1,714	261	1,975	35,531,908	9,378,885	44,910,794		89,420,776	8,694.35	1,304.18
120,285	1,329,006	53,367	2,272,800	4,379,228	111,397	9,358	120,755	304,601,066	81,084,755	385,685,824	47.4	813,470,258	13,472.72	2,560.93
14,869	115,565	9,774	239,626	429,145	5,171	803	5,974	27,603,706	6,877,739	34,481,459	49.2	70,036,499	12,450.94	1,930.51
3,022	25,424	4,650	60,601	107,274	162	23	185	6,306,347	1,591,548	7,897,899	50.9	15,503,513	9,619.46	1,079.28
11,847	90,141	5,124	179,025	321,871	5,009	780	5,789	21,297,360	5,286,191	26,583,560	48.7	54,532,986	13,588.02	2,488.50
1,082	16,230	1,021	32,868	58,385	829	105	934	3,454,560	946,140	4,400,700	48.9	8,991,715	10,133.55	1,517.18
505	5,601	646	12,458	22,021	21	0	21	1,198,581	310,026	1,508,608	50.0	3,014,770	8,626.37	1,006.00
577	10,629	375	20,410	36,364	808	105	913	2,255,980	636,114	2,892,092	48.4	5,976,945	11,112.91	2,040.07
3	364	15	689	1,228	0	0	0	74,737	21,241	95,978	48.3	198,866	10,666.50	1,328.37
33	1,277	41	2,694	4,531	0	0	0	253,447	68,875	322,323	48.4	666,279	8,415.37	1,297.38
0	758	8	991	1,943	0	0	0	120,343	22,622	142,964	34.0	420,474	9,457.15	2,328.99
221	3,013	52	5,584	10,062	228	4	232	646,601	151,813	798,414	50.7	1,575,836	11,087.36	2,254.93
13	622	18	1,189	1,993	0	0	0	104,015	21,551	125,566	44.2	284,393	9,767.58	1,884.02
107	2,448	18	4,939	8,799	573	99	672	547,829	207,287	755,116	48.7	1,549,981	18,510.77	2,739.73
7	355	10	570	1,092	0	0	0	79,558	21,403	100,961	46.7	216,024	7,090.65	1,910.51
54	803	25	1,410	2,607	2	0	2	157,074	36,349	193,422	48.7	396,872	10,879.76	2,465.13
139	989	188	2,344	4,109	5	2	7	272,375	84,974	357,348	53.5	668,221	9,074.66	1,685.81
1,720	15,567	1,351	25,626	51,954	15	399	414	3,215,978	724,835	3,940,812	50.2	7,848,856	10,938.65	1,632.44
459	4,384	701	9,803	18,423	1	0	1	982,460	229,031	1,211,490	53.6	2,258,492	9,413.01	911.4
1,261	11,183	650	15,823	33,531	14	399	413	2,233,518	495,804	2,729,322	48.8	5,590,364	11,705.09	2,399.31
840	6,052	203	8,391	17,963	1	385	386	1,233,364	275,283	1,508,647	48.6	3,104,978	12,647.67	2,728.17
51	330	34	729	1,286	0	0	0	89,141	16,500	105,641	49.8	212,306	7,675.57	2,172.35
21	233	23	366	750	0	0	0	56,688	11,020	67,707	52.9	128,056	7,817.84	885.36
273	1,451	326	2,676	5,464	0	14	14	393,933	92,017	485,951	55.4	877,876	12,945.35	2,501.03
76	3,117	64	3,661	8,068	13	0	13	460,392	100,984	561,376	44.3	1,267,148	10,537.70	2,117.22
6,064	26,206	2,414	70,790	116,667	2,255	105	2,360	7,736,518	2,052,172	9,788,695	52.5	18,651,841	15,072.46	2,207.59
747	4,624	1,237	12,906	21,657	8	8	16	1,406,229	377,489	1,783,720	50.7	3,517,488	10,797.96	1,067.81
5,317	21,582	1,177	57,884	95,010	2,247	97	2,344	6,330,289	1,674,684	8,004,975	52.9	15,134,353	16,599.73	2,935.94
545	1,905	270	5,185	8,559	7	0	7	719,527	183,470	902,997	59.8	1,509,928	16,520.90	2,062.43
15	113	40	323	560	1	1	2	24,492	5,786	30,279	54.6	55,472	9,575.63	523.98
148	472	78	883	1,801	0	0	0	134,645	35,255	169,900	47.8	355,214	13,365.46	3,899.03
2,345	13,425	427	26,012	47,243	975	96	1,071	4,293,952	1,141,837	5,435,790	52.7	10,310,421	16,805.16	3,449.06
2,240	4,129	141	22,101	31,137	1,249	0	1,249	809,040	215,834	1,024,875	49.0	2,093,542	17,571.97	2,683.23
24	1,538	221	3,380	5,710	15	0	15	348,633	92,502	441,134	54.5	809,777	14,645.99	1,775.08
3,418	36,210	2,694	69,125	124,673	1,827	137	1,964	7,791,414	1,932,172	9,723,592	45.5	21,355,922	11,844.75	2,262.21
588	4,151	1,096	10,424	18,109	41	6	47	1,011,561	263,758	1,275,321	49.5	2,576,713	7,749.07	1,628.34
2,830	32,059	1,598	58,701	106,564	1,786	131	1,917	6,779,853	1,668,414	8,448,271	45.0	18,779,209	12,770.91	2,389.86
192	1,089	137	2,518	4,333	0	8	8	293,543	60,361	353,904	46.4	762,905	15,960.35	3,437.33
36	1,577	234	3,942	6,203	387	17	404	344,985	108,880	453,866	40.0	1,135,212	15,386.03	3,067.58
97	580	136	1,297	2,289	9	0	9	138,076	35,604	173,679	46.8	370,874	9,833.59	2,343.62
243	1,379	67	2,504	4,960	23	0	23	337,265	67,105	404,370	51.4	787,024	11,016.89	2,144.51
522	7,122	207	14,107	24,508	198	106	304	1,709,289	413,432	2,122,723	45.7	4,649,751	14,022.59	2,329.69
959	3,709	412	10,177	16,664	0	0	0	732,173	185,536	917,709	44.0	2,083,751	11,407.63	2,389.07
180	771	193	2,070	3,393	0	0	0	256,836	64,645	321,481	56.4	570,103	14,140.87	3,308.86
601	15,832	212	22,086	44,214	1,169	0	1,169	2,967,686	732,853	3,700,539	44.0	8,419,589	12,288.43	2,275.42
760	10,221	820	20,283	36,763	46	9	55	2,300,614	572,848	2,873,465	48.5	5,924,356	12,910.33	1,883.36
287	3,364	608	7,903	14,054	18	2	20	784,209	206,253	990,462	48.5	2,042,410	11,152.30	1,327.49
473	6,857	212	12,380	22,709	28	7	35	1,516,405	366,595	1,883,003	48.5	3,881,946	14,077.93	2,415.52
12	319	29	663	1,207	0	0	0	61,871	18,277	80,148	42.0	190,794	11,472.19	1,034.47
32	1,892	49	2,857	5,509	13	6	19	307,305	88,560	395,866	44.4	890,660	12,584.04	1,931.31
429	4,646	134	8,860	15,993	15	1	16	1,147,229	259,758	1,406,989	50.2	2,800,492	14,869.42	2,912.69
1,197	5,413	1,011	10,229	20,312	99	35	134	1,606,296	307,989	1,914,282	50.8	3,764,651	14,385.75	1,997.97
165	1,375	164	2,927	5,431	71	6	77	432,802	86,404	519,204	52.8	982,871	12,853.20	1,102.96
1,032	4,038	847	7,302	14,881	28	29	57	1,173,494	221,585	1,395,078	50.2	2,781,779	15,018.46	2,801.08
258	1,368	159	2,202	4,704	2	0	2	325,645	58,288	383,933	42.0	914,817	15,528.00	3,354.97
561	2,100	409	2,826	6,685	0	0	0	561,678	108,765	670,444	51.4	1,303,112	15,418.35	2,914.77
213	570	279	2,274	3,492	26	29	55	286,170	54,531	340,701	60.4	563,850	13,491.49	2,062.63
628	5,718	463	10,705	20,391	100	13	113	1,498,328	341,583	1,839,913	52.6	3,499,158	13,505.20	1,333.03
271	1,925	198	4,180	7,579	2	1	3	490,506	118,588	609,094	54.8	1,110,768	10,641.07	701.41
357	3,793	265	6,525	12,812	98	12	110	1,007,822	222,996	1,230,819	51.5	2,388,390	15,437.65	2,293.61
35	686	36	1,551	2,725	0	2	2	229,544	45,687	275,232	48.5	567,821	14,533.05	1,720.68
322	3,107	229	4,974	10,087	98	10	108	778,277	177,309	955,587	52.5	1,820,569	15,743.28	2,559.39

TABLE 8

U.S. CENSUS DIVISION 7, WEST SOUTH CENTRAL

U.S. Community Hospitals
(Nonfederal, short-term general and other special hospitals)

2016 Utilization, Personnel and Finances

CLASSIFICATION	Hospitals	Beds	Admissions	Inpatient Days	Adjusted Inpatient Days	Average Daily Census	Adjusted Average Daily Census	Average Stay (days)	Surgical Operations	NEWBORNS Bassinets	NEWBORNS Births	OUTPATIENT VISITS Emergency	OUTPATIENT VISITS Total
UNITED STATES	4,840	780,272	33,424,253	182,291,689	386,210,917	499,407	1,056,009	5.5	27,227,227	55,149	3,727,427	142,557,879	747,089,013
Nonmetropolitan	1,825	111,987	3,103,592	20,547,750	68,564,794	56,294	187,486	6.6	3,578,377	9,181	371,659	22,118,524	126,900,302
Metropolitan	3,015	668,285	30,320,661	161,743,939	317,646,123	443,113	868,523	5.3	23,648,850	45,968	3,355,768	120,439,355	620,188,711
CENSUS DIVISION 7, WEST SOUTH CENTRAL	711	96,752	3,861,630	20,957,783	41,988,441	57,417	114,815	5.4	2,906,969	7,393	532,702	16,851,086	66,907,307
Nonmetropolitan	279	13,329	374,291	1,736,373	5,628,827	4,753	15,404	4.6	339,515	1,200	52,549	2,776,142	11,804,444
Metropolitan	432	83,423	3,487,339	19,221,410	36,359,614	52,664	99,411	5.5	2,567,454	6,193	480,153	14,074,944	55,102,863
Arkansas	80	9,419	352,722	1,810,494	3,888,967	4,961	10,623	5.1	281,511	753	35,864	1,503,862	6,003,881
Nonmetropolitan	47	3,102	86,274	440,328	1,311,261	1,208	3,581	5.1	66,940	223	9,754	555,914	2,448,327
Metropolitan	33	6,317	266,448	1,370,166	2,577,706	3,753	7,042	5.1	214,571	530	26,110	947,948	3,555,554
Fayetteville-Springdale-Rogers	5	975	46,285	183,666	356,931	503	976	4.0	42,485	91	7,381	207,846	639,251
Fort Smith	6	822	34,780	184,080	341,028	504	931	5.3	35,583	54	3,420	134,593	430,226
Hot Springs	3	496	18,712	96,147	177,399	263	485	5.1	17,215	27	1,408	65,248	218,519
Jonesboro	3	669	30,539	148,108	297,159	406	811	4.8	16,428	46	2,237	103,458	375,761
Little Rock-North Little Rock-Conway	14	2,997	126,927	706,294	1,295,317	1,935	3,539	5.6	98,086	276	10,937	385,656	1,692,725
Pine Bluff	1	333	8,988	51,162	106,905	140	292	5.7	4,552	36	727	49,697	190,052
Texarkana	1	25	217	709	2,967	2	8	3.3	222	0	0	1,450	9,020
Louisiana	118	14,052	548,316	3,012,767	6,574,274	8,256	17,973	5.5	446,210	942	60,923	2,853,225	11,613,838
Nonmetropolitan	38	1,887	57,269	280,989	787,414	770	2,159	4.9	55,175	136	7,470	353,906	1,209,003
Metropolitan	80	12,165	491,047	2,731,778	5,786,860	7,486	15,814	5.6	391,035	806	53,453	2,499,319	10,404,835
Alexandria	5	737	29,248	175,603	307,778	481	840	6.0	18,543	55	2,923	137,936	429,568
Baton Rouge	12	2,369	79,997	550,848	1,340,449	1,509	3,662	6.9	65,441	155	11,470	404,294	2,419,252
Hammond	3	280	11,658	63,671	137,337	174	375	5.5	14,356	26	1,324	110,965	562,548
Houma-Thibodaux	5	516	23,338	111,475	309,219	305	844	4.8	18,857	42	3,432	156,374	602,362
Lafayette	12	1,215	50,157	270,125	556,754	741	1,524	5.4	32,800	88	4,652	248,290	1,037,960
Lake Charles	7	730	27,220	144,806	344,265	398	941	5.3	25,433	54	3,067	143,264	556,773
Monroe	8	836	31,971	176,806	329,933	485	903	5.5	19,952	51	3,534	134,385	524,855
New Orleans-Metairie	17	3,510	145,916	809,341	1,656,503	2,217	4,526	5.5	125,739	194	16,493	772,144	3,162,837
Shreveport-Bossier City	11	1,972	91,542	429,103	804,622	1,176	2,199	4.7	69,914	141	6,558	391,667	1,108,680
Oklahoma	110	11,167	396,764	2,205,360	4,718,972	6,040	12,897	5.6	332,096	829	52,663	1,829,289	6,559,315
Nonmetropolitan	60	3,077	83,528	398,674	1,218,992	1,092	3,331	4.8	95,008	298	11,760	594,953	2,414,554
Metropolitan	50	8,090	313,236	1,806,686	3,499,980	4,948	9,566	5.8	237,088	531	40,903	1,234,336	4,144,761
Enid	2	331	9,244	52,288	111,807	143	306	5.7	7,767	16	1,345	34,081	162,522
Fort Smith	2	71	1,710	8,605	36,007	24	99	5.0	1,430	11	494	7,645	47,569
Lawton	2	540	13,826	122,875	315,586	337	863	8.9	13,359	43	1,859	71,706	236,039
Oklahoma City	22	4,157	151,296	924,717	1,699,557	2,533	4,645	6.1	129,682	290	21,674	681,343	2,125,289
Tulsa	22	2,991	137,160	698,201	1,337,023	1,911	3,653	5.1	84,850	171	15,531	439,561	1,573,342
Texas	403	62,114	2,563,828	13,929,162	26,806,228	38,160	73,322	5.4	1,847,152	4,869	383,252	10,664,710	42,730,273
Nonmetropolitan	134	5,263	147,220	616,382	2,311,160	1,683	6,333	4.2	122,392	543	23,565	1,271,369	5,732,560
Metropolitan	269	56,851	2,416,608	13,312,780	24,495,068	36,477	66,989	5.5	1,724,760	4,326	359,687	9,393,341	36,997,713
Abilene	6	704	23,350	125,705	273,490	344	748	5.4	19,197	46	2,721	96,659	396,574
Amarillo	5	906	39,894	201,833	333,519	553	914	5.1	20,809	54	4,426	118,766	386,398
Austin-Round Rock	24	3,278	159,015	782,865	1,361,389	2,146	3,749	4.9	124,236	373	27,158	732,414	2,903,277
Beaumont-Port Arthur	5	1,026	41,823	196,762	415,964	539	1,144	4.7	34,317	82	5,215	203,761	629,426
Brownsville-Harlingen	3	892	36,504	181,067	277,316	496	757	5.0	22,709	72	6,677	124,076	264,214
College Station-Bryan	3	392	18,292	76,467	162,584	210	444	4.2	15,392	58	2,680	89,070	307,570
Corpus Christi	6	1,288	54,905	310,868	503,533	852	1,376	5.7	36,868	73	7,119	255,032	577,463
Dallas-Plano-Irving	51	11,075	405,758	2,668,129	5,017,750	7,313	13,711	6.6	238,556	741	59,712	1,689,991	4,953,355
El Paso	6	1,657	82,033	389,762	661,711	1,068	1,808	4.8	46,181	169	15,410	346,114	1,271,345
Fort Worth-Arlington	27	4,819	224,283	1,176,658	2,014,787	3,223	5,507	5.2	159,300	398	33,439	965,529	3,311,807
Houston-The Woodlands-Sugar Land	59	14,429	632,222	3,553,388	6,785,456	9,738	18,543	5.6	441,360	1,161	98,972	2,192,998	10,481,980
Killeen-Temple	6	1,012	46,355	223,077	551,161	610	1,506	4.8	40,528	70	4,954	212,201	1,980,376
Laredo	2	509	21,771	117,888	218,995	323	598	5.4	20,138	66	5,726	81,736	260,894
Longview	4	696	25,250	126,146	251,611	346	687	5.0	27,108	77	3,959	156,293	323,306
Lubbock	6	1,150	55,962	273,218	501,809	749	1,371	4.9	37,372	95	5,661	169,412	798,814
McAllen-Edinburg-Mission	7	2,176	90,183	440,100	805,133	1,205	2,200	4.9	93,313	175	16,492	297,801	810,515
Midland	3	337	13,176	75,112	150,238	206	410	5.7	8,248	27	2,455	62,411	155,308
Odessa	2	581	18,758	105,876	197,485	290	540	5.6	15,107	42	4,193	72,667	399,270
San Angelo	2	442	17,282	82,369	181,374	225	495	4.8	20,266	36	2,029	66,258	181,042
San Antonio-New Braunfels	17	5,634	248,976	1,366,466	2,268,302	3,743	6,214	5.5	181,314	327	33,892	797,292	3,971,281
Sherman-Denison	2	434	21,023	98,702	176,621	270	482	4.7	18,258	45	1,518	87,237	165,339
Texarkana	5	692	23,018	128,160	230,966	352	630	5.6	11,473	31	2,880	113,234	260,724
Tyler	7	1,164	52,030	275,387	493,771	754	1,350	5.3	43,808	30	3,413	142,458	1,144,620
Victoria	3	533	17,066	89,912	172,213	246	470	5.3	15,266	30	2,124	75,885	220,652
Waco	3	591	29,939	160,885	339,090	441	929	5.4	18,825	28	4,769	154,427	654,876
Wichita Falls	5	434	17,740	85,978	148,800	235	406	4.8	14,811	20	2,093	89,619	187,287

MSAs

TABLE 8

U.S. CENSUS DIVISION 7, WEST SOUTH CENTRAL

U.S. Community Hospitals
(Nonfederal, short-term general and other special hospitals)

2016 Utilization, Personnel and Finances

	FULL-TIME EQUIVALENT PERSONNEL				FULL-TIME EQUIV. TRAINEES			EXPENSES						
								LABOR				TOTAL		
Physicians and Dentists	Registered Nurses	Licensed Practical Nurses	Other Salaried Personnel	Total Personnel	Medical and Dental Residents	Other Trainees	Total Trainees	Payroll (in thousands)	Employee Benefits (in thousands)	Total (in thousands)	Percent of Total	Amount (in thousands)	Adjusted per Admission	Adjusted per Inpatient Day
135,693	1,478,657	74,344	2,612,576	4,991,775	113,111	9,619	122,730	$340,132,974	$90,463,641	$430,596,618	47.7	$902,891,035	$12,777.25	$2,337.82
15,408	149,651	20,977	339,776	612,547	1,714	261	1,975	35,531,908	9,378,885	44,910,794	50.2	89,420,776	8,694.35	1,304.18
120,285	1,329,006	53,367	2,272,800	4,379,228	111,397	9,358	120,755	304,601,066	81,084,755	385,685,824	47.4	813,470,258	13,472.72	2,560.93
7,319	157,135	13,398	247,555	508,814	5,178	1,317	6,495	32,428,322	7,679,557	40,107,875	44.7	89,814,664	11,249.47	2,139.03
871	15,361	4,177	32,456	63,071	99	14	113	3,285,655	781,617	4,067,274	47.8	8,512,783	6,877.02	1,512.35
6,448	141,774	9,221	215,099	445,743	5,079	1,303	6,382	29,142,668	6,897,941	36,040,601	44.3	81,301,881	12,051.79	2,236.05
865	14,206	1,618	22,275	46,751	61	12	73	2,459,317	562,441	3,021,757	45.5	6,639,743	8,385.22	1,707.33
314	3,509	888	6,997	13,783	35	2	37	677,255	156,998	834,253	52.3	1,595,283	5,990.50	1,216.60
551	10,697	730	15,278	32,968	26	10	36	1,782,062	405,443	2,187,504	43.4	5,044,460	9,598.68	1,956.96
190	1,707	188	2,469	5,422	0	0	0	254,763	53,526	308,289	44.4	694,902	7,288.75	1,946.88
81	939	123	1,651	3,451	0	0	0	191,635	41,337	232,972	40.1	580,578	8,334.93	1,702.44
126	679	29	433	1,742	0	0	0	91,697	24,739	116,435	42.7	272,594	7,768.42	1,536.61
47	1,046	44	1,582	3,217	25	2	27	169,004	41,802	210,806	44.0	479,118	7,508.62	1,612.33
91	5,868	281	8,504	17,733	1	6	7	999,838	229,777	1,229,614	43.3	2,837,405	11,727.04	2,190.51
14	442	61	601	1,334	0	2	2	70,015	12,940	82,955	49.5	167,717	8,930.15	1,568.84
2	16	4	38	69	0	0	0	5,111	1,322	6,433	53.0	12,147	13,377.87	4,094.07
2,872	23,767	3,008	40,555	82,221	742	90	832	4,456,008	975,938	5,431,943	43.5	12,493,815	10,176.13	1,900.41
156	2,295	460	4,900	9,218	15	7	22	459,812	101,387	561,200	46.7	1,201,849	7,046.28	1,526.32
2,716	21,472	2,548	35,655	73,003	727	83	810	3,996,196	874,551	4,870,743	43.1	11,291,966	10,681.09	1,951.31
9	1,107	119	1,266	3,131	0	0	0	170,110	39,549	209,658	42.4	494,640	9,567.68	1,607.13
355	3,661	222	6,713	12,806	315	17	332	817,043	182,244	999,286	45.4	2,199,435	11,164.98	1,640.82
101	757	128	1,544	2,773	0	0	0	182,888	38,098	220,986	63.5	347,886	13,759.70	2,533.09
67	900	130	2,331	3,921	0	2	2	198,537	42,440	240,977	47.9	503,233	7,624.97	1,627.43
91	1,784	276	3,328	6,446	4	1	5	347,276	76,522	423,799	41.6	1,019,604	9,716.44	1,831.34
102	1,253	229	2,574	4,719	4	17	21	211,034	56,119	267,152	43.5	613,710	9,332.01	1,782.67
96	1,015	142	2,024	3,804	48	1	49	215,071	52,813	267,883	45.0	595,294	9,755.39	1,804.29
1,267	7,552	750	10,267	23,423	356	27	383	1,349,770	273,438	1,623,208	39.9	4,067,855	13,307.69	2,455.69
628	3,443	552	5,608	11,980	0	18	18	504,467	113,328	617,794	42.6	1,450,309	8,065.38	1,802.47
695	14,991	1,608	25,114	50,268	205	42	247	2,939,458	666,584	3,606,044	42.6	8,470,169	9,554.04	1,794.92
256	3,522	726	7,069	13,925	49	4	53	722,462	167,740	890,204	47.9	1,860,339	7,139.36	1,526.13
439	11,469	882	18,045	36,343	156	38	194	2,216,996	498,844	2,715,840	41.1	6,609,830	10,559.19	1,888.53
3	327	23	537	1,015	0	1	1	77,895	16,370	94,265	47.2	199,525	10,199.61	1,784.55
6	54	28	190	329	0	0	0	14,508	3,751	18,259	53.0	34,479	4,818.25	957.58
108	353	165	1,151	2,048	19	0	19	138,852	23,749	162,601	47.0	345,971	9,855.60	1,096.28
223	5,962	353	8,658	18,007	125	35	160	1,155,802	272,673	1,428,476	40.1	3,566,450	12,170.85	2,098.46
99	4,773	313	7,509	14,944	12	2	14	829,938	182,301	1,012,239	41.1	2,463,405	9,085.86	1,842.46
2,887	104,171	7,164	159,611	329,574	4,170	1,173	5,343	22,573,540	5,474,594	28,048,131	45.1	62,210,937	12,251.67	2,320.76
145	6,035	2,103	13,490	26,145	0	1	1	1,426,126	355,492	1,781,617	46.2	3,855,311	7,133.94	1,668.13
2,742	98,136	5,061	146,121	303,429	4,170	1,172	5,342	21,147,413	5,119,102	26,266,514	45.0	58,355,626	12,861.22	2,382.34
2	1,002	184	1,599	3,514	0	49	49	163,695	34,118	197,814	40.2	491,514	8,924.28	1,797.19
0	1,395	106	1,875	3,927	0	18	18	239,456	55,219	294,676	45.6	645,999	9,350.78	1,936.92
369	6,237	187	7,730	17,774	0	1	1	1,199,989	267,009	1,466,998	39.3	3,735,378	12,919.64	2,743.80
0	1,652	158	1,787	4,197	0	0	0	254,158	53,059	307,217	41.9	733,069	7,972.21	1,762.34
0	1,071	127	1,067	2,882	0	0	0	187,577	36,145	223,721	46.1	485,674	8,668.88	1,751.34
31	710	76	1,031	2,120	0	0	0	123,220	28,441	151,660	43.9	345,539	9,202.35	2,125.30
69	1,980	129	3,318	6,621	184	4	188	383,855	93,686	477,541	40.5	1,179,761	13,045.98	2,342.97
140	17,005	486	26,454	51,633	1,476	12	1,488	4,046,337	909,642	4,955,980	46.8	10,600,362	14,292.19	2,112.57
58	2,547	67	3,887	7,929	0	0	0	488,497	117,992	606,489	38.0	1,597,686	11,306.09	2,414.48
13	9,623	454	12,753	27,367	278	6	284	1,923,593	493,172	2,416,765	45.6	5,295,102	13,330.13	2,628.12
1,528	30,427	865	45,262	95,456	1,084	1,032	2,116	7,396,882	1,907,423	9,304,305	46.7	19,928,007	16,003.20	2,936.87
0	1,375	290	4,347	6,596	440	8	448	378,815	99,487	478,301	40.6	1,179,521	9,976.75	2,140.07
0	506	27	880	1,740	0	0	0	102,440	21,633	124,074	42.6	291,304	7,174.98	1,330.19
0	1,004	21	929	2,423	0	0	0	158,309	34,500	192,809	39.9	482,807	9,134.22	1,918.86
0	2,387	161	3,219	6,841	0	0	0	370,059	114,820	484,879	40.3	1,204,183	11,484.16	2,399.68
81	2,929	182	4,316	9,318	6	3	9	489,221	106,116	595,337	48.0	1,239,472	7,375.31	1,539.46
2	420	45	1,245	1,986	36	1	37	119,530	31,088	150,618	51.8	290,670	10,148.39	1,934.73
0	634	59	1,131	2,171	0	14	14	146,517	37,942	184,458	46.9	393,088	11,232.68	1,990.47
0	651	74	1,076	2,201	0	0	0	124,337	26,818	151,154	42.9	352,023	9,189.04	1,940.87
231	8,530	671	11,901	26,116	567	17	584	1,708,443	375,437	2,083,880	44.7	4,666,614	11,047.44	2,057.32
55	727	28	1,229	2,248	8	0	8	118,819	34,186	153,005	50.9	300,464	8,019.87	1,701.18
0	1,062	131	1,056	2,742	0	0	0	138,552	30,022	168,575	44.9	375,760	8,261.18	1,626.91
76	1,965	310	3,647	7,582	69	6	75	412,510	105,080	517,591	39.9	1,296,649	13,051.19	2,626.01
31	623	87	1,110	2,118	0	0	0	133,477	32,805	166,282	51.3	324,395	9,543.26	1,883.68
56	1,012	57	1,980	3,472	22	1	23	197,128	49,358	246,485	43.5	567,154	8,828.67	1,672.58
0	662	79	1,292	2,455	0	0	0	141,998	23,902	165,900	46.9	353,431	10,671.87	2,375.21

MSAs

TABLE 8

U.S. CENSUS DIVISION 8, MOUNTAIN

U.S. Community Hospitals
(Nonfederal, short-term general and other special hospitals)

2016 Utilization, Personnel and Finances

MSAs

CLASSIFICATION	Hospitals	Beds	Admissions	Inpatient Days	Adjusted Inpatient Days	Average Daily Census	Adjusted Average Daily Census	Average Stay (days)	Surgical Operations	NEWBORNS Bassinets	NEWBORNS Births	OUTPATIENT VISITS Emergency	OUTPATIENT VISITS Total
UNITED STATES	4,840	780,272	33,424,253	182,291,689	386,210,917	499,407	1,056,009	5.5	27,227,227	55,149	3,727,427	142,557,879	747,089,013
Nonmetropolitan	1,825	111,987	3,103,592	20,547,750	68,564,794	56,294	187,486	6.6	3,578,377	9,181	371,659	22,118,524	126,900,302
Metropolitan	3,015	668,285	30,320,661	161,743,939	317,646,123	443,113	868,523	5.3	23,648,850	45,968	3,355,768	120,439,355	620,188,711
CENSUS DIVISION 8, MOUNTAIN	381	47,589	1,996,485	10,420,637	22,365,109	28,555	61,145	5.2	1,627,503	3,995	266,519	8,370,732	46,470,440
Nonmetropolitan	189	8,651	205,421	1,516,783	5,155,633	4,160	14,095	7.4	286,758	840	38,279	1,668,560	9,775,753
Metropolitan	192	38,938	1,791,064	8,903,854	17,209,476	24,395	47,050	5.0	1,340,745	3,155	228,240	6,702,172	36,694,687
Arizona	70	13,371	621,129	2,989,208	5,686,389	8,191	15,551	4.8	434,654	988	75,727	2,097,304	8,330,869
Nonmetropolitan	9	327	12,529	39,960	167,614	110	459	3.2	16,623	48	2,968	84,887	339,576
Metropolitan	61	13,044	608,600	2,949,248	5,518,775	8,081	15,092	4.8	418,031	940	72,759	2,012,417	7,991,293
Flagstaff	3	345	16,601	76,762	165,438	211	453	4.6	12,714	33	1,743	37,714	197,683
Lake Havasu City-Kingman	4	591	25,598	128,284	268,987	352	736	5.0	20,107	33	1,815	144,024	549,920
Phoenix-Mesa-Scottsdale	35	8,620	411,361	2,020,791	3,700,213	5,535	10,120	4.9	276,966	673	51,563	1,144,465	5,094,917
Prescott	3	316	15,228	53,882	124,301	148	339	3.5	9,995	24	1,579	104,643	304,112
Sierra Vista-Douglas	4	160	6,835	28,734	100,468	79	276	4.2	4,359	10	1,033	45,162	162,379
Tucson	10	2,565	114,214	558,902	982,762	1,532	2,686	4.9	82,262	133	11,682	463,244	1,409,507
Yuma	2	447	18,763	81,893	176,606	224	482	4.4	11,628	34	3,344	73,165	272,775
Colorado	79	10,680	424,472	2,192,792	4,621,940	6,005	12,632	5.2	380,229	851	60,876	2,008,376	9,052,093
Nonmetropolitan	38	1,482	34,042	249,540	861,461	683	2,358	7.3	55,206	145	6,558	279,046	1,841,356
Metropolitan	41	9,198	390,430	1,943,252	3,760,479	5,322	10,274	5.0	325,023	706	54,318	1,729,330	7,210,737
Boulder	4	645	32,758	128,492	263,435	352	720	3.9	25,875	98	6,173	131,149	740,881
Colorado Springs	4	1,076	48,617	195,019	368,099	534	1,005	4.0	35,047	86	6,452	212,684	923,308
Denver-Aurora-Lakewood	22	5,630	231,076	1,227,106	2,227,270	3,360	6,085	5.3	204,057	389	31,847	1,016,724	4,188,850
Fort Collins	4	637	29,517	123,854	312,969	339	855	4.2	21,800	54	4,347	138,045	520,311
Grand Junction	3	439	15,448	99,064	228,017	272	623	6.4	11,240	32	1,725	69,935	342,223
Greeley	2	276	11,238	53,213	118,305	146	324	4.7	7,067	15	1,714	33,312	175,047
Pueblo	2	495	21,776	116,504	242,384	319	662	5.4	19,937	32	2,060	127,481	320,117
Idaho	40	3,296	130,266	654,000	1,645,451	1,793	4,493	5.0	127,621	294	19,192	668,997	5,505,531
Nonmetropolitan	26	1,018	28,199	171,059	578,961	469	1,580	6.1	42,232	107	5,969	190,991	1,666,003
Metropolitan	14	2,278	102,067	482,941	1,066,490	1,324	2,913	4.7	85,389	187	13,223	478,006	3,839,528
Boise City	8	1,332	60,279	274,428	620,984	752	1,696	4.6	55,308	114	8,622	248,425	2,868,244
Coeur d'Alene	1	292	13,722	66,780	157,819	183	431	4.9	11,987	18	1,704	52,567	309,319
Idaho Falls	2	336	13,676	87,513	163,306	240	447	6.4	5,607	13	610	103,618	253,920
Lewiston	1	123	4,981	16,996	38,932	47	106	3.4	3,913	22	772	32,067	132,932
Logan	1	20	663	2,667	14,295	7	39	4.0	847	5	127	1,102	6,788
Pocatello	1	175	8,746	34,557	71,154	95	194	4.0	7,727	15	1,388	40,227	268,325
Montana	50	3,644	93,184	781,200	2,172,330	2,143	5,940	8.4	90,224	218	10,933	421,448	3,955,513
Nonmetropolitan	44	2,176	39,673	424,635	1,378,971	1,167	3,772	10.7	38,413	130	4,979	252,763	1,929,730
Metropolitan	6	1,468	53,511	356,565	793,359	976	2,168	6.7	51,811	88	5,954	168,685	2,025,783
Billings	3	631	27,372	151,733	323,236	415	883	5.5	23,046	40	2,909	84,749	1,090,682
Great Falls	1	502	11,307	134,421	319,398	368	873	11.9	9,291	24	1,432	31,591	496,159
Missoula	2	335	14,832	70,411	150,725	193	412	4.7	19,474	24	1,613	52,345	438,942
Nevada	36	5,662	269,741	1,540,521	2,804,991	4,222	7,676	5.7	145,608	287	24,282	905,556	3,270,873
Nonmetropolitan	10	324	7,512	56,380	218,286	155	596	7.5	14,725	29	1,044	88,006	420,767
Metropolitan	26	5,338	262,229	1,484,141	2,586,705	4,067	7,080	5.7	130,883	258	23,238	817,550	2,850,106
Carson City	1	211	12,489	54,031	107,711	148	294	4.3	11,149	12	921	37,271	296,085
Las Vegas-Henderson-Paradise	18	3,879	198,088	1,155,249	1,996,898	3,165	5,469	5.8	77,903	171	16,265	581,118	1,778,013
Reno	7	1,248	51,652	274,861	482,096	754	1,317	5.3	41,831	75	6,052	199,161	776,008
New Mexico	36	3,798	177,167	854,001	2,008,519	2,341	5,490	4.8	148,751	505	20,145	1,032,462	6,641,640
Nonmetropolitan	23	1,252	44,862	180,796	528,313	496	1,445	4.0	54,539	156	7,092	487,959	1,942,354
Metropolitan	13	2,546	132,305	673,205	1,480,206	1,845	4,045	5.1	94,212	349	13,053	544,503	4,699,286
Albuquerque	8	1,774	93,126	495,892	1,061,878	1,359	2,901	5.3	63,423	267	8,753	356,580	3,520,601
Farmington	1	198	9,931	48,647	104,269	133	285	4.9	6,466	22	1,174	59,594	730,618
Las Cruces	3	355	17,425	78,765	173,652	216	475	4.5	13,650	36	1,877	79,966	306,649
Santa Fe	1	219	11,823	49,901	140,407	137	384	4.2	10,673	24	1,249	48,363	141,418

TABLE 8

U.S. CENSUS DIVISION 8, MOUNTAIN

U.S. Community Hospitals
(Nonfederal, short-term general and other special hospitals)

2016 Utilization, Personnel and Finances

FULL-TIME EQUIVALENT PERSONNEL					FULL-TIME EQUIV. TRAINEES			EXPENSES						
								LABOR				TOTAL		
Physicians and Dentists	Registered Nurses	Licensed Practical Nurses	Other Salaried Personnel	Total Personnel	Medical and Dental Residents	Other Trainees	Total Trainees	Payroll (in thousands)	Employee Benefits (in thousands)	Total (in thousands)	Percent of Total	Amount (in thousands)	Adjusted per Admission	Adjusted per Inpatient Day
135,693	1,478,657	74,344	2,612,576	4,991,775	113,111	9,619	122,730	$340,132,974	$90,463,641	$430,596,618	47.7	$902,891,035	$12,777.25	$2,337.82
15,408	149,651	20,977	339,776	612,547	1,714	261	1,975	35,531,908	9,378,885	44,910,794	50.2	89,420,776	8,694.35	1,304.18
120,285	1,329,006	53,367	2,272,800	4,379,228	111,397	9,358	120,755	304,601,066	81,084,755	385,685,824	47.4	813,470,258	13,472.72	2,560.93
7,956	91,095	3,332	160,241	303,566	3,133	391	3,524	19,964,327	4,892,993	24,857,327	46.2	53,755,294	12,823.90	2,403.53
1,743	12,005	1,207	29,784	52,251	52	32	84	3,172,481	785,099	3,957,584	50.2	7,876,895	11,219.79	1,527.82
6,213	79,090	2,125	130,457	251,315	3,081	359	3,440	16,791,846	4,107,894	20,899,743	45.6	45,878,399	13,146.61	2,665.88
2,118	27,664	635	38,646	79,829	899	77	976	5,109,328	1,207,649	6,316,980	44.8	14,098,474	11,787.94	2,479.34
84	674	50	1,462	2,683	5	4	9	180,162	43,916	224,079	49.9	448,783	8,608.26	2,677.48
2,034	26,990	585	37,184	77,146	894	73	967	4,929,166	1,163,733	6,092,901	44.6	13,649,691	11,932.86	2,473.32
72	755	38	1,419	2,703	24	1	25	180,567	47,062	227,629	47.9	475,491	13,065.10	2,874.13
84	1,103	56	1,968	3,827	17	0	17	226,034	56,844	282,879	49.0	577,081	10,859.23	2,145.39
1,745	19,092	336	24,510	52,527	800	64	864	3,397,638	809,697	4,207,336	44.7	9,402,536	12,393.56	2,541.08
15	542	11	1,123	1,933	4	0	4	135,500	37,546	173,047	46.7	370,856	10,296.12	2,983.53
8	281	20	603	1,057	0	0	0	58,493	11,777	70,269	45.1	155,865	7,203.29	1,551.39
74	4,538	117	6,387	12,838	31	2	33	767,938	160,067	928,005	41.5	2,235,326	11,295.12	2,274.53
36	679	7	1,174	2,261	18	6	24	162,996	40,740	203,736	47.1	432,536	10,782.13	2,449.16
1,927	21,141	583	37,290	69,334	672	100	772	4,854,926	1,193,381	6,048,306	45.7	13,247,938	15,192.12	2,866.32
423	2,550	240	6,625	11,301	5	15	20	689,887	181,103	870,991	50.4	1,726,733	14,082.45	2,004.42
1,504	18,591	343	30,665	58,033	667	85	752	4,165,039	1,012,278	5,177,315	44.9	11,521,205	15,373.68	3,063.76
115	1,253	24	2,685	4,362	0	2	2	331,951	83,518	415,469	48.3	860,839	12,812.20	3,267.75
167	1,496	48	2,598	4,967	166	12	178	384,036	96,347	480,383	43.7	1,099,253	12,117.66	2,986.30
826	12,178	183	18,765	36,497	419	31	450	2,688,147	635,645	3,323,791	45.6	7,290,990	17,294.32	3,273.51
103	1,239	26	1,852	3,699	20	1	21	315,730	89,172	404,901	43.3	934,828	13,805.33	2,986.97
107	755	32	1,493	2,699	26	2	28	160,606	42,353	202,959	39.9	508,364	15,935.19	2,229.50
115	703	9	1,432	2,499	0	0	0	107,497	24,462	131,959	36.4	362,422	14,857.62	3,063.45
71	967	21	1,840	3,310	36	37	73	177,072	40,781	217,853	46.9	464,509	10,116.94	1,916.42
1,027	6,556	543	17,891	29,745	52	37	89	1,909,133	429,718	2,338,852	52.5	4,455,757	13,927.90	2,707.92
235	1,612	279	4,550	7,864	9	2	11	443,044	110,883	553,928	51.1	1,083,298	11,707.53	1,871.11
792	4,944	264	13,341	21,881	43	35	78	1,466,089	318,835	1,784,924	52.9	3,372,459	14,831.43	3,162.20
606	3,161	157	9,962	15,571	5	34	39	1,020,544	222,184	1,242,728	54.6	2,274,889	16,496.30	3,663.36
105	542	9	1,681	2,558	18	0	18	205,398	49,897	255,295	57.1	447,146	13,788.46	2,833.28
15	591	34	748	1,661	20	1	21	96,169	21,833	118,002	44.3	266,501	11,066.38	1,631.91
30	245	2	416	796	0	0	0	61,684	10,487	72,171	47.7	151,159	13,247.94	3,882.64
6	53	18	168	289	0	0	0	8,567	2,303	10,869	52.9	20,549	5,782.02	1,437.52
30	352	44	366	1,006	0	0	0	73,727	12,132	85,859	40.5	212,215	11,784.48	2,982.47
1,076	4,879	438	13,138	22,129	53	14	67	1,380,208	300,505	1,680,716	51.3	3,278,884	13,318.08	1,509.39
442	2,511	222	6,886	11,586	7	1	8	653,163	149,163	802,327	51.9	1,545,312	11,862.47	1,120.63
634	2,368	216	6,252	10,543	46	13	59	727,045	151,343	878,389	50.7	1,733,572	14,953.74	2,185.10
373	1,129	53	3,337	5,417	26	13	39	414,006	92,240	506,247	53.1	953,094	16,623.83	2,948.60
122	617	82	1,399	2,511	0	0	0	177,442	38,103	215,545	55.3	389,902	14,512.31	1,220.74
139	622	81	1,516	2,615	20	0	20	135,598	20,999	156,597	40.1	390,576	12,309.74	2,591.31
218	8,645	317	12,359	25,775	324	26	350	1,956,521	471,161	2,427,685	45.7	5,316,360	10,698.04	1,895.32
31	425	32	930	1,716	0	0	0	112,969	26,929	139,899	50.0	279,956	9,821.30	1,282.52
187	8,220	285	11,429	24,059	324	26	350	1,843,552	444,232	2,287,786	45.4	5,036,404	10,751.39	1,947.03
0	430	6	717	1,305	0	0	0	83,600	20,557	104,156	42.2	246,975	9,919.87	2,292.94
182	5,967	253	7,935	17,217	321	23	344	1,401,637	337,694	1,739,333	46.4	3,749,027	10,742.35	1,877.43
5	1,823	26	2,777	5,537	3	3	6	358,315	85,982	444,297	42.7	1,040,402	11,003.72	2,158.08
927	8,298	335	14,241	28,017	71	37	108	1,973,533	419,978	2,393,516	45.2	5,291,810	12,281.89	2,634.68
220	1,972	152	3,813	7,338	19	2	21	490,079	105,211	595,292	46.6	1,276,871	9,518.87	2,416.88
707	6,326	183	10,428	20,679	52	35	87	1,483,454	314,767	1,798,224	44.8	4,014,939	13,530.98	2,712.42
514	4,869	146	7,289	15,062	27	34	61	1,067,062	216,215	1,283,279	42.9	2,990,596	14,651.74	2,816.33
79	473	7	900	1,811	0	0	0	140,708	40,339	181,047	61.5	294,327	13,827.24	2,822.76
28	683	24	1,027	2,045	25	0	25	131,877	26,427	158,305	44.2	358,320	9,415.10	2,063.44
86	301	6	1,212	1,761	0	1	1	143,807	31,786	175,593	47.2	371,697	11,173.48	2,647.28

Table continues

MSAs

TABLE 8

U.S. CENSUS DIVISION 8, MOUNTAIN
CONTINUED

U.S. Community Hospitals
(Nonfederal, short-term general and other special hospitals)

2016 Utilization, Personnel and Finances

CLASSIFICATION	Hospitals	Beds	Admissions	Inpatient Days	Adjusted Inpatient Days	Average Daily Census	Adjusted Average Daily Census	Average Stay (days)	Surgical Operations	NEWBORNS Bassinets	NEWBORNS Births	OUTPATIENT VISITS Emergency	OUTPATIENT VISITS Total
Utah	47	5,423	239,305	1,045,406	2,329,125	2,864	6,368	4.4	262,682	684	48,919	998,334	8,479,247
Nonmetropolitan	18	712	16,248	114,637	479,822	314	1,311	7.1	37,420	97	5,618	122,647	668,146
Metropolitan	29	4,711	223,057	930,769	1,849,303	2,550	5,057	4.2	225,262	587	43,301	875,687	7,811,101
Logan	2	161	7,414	21,562	57,599	59	157	2.9	10,782	36	2,611	32,524	349,572
Ogden-Clearfield	6	872	37,974	145,497	272,723	398	747	3.8	35,012	115	7,846	179,402	636,134
Provo-Orem	6	697	35,999	124,899	254,580	343	697	3.5	39,004	123	9,886	139,899	1,214,593
Salt Lake City	14	2,720	125,121	577,861	1,143,902	1,583	3,127	4.6	125,364	297	20,536	471,460	5,082,933
St. George	1	261	16,549	60,950	120,499	167	329	3.7	15,100	16	2,422	52,402	527,869
Wyoming	23	1,715	41,221	363,509	1,096,364	996	2,995	8.8	37,734	168	6,445	238,255	1,234,674
Nonmetropolitan	21	1,360	22,356	279,776	942,205	766	2,574	12.5	27,600	128	4,051	162,261	967,821
Metropolitan	2	355	18,865	83,733	154,159	230	421	4.4	10,134	40	2,394	75,994	266,853
Casper	1	217	8,578	33,858	54,694	93	149	3.9	5,077	24	1,132	34,789	84,116
Cheyenne	1	138	10,287	49,875	99,465	137	272	4.8	5,057	16	1,262	41,205	182,737

MSAs

TABLE 8

U.S. CENSUS DIVISION 8, MOUNTAIN CONTINUED

U.S. Community Hospitals
(Nonfederal, short-term general and other special hospitals)

2016 Utilization, Personnel and Finances

FULL-TIME EQUIVALENT PERSONNEL					FULL-TIME EQUIV. TRAINEES			EXPENSES						
								LABOR				TOTAL		
Physicians and Dentists	Registered Nurses	Licensed Practical Nurses	Other Salaried Personnel	Total Personnel	Medical and Dental Residents	Other Trainees	Total Trainees	Payroll (in thousands)	Employee Benefits (in thousands)	Total (in thousands)	Percent of Total	Amount (in thousands)	Adjusted per Admission	Adjusted per Inpatient Day
310	11,716	322	21,347	39,290	1,056	95	1,151	2,164,668	701,811	2,866,474	43.6	6,579,979	12,654.07	2,825.09
64	834	92	1,989	3,475	1	3	4	177,145	54,661	231,804	44.2	524,074	7,895.77	1,092.23
246	10,882	230	19,358	35,815	1,055	92	1,147	1,987,523	647,150	2,634,670	43.5	6,055,905	13,350.32	3,274.70
28	348	12	530	1,069	0	0	0	58,435	20,379	78,813	40.6	193,897	9,761.73	3,366.33
58	1,381	71	2,051	4,197	35	2	37	281,047	79,734	360,780	43.3	833,162	11,594.88	3,054.97
28	1,596	37	2,556	5,035	52	21	73	274,728	91,770	366,499	45.5	805,884	10,514.36	3,165.54
128	6,886	110	13,083	23,252	968	65	1,033	1,239,172	411,545	1,650,716	43.7	3,778,172	14,961.16	3,302.88
4	671	0	1,138	2,262	0	4	4	134,141	43,721	177,862	40.0	444,789	13,594.64	3,691.23
353	2,196	159	5,329	9,447	6	5	11	616,009	168,789	784,798	52.8	1,486,092	13,527.51	1,355.47
244	1,427	140	3,529	6,288	6	5	11	426,031	113,233	539,264	54.4	991,867	13,139.92	1,052.71
109	769	19	1,800	3,159	0	0	0	189,978	55,556	245,534	49.7	494,224	14,378.69	3,205.94
26	276	6	520	1,033	0	0	0	75,914	27,128	103,042	48.8	211,236	15,243.96	3,862.13
83	493	13	1,280	2,126	0	0	0	114,064	28,428	142,492	50.4	282,989	13,794.24	2,845.11

MSAs

TABLE 8

U.S. CENSUS DIVISION 9, PACIFIC

U.S. Community Hospitals
(Nonfederal, short-term general and other special hospitals)

2016 Utilization, Personnel and Finances

MSAs

CLASSIFICATION	Hospitals	Beds	Admissions	Inpatient Days	Adjusted Inpatient Days	Average Daily Census	Adjusted Average Daily Census	Average Stay (days)	Surgical Operations	NEWBORNS Bassinets	NEWBORNS Births	OUTPATIENT VISITS Emergency	OUTPATIENT VISITS Total
UNITED STATES	4,840	780,272	33,424,253	182,291,689	386,210,917	499,407	1,056,009	5.5	27,227,227	55,149	3,727,427	142,557,879	747,089,013
Nonmetropolitan	1,825	111,987	3,103,592	20,547,750	68,564,794	56,294	187,486	6.6	3,578,377	9,181	371,659	22,118,524	126,900,302
Metropolitan	3,015	668,285	30,320,661	161,743,939	317,646,123	443,113	868,523	5.3	23,648,850	45,968	3,355,768	120,439,355	620,188,711
CENSUS DIVISION 9, PACIFIC	534	93,016	4,388,359	22,446,883	41,771,631	61,491	114,214	5.1	3,190,254	7,171	605,737	18,480,477	88,794,484
Nonmetropolitan	109	4,481	147,344	813,787	2,697,800	2,232	7,376	5.5	212,775	442	25,487	1,245,029	7,634,767
Metropolitan	425	88,535	4,241,015	21,633,096	39,073,831	59,259	106,838	5.1	2,977,479	6,729	580,250	17,235,448	81,159,717
Alaska	21	1,647	51,022	384,938	936,341	1,057	2,561	7.5	70,235	191	9,687	342,017	2,059,121
Nonmetropolitan	15	593	11,873	125,360	440,010	345	1,204	10.6	23,349	50	2,664	113,211	800,994
Metropolitan	6	1,054	39,149	259,578	496,331	712	1,357	6.6	46,886	141	7,023	228,806	1,258,127
Anchorage	5	838	34,524	213,370	391,244	585	1,070	6.2	42,234	125	5,851	193,650	922,821
Fairbanks	1	216	4,625	46,208	105,087	127	287	10.0	4,652	16	1,172	35,156	335,306
California	341	70,082	3,298,740	16,955,615	30,105,018	46,445	82,324	5.1	2,165,321	5,092	450,858	13,420,209	58,516,196
Nonmetropolitan	30	1,337	48,168	262,133	798,739	718	2,182	5.4	65,768	111	6,871	449,548	2,332,240
Metropolitan	311	68,745	3,250,572	16,693,482	29,306,279	45,727	80,142	5.1	2,099,553	4,981	443,987	12,970,661	56,183,956
Anaheim-Santa Ana-Irvine	24	5,502	272,112	1,260,116	2,239,131	3,452	6,123	4.6	176,590	393	40,881	873,955	3,946,830
Bakersfield	10	1,534	65,858	342,748	689,147	939	1,887	5.2	50,144	79	13,161	280,785	963,609
Chico	4	530	33,144	139,564	290,492	382	795	4.2	18,134	47	3,022	81,982	681,448
El Centro	2	268	11,333	39,064	100,943	107	276	3.4	8,826	33	3,403	73,947	343,794
Fresno	8	1,816	81,941	458,437	871,290	1,255	2,382	5.6	41,728	150	11,410	324,410	1,299,606
Hanford-Corcoran	2	248	19,071	46,827	107,015	128	293	2.5	12,699	20	913	123,979	543,769
Los Angeles-Long Beach-Glendale	86	20,926	983,956	5,068,658	8,440,273	13,884	23,085	5.2	562,066	1,482	120,989	3,229,129	13,617,147
Madera	2	464	16,592	88,421	144,005	242	393	5.3	16,237	10	1,042	160,244	482,687
Merced	2	230	12,663	49,964	95,628	137	261	3.9	7,338	28	3,398	104,527	244,501
Modesto	4	1,036	53,621	278,081	467,881	761	1,279	5.2	33,162	87	8,078	256,041	495,698
Napa	2	236	12,841	57,995	104,152	159	285	4.5	12,457	10	954	34,626	224,931
Oakland-Hayward-Berkeley	19	4,093	189,224	980,591	1,720,910	2,686	4,705	5.2	104,932	301	24,985	1,047,052	4,678,362
Oxnard-Thousand Oaks-Ventura	6	1,221	63,205	312,559	629,924	856	1,723	4.9	37,319	101	9,616	253,767	1,235,355
Redding	3	464	20,691	122,068	274,782	334	752	5.9	12,564	10	1,892	76,935	229,741
Riverside-San Bernardino-Ontario	34	6,817	329,950	1,595,550	2,864,764	4,370	7,836	4.8	217,406	525	48,124	1,447,592	4,363,528
Sacramento-Roseville-Arden-Arcade	17	3,726	202,164	1,010,028	1,742,716	2,765	4,761	5.0	148,159	275	21,451	787,297	3,556,831
Salinas	4	754	33,060	154,206	242,644	423	663	4.7	20,718	79	6,349	169,855	637,757
San Diego-Carlsbad	20	5,605	288,487	1,497,824	2,460,796	4,105	6,728	5.2	210,836	374	40,017	998,768	3,531,080
San Francisco-Redwood City-South San Francisco	16	4,778	148,107	1,176,663	1,947,933	3,224	5,328	7.9	121,160	181	17,390	661,116	4,730,468
San Jose-Sunnyvale-Santa Clara	11	3,262	160,526	829,220	1,516,751	2,271	4,146	5.2	122,293	312	26,745	646,514	4,341,979
San Luis Obispo-Paso Robles-Arroyo Grande	3	325	13,984	53,933	97,651	147	267	3.9	10,252	39	2,449	77,834	210,927
San Rafael	3	332	15,284	65,828	127,711	181	349	4.3	12,824	15	1,331	57,998	324,781
Santa Cruz-Watsonville	3	359	16,380	69,458	142,204	190	389	4.2	15,339	50	2,947	76,409	313,761
Santa Maria-Santa Barbara	5	846	38,004	219,914	423,261	603	1,158	5.8	23,017	48	5,691	145,288	523,204
Santa Rosa	6	633	31,722	147,831	290,479	405	794	4.7	25,585	55	4,940	129,120	570,011
Stockton-Lodi	7	1,147	59,513	249,861	537,670	684	1,473	4.2	37,494	129	9,484	347,867	1,545,902
Vallejo-Fairfield	4	676	31,764	130,229	255,786	357	699	4.1	19,418	67	4,566	191,659	1,338,830
Visalia-Porterville	3	698	34,545	195,731	387,583	537	1,059	5.7	15,435	51	6,717	247,154	948,539
Yuba City	1	219	10,830	52,113	92,757	143	253	4.8	5,421	30	2,062	64,811	258,880
Hawaii	23	2,488	110,104	703,010	1,474,635	1,925	4,032	6.4	87,868	162	18,495	468,601	2,575,781
Nonmetropolitan	8	564	17,901	119,972	360,243	327	985	6.7	18,649	45	4,755	93,503	342,666
Metropolitan	15	1,924	92,203	583,038	1,114,392	1,598	3,047	6.3	69,219	117	13,740	375,098	2,233,115
Kahului-Wailuku-Lahaina	4	258	11,015	58,002	131,738	159	361	5.3	3,277	26	2,797	22,878	126,425
Urban Honolulu	11	1,666	81,188	525,036	982,654	1,439	2,686	6.5	65,942	91	10,943	352,220	2,106,690
Oregon	59	6,673	337,535	1,508,241	3,222,786	4,131	8,805	4.5	328,735	658	42,705	1,565,520	11,458,190
Nonmetropolitan	26	956	40,821	154,744	555,795	425	1,518	3.8	46,089	129	6,029	318,654	2,635,626
Metropolitan	33	5,717	296,714	1,353,497	2,666,991	3,706	7,287	4.6	282,646	529	36,676	1,246,866	8,822,564
Albany	2	95	4,302	14,204	60,114	38	165	3.3	9,064	14	857	49,923	533,261
Bend-Redmond	2	298	18,877	72,401	125,716	198	343	3.8	20,169	39	2,189	63,619	175,176
Corvallis	1	182	9,528	44,047	84,626	121	231	4.6	9,692	20	1,090	27,917	419,862
Eugene	5	631	35,724	164,219	282,344	450	772	4.6	23,983	56	3,648	165,302	444,920
Grants Pass	1	111	6,966	24,245	52,175	66	143	3.5	4,881	12	771	40,036	259,610
Medford	3	494	24,699	115,455	208,302	316	569	4.7	21,757	34	2,435	94,454	799,383
Portland-Vancouver-Hillsboro	15	3,372	167,703	798,112	1,594,357	2,186	4,357	4.8	174,384	305	20,642	640,986	5,504,112
Salem	4	534	28,915	120,814	259,357	331	707	4.2	18,716	49	5,044	164,629	686,240

FULL-TIME EQUIVALENT PERSONNEL					FULL-TIME EQUIV. TRAINEES			EXPENSES						
								LABOR				TOTAL		
Physicians and Dentists	Registered Nurses	Licensed Practical Nurses	Other Salaried Personnel	Total Personnel	Medical and Dental Residents	Other Trainees	Total Trainees	Payroll (in thousands)	Employee Benefits (in thousands)	Total (in thousands)	Percent of Total	Amount (in thousands)	Adjusted per Admission	Adjusted per Inpatient Day
135,693	1,478,657	74,344	2,612,576	4,991,775	113,111	9,619	122,730	$340,132,974	$90,463,641	$430,596,618	47.7	$902,891,035	$12,777.25	$2,337.82
15,408	149,651	20,977	339,776	612,547	1,714	261	1,975	35,531,908	9,378,885	44,910,794	50.2	89,420,776	8,694.35	1,304.18
120,285	1,329,006	53,367	2,272,800	4,379,228	111,397	9,358	120,755	304,601,066	81,084,755	385,685,824	47.4	813,470,258	13,472.72	2,560.93
14,949	200,688	8,815	328,146	638,708	13,211	1,332	14,543	52,174,156	16,510,635	68,684,791	48.7	141,159,569	17,113.44	3,379.32
875	8,531	789	20,278	35,337	35	16	51	2,564,162	782,334	3,346,494	52.5	6,379,585	13,225.50	2,364.74
14,074	192,157	8,026	307,868	603,371	13,176	1,316	14,492	49,609,994	15,728,301	65,338,297	48.5	134,779,984	17,354.93	3,449.37
396	3,180	146	6,005	11,614	113	6	119	948,625	220,609	1,169,233	51.0	2,291,294	19,338.91	2,447.07
135	868	80	2,556	4,250	14	4	18	372,330	117,071	489,401	55.5	881,659	20,954.46	2,003.72
261	2,312	66	3,449	7,364	99	2	101	576,295	103,538	679,832	48.2	1,409,635	18,449.27	2,840.11
206	1,995	47	2,519	5,905	98	2	100	486,751	77,509	564,259	48.8	1,155,197	17,532.74	2,952.63
55	317	19	930	1,459	1	0	1	89,544	26,029	115,573	45.4	254,438	24,190.67	2,421.21
9,183	147,759	6,943	231,183	456,317	10,296	1,102	11,398	37,458,123	12,901,861	50,359,983	48.9	102,994,932	17,385.10	3,421.19
113	2,726	279	5,723	10,270	6	4	10	716,075	251,085	967,159	49.0	1,974,078	13,886.50	2,471.49
9,070	145,033	6,664	225,460	446,047	10,290	1,098	11,388	36,742,048	12,650,776	49,392,824	48.9	101,020,855	17,471.12	3,447.07
197	11,017	298	16,782	32,833	126	14	140	2,317,450	716,889	3,034,340	44.4	6,830,364	13,868.59	3,050.45
125	2,650	175	4,560	8,870	31	3	34	618,675	174,631	793,307	46.5	1,706,845	13,452.97	2,476.75
24	1,481	73	2,466	4,567	2	1	3	356,244	130,176	486,420	49.8	977,607	14,671.08	3,365.35
44	402	41	880	1,600	12	2	14	88,022	26,143	114,165	50.3	227,020	7,752.09	2,248.99
259	2,817	132	5,388	9,989	212	14	226	696,073	187,488	883,561	46.6	1,894,973	11,977.13	2,174.91
47	621	47	1,128	2,222	11	1	12	123,752	30,753	154,506	44.9	344,360	7,883.51	3,217.86
3,052	44,607	2,539	69,125	139,215	3,443	497	3,940	10,440,865	3,312,876	13,753,744	48.0	28,633,149	17,241.82	3,392.44
3	776	38	1,760	2,981	0	4	4	221,370	96,513	317,883	52.2	608,613	21,849.32	4,226.33
1	520	40	747	1,454	0	0	0	119,970	41,684	161,654	48.2	335,689	13,162.73	3,510.36
17	2,649	49	2,279	5,770	4	6	10	495,000	169,732	664,732	51.6	1,288,642	14,922.26	2,754.21
1	541	4	1,064	1,753	0	0	0	133,902	55,405	189,308	38.7	489,381	21,097.65	4,698.72
458	7,856	432	14,112	25,614	328	25	353	2,554,188	1,036,140	3,590,326	52.0	6,905,867	20,347.94	4,012.92
90	2,276	117	3,783	7,244	85	4	89	672,305	203,140	875,444	48.8	1,802,319	13,974.93	2,861.17
45	794	29	1,289	2,531	16	2	18	223,278	58,746	282,024	45.6	618,034	15,796.40	2,249.18
1,598	14,092	857	17,697	40,727	530	61	591	2,754,840	790,850	3,545,690	48.1	7,373,153	12,495.45	2,573.74
273	9,622	243	13,879	26,857	884	6	890	2,666,450	968,076	3,634,526	49.9	7,287,860	20,532.19	4,181.90
51	1,573	32	2,379	4,711	33	1	34	498,139	228,662	726,800	61.8	1,176,718	22,784.74	4,849.57
118	13,364	427	17,404	36,202	1,095	386	1,481	2,885,726	914,588	3,800,315	47.6	7,979,456	16,715.56	3,242.63
1,692	7,200	378	13,164	25,559	1,795	36	1,831	2,973,593	1,234,345	4,207,938	50.9	8,267,689	30,449.54	4,244.34
545	9,415	303	16,933	30,474	1,383	22	1,405	3,141,227	1,429,765	4,570,991	51.5	8,881,565	30,844.12	5,855.65
6	578	11	692	1,481	2	0	2	136,748	33,580	170,328	48.0	354,879	13,805.31	3,634.16
25	744	19	1,544	2,580	5	1	6	231,407	74,825	306,232	53.1	576,284	19,262.75	4,512.40
28	707	13	995	1,914	9	2	11	213,683	65,667	279,350	49.4	566,027	16,582.98	3,980.39
60	1,330	42	2,686	4,635	78	1	79	444,344	131,131	575,474	47.0	1,223,754	17,695.05	2,891.25
33	1,459	39	2,037	4,184	43	0	43	344,455	138,442	482,897	45.8	1,053,563	16,794.67	3,626.98
210	2,613	117	4,704	8,838	74	6	80	547,830	156,760	704,589	49.1	1,435,206	11,202.22	2,669.31
68	1,475	49	2,660	4,712	21	2	23	407,589	112,670	520,259	51.6	1,009,076	16,059.91	3,945.00
0	1,267	116	2,564	4,931	68	1	69	310,225	89,386	399,610	50.4	792,351	11,563.45	2,044.34
0	587	4	759	1,599	0	0	0	124,698	41,714	166,411	43.7	380,409	19,733.81	4,101.13
520	5,220	196	8,673	17,210	47	39	86	1,405,546	375,429	1,780,976	50.1	3,556,187	16,047.27	2,411.57
53	804	56	1,512	2,832	8	3	11	213,684	69,105	282,789	50.5	559,926	11,795.36	1,554.30
467	4,416	140	7,161	14,378	39	36	75	1,191,862	306,324	1,498,187	50.0	2,996,261	17,206.34	2,688.70
42	421	23	785	1,496	14	1	15	116,310	30,588	146,898	47.1	311,678	13,542.39	2,365.89
425	3,995	117	6,376	12,882	25	35	60	1,075,552	275,736	1,351,289	50.3	2,684,583	17,764.34	2,731.97
1,702	16,488	181	27,847	53,324	1,236	56	1,292	4,328,430	1,293,103	5,621,535	49.3	11,398,930	15,257.30	3,536.98
390	2,164	72	5,780	9,675	2	5	7	718,804	198,759	917,562	53.3	1,722,306	11,599.90	3,098.82
1,312	14,324	109	22,067	43,649	1,234	51	1,285	3,609,627	1,094,344	4,703,973	48.6	9,676,624	16,164.43	3,628.29
89	292	8	808	1,422	0	13	13	124,132	38,251	162,383	56.4	288,033	15,815.54	4,791.44
108	826	5	2,095	3,259	3	0	3	223,272	45,406	268,678	58.6	458,478	13,793.78	3,646.93
103	452	9	821	1,637	103	8	111	162,304	50,474	212,778	52.1	408,077	22,292.01	4,822.13
115	1,316	15	1,984	3,841	0	0	0	320,514	90,626	411,141	43.5	944,942	15,243.22	3,346.78
15	296	7	466	957	0	0	0	57,834	21,916	79,749	52.7	151,436	10,101.77	2,902.46
29	1,232	15	1,780	3,599	0	3	3	223,126	90,512	313,639	44.7	701,573	15,393.14	3,368.06
727	8,502	41	11,517	24,237	1,128	27	1,155	2,121,586	657,318	2,778,904	47.3	5,880,441	17,252.08	3,688.28
126	1,408	9	2,596	4,697	0	0	0	376,859	99,842	476,701	56.5	843,644	12,886.36	3,252.83

Table continues

MSAs

TABLE 8

U.S. CENSUS DIVISION 9, PACIFIC CONTINUED

U.S. Community Hospitals
(Nonfederal, short-term general and other special hospitals)

2016 Utilization, Personnel and Finances

CLASSIFICATION	Hospitals	Beds	Admissions	Inpatient Days	Adjusted Inpatient Days	Average Daily Census	Adjusted Average Daily Census	Average Stay (days)	Surgical Operations	NEWBORNS Bassinets	Births	OUTPATIENT VISITS Emergency	Total
Washington..............	90	12,126	590,958	2,895,079	6,032,851	7,933	16,492	4.9	538,095	1,068	83,992	2,684,130	14,185,196
Nonmetropolitan..............	30	1,031	28,581	151,578	543,013	417	1,487	5.3	58,920	107	5,168	270,113	1,523,241
Metropolitan..............	60	11,095	562,377	2,743,501	5,489,838	7,516	15,005	4.9	479,175	961	78,824	2,414,017	12,661,955
Bellingham..............	1	253	15,102	65,694	130,915	180	358	4.4	6,771	20	1,878	21,185	107,493
Bremerton-Silverdale..............	1	260	12,892	54,633	108,872	150	297	4.2	7,978	22	1,924	81,017	297,003
Kennewick-Richland..............	4	449	23,911	95,273	244,106	260	667	4.0	20,356	44	4,823	212,080	853,589
Lewiston..............	1	25	1,210	3,859	16,737	11	46	3.2	2,136	0	0	16,693	95,584
Longview..............	1	180	7,234	29,904	77,945	82	213	4.1	4,575	14	857	46,511	216,239
Mount Vernon-Anacortes..............	3	241	11,331	45,611	135,476	124	370	4.0	12,394	35	1,638	74,762	828,273
Olympia-Tumwater..............	2	402	19,734	108,173	172,822	296	472	5.5	22,174	49	2,907	85,391	401,810
Portland-Vancouver-Hillsboro..............	2	577	34,521	146,213	276,457	401	756	4.2	12,705	82	5,433	115,312	490,002
Seattle-Bellevue-Everett..............	21	4,987	268,619	1,335,946	2,611,485	3,661	7,137	5.0	200,884	390	36,322	959,132	6,204,723
Spokane-Spokane Valley..............	9	1,563	59,059	340,980	609,227	935	1,665	5.8	95,337	106	7,091	239,352	1,055,158
Tacoma-Lakewood..............	6	1,331	72,859	361,728	729,796	990	1,995	5.0	52,981	105	9,777	325,625	949,740
Walla Walla..............	2	129	5,221	30,259	63,732	83	175	5.8	4,777	14	648	24,553	200,333
Wenatchee..............	3	232	11,771	52,234	105,675	143	289	4.4	8,806	25	1,801	46,441	213,092
Yakima..............	4	466	18,913	72,994	206,593	200	565	3.9	27,301	55	3,725	165,963	748,916

MSAs

TABLE **8**

U.S. CENSUS DIVISION 9, PACIFIC CONTINUED

U.S. Community Hospitals
(Nonfederal, short-term general and other special hospitals)

2016 Utilization, Personnel and Finances

FULL-TIME EQUIVALENT PERSONNEL					FULL-TIME EQUIV. TRAINEES			EXPENSES						
								LABOR				TOTAL		
Physicians and Dentists	Registered Nurses	Licensed Practical Nurses	Other Salaried Personnel	Total Personnel	Medical and Dental Residents	Other Trainees	Total Trainees	Payroll (in thousands)	Employee Benefits (in thousands)	Total (in thousands)	Percent of Total	Amount (in thousands)	Adjusted per Admission	Adjusted per Inpatient Day
3,148	28,041	1,349	54,438	100,243	1,519	129	1,648	8,033,432	1,719,633	9,753,064	46.6	20,918,227	16,911.26	3,467.39
184	1,969	302	4,707	8,310	5	0	5	543,269	146,314	689,583	55.5	1,241,617	12,149.96	2,286.53
2,964	26,072	1,047	49,731	91,933	1,514	129	1,643	7,490,163	1,573,319	9,063,481	46.1	19,676,610	17,340.04	3,584.19
81	846	35	1,535	2,935	33	1	34	183,310	49,806	233,116	47.3	493,283	16,390.87	3,767.97
63	640	27	1,161	2,249	26	1	27	141,957	37,569	179,526	47.2	379,991	14,790.81	3,490.25
211	1,134	55	2,383	4,599	22	26	48	370,261	62,362	432,623	52.3	827,741	13,386.50	3,390.91
12	95	10	243	413	1	2	3	26,511	7,126	33,637	48.9	68,814	13,112.51	4,111.52
37	348	34	763	1,374	10	2	12	111,451	29,465	140,916	53.4	263,899	13,996.25	3,385.71
84	678	65	1,544	2,838	18	1	19	205,471	47,062	252,532	50.8	496,795	14,595.73	3,667.03
19	1,065	34	1,315	2,839	3	0	3	209,767	24,918	234,684	52.6	445,891	13,592.99	2,580.06
119	1,476	56	2,463	4,833	56	5	61	335,554	87,150	422,704	50.4	838,710	12,792.43	3,033.78
1,734	12,806	359	25,250	46,010	1,224	85	1,309	4,009,340	852,423	4,861,762	45.0	10,796,490	20,664.29	4,134.23
74	2,523	59	4,394	7,838	35	2	37	596,464	89,830	686,295	41.0	1,673,670	16,693.63	2,747.20
354	2,781	219	4,977	9,527	73	4	77	825,884	187,925	1,013,809	46.4	2,187,197	14,703.15	2,997.00
64	275	10	528	1,047	0	0	0	98,669	9,611	108,280	57.3	188,853	14,733.42	2,963.24
55	454	27	890	1,640	7	0	7	115,698	30,696	146,394	39.5	370,990	16,840.22	3,510.67
57	951	57	2,285	3,791	6	0	6	259,826	57,376	317,203	49.2	644,285	11,867.46	3,118.62

MSAs

Statistics for Health Care Systems and their Hospitals

The following tables describing health care systems refers to information in section B of the 2018 *AHA Guide*. Table 1 shows the number of health care systems by type of control. Table 2 provides a breakdown of the number of systems that own, lease, sponsor or contract manage hospitals within each control category. Table 3 gives the number of hospitals and beds in each control category as well as total hospitals and beds. Finally, shows the percentage of hospitals and beds in each control category.

For more information on health care systems, please write to the Section for Health Care Systems, 155 N. Wacker Drive, Chicago, Illinois 60606 or call 312/422–3000.

Table 1. Multihospital Health Care Systems, by Type of Organizaton Control

Type of Control	Code	Numebr of Systems
Catholic (Roman) church–related	CC	30
Other church–related	CO	6
Subtotal, church–related		36
Other not–for–profit	NP	314
Subtotal, not–for–profit		350
Investor Owned	IO	78
Federal Government	FG	5
Total		433

Table 2. Multihospital Health Care Systems, by Type of Ownership and Control

Type of Ownership	Catholic Church–Related (CC)	Other Church–Related (CO)	Total Church–Related (CC + CO)	Other Not–for–Profit (NP)	Total Not–for–Profit (CC, CO, + NP)	Investor–Owned (IO)	Federal Govern–ment (FG)	All Systems
Systems that only own, lease or sponsor	22	5	27	188	215	20	0	235
Systems that only contract–manage	1	0	1	9	10	3	0	13
Systems that manage, own, lease, or sponsor	7	1	8	117	125	55	5	185
Total	30	6	38	314	350	78	5	433

Table 3. Hospitals and Beds in Multihospital Health Care Systems, by Type of Ownership and Control

Type of Ownership	Catholic Church–Related (CC)		Other Church–Related (CO)		Total Church–Related (CC + CO)		Other Not–for–Profit (NP)		Total Not–for–Profit (CC, CO, + NP)		Investor–Owned (IO)		Federal Govern–ment (FG)		All Systems	
	H	B	H	B	H	B	H	B	H	B	H	B	H	B	H	B
Owned, leased or sponsored	582	105,369	70	15,873	652	121,242	1,563	334,450	2,215	455,692	1,378	164,474	209	41,056	3,802	661,222
Contract–managed	44	2,290	3	465	46	2,755	113	10,169	159	12,924	92	5,120	0	0	256	18,044
Total	626	107,659	73	16,338	698	123,997	3,126	344,619	3,854	468,616	1,475	169,594	209	41,056	5,508	679,266

H = hospitals; B = beds.

Table 4. Hospitals and Beds in Multihospital Health Care Systems, by Type of Ownership and Control as a Percentage of All Systems

Type of Ownership	Catholic Church–Related (CC)		Other Church–Related (CO)		Total Church–Related (CC + CO)		Other Not–for–Profit (NP)		Total Not–for–Profit (CC, CO, + NP)		Investor–Owned (IO)		Federal Govern–ment (FG)		All Systems	
	H	B	H	B	H	B	H	B	H	B	H	B	H	B	H	B
Owned, leased or sponsored	15.3	15.9	1.8	2.4	17.2	18.3	41.1	50.6	58.3	68.9	36.2	24.9	5.5	6.2	99.9	100
Contract managed	17.2	12.7	0.8	2.6	17.9	15.3	44.1	50.6	62.1	71.6	37.9	24.9	0.0	0.0	100.0	97
Total	11.4	15.9	1.3	2.4	12.7	18.3	56.8	50.6	69.4	68.9	26.8	24.9	3.8	6.2	100.1	100

H = hospitals; B = beds.

*Please note that figures may not always equal the provided subtotal or total percentages due to rounding.

Glossary

This glossary explains specific terms as they are used in the tables and text of AHA Hospital Statistics

Ablation of Barrett's esophagus: Premalignant condition that can lead to adenocarcinoma of the esophagus. The non surgical ablation of the premalignant tissue in Barrett's esophagus by the application of thermal energy or light through an endoscope passed from the mouth into the esophagus.

Acute long term care: Providers specialized acute hospital care to medically complex patients who are critically ill, have multisystem complications and/or failure, and require hospitalization averaging 25 days, in a facility offering specialized treatment programs and therapeutic intervention on a 24 hour/7day a week basis.

Adjusted admission: An aggregate measure of workload reflecting the sum of admissions and equivalent admissions attributed to outpatient services. The number of equivalent admissions attributed to outpatient services is derived by multiplying admissions by the ratio of outpatient revenue to inpatient revenue.

$$\frac{\text{Adjusted}}{\text{admissions}} = \text{admissions} + [\text{ admissions} * \left(\frac{\text{outpatient revenue}}{\text{inpatient revenue}}\right)]$$

Adjusted average daily census: An estimate of the average number of patients (both inpatients and outpatients) receiving care each day during the reporting period, which is usually 12 months. The figure is derived by dividing the number of inpatient day equivalents (also called adjusted inpatient days) by the number of days in the reporting period.

Adjusted inpatient days: An aggregate measure of workload reflecting the sum of inpatient days and equivalent patient days attributed to outpatient services. The number of equivalent patient days attributed to outpatient services is derived by multiplying inpatient days by the ratio of outpatient revenue to inpatient revenue.

$$\frac{\text{Adjusted}}{\text{inpatient days}} = \text{inpatient days} + [\text{ inpatient days} * \left(\frac{\text{outpatient revenue}}{\text{inpatient revenue}}\right)]$$

Admissions: The number of patients, excluding newborns, accepted for inpatient service during the reporting period; the number includes patients who visit the emergency room and are later admitted for inpatient service.

Adult Cardiac Surgery: Includes minimally invasive procedures that include surgery done with only a small incision or no incision at all, such as through a laparoscope or an endoscope and more invasive major surgical procedures that include open chest and open heart surgery.

Adult Cardiology Services: An organized clinical service offering diagnostic and interventional procedures to manage the full range of adult heart conditions.

Adult day care program: Program providing supervision, medical and psychological care, and social activities for older adults who live at home or in another family setting, but cannot be alone or prefer to be with others during the day. May include intake assessment, health monitoring, occupational therapy, personal care, noon meal, and transportation services.

Adult Diagnostic/invasive catheterization: (also called coronary angiography or coronary arteriography) is used to assist in diagnosing complex heart conditions. Cardiac angiography involves the insertion of a tiny catheter into the artery in the groin then carefully threading the catheter up into the aorta where the coronary arteries originate. Once the catheter is in place, a dye is injected which allows the cardiologist to see the size, shape, and distribution of the coronary arteries. These images are used to diagnose heart disease and to determine, among other things, whether or not surgery is indicated.

Adult Interventional cardiac catheterization: Non surgical procedure that utilizes the same basic principles as diagnostic catheterization and then uses advanced techniques to improve the heart's function. It can be a less-invasive alternative to heart surgery.

Airborne infection isolation room: A single-occupancy room for patient care where environmental factors are controlled in an effort to minimize the transmission of those infectious agents, usually spread person to person by droplet nuclei associated with coughing and inhalation. Such rooms typically have specific ventilation requirements for controlled ventilation, air pressure and filtration.

Alcoholism-drug abuse or dependency inpatient care: Provides diagnosis and therapeutic services to patients with alcoholism or other drug dependencies. Includes care for inpatient/residential treatment for patients whose course of treatment involves more intensive care than provided in an outpatient setting or where patient requires supervised withdrawal.

Alcoholism-drug abuse or dependency outpatient services: Organized hospital services that provide medical care and/or rehabilitative treatment services to outpatients for whom the primary diagnosis is alcoholism or other chemical dependency.

Alzheimer Center: Facility that offers care to persons with Alzheimer's disease and their families through an integrated program of clinical services, research, and education.

Ambulance services: Provision of ambulance services to the ill and injured who require medical attention on a scheduled or unscheduled basis.

Ambulatory Surgery Center: Facility that provides care to patients requiring surgery who are admitted and discharged on the same day. Ambulatory surgery centers are distinct from same day surgical units within the hospital outpatient departments for purposes of Medicare payments.

Arthritis treatment center: Specifically equipped and staffed center for the diagnosis and treatment of arthritis and other joint disorders.

Assisted living: A special combination of housing, supportive services, personalized assistance and health care designed to respond to the individual needs of those who need help in activities of daily living and instrumental activities of daily living. Supportive services are available, 24 hours a day, to meet scheduled and unscheduled needs, in a way that promotes maximum independence and dignity for each resident and encourages the involvement of a resident's family, neighbor and friends.

Assistive Technology Center: A program providing access to specialized hardware and software with adaptations allowing individuals greater independence with mobility, dexterity, or increased communication options.

Auxiliary: A volunteer community organization formed to assist the hospital in carrying out its purpose and to serve as a link between the institution and the community.

Average daily census: The average number of people served on an inpatient basis on a single day during the reporting period; the figure is calculated by dividing the number of inpatient days by the number of days in the reporting period.

Bariatric/weight control services: Bariatrics is the medical practice of weight reduction.

Beds: Number of beds regularly maintained (set up and staffed for use) for inpatients as of the close of the reporting period. Excludes newborn bassinets.

Bed-size category: Hospitals are categorized by the number of beds set up and staffed for use at the end of the reporting period. The eight categories in Hospital Statistics are: 6 to 24 beds; 25 to 49; 50 to 99; 100 to 199; 200 to 299; 300 to 399; 400 to 499; and 500 or more.

Birthing room-LDR room-LDRP room: A single-room type of maternity care with a more homelike setting for families than the traditional three-room unit (labor/delivery/recovery) with a separate postpartum area. A birthing room combines labor and delivery in one room. An LDR room accommodates three stages in the birthing process—labor, delivery, and recovery. An LDRP room accommodates all four stages of the birth process—labor, delivery, recovery, and postpartum.

Births: Total number of infants born in the hospital during the reporting period. Births do not include infants transferred from other institutions, and are excluded from admission and discharge figures.

Blood Donor Center: A facility that performs, or is responsible for the collection, processing, testing or distribution of blood and components.

Bone marrow transplant: See definition for Transplant services on page 214.

Breast cancer screening/mammograms: Mammography screening – The use of breast x-ray to detect unsuspected breast cancer in asymptomatic women. Diagnostic mammography – The x-ray imaging of breast tissue in symptomatic women who are considered to have a substantial likelihood of having breast cancer already.

Burn care: Provides care to severely burned patients. Severely burned patients are those with any of the following: (1) second-degree burns of more than 25% total body surface area for adults or 20% total body surface area for children: (2) third-degree burns of more than 10% total body surface area; (3) any severe burns of the hands, face, eyes, ears, or feet; or (4) all inhalation injuries, electrical burns, complicated burn injuries involving fractures and other major traumas, and all other poor risk factors.

Cardiac electrophysiology: Evaluation and management of patients with complex rhythm or conduction abnormalities, including diagnostic testing, treatment of arrhythmias by catheter ablation or drug therapy, and pacemaker/defibrillator implantation and follow-up.

Cardiac intensive care: Provides patient care of a more specialized nature than the usual medical and surgical care, on the basis of physicians' orders and approved nursing care plans. The unit is staffed with specially trained nursing personnel and contains monitoring and specialized support or treatment equipment for patients who, because of heart seizure, open-heart surgery, or other life-threatening conditions, require intensified, comprehensive observation and care. May include myocardial infarction, pulmonary care, and heart transplant units.

Cardiac Rehabilitation: A medically supervised program to help heart patients recover quickly and improve their overall physical and mental functioning. The goal is to reduce risk of another cardiac event or to keep an already present heart condition from getting worse. Cardiac rehabilitation programs include: counseling to patients, an exercise program, helping patients modify risk factors such as smoking and high blood pressure, providing vocational guidance to enable the patient to return to work, supplying information on physical limitations and lending emotional support.

Case management: A system of assessment, treatment planning, referral and follow-up that ensures the provision of comprehensive and continuous services and the coordination of payment and reimbursement for care.

Chaplaincy/pastoral care services: A service ministering religious activities and providing pastoral counseling to patients, their families, and staff of a health care organization.

Chemotherapy: An organized program for the treatment of cancer by the use of drugs or chemicals.

Children's wellness program: A program that encourages improved health status and a healthful lifestyle of children through health education, exercise, nutrition and health promotion.

Chiropractic services: An organized clinical service including spinal manipulation or adjustment and related diagnostic and therapeutic services.

Closed physician-hospital organization (Closed PHO): A joint venture between the hospital and physicians who have been selected on the basis of cost-effectiveness and/or high quality. The PHO can act as a unified agent in managed care contracting, own a managed care plan, own and operate ambulatory care centers or ancillary services projects, or provide administrative services to physician members.

Community health education: Education that provides health information to individuals and populations, as well as support for personal, family and community health decisions with the objective of improving health status.

Community hospitals: All nonfederal, short-term general, and special hospitals whose facilities and services are available to the public. (Special hospitals include obstetrics and gynecology; eye, ear, nose, and throat; rehabilitation; orthopedic; and other individually described specialty services.) Short-term general and special childrens hospitals are also considered to be community hospitals.

A hospital may include a nursing-home-type unit and still be classified as short-term, provided that the majority of its patients are admitted to units where the average length of stay is less than 30 days. Therefore, statistics for community hospitals often include some data about such nursing-home-type units. An example

is furnished by Montana, where in 1995 63.6 percent of all hospitals classified as community hospitals include nursing-home-type units. Expense, revenue, utilization, and personnel data for these hospitals include data about their nursing-home-type units. Thus, total admissions to Montana community hospitals in 1995 were 96,154; total inpatient days, 997,759; total expenses, $791,806,393; and total payroll expenses, $352,583,331. If nursing-home-type unit data were excluded, these same items would be 94,034; 457,340; 752,567,865; and $328,911841, respectively.

Note that before 1972, hospital units of institutions such as prison and college infirmaries were included in the category of community hospitals. Including these units made this category equivalent to the short-term general and other special hospitals category. Although these hospital units are few in number and small in size, this change in definition should be taken into consideration when comparing data.

Community outreach: A program that systematically interacts with the community to identify those in need of services, alerting persons and their families to the availability of services, locating needed services, and enabling persons to enter the service delivery system.

Complementary and alternative medicine services: Organized hospital services or formal arrangements to providers that provide care or treatment not based solely on traditional western allopathic medical teachings as instructed in most U.S. medical schools. Includes any of the following: acupuncture, chiropractic, homeopathy, osteopathy, diet and lifestyle changes, herbal medicine, message therapy, etc.

Computer assisted orthopedic surgery (CAOS): Orthopedic surgery using computer technology, enabling three-dimensional graphic models to visualize a patient's anatomy.

Control: The type of organization responsible for establishing policy concerning the overall operation of hospitals. The three major categories are government (including federal, state, and local); nongovernment (nonprofit); and investor-owned (for-profit).

Crisis prevention: Services provided in order to promote physical and mental well being and the early identification of disease and ill health prior to the onset and recognition of symptoms so as to permit early treatment.

CT scanner: Computed tomographic scanner for head or whole body scans.

Deduction from revenue: The difference between revenue at full established rates (gross) and the payment actually received from payers (net).

Dental Services: An organized dental service or dentists on staff, not necessarily involving special facilities, providing dental or oral services to inpatients or outpatients.

Diagnostic radioisotope facility: The use of radioactive isotopes (Radiopharmaceuticals) as tracers or indicators to detect an abnormal condition or disease.

Electrodiagnostic Services: Diagnostic testing services for nerve and muscle function including services such as nerve conduction studies and needle electromyography.

Electron beam computed tomography (EBCT): A high tech computed tomography scan used to detect coronary artery disease by measuring coronary calcifications. This imaging procedure uses electron beams which are magnetically steered to produce a visual of the coronary artery and the images are produced faster than conventional CT scans.

Emergency department: Hospital facilities for the provision of unscheduled outpatient services to patients whose conditions require immediate care.

Emergency room visits: The number of visits to the emergency unit. When emergency outpatients are admitted to the inpatient areas of the hospital, they are counted as emergency room visits and subsequently, as inpatient admissions.

Emergency services: Health services that are provided after the onset of a medical condition that manifests itself by symptoms of sufficient severity, including severe pain, that the absence of immediate medical attention could reasonably be expected by a prudent layperson, who possesses an average knowledge of health and medicine, to result in placing the patient's health in serious jeopardy.

Enabling services: A program that is designed to help the patient access health care services by offering any of the following: transportation services and/or referrals to local social services agencies.

End of Life: Services offered to patients suffering from chronic, severe, and life-threatening diseases including comprehensive services that give patients and caregivers the resources and the confidence to manage symptoms, avoid emergency room admissions and frequent hospitalization, and remain in familiar and comfortable settings.

Endoscopic retrograde cholangiopancreatography (ERCP): A procedure in which a catheter is introduced through an endoscope into the bile ducts and pancreatic ducts. Injection of contrast materials permits detailed x-ray of these structures. The procedure is used diagnostically as well as therapeutically to relieve obstruction or remove stones.

Endoscopic ultrasound: Specially designed endoscope that incorporates an ultrasound transductor used to obtain detailed images of organs in the chest and abdomen. The endoscope can be passed through the mouth or the anus. When combined with needle biopsy the procedure can assist in diagnosis and staging of cancer.

Enrollment (insurance) assistance services: A program that provides enrollment assistance for patients who are potentially eligible for public health insurance programs such as Medicaid, State Children's Health Insurance, or local/state indigent care programs. The specific services offered could include explanation of benefits, assist applicants in completing the application and locating all relevant documents, conduct eligibility interviews, and/or forward applications and documentation to state/local social service or health agency.

Equity model: An arrangement that allows established practitioners to become shareholders in a professional corporation in exchange for tangible and intangible assets of their existing practices.

Esophageal impedance study: A test in which a catheter is placed through the nose into the esophagus to measure whether gas or liquids are passing from the stomach into the esophagus and causing symptoms.

Expenses: Includes all expenses for the reporting period including payroll, non-payroll, and all operating expenses. *Payroll expenses* include all salaries and wages. *Non-payroll expenses* are all professional fees and those salary expenditures excluded from payroll. *Labor related expenses* are defined as payroll expenses plus employee benefits. *Non-labor related expenses* are all other non-payroll expenses. Bad debt has been reclassified from an expense to a deduction from revenue in accordance with the revised AICPA Audit Guide. Note: Financial data may not add due to rounding.

Expenses per adjusted admission stay: Total expenses divided by adjusted admissions (see *adjusted admission*).

Expenses per adjusted inpatient days: Expenses divided by adjusted inpatient days (see *adjusted inpatient days*).

Extracorporeal shock wave lithotripter (ESWL): A medical device used for treating stones in the kidney or urethra. The device disintegrates kidney stones noninvasively through the transmission of acoustic shock waves directed at the stones.

Fertility Clinic: A specialized program set in an infertility center that provides counseling and education as well as advanced reproductive techniques such as: injectable therapy, reproductive surgeries, treatment for endometriosis, male factor infertility, tubal reversals, in vitro fertilization (IVF), donor eggs, and other such services to help patients achieve successful pregnancies.

Fitness center: Provides exercise, testing, or evaluation programs and fitness activities to the community and hospital employees.

Foundation: A corporation, organized as a hospital affiliate or subsidiary, that purchases both tangible and intangible assets of one or more medical group practices. Physicians remain in a separate corporate entity but sign a professional services agreement with the foundation.

Freestanding outpatient care center: A facility owned and operated by the hospital, that is physically separate from the hospital and provides various medical treatments and diagnostic services on an outpatient basis only. Laboratory and radiology services are usually available.

Full-field digital mammography (FFDM): Combines the x-ray generators and tubes used in analog screen-film mammography (SFM) with a detector plate that converts the x-rays into a digital signal.

Full time equivalent employees (FTE): Full time personnel on payroll plus one half of the part time personnel on payroll. For purposes of *AHA Hospital Statistics*, full time and part time medical and dental residents/interns and other trainees are excluded from the calculation.

General medical-surgical care: Provides acute care to patients in medical and surgical units on the basis of physicians' orders and approved nursing care plans.

Genetic testing/counseling: A service equipped with adequate laboratory facilities and directed by a qualified physician to advise parents and prospective parents on potential problems in cases of genetic defects. A genetic test is the analysis of human DNA, RNA, chromosomes, proteins, and certain metabolites in order to detect heritable disease-related genotypes, mutations, phenotypes, or karyotypes for clinical purposes. Genetic tests can have diverse purposes, including the diagnosis of genetic diseases in newborns, children, and adults; the identification of future health risks; the prediction of drug responses; and the assessment of risks to future children.

Geriatric services: The branch of medicine dealing with the physiology of aging and the diagnosis and treatment of disease affecting the aged. Services could include: Adult day care; Alzheimer's diagnostic-assessment services; Comprehensive geriatric assessment; Emergency response system; Geriatric acute care unit; and/or Geriatric clinics.

Government, nonfederal, state, local: Controlled by an agency of state, county, or city government.

Gross inpatient revenue: Revenue from services rendered to inpatients at full established rates (also known as "charges").

Gross outpatient revenue: Revenue from services rendered to outpatients at full established rates.

Group practice without walls: In this organization, the hospital sponsors the formation of a physician group or provides capital to physicians to establish one. The group shares administrative expenses, although the physicians remain independent practitioners.

Group Purchasing Organization: An organization whose primary function is to negotiate contracts for the purpose of purchasing for members of the group or has a central supply site for its members.

Health fair: Community health education events that focus on the prevention of disease and promotion of health through such activities as audiovisual exhibits and free diagnostic services.

Health maintenance organization (HMO): A health care organization that acts as both insurer and provider of comprehensive but specified medical services in return for prospective per capita (capitation) payments.

Health Research: Organized hospital research program in any of the following areas: basic research, clinical research, community health research, and/or research on innovative health care delivery.

Health screening: A preliminary procedure such as a test or examination to detect the most characteristic sign or signs of a disorder that may require further investigation.

Heart transplant: See definition for Transplant services on page 214.

Hemodialysis: Provision of equipment and personnel for the treatment of renal insufficiency on an inpatient or outpatient basis.

HIV-AIDS services: (could include). *HIV-AIDS unit* – Special unit or team designated and equipped specifically for diagnosis, treatment, continuing care planning, and counseling services for HIV-AIDS patients and their families. *General inpatient care for HIV-AIDS* – Inpatient diagnosis and treatment for human immunodeficiency virus and acquired immunodeficiency syndrome patients, but dedicated unit is not available. *Specialized outpatient program for HIV-AIDS* – Special outpatient program providing diagnostic, treatment, continuing care planning, and counseling for HIV-AIDS patients and their families.

Home health services: Service providing nursing, therapy, and health-related homemaker or social services in the patient's home.

Hospice: A program providing palliative care, chiefly medical relief of pain and supportive services, addressing the emotional, social, financial, and legal needs of terminally ill patients and their families. Care can be provided in a variety of settings, both inpatient and at home.

Hospital unit: The hospital operation, excluding activity pertaining to nursing-home-type unit (as described below), for the following items: Admissions, Beds, FTEs (full-time, part-time, and total), Inpatient Days, Length of Stay, Net Revenue, and Total Expense.

Hospital unit of institutions: A hospital unit that is not open to the public and is contained within a nonhospital unit. An example is an infirmary that is contained within a college.

Hospitals in a network: Hospitals participating in a group that may include other hospitals, physicians, other providers, insurers, and/or community agencies that work together to coordinate and deliver a broad spectrum of services to the community.

Hospitals in a system: Hospitals belonging to a corporate body that owns and/or manages health provider facilities or health-related subsidiaries; the system may also own non-health-related facilities.

Image-guided radiation therapy (IGRT): Automated system for image-guided radiation therapy that enables clinicians to obtain high-resolution x-ray images to pinpoint tumor sites, adjust patient positioning when necessary, and complete a treatment, all within the standard treatment time slot, allowing for more effective cancer treatments.

Immunization program: Program that plans, coordinates and conducts immunization services in the community.

Indemnity fee for service: The traditional type of health insurance, in which the insured is reimbursed for covered expenses without regard to choice of provider. Payment up to a stated limit may be made either to the individual incurring and claiming the expense, or directly to providers.

Independent practice association (IPA): An IPA is a legal entity that holds managed care contracts and contracts with physicians, usually in solo practice, to provide care either on a fee-for-services or capitated basis. The purpose of an IPA is to assist solo physicians in obtaining managed care contracts.

Indigent care clinic: Health care services for uninsured and underinsured persons where care is free of charge or charged on a sliding scale. This would include "free clinics" staffed by volunteer practitioners, but could also be staffed by employees with sponsoring health care organizations subsidizing the cost of service.

Inpatient days: The number of adult and pediatric days of care, excluding newborn days of care, rendered during the entire reporting period.

Inpatient palliative care unit: An inpatient palliative care ward is a physically discreet, inpatient nursing unit where the focus is palliative care. The patient care focus is on symptom relief for complex patients who may be continuing to undergo primary treatment. Care is delivered by palliative medicine specialists.

Inpatient surgeries: Surgical services provided to patients who remain in the hospital overnight.

Insurance product: In tables 3 through 6, the insurance product can be owned by the hospital, the hospital's system or network, or co-owned with an insurer.

Integrated salary model: In this arrangement, physicians are salaried by the hospital or other entity of a health system to provide medical services for primary care and specialty care.

Intensity-Modulated Radiation Therapy (IMRT): A type of three-dimensional radiation therapy, which improves the targeting of treatment delivery in a way that is likely to decrease damage to normal tissues and allows varying intensities.

Intermediate nursing care: Provides health-related services (skilled nursing care and social services) to residents with a variety of physical conditions or functional disabilities. These residents do not require the care provided by a hospital or skilled nursing facility, but do need supervision and support services.

Intraoperative magnetic resonance imaging: An integrated surgery system which provides an MRI system in an operating room. The system allows for immediate evaluation of the degree to tumor resection while the patient is undergoing a surgical resection. Intraoperative MRI exists when a MRI (low-field or high-field) is placed in the operating theater and is used during surgical resection without moving the patient from the operating room to the diagnostic imaging suite.

Investor-owned, for-profit: Investor-owned, for-profit hospitals are those controlled on a for-profit basis by an individual, partnership, or profit-making corporation.

Kidney transplant: See definition for Transplant services on page 214.

Labor-related expenses: Payroll expenses plus employee benefits. *Non-labor-related expenses refers* to all other nonpayroll expenses, such as interest depreciation, supplies, purchased services, professional fees, and others.

Length of stay (LOS): LOS refers to the average number of days a patient stays at the facility. Short-term hospitals are those where the average LOS is less than 30 days. Long-term hospitals are those where the average LOS is 30 days or more. The figure is derived by dividing the number of inpatient days by the number of admissions.

Note that this publication carries two LOS variables: *total facility length of stay and hospital unit length of stay. Total facility* includes admissions and inpatient days from nursing-home-type units under control of the hospital. In *hospital unit length of stay*, nursing home utilization is subtracted.

Licensed practical nurse (LPN): A nurse who has graduated from an approved school of practical (vocational) nursing and works under the supervision of registered nurses and/or physicians.

Linguistic/Translation services: Services provided by the hospital designed to make health care more accessible to non-English speaking patients and their physicians.

Liver transplant: See definition for Transplant services on page 214.

Long-term: Hospitals are classified either short-term or long-term according to the average length of stay (LOS). A long-term hospital is one in which the average LOS is 30 days or more.

Lung transplant: See definition for Transplant services on page 214.

Magnetic resonance imaging (MRI): The use of a uniform magnetic field and radio frequencies to study tissue and structure of the body. This procedure enables the visualization of biochemical activity of the cell in vivo without the use of ionizing radiation, radio-isotopic substances, or high-frequency sound.

Magnetoencephalography: a noninvasive neurophysiological measurement tool used to study magnetic fields generated by neuronal activity of the brain. The primary uses of MEG include assisting surgeons in localizing the source of epilepsy, sensory mapping, and the study of brain function. When it is combined with structural imaging, it is known as magnetic source imaging (MSI).

Managed care: A term covering a broad spectrum of arrangements for health care delivery and financing, including managed indemnity plans (MIP), health maintenance organizations (HMO), preferred provider organizations (PPO), point-of-service plans (POS), and direct contracting arrangements between employers and providers.

Managed care contract: A contract between the hospital and a managed care organization.

Management services organization (MSO): A corporation owned by the hospital or a physician/hospital joint venture that provides management services to one or more medical group practices. As part of a full-service management agreement, the MSO purchases the tangible assets of the practices and leases them back, employs all non-physician staff, and provides all supplies/administrative systems for a fee.

Meals on wheels: A hospital sponsored program which delivers meals to people, usually the elderly, who are unable to prepare their own meals. Low cost, nutritional meals are delivered to individuals' homes on a regular basis.

Medical surgical intensive care: Provides patient care of a more intensive nature than the usual medical and surgical care, on the basis of physicians' orders and approved nursing care plans. These units are staffed with specially trained nursing personnel and contain monitoring and specialized support equipment for patients who, because of shock, trauma, or other life-threatening conditions, require

intensified, comprehensive observation and care. Includes mixed intensive care units.

Mobile health services: Vans and other vehicles used to deliver primary care services.

Multi-slice spiral computed tomography (<64 slice CT): A specialized computed tomography procedure that provides three-dimensional processing and allows narrower and multiple slices with increased spatial resolution and faster scanning times as compared to a regular computed tomography scan.

Multi-slice spiral computed tomography (64+ slice CT): Involves the acquisition of volumetric tomographic x-ray absorption data expressed in Hounsfield units using multiple rows of detectors. 64+ systems reconstruct the equivalent of 64 or greater slices to cover the imaged volume.

Neonatal intensive care: A unit that must be separate from the newborn nursery providing intensive care to all sick infants including those with the very lowest birth weights (less than 1500 grams). NICU has potential for providing mechanical ventilation, neonatal surgery, and special care for the sickest infants born in the hospital or transferred from another institution. A full-time neonatologist serves as director of the NICU.

Neonatal intermediate care: A unit that must be separate from the normal newborn nursery and that provides intermediate and/or recovery care and some specialized services, including immediate resuscitation, intravenous therapy, and capacity for prolonged oxygen therapy and monitoring.

Net patient revenue: The estimated net realizable amounts from patients, third-party payers, and others for services rendered. The number includes estimated retroactive adjustments called for by agreements with third-party payers; retroactive adjustments are accrued on an estimated basis in the period the related services are rendered and then adjusted later as final settlements are determined.

Net total revenue: Net patient revenue plus all other revenue, including contributions, endowment revenue, governmental grants, and all other payments not made on behalf of individual patients.

Neurological services: Services provided by the hospital dealing with the operative and nonoperative management of disorders of the central, peripheral, and autonomic nervous system.

Nongovernment, nonprofit: Hospitals that are nongovernment, nonprofit are controlled by not-for-profit organizations, including religious organizations (Catholic hospitals, for example), fraternal societies, and others.

Nursing-home-type unit/facility: A unit/facility that primarily offers the following type of services to a majority of all admissions:

- *Skilled nursing:* The provision of medical and nursing care services, health-related services, and social services under the supervision of a registered nurse on a 24-hour basis.

- *Intermediate care:* The provision, on a regular basis, of health-related care and services to individuals who do not require the degree of care or treatment that a skilled nursing unit is designed to provide.

- *Personal care:* The provision of general supervision and direct personal care services for residents who require assistance in activities of daily living but who do not need nursing services or inpatient care. Medical and nursing services are available as needed.

- *Sheltered/residential care:* The provision of general supervision and protective services for residents who do not need nursing services or continuous personal care services in the conduct of daily life. Medical and nursing services are available as needed.

Nutrition programs: Those services within a health care facility which are designed to provide inexpensive, nutritionally sound meals to patients.

Obstetrics: Levels should be designated: (1) unit provides services for uncomplicated maternity and newborn cases; (2) unit provides services for uncomplicated cases, the majority of complicated problems, and special neonatal services; and (3) unit provides services for all serious illnesses and abnormalities and is supervised by a full-time maternal/fetal specialist.

Occupational health services: Includes services designed to protect the safety of employees from hazards in the work environment.

Oncology services: Inpatient and outpatient services for patients with cancer, including comprehensive care, support and guidance in addition to patient education and prevention, chemotherapy, counseling and other treatment methods.

Open physician hospital organization (Open PHO): A joint venture between the hospital and all members of the medical staff who wish to participate. The open PHO can act as a unified agent in managed care contracting, own a managed care plan, own and operate ambulatory care centers or ancillary services projects, or provide administrative services to physician members.

Optical colonoscopy: An examination of the interior of the colon using a long, flexible, lighted tube with a small built-in camera.

Orthopedic services: Services provided for the prevention or correction of injuries or disorders of the skeletal system and associated muscles, joints and ligaments.

Osteopathic hospitals: Osteopathic medicine is a medical practice based on a theory that diseases are due chiefly to a loss of structural integrity, which can be restored by manipulation of the neuro-muscular and skeletal systems, supplemented by therapeutic measures (such as medicine or surgery).

Other Intensive Care: A specially staffed, specialty equipped, separate section of a hospital dedicated to the observation, care, and treatment of patients with life threatening illnesses, injuries, or complications from which recovery is possible. It provides special expertise and facilities for the support of vital function and utilizes the skill of medical nursing and other staff experienced in the management of these problems.

Other long-term care: Provision of long-term care other than skilled nursing care or intermediate care for those who do not require daily medical or nursing services, but may require some assistance in the activities of daily living. This can include residential care, elderly care, or sheltered care facilities for developmentally disabled.

Other special care: Provides care to patients requiring care more intensive than that provided in the acute area, yet not sufficiently intensive to require admission to an intensive care unit. Patients admitted to this area are usually transferred here from an intensive care unit once their condition has improved. These units are sometimes referred to as definitive observation, step-down, or progressive care units.

Other transplant: See definition for Transplant services on page 214.

Outpatient care: Treatment provided to patients who do not remain in the hospital for overnight care. Hospitals may deliver outpatient care on site or through a facility owned and operated by the hospital, but physically separate from the hospital. In addition to treating minor illnesses or injuries, a free-standing center will stabilize seriously ill or injured patients before transporting them to a hospital. Laboratory and radiology services are usually available.

Outpatient care center (Freestanding): A facility owned and operated by the hospital, but physically separate from the hospital, that provides various medical treatments on an outpatient basis only. In addition to treating minor illnesses or injuries, the center will stabilize seriously ill or injured patients before transporting them to a hospital. Laboratory and radiology services are usually available.

Outpatient care center-services (Hospital-based): Organized hospital health care services offered by appointment on an ambulatory basis. Services may include outpatient surgery, examination, diagnosis, and treatment of a variety of medical conditions on a nonemergency basis, and laboratory and other diagnostic testing as ordered by staff or outside physician referral.

Outpatient surgery: Scheduled surgical services provided to patients who do not remain in the hospital overnight. The surgery may be performed in operating suites also used for inpatient surgery, specially designated surgical suites for outpatient surgery, or procedure rooms within an outpatient care facility.

Outpatient visit: A visit by a patient who is not lodged in the hospital while receiving medical, dental, or other services. Each visit an outpatient makes to a discrete unit constitutes one visit regardless of the number of diagnostic and/or therapeutic treatments that the patient receives. Total outpatient visits should include all clinic visits, referred visits, observation services, outpatient surgeries, and emergency room visits.

Pain Management Program: A recognized clinical service or program providing specialized medical care, drugs or therapies for the management of acute or chronic pain or other distressing symptom, administered by specially trained physicians and other clinicians, to patients suffering from acute illness of diverse causes.

Palliative Care Inpatient Unit: An inpatient palliative care ward is a physically discreet, inpatient nursing unit where the focus is palliative care. The patient care focus is on symptom relief for complex patients who may be continuing to undergo primary treatment. Care is delivered by palliative medicine specialists.

Palliative care program: An organized program providing specialized medical care, drugs or therapies for the management of acute or chronic pain and/or the control of symptoms administered by specially trained physicians and other clinicians; and supportive care services, such as counseling on advanced directives, spiritual care, and social services, to patients with advanced disease and their families.

Patient Controlled Analgesia (PCA): Patient-controlled Analgesia (PCA) is intravenously administered pain medicine under the patient's control. The patient has a button on the end of a cord than can be pushed at will, whenever more pain medicine is desired. This button will only deliver more pain medicine at pre-determined intervals, as programmed by the doctor's order.

Patient education center: Written goals and objectives for the patient and/or family related to therapeutic regimens, medical procedures, and self care.

Patient representative services: Organized hospital services providing personnel through whom patients and staff can seek solutions to institutional problems affecting the delivery of high-quality care and services.

Payroll expenses: Includes all salaries and wages. All professional fees and salary expenditures excluded from payroll, such as employee benefits, are defined as nonpayroll expenses and are included in total expenses.

Pediatric Cardiac Surgery: Includes minimally invasive procedures that include surgery done with only a small incision or no incision at all, such as through a laparoscope or an endoscope and more invasive major surgical procedures that include open chest and open heart surgery.

Pediatric Cardiology Services: An organized clinical service offering diagnostic and interventional procedures to manage the full range of pediatric heart conditions.

Pediatric Diagnostic/invasive catheterization: (also called coronary angiography or coronary arteriography) is used to assist in diagnosing complex heart conditions. Cardiac angiography involves the insertion of a tiny catheter into the artery in the groin then carefully threading the catheter up into the aorta where the coronary arteries originate. Once the catheter is in place, a dye is injected which allows the cardiologist to see the size, shape, and distribution of the coronary arteries. These images are used to diagnose heart disease and to determine, among other things, whether or not surgery is indicated.

Pediatric intensive care: Provides care to pediatric patients that is of a more intensive nature than that usually provided to pediatric patients. The unit is staffed with specially trained personnel and contains monitoring and specialized support equipment for treatment of patients who, because of shock, trauma, or other life-threatening conditions, require intensified, comprehensive observation and care.

Pediatric Interventional cardiac catheterization: Non surgical procedure that utilizes the same basic principles as diagnostic catheterization and then uses advanced techniques to improve the heart's function. It can be a less-invasive alternative to heart surgery.

Pediatric medical-surgical care: Provides acute care to pediatric patients on the basis of physicians' orders and approved nursing care plans.

Personnel: Number of persons on the hospital payroll at the end of the reporting period. Personnel are recorded in *Hospital Statistics* as full-time equivalents (FTEs), which are calculated by adding the number of full-time personnel to one-half the number of part-time personnel, excluding medical and dental residents, interns, and other trainees. *Per 100 adjusted census* indicates the ratio of personnel to adjusted average daily census, calculated on a per-100 basis.

Physical rehabilitation inpatient care: Provides care encompassing a comprehensive array of restoration services for the disabled and all support services necessary to help patients attain their maximum functional capacity.

Physical rehabilitation outpatient services: Outpatient program providing medical, health-related, therapy, social, and/or vocational services to help disabled persons attain or retain their maximum functional capacity.

Population: Population refers to the residential population of the United States. This includes both civilian and military personnel. Note that population is being used to calculate the values *for community health indicators per 1000 population.*

Positron emission tomography/CT (PET/CT): Provides metabolic functional information for the monitoring of chemotherapy, radiotherapy and surgical planning.

Positron emission tomography scanner (PET): A nuclear medicine imaging technology which uses radioactive (positron emitting) isotopes created in a cyclotron or generator and computers to produce composite pictures of the brain and heart at work. PET scanning produces sectional images depicting metabolic activity or blood flow rather than anatomy.

Preferred provider organization (PPO): A pre-set arrangement in which purchasers and providers agree to furnish specified health services to a group of employees/patients.

Primary care department: A unit or clinic within the hospital that provides primary care services (e.g. general pediatric care, general internal medicine, family practice, gynecology) through hospital-salaried medical and/or nursing staff, focusing on evaluating and diagnosing medical problems and providing medical treatment on an outpatient basis.

Prosthetic and Orthotic Services: Services providing comprehensive prosthetic and orthotic evaluation, fitting, and training.

Proton beam therapy: A form of radiation therapy which administers proton beams. While producing the same biologic effects as x-ray beams, the energy distribution of protons differs from conventional x-ray beams in that they can be more precisely focused in tissue volumes in a three-dimensional pattern resulting in less surrounding tissue damage than conventional radiation therapy permitting administration of higher doses.

Psychiatric child-adolescent services: Provides care to emotionally disturbed children and adolescents, including those admitted for diagnosis and those admitted for treatment.

Psychiatric consultation-liaison services: Provides organized psychiatric consultation/liaison services to nonpsychiatric hospital staff and/or departments on psychological aspects of medical care that may be generic or specific to individual patients.

Psychiatric education services: Provides psychiatric educational services to community agencies and workers such as schools, police, courts, public health nurses, welfare agencies, clergy, and so

forth. The purpose is to expand the mental health knowledge and competence of personnel not working in the mental health field and to promote good mental health through improved understanding, attitudes, and behavioral patterns.

Psychiatric emergency services: Services of facilities available on a 24-hour basis to provide immediate unscheduled out-patient care, diagnosis, evaluation, crisis intervention, and assistance to persons suffering acute emotional or mental distress.

Psychiatric geriatric services: Provides care to emotionally disturbed elderly patients, including those admitted for diagnosis and those admitted for treatment.

Psychiatric inpatient care: Provides acute or long-term care to emotionally disturbed patients, including patients admitted for diagnosis and those admitted for treatment of psychiatric problems, on the basis of physicians' orders and approved nursing care plans. Long-term care may include intensive supervision to the chronically mentally ill, mentally disordered, or other mentally incompetent persons.

Psychiatric outpatient services: Provides medical care, including diagnosis and treatment, of psychiatric outpatients.

Psychiatric partial hospitalization program: Organized hospital services of intensive day/evening outpatient services of three hours of more duration, distinguished from other outpatient visits of one hour.

Psychiatric residential treatment: Overnight psychiatric care in conjunction with an intensive treatment program in a setting other than a hospital.

Radiology, diagnostic: The branch of radiology that deals with the utilization of all modalities of radiant energy in medical diagnoses and therapeutic procedures using radiologic guidance. This includes, but is not restricted to, imaging techniques and methodologies utilizing radiation emitted by x-ray tubes, radionnuclides, and ultrasonographic devices and the radiofrequency electromagnetic radiation emitted by atoms.

Radiology, therapeutic: The branch of medicine concerned with radioactive substances and using various techniques of visualization, with the diagnosis and treatment of disease using any of the various sources of radiant energy. Services could include: megavoltage radiation therapy; radioactive implants; stereotactic radiosurgery; therapeutic radioisotope facility; X-ray radiation therapy.

Registered nurse (RN): A nurse who has graduated from an approved school of nursing and who is currently registered by the state. RNs are responsible for the nature and quality of all nursing care that patients receive. In these tables, the number of RNs does not include those registered nurses more appropriately reported in other occupational categories, such as facility administrators, which are listed under *all other personnel* (Tables 1 and 2).

Rehabilitation services: A wide array of restoration services for disabled and recuperating patients, including all support services necessary to help them attain their maximum functional capacity.

Retirement housing: A facility which provides social activities to senior citizens, usually retired persons, who do not require health care but some short-term skilled nursing care may be provided. A retirement center may furnish housing and may also have acute hospital and long-term care facilities, or it may arrange for acute and long term care through affiliated institutions.

Robot-assisted walking therapy: A form of physical therapy that uses a robotic device to assist patients who are relearning how to walk.

Robotic surgery: The use of mechanical guidance devices to remotely manipulate surgical instrumentation.

Rural: A rural hospital is located outside a Metropolitan Statistical Area (MSA), as designated by the U.S. Office of Management and Budget (OMB) effective June 6, 2003. An urban area is a geographically defined, integrated social and economic unit with a large population nucleus. Micropolitan areas, which are new to the OMB June 6, 2003 definitions, continue to be classified as rural for purposes of this publication.

Rural Health Clinic: A clinic located in a rural, medically under-served area in the United States that has a separate reimbursement structure from the standard medical office under the Medicare and Medicaid programs.

Satellite Emergency Department: A facility owned and operated by the hospital but physically separate from the hospital for the provision of unscheduled outpatient services to patients whose conditions require immediate care. A freestanding ED is not physically connected to a hospital, but has all necessary emergency staffing and equipment on-site.

Shaped beam radiation system: A precise, non-invasive treatment that involves targeting beams of radiation that mirrors the exact size and shape of a tumor at a specific area of a tumor to shrink or destroy cancerous cells. This procedure delivers a therapeutic dose of radiation that conforms precisely to the shape of the tumor, thus minimizing the risk to nearby tissues.

Simulated rehabilitation environment: Rehabilitation focused on retraining functional skills in a contextually appropriate environment (simulated home and community settings) or in a traditional setting (gymnasium) using motor learning principles.

Single photon emission computerized tomography (SPECT): A nuclear medicine imaging technology that combines existing technology of gamma camera imaging with computed tomographic imaging technology to provide a more precise and clear image.

Skilled nursing care: Provides non-acute medical and skilled nursing care services, therapy, and social services under the supervision of a licensed registered nurse on a 24-hour basis.

Sleep Center: Specially equipped and staffed center for the diagnosis and treatment of sleep disorders.

Social work services (could include): Organized services that are properly directed and sufficiently staffed by qualified individuals who provide assistance and counseling to patients and their families in dealing with social, emotional, and environmental problems associated with illness or disability, often in the context of financial or discharge planning coordination.

Sports medicine: Provision of diagnostic screening and assessment and clinical and rehabilitation services for the prevention and treatment of sports-related injuries.

Stereotactic radiosurgery: Stereotactic radiosurgery (SRS) is a radiotherapy modality that delivers a high dosage of radiation to a discrete treatment area in as few as one treatment session. Includes gamma knife, cyberknife, etc.

Support groups: A hospital sponsored program that allows a group of individuals with the same or similar problems who meet periodically to share experiences, problems, and solutions in order to support each other.

Surgical operations: Those surgical operations, whether major or minor, performed in the operating room(s). A surgical operation involving more than one surgical procedure is still considered only one surgical operation.

Swing bed services: A hospital bed that can be used to provide either acute or long-term care depending on community or patient needs. To be eligible a hospital must have a Medicare provider agreement in place, have fewer than 100 beds, be located in a rural area, do not have a 24 hour nursing service waiver in effect, have not been terminated from the program in the prior two years, and meet various service conditions.

Teen outreach services: A program focusing on the teenager which encourages an improved health status and a healthful lifestyle including physical, emotional, mental, social, spiritual and economic health through education, exercise, nutrition and health promotion.

Tissue transplant: See definition for Transplant services on page 214.

Tobacco treatment/cessation program: Organized hospital services with the purpose of ending tobacco-use habits of patients addicted to tobacco/nicotine.

Transplant services: The branch of medicine that transfers an organ or tissue from one person to another or from one body part to another to replace a diseased structure or to restore function or to change appearance. Services could include: bone marrow transplant program; heart, lung, kidney, intestine, or tissue transplant. The other transplant services include transplant services other than bone marrow, heart, kidney, liver, lung, tissue and heart/lung or other multi-transplant surgeries.

Transportation to health facilities: A long-term care support service designed to assist the mobility of the elderly. Some programs offer improved financial access by offering reduced rates and barrier-free buses or vans with ramps and lifts to assist the elderly or handicapped; others offer subsidies for public transport systems or operate mini-bus services exclusively for use by senior citizens.

Trauma center (certified): A facility to provide emergency and specialized intensive care to critically ill and injured patients. **Level 1:** A regional resource trauma center, which is capable of providing total care for every aspect of injury and plays a leadership role in trauma research and education. **Level 2:** A community trauma center, which is capable of providing trauma care to all but the most severely injured patients who require highly specialized care. **Level 3:** A rural trauma hospital, which is capable of providing care to a large number of injury victims and can resuscitate and stabilize more severely injured patients so that they can be transported to Level 1 or 2 facilities.

Ultrasound: The use of acoustic waves above the range of 20,000 cycles per second to visualize internal body structures.

Urban: An urban hospital is located inside a Metropolitan Statistical Area (MSA), designated by the U.S. Office of Management and Budget effective June 6, 2003. An urban areas is a geographically defined, integrated social and economic unit with a large population base. Micropolitan areas, which are new to the OMB June 6, 2003 definitions, are not considered to be urban for purposes of this publication.

Urgent care center: A facility that provides care and treatment for problems that are not life-threatening but require attention over the short term.

Violence prevention programs for the workplace: A violence prevention program with goals and objectives for preventing workplace violence against staff and patients.

Violence prevention programs for the community: An organized program that attempts to make a positive impact on the type(s) of violence a community is experiencing. For example, it can assist victims of violent crimes, e.g., rape, or incidents, e.g., bullying, to hospital or to community services to prevent further victimization or retaliation. A program that targets the underlying circumstances that contribute to violence such as poor housing, insufficient job training, and/or substance abuse through means such as direct involvement and support, education, mentoring, anger management, crisis intervention and training programs would also qualify.

Virtual colonoscopy: Noninvasive screening procedure used to visualize, analyze and detect cancerous or potentially cancerous polyps in the colon.

Volunteer services department: An organized hospital department responsible for coordinating the services of volunteers working within the institution.

Women's health center/services: An area set aside for coordinated education and treatment services specifically for and promoted to women as provided by this special unit. Services may or may not include obstetrics but include a range of services other than OB.

Wound Management Services: Services for patients with chronic wounds and nonhealing wounds often resulting from diabetes, poor circulation, improper seating and immunocompromising conditions. The goals are to progress chronic wounds through stages of healing, reduce and eliminate infections, increase physical function to minimize complications from current wounds and prevent future chronic wounds. Wound management services are provided on an inpatient or outpatient basis, depending on the intensity of service needed.

2016 AHA Annual Survey
Health Forum, L.L.C.

> **Please return to:**
> **AHA Annual Survey**
> **155 N Wacker Drive**
> **Suite 400**
> **Chicago IL 60606**

A. REPORTING PERIOD (please refer to the instructions and definitions at the end of this questionnaire)

Report data for a full 12-month period, preferably your last completed fiscal year (366 days). Be consistent in using the same reporting period for responses throughout various sections of this survey.

1. Reporting Period used (beginning and ending date) ...... ___/___/___ ___ to ___/___/___ ___
   Month   Day   Year   Month   Day   Year

2. a. Were you in operation 12 full months
   at the end of your reporting period? .... YES ☐   NO ☐

   b. Number of days open
   during reporting period .... _____

3. Indicate the beginning of your current fiscal year .... ___/___/___ ___
   Month   Day   Year

B. ORGANIZATIONAL STRUCTURE

1. CONTROL
Indicate the type of organization that is responsible for establishing policy for overall operation of your hospital. CHECK ONLY ONE:

Government, nonfederal
- ☐ 12 State
- ☐ 13 County
- ☐ 14 City
- ☐ 15 City-County
- ☐ 16 Hospital district or authority

Nongovernment, not-for-profit (NFP)
- ☐ 21 Church-operated
- ☐ 23 Other not-for-profit (including NFP Corporation)

Investor-owned, for-profit
- ☐ 31 Individual
- ☐ 32 Partnership
- ☐ 33 Corporation

Government, federal
- ☐ 41 Air Force
- ☐ 42 Army
- ☐ 43 Navy
- ☐ 44 Public Health Service
- ☐ 45 Veterans' Affairs
- ☐ 46 Federal other than 41-45 or 47-48
- ☐ 47 PHS Indian Service
- ☐ 48 Department of Justice

2. SERVICE
Indicate the ONE category that BEST describes your hospital or the type of service it provides to the MAJORITY of patients:

- ☐ 10 General medical and surgical
- ☐ 11 Hospital unit of an institution (prison hospital, college infirmary)
- ☐ 12 Hospital unit within a facility for persons with intellectual disabilities
- ☐ 13 Surgical
- ☐ 22 Psychiatric
- ☐ 33 Tuberculosis and other respiratory diseases
- ☐ 41 Cancer
- ☐ 42 Heart
- ☐ 44 Obstetrics and gynecology
- ☐ 45 Eye, ear, nose, and throat

- ☐ 46 Rehabilitation
- ☐ 47 Orthopedic
- ☐ 48 Chronic disease
- ☐ 62 Intellectual disabilities
- ☐ 80 Acute long-term care hospital
- ☐ 82 Alcoholism and other chemical dependency
- ☐ 49 Other - specify treatment area: _____

B. ORGANIZATIONAL STRUCTURE (continued)

3. OTHER

a. Does your hospital restrict admissions primarily to children? .... YES ☐   NO ☐

b. Does the hospital itself operate subsidiary corporations? .... YES ☐   NO ☐

c. Is the hospital contract managed? If yes, please provide the name, city, and state of the organization.... YES ☐   NO ☐

Name: _____   City: _____   State: _____

d. Is the hospital a participant in a network? ....YES ☐   NO ☐
   If yes, please provide the name, city, state and telephone number of the network(s).

Name: _____   City: _____   State: _____ Telephone_____

Name: _____   City: _____   State: _____ Telephone_____

Name: _____   City: _____   State: _____ Telephone_____

e. Is your hospital owned in whole or in part by physicians or a physician group?... YES ☐   NO ☐

f. If you checked 80 Acute long-term care hospital (LTCH) in Section B2 (Service), please indicate if you are a freestanding LTCH or a LTCH arranged within a general acute care hospital.
   ☐ Free standing LTCH   ☐ LTCH arranged in a general acute care hospital

   If you are arranged in a general acute care hospital, what is your host hospital's name?

   Name_____ City_____ State_____

C. FACILITIES AND SERVICES

For each service or facility listed below, please check all the categories that describe how each item is provided **as of the last day of the reporting period**. Check all categories that apply for an item. If you check column (1) C1-19, please include the number of **staffed beds**.
The sum of the beds reported in 1-19 should equal Section D(1b), beds set up and staffed on page 9.

	(1) Owned or provided by my hospital or its subsidiary	(2) Provided by my Health System (in my local community)	(3) Provided through a formal contractual arrangement or joint venture with another provider that is not in my system (in my local community)	(4) Do Not Provide
1. General medical-surgical care .... (#Beds____)	☐	☐	☐	☐
2. Pediatric medical-surgical care .... (#Beds____)	☐	☐	☐	☐
3. Obstetrics............[Hospital level of unit (1-3):(____)] (#Beds____)	☐	☐	☐	☐
4. Medical-surgical intensive care.................. (#Beds____)	☐	☐	☐	☐
5. Cardiac intensive care .... (#Beds____)	☐	☐	☐	☐
6. Neonatal intensive care .... (#Beds____)	☐	☐	☐	☐
7. Neonatal intermediate care .... (#Beds____)	☐	☐	☐	☐
8. Pediatric intensive care .... (#Beds____)	☐	☐	☐	☐
9. Burn care .... (#Beds____)	☐	☐	☐	☐
10. Other special care _____.......... (#Beds____)	☐	☐	☐	☐
11. Other intensive care_____.......... (#Beds____)	☐	☐	☐	☐
12. Physical rehabilitation .... (#Beds____)	☐	☐	☐	☐
13. Alcoholism-drug abuse or dependency care .... (#Beds____)	☐	☐	☐	☐
14. Psychiatric care .... (#Beds____)	☐	☐	☐	☐
15. Skilled nursing care .... (#Beds____)	☐	☐	☐	☐
16. Intermediate nursing care .... (#Beds____)	☐	☐	☐	☐
17. Acute long-term care .... (#Beds____)	☐	☐	☐	☐
18. Other long-term care................................. (#Beds____)	☐	☐	☐	☐
19. Other care _____.................. (#Beds____)	☐	☐	☐	☐
20. Adult day care program	☐	☐	☐	☐
21. Airborne infection isolation room...................... (#rooms ____)	☐	☐	☐	☐
22. Alcoholism-drug abuse or dependency outpatient services	☐	☐	☐	☐
23. Alzheimer Center	☐	☐	☐	☐
24. Ambulance services..	☐	☐	☐	☐
25. Ambulatory surgery center.....................................	☐	☐	☐	☐
26. Arthritis treatment center	☐	☐	☐	☐
27. Assisted living	☐	☐	☐	☐
28. Auxiliary	☐	☐	☐	☐
29. Bariatric/weight control services	☐	☐	☐	☐
30. Birthing room/LDR room/LDRP room	☐	☐	☐	☐
31. Blood Donor Center	☐	☐	☐	☐
32. Breast cancer screening/mammograms	☐	☐	☐	☐

C. FACILITIES AND SERVICES (continued)

	(1) Owned or provided by my hospital or its subsidiary	(2) Provided by my Health System (in my local community)	(3) Provided through a formal contractual arrangement or joint venture with another provider that is not in my system (in my local community)	(4) Do Not Provide
33. Cardiology and cardiac surgery services				
a. Adult cardiology services	☐	☐	☐	☐
b. Pediatric cardiology services	☐	☐	☐	☐
c. Adult diagnostic catheterization	☐	☐	☐	☐
d. Pediatric diagnostic catheterization	☐	☐	☐	☐
e. Adult interventional cardiac catheterization	☐	☐	☐	☐
f. Pediatric interventional cardiac catheterization	☐	☐	☐	☐
g. Adult cardiac surgery	☐	☐	☐	☐
h. Pediatric cardiac surgery	☐	☐	☐	☐
i. Adult cardiac electrophysiology	☐	☐	☐	☐
j. Pediatric cardiac electrophysiology	☐	☐	☐	☐
k. Cardiac rehabilitation	☐	☐	☐	☐
34. Case management	☐	☐	☐	☐
35. Chaplaincy/pastoral care services	☐	☐	☐	☐
36. Chemotherapy	☐	☐	☐	☐
37. Children's wellness program	☐	☐	☐	☐
38. Chiropractic services	☐	☐	☐	☐
39. Community outreach	☐	☐	☐	☐
40. Complementary and alternative medicine services	☐	☐	☐	☐
41. Computer assisted orthopedic surgery (CAOS)	☐	☐	☐	☐
42. Crisis prevention	☐	☐	☐	☐
43. Dental services	☐	☐	☐	☐
44. Emergency services				
a. Emergency department	☐	☐	☐	☐
b. Pediatric emergency department	☐	☐	☐	☐
c. Satellite emergency department	☐	☐	☐	☐
d. If you checked column 1 for Satellite ED (44c), is the department open 24 hours a day, 7 days a week? Yes ☐ No ☐				
e. Trauma center (certified) ....[Hospital level of unit (1-3) _____]	☐	☐	☐	☐
45. Enabling services	☐	☐	☐	☐
46. Endoscopic services				
a. Optical colonoscopy	☐	☐	☐	☐
b. Endoscopic ultrasound	☐	☐	☐	☐
c. Ablation of Barrett's esophagus	☐	☐	☐	☐
d. Esophageal impedance study	☐	☐	☐	☐
e. Endoscopic retrograde cholangiopancreatography (ERCP)	☐	☐	☐	☐
47. Enrollment (insurance) assistance services	☐	☐	☐	☐
48. Extracorporeal shock wave lithotripter (ESWL)	☐	☐	☐	☐
49. Fertility clinic	☐	☐	☐	☐
50. Fitness center	☐	☐	☐	☐
51. Freestanding outpatient care center	☐	☐	☐	☐
52. Geriatric services	☐	☐	☐	☐
53. Health fair	☐	☐	☐	☐

C. FACILITIES AND SERVICES (continued)

	(1) Owned or provided by my hospital or its subsidiary	(2) Provided by my Health System (in my local community)	(3) Provided through a formal contractual arrangement or joint venture with another provider that is not in my system (in my local community)	(4) Do Not Provide
54. Community health education	☐	☐	☐	☐
55. Genetic testing/counseling	☐	☐	☐	☐
56. Health screenings	☐	☐	☐	☐
57. Health research	☐	☐	☐	☐
58. Hemodialysis	☐	☐	☐	☐
59. HIV/AIDS services	☐	☐	☐	☐
60. Home health services	☐	☐	☐	☐
61. Hospice program	☐	☐	☐	☐
62. Hospital-based outpatient care center services	☐	☐	☐	☐
63. Immunization program	☐	☐	☐	☐
64. Indigent care clinic	☐	☐	☐	☐
65. Linguistic/translation services	☐	☐	☐	☐
66. Meals on wheels	☐	☐	☐	☐
67. Mobile health services	☐	☐	☐	☐
68. Neurological services	☐	☐	☐	☐
69. Nutrition program	☐	☐	☐	☐
70. Occupational health services	☐	☐	☐	☐
71. Oncology services	☐	☐	☐	☐
72. Orthopedic services	☐	☐	☐	☐
73. Outpatient surgery	☐	☐	☐	☐
74. Pain management program	☐	☐	☐	☐
75. Palliative care program	☐	☐	☐	☐
76. Palliative care inpatient unit	☐	☐	☐	☐
77. Patient controlled analgesia (PCA)	☐	☐	☐	☐
78. Patient education center	☐	☐	☐	☐
79. Patient representative services	☐	☐	☐	☐
80. Physical rehabilitation services				
a. Assistive technology center	☐	☐	☐	☐
b. Electrodiagnostic services	☐	☐	☐	☐
c. Physical rehabilitation outpatient services	☐	☐	☐	☐
d. Prosthetic and orthotic services	☐	☐	☐	☐
e. Robot-assisted walking therapy	☐	☐	☐	☐
f. Simulated rehabilitation environment	☐	☐	☐	☐
81. Primary care department	☐	☐	☐	☐
82. Psychiatric services				
a. Psychiatric child-adolescent services	☐	☐	☐	☐
b. Psychiatric consultation-liaison services	☐	☐	☐	☐
c. Psychiatric education services	☐	☐	☐	☐
d. Psychiatric emergency services	☐	☐	☐	☐
e. Psychiatric geriatric services	☐	☐	☐	☐
f. Psychiatric outpatient services	☐	☐	☐	☐
g. Psychiatric partial hospitalization services	☐	☐	☐	☐
h. Psychiatric residential treatment	☐	☐	☐	☐

C. FACILITIES AND SERVICES (continued)

	(1) Owned or provided by my hospital or its subsidiary	(2) Provided by my Health System (in my local community)	(3) Provided through a formal contractual arrangement or joint venture with another provider that is not in my system (in my local community)	(4) Do Not Provide
83. Radiology, diagnostic				
a. CT Scanner	☐	☐	☐	☐
b. Diagnostic radioisotope facility	☐	☐	☐	☐
c. Electron beam computed tomography (EBCT)	☐	☐	☐	☐
d. Full-field digital mammography (FFDM)	☐	☐	☐	☐
e. Magnetic resonance imaging (MRI)	☐	☐	☐	☐
f. Intraoperative magnetic resonance imaging	☐	☐	☐	☐
g. Magnetoencephalography (MEG)	☐	☐	☐	☐
h. Multi-slice spiral computed tomography (<64+ slice CT)	☐	☐	☐	☐
i. Multi-slice spiral computed tomography (64+ slice CT)	☐	☐	☐	☐
j. Positron emission tomography (PET)	☐	☐	☐	☐
k. Positron emission tomography/CT (PET/CT)	☐	☐	☐	☐
l. Single photon emission computerized tomography (SPECT)	☐	☐	☐	☐
m. Ultrasound	☐	☐	☐	☐
84. Radiology, therapeutic				
a. Image-guided radiation therapy (IGRT)	☐	☐	☐	☐
b. Intensity-modulated radiation therapy (IMRT)	☐	☐	☐	☐
c. Proton beam therapy	☐	☐	☐	☐
d. Shaped beam radiation system	☐	☐	☐	☐
e. Stereotactic radiosurgery	☐	☐	☐	☐
85. Retirement housing	☐	☐	☐	☐
86. Robotic surgery	☐	☐	☐	☐
87. Rural health clinic	☐	☐	☐	☐
88. Sleep center	☐	☐	☐	☐
89. Social work services	☐	☐	☐	☐
90. Sports medicine	☐	☐	☐	☐
91. Support groups	☐	☐	☐	☐
92. Swing bed services	☐	☐	☐	☐
93. Teen outreach services	☐	☐	☐	☐
94. Tobacco treatment/cessation program	☐	☐	☐	☐
95. Transplant services				
a. Bone marrow	☐	☐	☐	☐
b. Heart	☐	☐	☐	☐
c. Kidney	☐	☐	☐	☐
d. Liver	☐	☐	☐	☐
e. Lung	☐	☐	☐	☐
f. Tissue	☐	☐	☐	☐
g. Other	☐	☐	☐	☐

C. FACILITIES AND SERVICES (continued)

	(1) Owned or provided by my hospital or its subsidiary	(2) Provided by my Health System (in my local community)	(3) Provided through a formal contractual arrangement or joint venture with another provider that is not in my system (in my local community)	(4) Do Not Provide
96. Transportation to health services	☐	☐	☐	☐
97. Urgent care center	☐	☐	☐	☐
98. Violence Prevention Programs				
a. For the workplace	☐	☐	☐	☐
b. For the community	☐	☐	☐	☐
99. Virtual colonoscopy	☐	☐	☐	☐
100. Volunteer services department	☐	☐	☐	☐
101. Women's health center/services	☐	☐	☐	☐
102. Wound management services	☐	☐	☐	☐

103. In which of the following physician arrangements does your hospital or system/network participate? Column 3 refers to the networks that were identified in section B, question 3d. For hospital level physician arrangements that are reported in column 1, please report the number of physicians involved.

		(1) My Hospital	(2) My Health System	(3) My Health Network	(4) Do Not Provide
a. Independent Practice Association (IPA)	(# of physicians _____)	☐	☐	☐	☐
b. Group practice without walls	(# of physicians _____)	☐	☐	☐	☐
c. Open Physician-Hospital Organization (PHO)	(# of physicians _____)	☐	☐	☐	☐
d. Closed Physician-Hospital Organization (PHO)	(# of physicians _____)	☐	☐	☐	☐
e. Management Service Organization (MSO)	(# of physicians _____)	☐	☐	☐	☐
f. Integrated Salary Model	(# of physicians _____)	☐	☐	☐	☐
g. Equity Model	(# of physicians _____)	☐	☐	☐	☐
h. Foundation	(# of physicians _____)	☐	☐	☐	☐
i. Other, please specify _____	(# of physicians _____)	☐	☐	☐	☐

104. Looking across all the relationships identified in question **103**, what is the total number of physicians (count each physician only once) that are engaged in an arrangement with your hospital that allows for joint contracting with payors or shared responsibility for financial risk or clinical performance between the hospital and physician? (arrangement may be at the hospital, system or network level) # of physicians _____

105a. Does your hospital participate in any joint venture arrangements with physicians or physician groups? YES ☐   NO ☐

105b. If your hospital participates in any joint ventures with physicians or physician groups, please indicate which types of services are involved in those joint ventures. (Check all that apply)

    1. ☐   Limited service hospital
    2. ☐   Ambulatory surgical centers
    3. ☐   Imaging centers
    4. ☐   Other _____

105c. If you selected 'a. Limited service hospital', please tell us what type(s) of services are provided. (Check all that apply)

    1. ☐   Cardiac
    2. ☐   Orthopedic
    3. ☐   Surgical
    4. ☐   Other _____

105d. Does your hospital participate in joint venture arrangements with organizations other than physician groups? YES ☐   NO ☐

C. FACILITIES AND SERVICES (continued)

106a. Has your hospital or health care system established an accountable care organization (ACO)? YES ☐ NO ☐

106b. If yes, please indicate the patient population that participates in the ACO. (Check all that apply)

    1. ☐ Medicaid

    2. ☐ Medicare

    3. ☐ Privately insured

    4. ☐ Other, please specify_____

107. Does your hospital have an established medical home program? YES ☐ NO ☐

108. Does your hospital participate in a bundled payment program involving inpatient, physician, and/or post-acute care services where the hospital receives a single payment from a payor for a package of services and then distributes payments to participating providers of care (such as a single fee for hospital and physician services for a specific procedure, e.g., hip replacement, CABG)? YES ☐ NO ☐

109. Does your hospital, health system or health network have an equity interest in any of the following insurance products? (Check all that apply) Contractual relationships with HMOs and PPOs should not be reported here but in Question 110. Column 3 refers to the networks that were identified in section B, question 3d.

	(1) My Hospital	(2) My Health System	(3) My Health Network	(4) Joint Venture with Insurer	(5) Do Not Provide
a. Health Maintenance Organization	☐	☐	☐	☐	☐
b. Preferred Provider Organization.	☐	☐	☐	☐	☐
c. Indemnity Fee for Service Plan	☐	☐	☐	☐	☐

110. Does your hospital have a formal written contract that specifies the obligations of each party with:

    a. Health maintenance organization (HMO)...............YES ☐ NO .... ☐ **b.** If YES, how many contracts? _____

    c. Preferred provider organization (PPO) ....YES ☐ NO........ ☐ **d.** If YES, how many contracts? _____

111. What percentage of the hospital's net patient revenue is paid on a capitated basis? If the hospital does not participate in capitated arrangements, please enter "0" _____ %

112. What percentage of the hospital's net patient revenue is paid on a shared risk basis? _____ %

113. Does your hospital contract directly with employers or a coalition of employers to provide care on a capitated, predetermined, or shared risk basis? ....YES ☐ NO ☐

114. If your hospital has arrangements to care for a specific group of enrollees in exchange for a capitated payment, how many lives are covered? _____

115. Does your hospital have contracts with commercial payors where payment is tied to performance on quality/safety metrics? YES ☐ NO ☐

116a. Does your hospital conduct an internal survey of the hospital's quality/safety culture at least every 18 months? YES ☐ NO ☐

116b. If yes, please indicate the response rate for the most recent survey. _____ %

116c. If yes, are valid results available at the level of individual units (e.g., medical ICUs, cardiothoracic surgery)? YES ☐ NO ☐

D. TOTAL FACILITY BEDS, UTILIZATION, FINANCES, AND STAFFING

Please report beds, utilization, financial, and staffing data for the 12-month period that is consistent with the period reported on page 1. Report financial data for reporting period only. Include within your operations all activities that are wholly owned by the hospital, including subsidiary corporations regardless of where the activity is physically located. Please do not include within your operations distinct and separate divisions that may be owned by your hospital's parent corporation. If final figures are not available, please estimate. Round to the nearest dollar. Report all personnel who were on the payroll and whose payroll expenses are reported in D3f. (Please refer to specific definitions on pages 21-23.)

Fill out column (2) if hospital owns and operates a nursing home type unit/facility. Column (1) should be the combined total of hospital plus nursing home unit/facility.	(1) Total Facility	(2) Nursing Home Unit/Facility

1. BEDS AND UTILIZATION

		Total Facility	Nursing Home
a.	Total licensed beds..	_____	_____
b.	Beds set up and staffed for use at the end of the reporting period	_____	_____
c.	Bassinets set up and staffed for use at the end of the reporting period	_____	
d.	Births (exclude fetal deaths)	_____	
e.	Admissions (exclude newborns; include neonatal & swing admissions)	_____	_____
f.	Inpatient days (exclude newborns; include neonatal & swing days)	_____	_____
g.	Emergency department visits...	_____	
h.	Total outpatient visits (include emergency department visits & outpatient surgeries)....	_____	
i.	Inpatient surgical operations	_____	
j.	Number of operating rooms	_____	
k.	Outpatient surgical operations...	_____	

2. MEDICARE/MEDICAID UTILIZATION (exclude newborns; include neonatal & swing days and deaths)

		Total Facility	Nursing Home
a1.	Total Medicare (Title XVIII) inpatient discharges (including Medicare Managed Care)	_____	_____
a2.	How many Medicare inpatient discharges were Medicare Managed Care?............	_____	_____
b1.	Total Medicare (Title XVIII) inpatient days (including Medicare Managed Care)	_____	_____
b2.	How many Medicare inpatient days were Medicare Managed Care?...................	_____	_____
c1.	Total Medicaid (Title XIX) inpatient discharges (including Medicaid Managed Care)	_____	_____
c2.	How many Medicaid inpatient discharges were Medicaid Managed Care?............	_____	_____
d1.	Total Medicaid (Title XIX) inpatient days (including Medicaid Managed Care)	_____	_____
d2.	How many Medicaid inpatient days were Medicaid Managed Care?..................	_____	_____

3. FINANCIAL

		Total Facility	Nursing Home
*a.	Net patient revenue (treat bad debt as a deduction from gross revenue)...........	.00	.00
*b.	Tax appropriations	.00	
*c.	Other operating revenue...	.00	
*d.	Nonoperating revenue	.00	
*e.	TOTAL REVENUE (add 3a thru 3d)	.00	.00
f.	Payroll expenses (only)	.00	.00
g.	Employee benefits	.00	.00
h.	Depreciation expense (for reporting period only)	.00	
i.	Interest expense	.00	
j.	Pharmacy Expense...	.00	
k.	Supply expense (other than pharmacy)	.00	
l.	All other expenses..	.00	
m.	TOTAL EXPENSES (add 3f thru 3l. Exclude bad debt)	.00	.00

4. REVENUE BY TYPE

		Total Facility
*a.	Total gross inpatient revenue...	.00
*b.	Total gross outpatient revenue	.00
*c.	Total gross patient revenue	.00

D. TOTAL FACILITY BEDS, UTILIZATION, FINANCES, AND STAFFING (continued)

*5. UNCOMPENSATED CARE & PROVIDER TAXES

a. Bad debt (Revenue forgone at full established rates. Include in gross revenue) .... _____ .00

b. Financial Assistance (includes Charity Care) (Revenue forgone at full-established rates. Include in gross revenue.)........ _____ .00

c. Is your bad debt (5a) reported on the basis of full charges?　　　　　　　YES ☐　　　　NO ☐

d.　Does your state have a provider Medicaid tax/assessment program?　　　YES ☐　　　NO ☐

e.　If yes, please report the total gross amount paid into the program.. _____ .00

f.　Due to differing accounting standards, please indicate whether the provider tax/assessment amount is included in:
　　　　1. Total expenses　　　　　　　　　　　　　　　　　　　YES ☐　　　NO ☐
　　　　2. Deductions from net patient revenue　　　　　　　　　　YES ☐　　　NO ☐

*6. REVENUE BY PAYOR (report total facility gross and net figures)

		(1) Gross	(2) Net
*a. GOVERNMENT　(1) Medicare:			
a) Fee for service patient revenue		_____ .00	_____ .00
b) Managed care revenue		_____ .00	_____ .00
c) Total (a + b)		_____ **.00**	_____ **.00**
(2) Medicaid:			
a)　Fee for service patient revenue................................		_____ .00	_____ .00
b)　Managed care revenue		_____ .00	_____ .00
c) Medicaid Disproportionate Share Hospital Payments (DSH)			_____ .00
d) Medicaid supplemental payments: not including Medicaid Disproportionate Share Hospital Payments (DSH)			_____ .00
e) Total (a + b + c + d)		_____ **.00**	_____ **.00**
(3) Other government		_____ .00	_____ .00
*b. NONGOVERNMENT　(1)　Self-pay....................................		_____ .00	_____ .00
(2)　Third-party payors:			
a)　Managed care (includes HMO and PPO)		_____ .00	_____ .00
b)　Other third-party payors		_____ .00	_____ .00
c)　Total third-party payors (a + b)		_____ **.00**	_____ **.00**
(3) All Other nongovernment.............................		_____ .00	_____ .00
*c. TOTAL		_____ **.00**	_____ **.00**

(Total gross should equal 4c on page 9. Total net should equal 3a on page 9.)

Are the financial data on pages 9 and 10 from your audited financial statement? .... YES ☐　NO ☐

---

7. FIXED ASSETS

a.　Property, plant and equipment at <u>cost</u> .... _____ .00

b.　Accumulated <u>depreciation</u> .... _____ .00

c.　Net property, plant and equipment (a-b) .... _____ .00

d.　Total gross square feet of your physical plant used for or in support of your healthcare activities.. _____

8. TOTAL CAPITAL EXPENSES

Include all expenses used to acquire assets, including buildings, remodeling projects, equipment, or property.　_____ .00

D. TOTAL FACILITY BEDS, UTILIZATION, FINANCES, AND STAFFING (continued)

9. INFORMATION TECHNOLOGY

*a. IT operating expense.._____.00

*b. IT capital expense.._____.00

*c. Number of employed IT staff (in FTEs) ...._____

*d. Number of outsourced IT staff (in FTEs).._____

    e. Does your hospital have an electronic health record? (see definition)

        ☐ Yes, fully implemented   ☐ Yes, partially implemented   ☐ No

10. STAFFING

Report full-time (35 hours or more) and part-time (less than 35 hours) personnel who were on the hospital/facility **payroll at the end of your reporting period.** Include members of religious orders for whom dollar equivalents were reported. Exclude private-duty nurses, volunteers, and all personnel whose salary is financed entirely by outside research grants. Exclude physicians and dentists who are paid on a fee basis. FTE is the total number of hours worked by all employees over the full (12 month) reporting period divided by the normal number of hours worked by a full-time employee for that same time period. For example, if your hospital considers a normal workweek for a full-time employee to be 40 hours, a total of 2,080 would be worked over a full year (52 weeks). If the total number of hours worked by all employees on the payroll is 208,000, then the number of Full-Time Equivalents (FTE) is 100 (employees). The FTE calculation for a specific occupational category such as registered nurses is exactly the same. The calculation for each occupational category should be based on the number of hours worked by staff employed in that specific category.

For each occupational category, please report the number of staff vacancies as of the last day of your reporting period. A vacancy is defined as a budgeted staff position which is unfilled as of the last day of the reporting period and for which the hospital is actively seeking either a full-time or part-time permanent replacement. Personnel who work in more than one area should be included only in the category of their primary responsibility and should be counted only once.

	(1) Full-Time (35 hr/wk or more) On Payroll	(2) Part-Time (Less than 35hr/wk) On Payroll	(3) FTE	(4) Vacancies
a. Physicians	_____	_____	_____	_____
b. Dentists	_____	_____	_____	_____
c. Medical and dental residents/interns	_____	_____	_____	_____
d. Other trainees	_____	_____	_____	_____
e. Registered nurses	_____	_____	_____	_____
f. Licensed practical (vocational) nurses	_____	_____	_____	_____
g. Nursing assistive personnel	_____	_____	_____	_____
h. Radiology technicians	_____	_____	_____	_____
i. Laboratory technicians	_____	_____	_____	_____
j. Pharmacists, licensed	_____	_____	_____	_____
k. Pharmacy technicians	_____	_____	_____	_____
l. Respiratory therapists	_____	_____	_____	_____
m. All other personnel	_____	_____	_____	_____
n. Total facility personnel (add 10a through 10m)	_____	_____	_____	_____

(Total facility personnel (a-n) should include hospital plus nursing home type unit/facility personnel also reported separately in 10o and 10p.)

o. Nursing home type unit/facility registered nurses	_____	_____	_____	_____
p. Total nursing home type unit/facility personnel	_____	_____	_____	_____

q. For your employed RN FTEs reported above (D.10.e, column 3), please report the number of full time equivalents who are involved in direct patient care.

    _____ Number of direct patient care FTEs

D. TOTAL FACILITY BEDS, UTILIZATION, FINANCES, AND STAFFING (continued)

11. PRIVILEGED PHYSICIANS

Report the total number of physicians with privileges at your hospital by type of relationship with the hospital. The sum of the physicians reported in 11a-11f should equal the total number of privileged physicians (11g) in the hospital.

	(1) Total Employed	(2) Total Individual Contract	(3) Total Group Contract	(4) Not Employed or Under Contract	(5) Total Privileged (add columns 1-4)
a. Primary care (general practitioner, general internal medicine, family practice, general pediatrics, obstetrics/gynecology, geriatrics)	_____	_____	_____	_____	_____
b. Emergency medicine	_____	_____	_____	_____	_____
c. Hospitalist	_____	_____	_____	_____	_____
d. Intensivist	_____	_____	_____	_____	_____
e. Radiologist/pathologist/anesthesiologist	_____	_____	_____	_____	_____
f. Other specialist	_____	_____	_____	_____	_____
g. Total (add 11a-11f)	_____	_____	_____	_____	_____

12. HOSPITALISTS

a. Do hospitalists provide care for patients in your hospital? (if no, please skip to 13)........... YES ☐   NO ☐ (if yes, please report in D.11c.)

b. If yes, please report the total number of full-time equivalents (FTE) hospitalists.....................FTE _____

13. INTENSIVISTS

a. Do intensivists provide care for patients in your hospital? (If no, please skip to 14) YES ☐   NO ☐ (if yes, please report in D.11d.)

b. If yes, please report the total number of FTE intensivists and assign them to the following areas. Please indicate whether the intensive care area is closed to intensivists. (Meaning that only intensivists are authorized to care for ICU patients.)

		FTE	Closed to Intensivists
1.	Medical-surgical intensive care	_____	☐
2.	Cardiac intensive care	_____	☐
3.	Neonatal intensive care	_____	☐
4.	Pediatric intensive care	_____	☐
5.	Other intensive care	_____	☐
6.	Total	_____	

14. ADVANCED PRACTICE REGISTERED NURSES/PHYSICIAN ASSISTANTS

a. Do advanced practice nurses/physician assistants provide care for patients in your hospital? .... YES ☐   NO ☐
(if no, please skip to 15)

b. If yes, please report the number of full time, part time and FTE advanced practice nurses and physician assistants who provide care for patients in your hospital.

Advanced Practice Registered Nurses   _____ Full-time   _____ Part-time   _____ FTE

Physician Assistants   _____ Full-time   _____ Part-time   _____ FTE

c. If yes, please indicate the type of service provided. (check all that apply)

☐ Primary care   ☐ Anesthesia services (Certified registered nurse anesthetist)   ☐ Emergency department care

☐ Other specialty care   ☐ Patient education   ☐ Case management   ☐ Other

15. FOREIGN EDUCATED NURSES

a. Did your facility hire more foreign-educated nurses (including contract or agency nurses) to help fill RN vacancies in 2016 vs. 2015?

More ☐   Less ☐   Same ☐   Did not hire foreign nurses ☐

b. From which countries/continents are you recruiting foreign-educated nurses? (check all that apply)

Africa ☐   South Korea ☐   Canada ☐   Philippines ☐   China ☐   India ☐   Other ☐

E. SUPPLEMENTAL INFORMATION

1. Does your hospital provide services through one or more satellite facilities?   YES ☐   NO ☐

2. Does the hospital participate in a group purchasing arrangement?   YES ☐   NO ☐

   If yes, please provide the name, city, and state of the group purchasing organization(s).

   Name: _____ City: _____ State: _____

   Name: _____ City: _____ State: _____

   Name: _____ City: _____ State: _____

3. Does the hospital purchase medical/surgical supplies directly through a distributor?   YES ☐   NO ☐
   If yes, please provide the name of the distributor(s).

   Name: _____

   Name: _____

   Name: _____

4. If your hospital hired RNs during the reporting period, how many were new graduates from nursing schools? _____

5. Describe the extent of your hospital's current partnerships with the following types of organizations for community or population health improvement initiatives

		Not Involved	Collaboration	Formal Alliance
a.	Health care providers outside your system	☐	☐	☐
b.	Local or state public health organizations	☐	☐	☐
c.	Local or state human/social service organizations	☐	☐	☐
d.	Other local or state government	☐	☐	☐
e.	Non-profit organizations	☐	☐	☐
f.	Faith-based organizations	☐	☐	☐
g.	Health insurance companies	☐	☐	☐
h.	Schools	☐	☐	☐
i.	Local businesses or chambers of commerce	☐	☐	☐
j.	Other (list)_____	☐	☐	☐

Use this space for comments or to elaborate on any information supplied on this survey. Refer to the response by page, section and item name.

_____

_____

_____

_____

_____

_____

_____

_____

_____

_____

_____

_____

_____

As declared previously, hospital specific revenue data are treated as confidential. AHA's policy is not to release these data without written permission from your institution. The AHA will however, share these data with your respective state hospital association and if requested with your appropriate metropolitan/regional association.

On occasion, the AHA is asked to provide these data to external organizations, both public and private, for their use in analyzing crucial health care policy or research issues. The AHA is requesting your permission to allow us to release your confidential data to those requests that we consider legitimate and worthwhile. In every instance of disclosure, the receiving organization will be prohibited from releasing hospital specific information.

Please indicate below whether or not you agree to these types of disclosure:

[ ] I hereby grant AHA permission to release my hospital's revenue data to external users that the AHA determines have a legitimate and worthwhile need to gain access to these data subject to the user's agreement with the AHA not to release hospital specific information.

_____   _____
Chief Executive Officer   Date

[ ] I do not grant AHA permission to release my confidential data.

_____   _____
Chief Executive Officer   Date

Does your hospital or health system have an Internet or Homepage address?   Yes ☐   No ☐

If yes, please provide the address: http:// _____

Thank you for your cooperation in completing this survey. If there are any questions about your responses to this survey, who should be contacted?

_____   _____   (   )_____
Name (please print)   Title   (Area Code) Telephone Number

____/____/____   _____   (   )_____
Date of Completion   Chief Executive Officer   Hospital's Main Fax Number

Contact Email address: _____

NOTE: PLEASE PHOTOCOPY THE INFORMATION FOR YOUR HOSPITAL FILE BEFORE RETURNING THE ORIGINAL FORM TO THE AMERICAN HOSPITAL ASSOCIATION. ALSO, PLEASE FORWARD A PHOTOCOPY OF THE COMPLETED QUESTIONNAIRE TO YOUR STATE HOSPITAL ASSOCIATION.

THANK YOU

INSTRUCTIONS AND DEFINITIONS FOR THE 2016 ANNUAL SURVEY OF HOSPITALS.
For purposes of this survey, a hospital is defined as the organization or corporate entity licensed or registered as a hospital by a state to provide diagnostic and therapeutic patient services for a variety of medical conditions, both surgical and nonsurgical.

1. **Reporting period used (beginning and ending date):** Record the beginning and ending dates of the reporting period in an eight-digit number: for example, January 1, 2016 should be shown as 01/01/2016. Number of days should equal the time span between the two dates that the hospital was open. If you are reporting for less than 366 days, utilization and finances should be presented for days reported only.
2. **Were you in operation 12 full months at the end of your reporting period?** If you are reporting for less than 366 days, utilization and finances should be presented for days reported only.
3. **Number of days open during reporting period:** Number of days should equal the time span between the two dates that the hospital was open.

SECTION B
ORGANIZATIONAL STRUCTURE
Instructions and Definitions

1. **CONTROL**
   Check the box to the left of the type of organization that is responsible for establishing policy for overall operation of the hospital.
   Government, nonfederal.
   State. Controlled by an agency of state government.
   County. Controlled by an agency of county government.
   City. Controlled by an agency of municipal government.
   City-County. Controlled jointly by agencies of municipal and county governments.
   Hospital district or authority. Controlled by a political subdivision of a state, county, or city created solely for the purpose of establishing and maintaining medical care or health-related care institutions.
   Nongovernment, not for profit. Controlled by not-for-profit organizations, including religious organizations (Catholic hospitals, for example), community hospitals, cooperative hospitals, hospitals operated by fraternal societies, and so forth.
   Investor owned, for profit. Controlled on a for profit basis by an individual, partnership, or a profit making corporation.
   Government, federal. Controlled by an agency or department of the federal government.

2. **SERVICE**
   Indicate the ONE category that best describes the type of service that your hospital provides to the majority of patients.
   General medical and surgical. Provides diagnostic and therapeutic services to patients for a variety of medical conditions, both surgical and nonsurgical.
   Hospital unit of an institution. Provides diagnostic and therapeutic services to patients in an institution.
   Hospital unit within a facility for persons with intellectual disabilities. Provides diagnostic and therapeutic services to persons with intellectual disabilities.
   Surgical. An acute care specialty hospital where 2/3 or more of its inpatient claims are for surgical/diagnosis related groups.
   Psychiatric. Provides diagnostic and therapeutic services to patients with mental or emotional disorders.
   Tuberculosis and other respiratory diseases. Provides medical care and rehabilitative services to patients for whom the primary diagnosis is tuberculosis or other respiratory diseases.
   Cancer. Provides medical care to patients for whom the primary diagnosis is cancer.
   Heart. Provides diagnosis and treatment of heart disease.
   Obstetrics and gynecology. Provides medical and surgical treatment to pregnant women and to mothers following delivery. Also provides diagnostic and therapeutic services to women with diseases or disorders of the reproductive organs.
   Eye, ear, nose, and throat. Provides diagnosis and treatment of diseases and injuries of the eyes, ears, nose, and throat.
   Rehabilitation. Provides a comprehensive array of restoration services for people with disabilities and all support services necessary to help them attain their maximum functional capacity.
   Orthopedic. Provides corrective treatment of deformities, diseases, and ailments of the locomotive apparatus, especially affecting the limbs, bones, muscles, and joints.
   Chronic disease. Provides medical and skilled nursing services to patients with long-term illnesses who are not in an acute phase, but who require an intensity of services not available in nursing homes.
   Intellectual Disabilities. Provides health-related care on a regular basis to patients with developmental or intellectual disabilities who cannot be treated in a skilled nursing unit.
   Acute long-term care hospital. Provides high acuity interdisciplinary services to medically complex patients that require more intensive recuperation and care than can be provided in a typical nursing facility.
   Alcoholism and other chemical dependency. Provides diagnostic and therapeutic services to patients with alcoholism or other drug dependencies.

3. **OTHER**
   a. **Children admissions.** A hospital whose primary focus is the health and treatment of children and adolescents.
   b. **Subsidiary.** A company that is wholly controlled by another or one that is more than 50% owned by another organization.
   c. **Contract managed.** General day-to-day management of an entire organization by another organization under a formal contract. Managing organization reports directly to the board of trustees or owners of the managed organization; managed organization retains total legal responsibility and ownership of the facility's assets and liabilities.
   d. **Network.** A group of hospitals, physicians, other providers, insurers and/or community agencies that voluntarily work together to coordinate and deliver health services.

Owned/provided by the hospital or its subsidiary. All patient revenues, expenses and utilization related to the provision of the service are reflected in the hospital's statistics reported elsewhere in this survey.

Provided by my Health System (in my local community). Another health care provider in the same system as your hospital provides the service and patient revenue, expenses, and utilization related to the provision of the service are recorded at the point where the service was provided and would not be reflected in your hospital's statistics reported elsewhere in this survey. (A system is a corporate body that owns, leases, religiously sponsors and/or manages health providers)

Provided through a formal contractual arrangement or joint venture with another provider that is not in my system. All patient revenues and utilization related to the provision of the service are recorded at the site where the service was provided and would not be reflected in your hospital statistics reported elsewhere in this survey. (A joint venture is a contractual arrangement between two or more parties forming an unincorporated business. The participants in the arrangement remain independent and separate outside of the venture's purpose.)

1. **General medical-surgical care.** Provides acute care to patients in medical and surgical units on the basis of physicians' orders and approved nursing care plans.
2. **Pediatric medical-surgical care.** Provides acute care to pediatric patients on the basis of physicians' orders and approved nursing care plans.
3. **Obstetrics.** For service owned or provided by the hospital, level should be designated: (1) unit provides services for uncomplicated maternity and newborn cases; (2) unit provides services for uncomplicated cases, the majority of complicated problems, and special neonatal services; and (3) unit provides services for all serious illnesses and abnormalities and is supervised by a full-time maternal/fetal specialist.
4. **Medical-surgical intensive care.** Provides patient care of a more intensive nature than the usual medical and surgical care, on the basis of physicians' orders and approved nursing care plans. These units are staffed with specially trained nursing personnel and contain monitoring and specialized support equipment for patients who because of shock, trauma or other life-threatening conditions require intensified comprehensive observation and care. Includes mixed intensive care units.
5. **Cardiac intensive care.** Provides patient care of a more specialized nature than the usual medical and surgical care, on the basis of physicians' orders and approved nursing care plans. The unit is staffed with specially trained nursing personnel and contains monitoring and specialized support or treatment equipment for patients who, because of heart seizure, open-heart surgery, or other life-threatening conditions, require intensified, comprehensive observation and care. May include myocardial infarction, pulmonary care, and heart transplant units.
6. **Neonatal intensive care.** A unit that must be separate from the newborn nursery providing intensive care to all sick infants including those with the very lowest birth weights (less than 1500 grams). NICU has potential for providing mechanical ventilation, neonatal surgery, and special care for the sickest infants born in the hospital or transferred from another institution. A full-time neonatologist serves as director of the NICU.
7. **Neonatal intermediate care.** A unit that must be separate from the normal newborn nursery and that provides intermediate and/or recovery care and some specialized services, including immediate resuscitation, intravenous therapy, and capacity for prolonged oxygen therapy and monitoring.
8. **Pediatric intensive care.** Provides care to pediatric patients that is of a more intensive nature than that usually provided to pediatric patients. The unit is staffed with specially trained personnel and contains monitoring and specialized support equipment for treatment of patients who, because of shock, trauma, or other life-threatening conditions, require intensified, comprehensive observation and care.
9. **Burn care.** Provides care to severely burned patients. Severely burned patients are those with any of the following: (1) second-degree burns of more than 25% total body surface area for adults or 20% total body surface area for children: (2) third-degree burns of more than 10% total body surface area; (3) any severe burns of the hands, face, eyes, ears, or feet; or (4) all inhalation injuries, electrical burns, complicated burn injuries involving fractures and other major traumas, and all other poor risk factors.
10. **Other special care.** Provides care to patients requiring care more intensive than that provided in the acute area, yet not sufficiently intensive to require admission to an intensive care unit. Patients admitted to this area are usually transferred here from an intensive care unit once their condition has improved. These units are sometimes referred to as definitive observation, step-down or progressive care units.
11. **Other intensive care.** A specially staffed, specialty equipped, separate section of a hospital dedicated to the observation, care, and treatment of patients with life-threatening illnesses, injuries, or complications from which recovery is possible. It provides special expertise and facilities for the support of vital function and utilizes the skill of medical nursing and other staff experienced in the management of these problems.
12. **Physical rehabilitation.** Provides care encompassing a comprehensive array of restoration services for people with disabilities and all support services necessary to help patients attain their maximum functional capacity.
13. **Alcoholism-drug abuse or dependency care.** Provides diagnosis and therapeutic services to patients with alcoholism or other drug dependencies. Includes care for inpatient/residential treatment for patients whose course of treatment involves more intensive care than provided in an outpatient setting or where patient requires supervised withdrawal.
14. **Psychiatric care.** Provides acute or long-term care to patients with mental or emotional disorders, including patients admitted for diagnosis and those admitted for treatment of psychiatric disorders, on the basis of physicians' orders and approved nursing care plans. Long-term care may include intensive supervision to persons with chronic/severe mental illness.
15. **Skilled nursing care.** Provides non-acute medical and skilled nursing care services, therapy, and social services under the supervision of a licensed registered nurse on a 24-hour basis.
16. **Intermediate nursing care.** Provides health-related services (skilled nursing care and social services) to residents with a variety of physical conditions or functional disabilities. These residents do not require the care provided by a hospital or skilled nursing facility, but do need supervision and support services.
17. **Acute long-term care.** Provides specialized acute hospital care to medically complex patients who are critically ill, have multisystem complications and/or failure, and require hospitalization averaging 25 days, in a facility offering specialized treatment programs and therapeutic intervention on a 24-hour/7 days a week basis.
18. **Other long-term care.** Provision of long-term care other than skilled nursing care or intermediate care for those who do not require daily medical or nursing services, but may requires some assistance in the activities of daily living. This can include residential care, elderly care, or care facilities for those with developmental or intellectual disabilities.
19. **Other care.** (specify) Any type of care other than those listed above.
    The sum of the beds reported in Section C 1-19 should equal what you have reported in Section D(1b) for beds set up and staffed.
20. **Adult day care program.** Program providing supervision, medical and psychological care, and social activities for older adults who live at home or in another family setting, but cannot be alone or prefer to be with others during the day. May include intake assessment, health monitoring, occupational therapy, personal care, noon meal, and transportation services.
21. **Airborne infection isolation room.** A single-occupancy room for patient care where environmental factors are controlled in an effort to minimize the transmission of those infectious agents, usually spread person to person by droplet nuclei associated with coughing and inhalation. Such rooms typically have specific ventilation requirements for controlled ventilation, air pressure and filtration.
22. **Alcoholism-drug abuse or dependency outpatient services.** Organized hospital services that provide medical care and/or rehabilitative treatment services to outpatients for whom the primary diagnosis is alcoholism or other chemical dependency.

23. **Alzheimer center.** Facility that offers care to persons with Alzheimer's disease and their families through an integrated program of clinical services, research, and education.
24. **Ambulance services.** Provision of ambulance service to the ill and injured who require medical attention on a scheduled and unscheduled basis.
25. **Ambulatory surgery center.** Facility that provides care to patients requiring surgery that are admitted and discharged on the same day. Ambulatory surgery centers are distinct from same day surgical units within the hospital outpatient departments for purposes of Medicare payment.
26. **Arthritis treatment center.** Specifically equipped and staffed center for the diagnosis and treatment of arthritis and other joint disorders.
27. **Assisted living.** A special combination of housing, supportive services, personalized assistance and health care designed to respond to the individual needs of those who need help in activities of daily living and instrumental activities of daily living. Supportive services are available, 24 hours a day, to meet scheduled and unscheduled needs, in a way that promotes maximum independence and dignity for each resident and encourages the involvement of a resident's family, neighbor and friends.
28. **Auxiliary.** A volunteer community organization formed to assist the hospital in carrying out its purpose and to serve as a link between the institution and the community.
29. **Bariatric/weight control services.** The medical practice of weight reduction.
30. **Birthing room/LDR room/LDRP room.** A single-room type of maternity care with a more homelike setting for families than the traditional three-room unit (labor/delivery/recovery) with a separate postpartum area. A birthing room combines labor and delivery in one room. An LDR room accommodates three stages in the birthing process--labor, delivery, and recovery. An LDRP room accommodates all four stages of the birth process--labor, delivery, recovery, and postpartum.
31. **Blood donor center.** A facility that performs, or is responsible for the collection, processing, testing or distribution of blood and components.
32. **Breast cancer screening/mammograms.** Mammography screening - The use of breast x-ray to detect unsuspected breast cancer in asymptomatic women. Diagnostic mammography - The x-ray imaging of breast tissue in symptomatic women who are considered to have a substantial likelihood of having breast cancer already.
33. **Cardiology and cardiac surgery services.** Services which include the diagnosis and treatment of diseases and disorders involving the heart and circulatory system.
   a-b. Cardiology services. An organized clinical service offering diagnostic and interventional procedures to manage the full range of heart conditions.
   c-d. Diagnostic catheterization. (also called coronary angiography or coronary arteriography) is used to assist in diagnosing complex heart conditions. Cardiac angiography involves the insertion of a tiny catheter into the artery in the groin then carefully threading the catheter up into the aorta where the coronary arteries originate. Once the catheter is in place, a dye is injected which allows the cardiologist to see the size, shape, and distribution of the coronary arteries. These images are used to diagnose heart disease and to determine, among other things, whether or not surgery is indicated.
   e-f. Interventional cardiac catheterization. Nonsurgical procedure that utilizes the same basic principles as diagnostic catheterization and then uses advanced techniques to improve the heart's function. It can be a less invasive alternative to heart surgery.
   g-h. Cardiac surgery. Includes minimally invasive procedures that include surgery done with only a small incision or no incision at all, such as through a laparoscope or an endoscope and more invasive major surgical procedures that include open chest and open heart surgery.
   i-j. Cardiac electrophysiology. Evaluation and management of patients with complex rhythm or conduction abnormalities, including diagnostic testing, treatment of arrhythmias by catheter ablation or drug therapy, and pacemaker/defibrillator implantation and follow-up.
   k. Cardiac rehabilitation. A medically supervised program to help heart patients recover quickly and improve their overall physical and mental functioning. The goal is to reduce risk of another cardiac event or to keep an already present heart condition from getting worse. Cardiac rehabilitation programs include: counseling to patients, an exercise program, helping patients modify risk factors such as smoking and high blood pressure, providing vocational guidance to enable the patient to return to work, supplying information on physical limitations and lending emotional support.
34. **Case management.** A system of assessment, treatment planning, referral and follow-up that ensures the provision of comprehensive and continuous services and the coordination of payment and reimbursement for care.
35. **Chaplaincy/pastoral care services.** A service ministering religious activities and providing pastoral counseling to patients, their families, and staff of a health care organization.
36. **Chemotherapy.** An organized program for the treatment of cancer by the use of drugs or chemicals.
37. **Children's wellness program.** A program that encourages improved health status and a healthful lifestyle of children through health education, exercise, nutrition and health promotion.
38. **Chiropractic services.** An organized clinical service including spinal manipulation or adjustment and related diagnostic and therapeutic services.
39. **Community outreach.** A program that systematically interacts with the community to identify those in need of services, alerting persons and their families to the availability of services, locating needed services, and enabling persons to enter the service delivery system.
40. **Complementary and alternative medicine services.** Organized hospital services or formal arrangements to providers that provide care or treatment not based solely on traditional western allopathic medical teachings as instructed in most U.S. medical schools. Includes any of the following: acupuncture, chiropractic, homeopathy, osteopathy, diet and lifestyle changes, herbal medicine, massage therapy, etc.
41. **Computer assisted orthopedic surgery (CAOS).** Orthopedic surgery using computer technology, enabling three-dimensional graphic models to visualize a patient's anatomy.
42. **Crisis prevention.** Services provided in order to promote physical and mental wellbeing and the early identification of disease and ill health prior to the onset and recognition of symptoms so as to permit early treatment.
43. **Dental Services.** An organized dental service or dentists on staff, not necessarily involving special facilities, providing dental or oral services to inpatients or outpatients.
44. **Emergency services.** Health services that are provided after the onset of a medical condition that manifests itself by symptoms of sufficient severity, including severe pain, that the absence of immediate medical attention could reasonably be expected by a prudent layperson, who possesses an average knowledge of health and medicine, to result in placing the patient's health in serious jeopardy.
   a-b. Emergency department. Hospital facilities for the provision of unscheduled outpatient services to patients whose conditions require immediate care.
   c. Satellite Emergency Department. A facility owned and operated by the hospital but physically separate from the hospital for the provision of unscheduled outpatient services to patients whose conditions require immediate care. A freestanding ED is not physically connected to a hospital, but has all necessary emergency staffing and equipment on-site.
   e. Trauma center (certified). A facility to provide emergency and specialized intensive care to critically ill and injured patients. For service owned or provided by the hospital, please specify trauma level. Level 1: A regional resource trauma center, which is capable of providing total care for every aspect of injury and plays a leadership role in trauma research and education. Level 2: A community trauma center, which is capable of providing trauma care to all but the most severely injured patients who require highly specialized care. Level 3: A rural trauma hospital, which is capable of providing care to a large number of injury victims and can resuscitate and stabilize more severely injured patients so that they can be transported to level 1 or 2 facilities. Please provide explanation on page 13 if necessary.
45. **Enabling services.** A program that is designed to help the patient access health care services by offering any of the following: transportation services and/or referrals to local social services agencies.

---

46. **Endoscopic services.**
   a. **Optical colonoscopy.** An examination of the interior of the colon using a long, flexible, lighted tube with a small built-in camera.
   b. **Endoscopic ultrasound.** Specially designed endoscope that incorporates an ultrasound transducer used to obtain detailed images of organs in the chest and abdomen. The endoscope can be passed through the mouth or the anus. When combined with needle biopsy the procedure can assist in diagnosis of disease and staging of cancer.
   c. **Ablation of Barrett's esophagus.** Premalignant condition that can lead to adenocarcinoma of the esophagus. The nonsurgical ablation of premalignant tissue in Barrett's esophagus by the application of thermal energy or light through an endoscope passed from the mouth into the esophagus.
   d. **Esophageal impedance study.** A test in which a catheter is placed through the nose into the esophagus to measure whether gas or liquids are passing from the stomach into the esophagus and causing symptoms.
   e. **Endoscopic retrograde cholangiopancreatography (ERCP).** A procedure in which a catheter is introduced through an endoscope into the bile ducts and pancreatic ducts. Injection of contrast material permits detailed x-ray of these structures. The procedure is used diagnostically as well as therapeutically to relieve obstruction or remove stones.

47. **Enrollment (insurance) assistance services.** A program that provides enrollment assistance for patients who are potentially eligible for public health insurance programs such as Medicaid, State Children's Health Insurance, or local/state indigent care programs. The specific services offered could include explanation of benefits, assist applicants in completing the application and locating all relevant documents, conduct eligibility interviews, and/or forward applications and documentation to state/local social service or health agency.

48. **Extracorporeal shock wave lithotripter (ESWL).** A medical device used for treating stones in the kidney or urethra. The device disintegrates kidney stones noninvasively through the transmission of acoustic shock waves directed at the stones.

49. **Fertility clinic.** A specialized program set in an infertility center that provides counseling and education as well as advanced reproductive techniques such as: injectable therapy, reproductive surgeries, treatment for endometriosis, male factor infertility, tubal reversals, in vitro fertilization (IVF), donor eggs, and other such services to help patients achieve successful pregnancies.

50. **Fitness center.** Provides exercise, testing, or evaluation programs and fitness activities to the community and hospital employees.

51. **Freestanding outpatient care center.** A facility owned and operated by the hospital, that is physically separate from the hospital and provides various medical treatments and diagnostic services on an outpatient basis only. Laboratory and radiology services are usually available.

52. **Geriatric services.** The branch of medicine dealing with the physiology of aging and the diagnosis and treatment of disease affecting the aged. Services could include: Adult day care; Alzheimer's diagnostic-assessment services; Comprehensive geriatric assessment; Emergency response system; Geriatric acute care unit; and/or Geriatric clinics.

53. **Health fair.** Community health education events that focus on the prevention of disease and promotion of health through such activities as audiovisual exhibits and free diagnostic services.

54. **Community health education.** Education that provides health information to individuals and populations as well as support for personal, family and community health decisions with the objective of improving health status.

55. **Genetic testing/counseling.** A service equipped with adequate laboratory facilities and directed by a qualified physician to advise patients on potential genetic diagnosis of vulnerabilities to inherited diseases. A genetic test is the analysis of human DNA, RNA, chromosomes, proteins, and certain metabolites in order to detect heritable disease-related genotypes, mutations, phenotypes, or karyotypes for clinical purposes. Genetic tests can have diverse purposes, including the diagnosis of genetic diseases in newborns, children, and adults; the identification of future health risks; the prediction of drug responses; and the assessment of risks to future children.

56. **Health screening.** A preliminary procedure such as a test or examination to detect the most characteristic sign or signs of a disorder that may require further investigation.

57. **Health research.** Organized hospital research program in any of the following areas: basic research, clinical research, community health research, and/or research on innovative health care delivery.

58. **Hemodialysis.** Provision of equipment and personnel for the treatment of renal insufficiency on an inpatient or outpatient basis.

59. **HIV/AIDS services.** Diagnosis, treatment, continuing care planning, and counseling services for HIV/AIDS patients and their families. Could include: HIV/AIDS unit, special unit or designated team, general inpatient care, or specialized outpatient program.

60. **Home health services.** Service providing nursing, therapy, and health-related homemaker or social services in the patient's home.

61. **Hospice.** A program providing palliative care, chiefly medical relief of pain and supportive services, addressing the emotional, social, financial, and legal needs of terminally ill patients and their families. Care can be provided in a variety of settings, both inpatient and at home.

62. **Hospital-based outpatient care center-services.** Organized hospital health care services offered by appointment on an ambulatory basis. Services may include outpatient surgery, examination, diagnosis, and treatment of a variety of medical conditions on a nonemergency basis, and laboratory and other diagnostic testing as ordered by staff or outside physician referral.

63. **Immunization program.** Program that plans, coordinates and conducts immunization services in the community.

64. **Indigent care clinic.** Health care services for uninsured and underinsured persons where care is free of charge or charged on a sliding scale. This would include "free clinics" staffed by volunteer practitioners, but could also be staffed by employees with the sponsoring health care organization subsidizing the cost of service.

65. **Linguistic/translation services.** Services provided by the hospital designed to make health care more accessible to non-English speaking patients and their physicians.

66. **Meals on wheels.** A hospital sponsored program which delivers meals to people, usually the elderly, who are unable to prepare their own meals. Low cost, nutritional meals are delivered to individuals' homes on a regular basis.

67. **Mobile health services.** Vans and other vehicles used for delivery to primary care services.

68. **Neurological services.** Services provided by the hospital dealing with the operative and nonoperative management of disorders of the central, peripheral, and autonomic nervous systems.

69. **Nutrition programs.** Services within a health care facility which are designed to provide inexpensive, nutritionally sound meals to patients.

70. **Occupational health services.** Includes services designed to protect the safety of employees from hazards in the work environment.

71. **Oncology services.** Inpatient and outpatient services for patients with cancer, including comprehensive care, support and guidance in addition to patient education and prevention, chemotherapy, counseling and other treatment methods.

72. **Orthopedic services.** Services provided for the prevention or correction of injuries or disorders of the skeletal system and associated muscles, joints and ligaments.

73. **Outpatient surgery.** Scheduled surgical services provided to patients who do not remain in the hospital overnight. The surgery may be performed in operating suites also used for inpatient surgery, specially designated surgical suites for outpatient surgery, or procedure rooms within an outpatient care facility.

74. **Pain management program.** A recognized clinical service or program providing specialized medical care, drugs or therapies for the management of acute or chronic pain and other distressing symptoms, administered by specially trained physicians and other clinicians, to patients suffering from acute illnesses of diverse causes.

75. **Palliative care program.** An organized program providing specialized medical care, drugs or therapies for the management of acute or chronic pain and/or the control of symptoms administered by specially trained physicians and other clinicians; and supportive care services, such as counseling on advanced directives, spiritual care, and social services, to patients with advanced diseases and their families.

76. **Palliative care inpatient unit.** An inpatient palliative care ward is a physically discreet, inpatient nursing unit where the focus is palliative care. The patient care focus is on symptom relief for complex patients who may be continuing to undergo primary treatment. Care is delivered by palliative medicine specialists.
77. **Patient controlled analgesia (PCA).** Intravenously administered pain medicine under the patient's control. The patient has a button on the end of a cord than can be pushed at will, whenever more pain medicine is desired. This button will only deliver more pain medicine at predetermined intervals, as programmed by the doctor's order.
78. **Patient education center.** Written goals and objectives for the patient and/or family related to therapeutic regimens, medical procedures, and self-care.
79. **Patient representative services.** Organized hospital services providing personnel through whom patients and staff can seek solutions to institutional problems affecting the delivery of high quality care and services.
80. **Physical rehabilitation services.** Program providing medical, health-related, therapy, social, and/or vocational services to help people with disabilities attain or retain their maximum functional capacity.
    a. **Assistive technology center.** A program providing access to specialized hardware and software with adaptations allowing individuals greater independence with mobility, dexterity, or increased communication options.
    b. **Electrodiagnostic services.** Diagnostic testing services for nerve and muscle function such as nerve conduction studies and needle electromyography.
    c. **Physical rehabilitation outpatient services.** Outpatient program providing medical, health-related, therapy, social, and/or vocational services to help people with disabilities attain or retain their maximum functional capacity.
    d. **Prosthetic and orthotic services.** Services providing comprehensive prosthetic and orthotic evaluation, fitting, and training.
    e. **Robot-assisted walking therapy.** A form of physical therapy that uses a robotic device to assist patients who are relearning how to walk.
    f. **Simulated rehabilitation environment.** Rehabilitation focused on retraining functional skills in a contextually appropriate environment (simulated home and community settings) or in a traditional setting (gymnasium) using motor learning principles.
81. **Primary care department.** A unit or clinic within the hospital that provides primary care services (e.g., general pediatric care, general internal medicine, family practice, gynecology) through hospital-salaried medical and/or nursing staff, focusing on evaluating and diagnosing medical problems and providing medical treatment on an outpatient basis.
82. **Psychiatric services.** Services provided by the hospital that offer immediate initial evaluation and treatment to patients with mental or emotional disorders.
    a. **Psychiatric child-adolescent services.** Provides care to children and adolescents with mental or emotional disorders, including those admitted for diagnosis and those admitted for treatment.
    b. **Psychiatric consultation-liaison services.** Provides organized psychiatric consultation/liaison services to nonpsychiatric hospital staff and/or departments on psychological aspects of medical care that may be generic or specific to individual patients.
    c. **Psychiatric education services.** Provides psychiatric educational services to community agencies and workers such as schools, police, courts, public health nurses, welfare agencies, clergy, and so forth. The purpose is to expand the mental health knowledge and competence of personnel not working in the mental health field and to promote good mental health through improved understanding, attitudes, and behavioral patterns.
    d. **Psychiatric emergency services.** Services of facilities available on a 24-hour basis to provide immediate unscheduled outpatient care, diagnosis, evaluation, crisis intervention, and assistance to persons suffering acute emotional or mental distress.
    e. **Psychiatric geriatric services.** Provides care to elderly patients with mental or emotional disorders, including those admitted for diagnosis and those admitted for treatment.
    f. **Psychiatric outpatient services.** Provides medical care, including diagnosis and treatment, of psychiatric outpatients.
    g. **Psychiatric partial hospitalization program.** Organized hospital services providing intensive day/evening outpatient services of three hours or more duration, distinguished from other outpatient visits of one hour.
    h. **Psychiatric residential treatment.** Overnight psychiatric care in conjunction with an intensive treatment program in a setting other than a hospital.
83. **Radiology, diagnostic.** The branch of radiology that deals with the utilization of all modalities of radiant energy in medical diagnoses and therapeutic procedures using radiologic guidance. This includes, but is not restricted to, imaging techniques and methodologies utilizing radiation emitted by x-ray tubes, radionuclides, and ultrasonographic devices and the radiofrequency electromagnetic radiation emitted by atoms.
    a. **CT Scanner.** Computed tomographic scanner for head or whole body scans.
    b. **Diagnostic radioisotope facility.** The use of radioactive isotopes (Radiopharmaceuticals) as tracers or indicators to detect an abnormal condition or disease.
    c. **Electron beam computed tomography (EBCT).** A high tech computed tomography scan used to detect coronary artery disease by measuring coronary calcifications. This imaging procedure uses electron beams which are magnetically steered to produce a visual of the coronary artery and the images are produced faster than conventional CT scans.
    d. **Full-field digital mammography (FFDM).** Combines the x-ray generators and tubes used in analog screen-film mammography (SFM) with a detector plate that converts the x-rays into a digital signal.
    e. **Magnetic resonance imaging (MRI).** The use of a uniform magnetic field and radio frequencies to study tissue and structure of the body. This procedure enables the visualization of biochemical activity of the cell in vivo without the use of ionizing radiation, radioisotopic substances or high-frequency sound.
    f. **Intraoperative magnetic resonance imaging.** An integrated surgery system which provides an MRI system in an operating room. The system allows for immediate evaluation of the degree to tumor resection while the patient is undergoing a surgical resection. Intraoperative MRI exists when a MRI (low-field or high-field) is placed in the operating theater and is used during surgical resection without moving the patient from the operating room to the diagnostic imaging suite.
    g. **Magnetoencephalography (MEG).** A noninvasive neurophysiological measurement tool used to study magnetic fields generated by neuronal activity of the brain. MEG provides direct information about the dynamics of evoked and spontaneous neural activity and its location in the brain. The primary uses of MEG include assisting surgeons in localizing the source of epilepsy, sensory mapping, and the study of brain function. When it is combined with structural imaging, it is known as *magnetic source imaging* (MSI).
    h. **Multi-slice spiral computed tomography (<64+slice CT).** A specialized computed tomography procedure that provides three-dimensional processing and allows narrower and multiple slices with increased spatial resolution and faster scanning times as compared to a regular computed tomography scan.
    i. **Multi-slice spiral computed tomography (64+ slice CT).** Involves the acquisition of volumetric tomographic x-ray absorption data expressed in Hounsfield units using multiple rows of detectors. 64+ systems reconstruct the equivalent of 64 or more slices to cover the imaged volume.
    j. **Positron emission tomography (PET).** A nuclear medicine imaging technology which uses radioactive (positron emitting) isotopes created in a cyclotron or generator and computers to produce composite pictures of the brain and heart at work. PET scanning produces sectional images depicting metabolic activity or blood flow rather than anatomy.
    k. **Positron emission tomography/CT (PET/CT).** Provides metabolic functional information for the monitoring of chemotherapy, radiotherapy and surgical planning.
    l. **Single photon emission computerized tomography (SPECT).** A nuclear medicine imaging technology that combines existing technology of gamma camera imaging with computed tomographic imaging technology to provide a clearer and more precise image.

---

m. **Ultrasound.** The use of acoustic waves above the range of 20,000 cycles per second to visualize internal body structures.

84. **Radiology, therapeutic.** The branch of medicine concerned with radioactive substances and using various techniques of visualization, with the diagnosis and treatment of disease using any of the various sources of radiant energy. Services could include: megavoltage radiation therapy; radioactive implants; stereotactic radiosurgery; therapeutic radioisotope facility; X-ray radiation therapy.

   a. **Image-guided radiation therapy (IGRT).** Automated system for image-guided radiation therapy that enables clinicians to obtain high-resolution x-ray images to pinpoint tumor sites, adjust patient positioning when necessary, and complete a treatment, all within the standard treatment time slot, allowing for more effective cancer treatments.

   b. **Intensity-Modulated Radiation Therapy (IMRT).** A type of three-dimensional radiation therapy which improves treatment delivery by targeting a tumor in a way that is likely to decrease damage to normal tissues and allows for varying intensities.

   c. **Proton beam therapy.** A form of radiation therapy which administers proton beams. While producing the same biologic effects as x-ray beams, the energy distribution of protons differs from conventional x-ray beams: proton beams can be more precisely focused in tissue volumes in a three-dimensional pattern, resulting in less surrounding tissue damage than conventional radiation therapy, permitting administration of higher doses.

   d. **Shaped beam radiation system.** A precise, noninvasive treatment that involves targeted beams of radiation that mirror the exact size and shape of a tumor at a specific area to shrink or destroy cancerous cells. This procedure delivers a therapeutic dose of radiation that conforms precisely to the shape of the tumor, thus minimizing the risk to nearby tissues.

   e. **Stereotactic radiosurgery.** A radiotherapy modality that delivers a high dosage of radiation to a discrete treatment area in as few as one treatment session. Includes Gamma Knife, Cyberknife, etc.

85. **Retirement housing.** A facility that provides social activities to senior citizens, usually retired persons, who do not require health care but some short-term skilled nursing care may be provided. A retirement center may furnish housing and may also have acute hospital and long-term care facilities, or it may arrange for acute and long-term care through affiliated institutions.

86. **Robotic surgery.** The use of mechanical guidance devices to remotely manipulate surgical instrumentation.

87. **Rural health clinic.** A clinic located in a rural, medically under-served area in the United States that has a separate reimbursement structure from the standard medical office under the Medicare and Medicaid programs.

88. **Sleep center.** Specially equipped and staffed center for the diagnosis and treatment of sleep disorders.

89. **Social work services.** Could include: organized services that are properly directed and sufficiently staffed by qualified individuals who provide assistance and counseling to patients and their families in dealing with social, emotional, and environmental problems associated with illness or disability, often in the context of financial or discharge planning coordination.

90. **Sports medicine.** Provision of diagnostic screening, assessment, clinical and rehabilitation services for the prevention and treatment of sports-related injuries.

91. **Support groups.** A hospital sponsored program that allows a group of individuals with common experiences or issues who meet periodically to share experiences, problems, and solutions in order to support each other.

92. **Swing bed services.** A hospital bed that can be used to provide either acute or long-term care depending on community or patient needs. To be eligible a hospital must have a Medicare provider agreement in place, have fewer than 100 beds, be located in a rural area, not have a 24-hour nursing service waiver in effect, have not been terminated from the program in the prior two years, and meet various service conditions.

93. **Teen outreach services.** A program focusing on the teenager which encourages an improved health status and a healthful lifestyle including physical, emotional, mental, social, spiritual and economic health through education, exercise, nutrition and health promotion.

94. **Tobacco treatment/cessation program.** Organized hospital services with the purpose of ending tobacco-use habits of patients addicted to tobacco/nicotine.

95. **Transplant services.** The branch of medicine that transfers an organ or tissue from one person to another or from one body part to another, to replace a diseased structure or to restore function or to change appearance. Services could include: Bone marrow, heart, lung, kidney, intestine, or tissue transplant. Please include heart/lung or other multi-transplant surgeries in 'other'.

96. **Transportation to health facilities.** A long-term care support service designed to assist the mobility of the elderly. Some programs offer improved financial access by offering reduced rates and barrier-free buses or vans with ramps and lifts to assist the elderly or people with disabilities; others offer subsidies for public transport systems or operate mini-bus services exclusively for use by senior citizens.

97. **Urgent care center.** A facility that provides care and treatment for problems that are not life threatening but require attention over the short term.

98. **Violence Prevention**

   a. **Workplace.** A violence prevention program with goals and objectives for preventing workplace violence against staff and patients.

   b. **Community.** An organized program that attempts to make a positive impact on the type(s) of violence a community is experiencing. For example, it can assist victims of violent crimes, e.g., rape, or incidents, e.g., bullying, to hospital or to community services to prevent further victimization or retaliation. A program that targets the underlying circumstances that contribute to violence such as poor housing, insufficient job training, and/or substance abuse through means such direct involvement and support, education, mentoring, anger management, crisis intervention and training programs would also qualify.

99. **Virtual colonoscopy.** Noninvasive screening procedure used to visualize, analyze and detect cancerous or potentially cancerous polyps in the colon.

100. **Volunteer services department.** An organized hospital department responsible for coordinating the services of volunteers working within the institution.

101. **Women's health center/services.** An area set aside for coordinated education and treatment services specifically for and promoted to women as provided by this special unit. Services may or may not include obstetrics but include a range of services other than OB.

102. **Wound management services.** Services for patients with chronic wounds and nonhealing wounds often resulting from diabetes, poor circulation, improper seating and immunocompromising conditions. The goals are to progress chronic wounds through stages of healing, reduce and eliminate infections, increase physical function to minimize complications from current wounds and prevent future chronic wounds. Wound management services are provided on an inpatient or outpatient basis, depending on the intensity of service needed.

103. **Physician arrangements.** An integrated healthcare delivery program implementing physician compensation and incentive systems for managed care services.

   a. **Independent practice association (IPA).** A legal entity that holds managed care contracts. The IPA then contracts with physicians, usually in solo practice, to provide care either on a fee-for-service or capitated basis. The purpose of an IPA is to assist solo physicians in obtaining managed care contracts.

   b. **Group practice without walls.** Hospital sponsors the formation of, or provides capital to physicians to establish, a "quasi" group to share administrative expenses while remaining independent practitioners.

   c. **Open physician-hospital organization (PHO).** A joint venture between the hospital and all members of the medical staff who wish to participate. The PHO can act as a unified agent in managed care contracting, own a managed care plan, own and operate ambulatory care centers or ancillary services projects, or provide administrative services to physician members.

   d. **Closed physician-hospital organization (PHO).** A PHO that restricts physician membership to those practitioners who meet criteria for cost effectiveness and/or high quality.

   e. **Management services organization (MSO).** A corporation, owned by the hospital or a physician/hospital joint venture, that provides management services to one or more medical group practices. The MSO purchases the tangible assets of the practices and leases them back as part of a full-service management agreement, under which the MSO employs all non-physician staff and provides all supplies/administrative systems for a fee.

    f.   **Integrated salary model.** Physicians are salaried by the hospital or another entity of a health system to provide medical services for primary care and specialty care.

    g.   **Equity model.** Allows established practitioners to become shareholders in a professional corporation in exchange for tangible and intangible assets of their existing practices.

    h.   **Foundation.** A corporation, organized either as a hospital affiliate or subsidiary, which purchases both the tangible and intangible assets of one or more medical group practices. Physicians remain in a separate corporate entity but sign a professional services agreement with the foundation.

104. Of all physician arrangements listed in question 103 (a-i), indicate the total number of physicians (count each physician only once) that are engaged in an arrangement with your hospital that allows for joint contracting with payors or shared responsibility for financial risk or clinical performance between the hospital and physician (arrangement may be at the hospital, system or network level). *Joint contracting* does not include contracting between physicians participating in an independent practice.

105. **Joint venture.** A contractual arrangement between two or more parties forming an unincorporated business. The participants in the arrangement remain independent and separate outside of the venture's purpose.

106. **Accountable Care Organization (ACO) Contract.** An ACO contract has two essential elements: (1) accountability for the total costs of care for the population of patients attributed to the primary care physicians in the organization; (2) financial incentives that link the magnitude of bonus payments to performance on quality measures (which could include technical quality, patient experience and/or health outcome measures) This will generally involve a contract where the payor establishes a target budget for one or more years for the total costs of care for the agreed-upon patient population, the payor tracks actual spending and performance on quality; and the provider receives bonus payments that could include a share of savings that are (or are not) contingent on meeting quality targets, with (or without) additional bonuses related to performance on those quality measures.

107. **Patient-Centered Medical Home.** The medical home concept refers to the provision of comprehensive primary care services that facilitates communication and shared decision-making between the patient, his/her primary care providers, other providers, and the patient's family.

108. **Bundling.** Bundling is a payment mechanism whereby a provider entity receives a single payment for services provided across one or parts of the care continuum. For example, an entity might receive a single payment for the hospital and physician services provided as part of an inpatient stay or might receive a single payment for the post-acute care services involved in a single episode of care. The entity then has responsibility for compensating each of the individual providers involved in the episode of care.

111. **Capitation.** An at-risk payment arrangement in which an organization receives a fixed prearranged payment and in turn guarantees to deliver or arrange all medically necessary care required by enrollees in the capitated plan. The fixed amount is specified within contractual agreements between the payor and the involved organization. The fixed payment amount is based on an actuarial assessment of the services required by enrollees and the costs of providing these services, recognizing enrollees' adjustment factors such as age, sex, and family size.

112. **Shared risk payments.** A payment arrangement in which a hospital and a managed care organization share the risk of adverse claims experience. Methods for sharing risk could include: capitation with partial refunds or supplements if billed hospital charges or costs differ from capitated payments, and service or discharge-based payments with withholds and bonus payouts that depend on expenditure targets.

116. **Quality/Safety Survey.** Examples of a patient safety culture survey are the Safety Attitudes Questionnaire and the AHRQ Hospital Survey on Patient Safety Culture. Impromptu surveys of only certain staff or units, and other narrowly based initiatives do not qualify as quality/safety surveys for the purpose of this question.

SECTION D
TOTAL FACILITY BEDS, UTILIZATION, FINANCES, AND STAFFING
Instructions and Definitions

For the purposes of this survey, a nursing home type unit/facility provides **long-term care for the elderly or other patients requiring chronic care** in a non-acute setting in any of the following categories: *Skilled nursing care *Intermediate care *Other long-term care (see page 16) The nursing home type unit/facility is to be owned and operated by the hospital. Only one legal entity may be vested with title to the physical property or operate under the authority of a duly executed lease of the physical property.

1. a. **Total licensed beds.** Report the total number of beds authorized by the state licensing (certifying) agency.

    b. **Beds set up and staffed.** Report the number of beds regularly available (those set up and staffed for use) at the end of the reporting period. Report only operating beds, not constructed bed capacity. Include all bed facilities that are set up and staffed for use by inpatients that have no other bed facilities, such as pediatric bassinets, isolation units and quiet rooms. Exclude newborn bassinets and bed facilities for patients receiving special procedures for a portion of their stay and who have other bed facilities assigned to or reserved for them. Exclude, for example, labor room, post anesthesia, or postoperative recovery room beds, psychiatric holding beds, observation beds, and beds that are used only as holding facilities for patients prior to their transfer to another hospital.

    c. **Bassinets set up and staffed.** Report the number of normal newborn bassinets. Do not include neonatal intensive care or intermediate care bassinets. These should be reported on page 3, C6 and C7.

    d. **Births.** Total births should exclude fetal deaths.

    e. **Admissions.** Include the number of adult and pediatric admissions (exclude births). This figure should include all patients admitted during the reporting period, including neonatal and swing admissions.

    f. **Inpatient days.** Report the number of adult and pediatric days of care rendered during the entire reporting period. Do not include days of care rendered for normal infants born in the hospital, but do include those for their mothers. Include days of care for infants born in the hospital and transferred into a neonatal care unit. Also include swing bed inpatient days. An inpatient day of care (also commonly referred to as a <u>patient day</u> or a <u>census day</u>, or by some federal hospitals as an <u>occupied bed day</u>) is a period of service between the census-taking hours on two successive calendar days, the day of discharge being counted only when the patient was admitted the same day.

    g. **Emergency department visits.** Should reflect the number of visits to the emergency unit. Emergency outpatients can be admitted to the inpatient areas of the hospital, but they are still counted as emergency visits and subsequently as inpatient admissions.

    h. **Total outpatient visits.** A visit by a patient who is not lodged in the hospital while receiving medical, dental, or other services. Each appearance of an outpatient in each unit constitutes one visit regardless of the number of diagnostic and/or therapeutic treatments that the patient receives. Total outpatient visits should include all clinic visits, referred visits, observation services, outpatient surgeries (also reported on line D1k), home health service visits, and emergency department visits (also reported on line D1g).

    Clinic visits should reflect total number of visits to each specialized medical unit that is responsible for the diagnosis and treatment of patients on an outpatient, nonemergency basis. (e.g., alcoholism, dental, gynecology.) Visits to the satellite clinics and primary group practices should be included if revenue is received by the hospital.

    Referred visits should reflect total number of outpatient ancillary visits to each specialty unit of the hospital established for providing technical aid used in the diagnosis and treatment of patients. Examples of such units are diagnostic radiology, EKG, pharmacy, etc.

    Observation services are those services furnished on a hospital's premises, including use of a bed and periodic monitoring by a hospital's nursing or other staff, which are reasonable and necessary to evaluate an outpatient's condition or determine the need for a possible admission to the hospital as an inpatient. Observation services usually do not exceed 24 hours; however, there is no hourly limit on the extent to which they may be used.

Home health service visits are visits by home health personnel to a patient's residence.

i. **Inpatient surgical operations.** Count each patient undergoing surgery as one surgical operation regardless of the number of surgical procedures that were performed while the patient was in the operating or procedure room.

j. **Operating room.** A unit/room of a hospital or other health care facility in which surgical procedures requiring anesthesia are performed.

k. **Outpatient surgical operations.** For outpatient surgical operations, please record operations performed on patients who do not remain in the hospital overnight. Include all operations whether performed in the inpatient operating rooms or in procedure rooms located in an outpatient facility. Include an endoscopy only when used as an operative tool and not when used for diagnosis alone. Count each patient undergoing surgery as one surgical operation regardless of the number of surgical procedures that were performed while the patient was in the operating or procedure room.

2a2. Managed Care Medicare Discharges. A discharge day where a Medicare Managed Care Plan is the source of payment.

2b2. Managed Care Medicare Inpatient Days. An inpatient day where a Medicare Managed Care Plan is the source of payment.

2c2. Managed Care Medicaid Discharges. A discharge day where a Medicaid Managed Care Plan is the source of payment.

2d2. Managed Care Medicaid Inpatient Days. An inpatient day where a Medicaid Managed Care Plan is the source of payment.

3a. Net patient revenue. Reported at the estimated net realizable amounts from patients, third-party payors, and others for services rendered, including estimated retroactive adjustments under reimbursement agreements with third-party payors. Retroactive adjustments are accrued on an estimated basis in the period the related services are rendered and adjusted in future periods, as final settlements are determined.

3b. Tax appropriations. A predetermined amount set aside by the government from its taxing authority to support the operation of the hospital.

3c. Other operating revenue. Revenue that arises from the normal day-to-day operations from services other than health care provided to patients. Includes sales and services to nonpatients, and revenue from miscellaneous sources (rental of hospital space, sale of cafeteria meals, gift shop sales). Also include operating gains in this category.

3d. Nonoperating revenue. Includes investment income, extraordinary gains and other nonoperating gains.

3e. Total revenue. Add net patient revenue, tax appropriations, other operating revenue and nonoperating revenue.

3f. Payroll expenses. Include payroll for all personnel including medical and dental residents/interns and trainees.

3g. Employee benefits. Includes social security, group insurance, retirement benefits, workman's compensation, unemployment insurance, etc.

3h. Depreciation expense (for reporting period only). Report only the depreciation expense applicable to the reporting period. The amount should also be included in accumulated depreciation (D7b).

3i. Interest expense. Report interest expense for the reporting period only.

3j. Pharmacy Expense. Includes the cost of drugs and pharmacy supplies requested to patient care departments and drugs charged to patients.

3k. Supply expense. The net cost of all tangible items that are expensed including freight, standard distribution cost, and sales and use tax minus rebates. This would exclude labor, labor-related expenses and services as well as some tangible items that are frequently provided as part of labor costs.

3l. All other expenses. Any total facility expenses not included in 3f-3k.

3m. Total expenses. Add 3f-3l. Includes all payroll and non-payroll expenses as well as any nonoperating losses (including extraordinary losses). **Treat bad debt as a deduction from gross patient revenue and not as an expense.**

4a. Total gross inpatient revenue. The hospital's full-established rates (charges) for all services rendered to inpatients.

4b. Total gross outpatient revenue. The hospital's full-established rates (charges) for all services rendered to outpatients.

4c. Total gross patient revenue. Add total gross inpatient revenue and total gross outpatient revenue.

5. **Uncompensated care.** Care for which no payment is expected or no charge is made. It is the sum of bad debt and charity care absorbed by a hospital or other health care organization in providing medical care for patients who are uninsured or are unable to pay.

5a. Bad debt. The provision for actual or expected uncollectibles resulting from the extension of credit. Report as a deduction from gross revenue. **For Question 6 (Revenue by payor), if you cannot break out your bad debt by payor, deduct the amount from self-pay.**

5b. Financial Assistance (Includes Charity care). Financial assistance and charity care refer to health services provided free of charge or at reduced rates to individuals who meet certain financial criteria. For purposes of this survey, charity care is measured on the basis of revenue forgone, at full-established rates.

5d. Medicaid Provider Tax, Fee or Assessment. Dollars paid as a result of a state law that authorizes collecting revenue from specified categories of providers. Federal matching funds may be received for the revenue collected from providers and some or all of the revenues may be returned directly or indirectly back to providers in the form of a Medicaid payment.

6. **REVENUE BY PAYOR**

6a1. Medicare. Should agree with the Medicare utilization reported in questions D2a1-D2b2.

6a1a. Fee for service patient revenue. Include traditional Medicare fee-for-service.

6a1c. Total. Medicare revenue (add Medicare fee for service patient revenue and Medicare managed care revenue).

6a2. Medicaid. Should agree with Medicaid utilization reported in questions D2c1-D2d2.

6a2a. Fee for service patient revenue. Do not include Medicaid disproportionate share payments (DSH) or other Medicaid supplemental payments.

6a2c. Medicaid disproportionate share payment (DSH). DSH minus associated provider taxes or assessments. Report in 'Net' column only.

6a2d. Medicaid supplemental payments. Supplemental payments the Medicaid program pays the hospital that are NOT Medicaid DSH, minus associated provider taxes or assessments. Report in 'Net' column only.

7a-c. Fixed Assets. Represent land and physical properties that are consumed or used in the creation of economic activity by the health care entity. The historical or acquisition costs are used in recording fixed assets. Net plant, property, and equipment represent the original costs of these items less accumulated depreciation and amortization.

7d. Gross Square Footage. Include all inpatient, outpatient, office, and support space used for or in support of your health care activities. Exclude exterior, roof, and garage space in the figure.

8. **Capital Expenses.** Expenses used to acquire assets, including buildings, remodeling projects, equipment, or property.

9. **Information Technology.**

a. **IT Operating expense.** Exclude department depreciation and operating dollars paid against capital leases.

b. **IT Capital expense.** Include IT capital expense for the current year only. Any capital expense that is carried forward from the previous year should be excluded from this figure. Include IT related capital included in the budget of other departments. (e.g., lab, radiology) if known or can be reasonably estimated. Include the total value of capital leases to be signed in the current year.

c. **Number of Employed IT staff (in FTEs).** Number of full-time equivalent (FTE) staff employed in the IT department/organization and on the hospital payroll.

d. **Total number of outsourced IT staff (in FTEs).** i.e., contracted staff.

e. **Electronic Health Record.** An electronic health record (EHR) integrates electronically originated and maintained patient-level clinical health information, derived from multiple sources, into one point of access. An EHR replaces the paper medical record as the primary source of patient information.

10. **Full-Time Equivalent (FTE)** is the total number of hours worked by all employees over the full 12-month reporting period, divided by the normal number of hours worked by a full-time employee for that same time period. For example, if your hospital considers a normal workweek for a full-time employee to be 40 hours, a total of 2,080 would be worked over a full year (52 weeks). If the total number of hours worked by all employees on the payroll is 208,000, then the number of full-time equivalents (FTE) is 100 (employees). The FTE calculation for a specific occupational category such as registered nurses is exactly the same. The calculation for each occupational category should be based on the number of hours worked by staff employed in that specific category.

   a-b. **Physicians and dentists.** Include only those physicians and dentists engaged in clinical practice and on the payroll. Those who hold administrative positions should be reported in all other personnel. (10m)

   d. **Other trainees.** A trainee is a person who has not completed the necessary requirements for certification or met the qualifications required for full salary under a related occupational category. Exclude medical and dental residents/interns who should be reported on line 10c.

   e. **Registered nurses.** Nurses who have graduated from approved schools of nursing and who are currently registered by the state. They are responsible for the nature and quality of all nursing care that patients receive. Do not include any registered nurses more appropriately reported in other occupational categories, such as facility administrators, and therefore listed under all other personnel. (10m)

   f. **Licensed practical (vocational) nurses.** Nurses who have graduated from an approved school of practical (vocational) nursing who work under the supervision of registered nurses and/or physicians.

   g. **Nursing assistive personnel.** Certified nursing assistant or equivalent unlicensed staff who assist registered nurses in providing patient care related services as assigned by and under the supervision of a registered nurse.

   h. **Radiology technicians.** Technical positions in imaging fields, including, but not limited to, radiology, sonography, nuclear medicine, radiation therapy, CT, MRI.

   i. **Laboratory technicians.** Professional and technical positions in all areas of the laboratory, including, but not limited to, histology, phlebotomy, microbiology, pathology, chemistry, etc.

   j. **Pharmacists, licensed.** Persons licensed within the state who are concerned with the preparation and distribution of medicinal products.

   k. **Pharmacy technicians.** Persons who assist the pharmacist with selected activities, including medication profile reviews for drug incompatibilities, typing labels and prescription packaging, handling of purchase records and inventory control.

   l. **Respiratory Therapists.** An allied health professional who specializes in scientific knowledge and theory of clinical problems of respiratory care. Duties include the collection and evaluation of patient data to determine an appropriate care plan, selection and assembly of equipment, conduction of therapeutic procedures, and modification of prescribed plans to achieve one or more specific objectives.

   m. **All other personnel.** This should include all other personnel not already accounted for in other categories.

   n. **Total facility personnel.** Add 10a-10m. Includes the total facility personnel - hospital plus nursing home type unit/facility personnel (for those hospitals that own and operate a nursing home type unit/facility.)

   o-p. **Nursing home type unit/facility personnel.** These lines should be filled out only by hospitals that own and operate a nursing home type unit/facility, where only one legal entity is vested with title to the physical property or operates under the authority of a duly executed lease of the physical property. If nursing home type unit/facility personnel are reported on the total facility personnel lines (10a-m), but cannot be broken out, please write "cannot break out" on this line.

   q. **Direct patient care RN.** Registered nurses providing care directly to patients. Direct patient care responsibilities are patient-centered nursing activities carried out in the presence of the patient (such as admission, transfer/discharge, patient teaching, patient communication, treatments, counseling, and administration of medication.)

11. **Privileged Physicians.** Report the total number of physicians (by type) on the medical staff with privileges except those with courtesy, honorary and provisional privileges. Do not include residents or interns. Physicians that provide only non-clinical services (administrative services, medical director services, etc.) should be excluded.

   Employed by your hospital. Physicians that are either direct hospital employees or employees of a hospital subsidiary corporation.

   Individual contract. An independent physician under a formal contract to provide services at your hospital including at outpatient facilities, clinics and offices

   Group contract. A physician that is part of a group (group practice, faculty practice plan or medical foundation) under a formal contract to provide services at your hospital including at inpatient and outpatient facilities, clinics and offices.

   Not employed or under contract. Other physicians with privileges that have no employment or contractual relationship with the hospital to provide services.

   __The sum of the physicians reported in 11a-11f should equal the total number of privileged physicians in the hospital.__

   a. **Primary care.** A physician that provides primary care services including general practice, general internal medicine, family practice, general pediatrics, obstetrics/gynecology and geriatrics.

   b. **Emergency medicine.** Physicians who provide care in the emergency department.

   c. **Hospitalist.** Physicians whose primary professional focus is the care of hospitalized medical patients (through clinical, education, administrative and research activity).

   d. **Intensivist.** A physician with special training to work with critically ill patients. Intensivists generally provided medical-surgical, cardiac, neonatal, pediatric and other types of intensive care.

   e. **Radiologist/pathologist/anesthesiologist. Radiologist.** A physician who has specialized training in imaging, including but not limited to radiology, sonography, nuclear medicine, radiation therapy, CT, MRI. **Pathologist.** A physician who examines samples of body tissues for diagnostic purposes. **Anesthesiologist.** A physician who specializes in administering medications or other agents that prevent or relieve pain, especially during surgery.

   f. **Other specialist.** Other physicians not included in the above categories that specialize in a specific type of medical care.

14. **Advanced Practice Registered Nurses.** Registered nurses with advanced didactic and clinical education, knowledge, skills, and scope of practice. Includes: **Physician assistant.** A healthcare professional licensed to practice medicine with supervision of a licensed physician. **Nurse practitioner.** A registered nurse with at least a master's degree in nursing and advanced education in primary care, capable of independent practice in a variety of settings. **Clinical nurse specialist (CNS).** A registered nurse who, through a formal graduate degree (masters or doctorate) CNS education program, has expertise in a specialty area of nursing practice. CNSs are clinical experts in the diagnosis and treatment of illness, and the delivery of evidence-based nursing interventions.

14c. **Primary care.** Medical services including general practice, general internal medicine, family practice, general pediatrics, obstetrics/gynecology. **Emergency department care.** The provision of unscheduled outpatient services to patients whose conditions require immediate care in the emergency department setting. **Other specialty care.** A clinic that provides specialized medical care beyond the scope of primary care. **Patient education.** Goals and objectives for the patient and/or family related to therapeutic regimens, medical procedures and self-care. **Case management.** A system of assessment, treatment planning, referral and follow-up that ensures the provision of comprehensive and continuous services and the coordination of payment and reimbursement for care. **Other.** Any type of care other than those listed above.

15. **Foreign-educated nurses.** Individuals who are foreign born and received basic nursing education in a foreign country. In general many of these nurses come to the US on employment-based visas which allow them to obtain a green card.

SECTION E. SUPPLEMENTAL INFORMATION
DEFINITIONS

1. **Satellite facility.** Services are available at a facility geographically remote from the hospital campus.
2. **Group Purchasing Organization.** An organization whose primary function is to negotiate contracts for the purpose of purchasing for members of the group or has a central supply site for its members.
3. **Distributor.** An entity that typically does not manufacture most of its own products but purchases and re-sells these products. Such a business usually maintains an inventory of products for sales to hospitals and physician offices and others.
5. **Types of Partnerships:**
   a. Health care providers outside your system (Include other hospitals health care systems, FQHCs, community clinics)
   b. Local or state public health organizations (Include public health departments, institutes, etc.)
   c. Local or state human/social service organizations (Include food, housing/rental assistance, energy assistance, transportation assistance)
   d. Local or state government (Include municipal, city or county government, including public safety and policy/legislative initiatives at a local level)
   e. Non-profit organizations (Include National health associations, United Way, YMCA, Service leagues, healthy communities coalitions)
   f. Faith-based organizations
   g. Health insurance companies
   h. Schools (Include childhood, primary and secondary schools and colleges/universities)
   i. Local businesses or chambers of commerce
   j. Other (list)

   Scale of partnerships:
   Not involved.   No current partnerships with this type of organization
   Collaboration.   Exchange information and share resources for a similar mission to enhance the capacity of the other partner
   Formal Alliance. Formalized partnership (binding agreement) among multiple organizations with merged initiatives, common goals and metrics